COLLEGE ZOOLOGY

THE MACMILLAN COMPANY
NEW YORK · BOSTON · CHICAGO · DALLAS
ATLANTA · SAN FRANCISCO

MACMILLAN & CO., Limited
LONDON · BOMBAY · CALCUTTA
MELBOURNE

THE MACMILLAN CO. OF CANADA, Ltd.
TORONTO

COLLEGE ZOOLOGY

BY

ROBERT W. HEGNER, Ph.D.

PROFESSOR OF PROTOZOOLOGY AND HEAD OF THE DEPARTMENT
OF MEDICAL ZOOLOGY IN THE SCHOOL OF HYGIENE
AND PUBLIC HEALTH OF THE JOHNS
HOPKINS UNIVERSITY

REVISED EDITION

New York

THE MACMILLAN COMPANY

1926

COPYRIGHT, 1912 AND 1926,

By THE MACMILLAN COMPANY.

Set up and electrotyped. Published July, 1912.
Revised edition, September, 1926. Reprinted November, 1926.

Norwood Press
J. S. Cushing Co. — Berwick & Smith Co.
Norwood, Mass., U.S.A.

PREFACE TO THE REVISED EDITION

ADVANCES in the science of zoology since the publication of the first edition have made it desirable to revise this book. The original plan has not been materially altered and the author believes that the method of teaching that directs attention to animals in phylogenetic groups and leads to the deduction of general principles is superior to any other. This book is arranged so that the student learns where each animal belongs in the animal kingdom; its characteristics and those of the other animals in its class or phylum. One common species is generally used as a type of each large group and then the classification and characteristics of other members of the group are presented more briefly. The groups in the animal kingdom are considered approximately in order of their supposed evolution and thus biological facts and theories fall into a series from the comparatively simple to the more complex in such a way that their gradual evolution is clearly evident. In each group the fundamental biological subjects are studied, — morphology, physiology, behavior, reproduction, embryology, classification, geographical distribution, evolution, paleontology, — thus furnishing the data from which the student arrives at generalizations. Various biological phenomena are emphasized in connection with the group of animals that furnishes the best illustrative material; for example, pure lines in PROTOZOA; polymorphism and metagenesis in CŒLENTERATA; regeneration in *Hydra*, *Planaria*, and echinoderms; artificial parthenogenesis in echinoderms; metamerism, the cœlom and trochophore in annelids; functional adaptations in the appendages of the crayfish and honey bee; autotomy in echinoderms and CRUSTACEA; the biogenetic law in CRUSTACEA; metamorphosis in insects; mimicry in butterflies; color and color changes in AMPHIBIA; hibernation in AMPHIBIA and mammals; form and function in birds; and migration and domestication in birds and mammals. Various other biological facts and theories are presented in special chapters, — Chapter I, *Introduction*, Chapter III,

An Introduction to the Metazoa, Chapter XIV, *Phylum Chordata: Introduction,* and Chapter XXII, *The Ancestors and Interrelations of the Vertebrates.*

Teachers are advised to arrange the work so that sufficient time may be allowed students at intervals during the course, or at its completion, to build up generalizations on the basis of the facts and theories studied in the various phyla. Suggested subjects for such exercises are (1) the cell theory, (2) the structure and physiology of protoplasm, (3) cell division, (4) the origin of METAZOA, (5) symmetry, (6) metamerism, (7) physiology of organs, (8) methods of reproduction, (9) breeding habits, (10) the germ-cell cycle, (11) embryology, (12) organogeny in vertebrates, (13) metamorphosis, (14) taxonomy, (15) the biogenetic law, (16) animal habitats, (17) commensalism, symbiosis, and parasitism, (18) animal communities, (19) the migration of animals, (20) geographical distribution, (21) genetics, (22) evolution, (23) fossil animals, (24) regeneration, (25) metagenesis, (26) polymorphism, (27) origin of the vertebrates, (28) hibernation, (29) domestication of animals, (30) economic importance of animals, (31) animal behavior.

Among the important changes in this edition are the addition of about 70 new illustrations and the modification of about 200 others by the substitution of names for guide letters, etc., thus making the figures of more value.

The writer wishes to thank those who have sent him suggestions which have been of use in correcting errors and increasing the value of the book, and to express his appreciation of the efforts made by The Macmillan Co., to improve the book in every possible way. He is very grateful indeed to Dr. Justin M. Andrews for generous assistance in the proofreading and indexing.

ROBERT W. HEGNER.

AUGUST, 1926.

PREFACE TO THE FIRST EDITION

THIS book is intended to serve as a text for beginning students in universities and colleges, or for students who have already taken a course in general biology and wish to gain a more comprehensive view of the animal kingdom. It differs from many of the college textbooks of zoology now on the market in several important respects: (1) the animals and their organs are not only described, but their functions are pointed out; (2) the animals described are in most cases native species; (3) the relations of the animals to man are emphasized. Besides serving as a textbook, it is believed that this book will be of interest to the general reader, since it gives a bird's-eye view of the entire animal kingdom as we know it at the present time.

Within the past decade there has been a tendency for teachers of zoology to pay less attention to morphology and more to physiology. As a prominent morphologist recently said, "Morphology . . . is no longer in favor . . . and among a section of the zoological world has almost fallen into disgrace" (Bourne). The study of the form and structure of animals is, however, of fundamental importance, and is absolutely necessary before physiological processes can be fully understood; but a course which is built up on the "old-fashioned morphological lines" is no longer adequate for the presentation of zoological principles.

In writing this book the author has attempted, not only to describe the most important structural features of the various types of animals, but also to point out the vital phenomena as expressed in the functions of the organs. Furthermore, an endeavor has been made to compare the animals in each phylum with those of the members of nearly related phyla, so that the student may realize the unity as well as the variety in animal life.

So far as possible in a limited space, the relations of the animals to other animals, to plants, and to environmental factors in general are considered, and the animals of special economic importance are emphasized. By this method the student is brought into closer contact with and gains a broader idea of natural phenomena. Questions naturally arise in the student's mind, such as, "Where does the animal live?" "What does the animal do?" and "What is this or that particular organ for?" and stimulate interest in the work leading to more careful observations and more accurate inferences.

Each phylum is introduced by a more or less complete account of the anatomy, physiology, and ecology of one, or in certain cases, two or more types. These types were selected with the following requirements in mind : (1) they must represent as nearly as possible an average of the phylum; (2) they must illustrate clearly the characteristics of the phylum so as to serve as an introduction to a comparative study of other members of the group; (3) they must be common native species which can be obtained for direct observations in the laboratory; (4) they must occupy an important position in the animal series; and (5) they must be of special importance to man. Very few types fulfill all of these requirements; in several cases two types have been employed because one was not considered adequate.

It is impossible in one small volume to describe as many different animals under each phylum as might be desired, or to give a full classification of each group. However, a general idea of the various kinds of animals and their habitats can be obtained from the short account included in each chapter. The species mentioned are in most cases the commonest and most representative of those living in North America.

More space has been devoted to the Chordata than to any other phylum, and the classes under the subphylum Vertebrata have been treated in a somewhat different manner from those of the invertebrates. It is customary in studying the vertebrates to select one species as a type to be examined in considerable detail, and then to compare species belonging to the other classes with it. The animal usually chosen for detailed study is the frog, and this form has therefore been treated more fully in this book than any other vertebrate type. The vertebrates are, as a rule, larger than the invertebrates, are fewer in number, and are usually more interesting to beginning students; they are, on the whole, better known than the invertebrates and more easily observed. For these reasons they have been discussed largely from the natural history standpoint, and it is hoped that this treatment will give students a better idea of the everyday events in the lives of the more common vertebrates than can be obtained from a purely morphological course.

A book covering such a large field as this one must necessarily be more or less of a compilation, and the facts and figures must be selected from numerous textbooks and scientific periodicals. The sources from which the author has obtained a large part of his material are as follows : —

Bourne, G. C. *Comparative Anatomy of Animals,* 2 vols., 1909.
Bronn, H. G. *Klassen und Ordnungen des Tierreichs.*
Calkins, G. N. *Protozoa,* 1901.
—— *Protozoology,* 1909.
Cambridge Natural History, 10 vols.
Dean, B. *Fishes, Living and Fossil,* 1895.
Dickerson, M. C. *The Frog Book,* 1907.
Ditmars, R. L. *The Reptile Book,* 1907.
—— *Reptiles of the World,* 1910.
Flower, W. H., and Lydekker, R. *Mammals, Living and Extinct,* 1891.
Hertwig, R. *Manual of Zoology,* 1905.
Holmes, S. J. *Biology of the Frog,* 1906.
Jennings, H. S. *Behavior of the Lower Organisms,* 1906.
Jordan, D. S. *Guide to the Study of Fishes,* 2 vols., 1905.
—— and Evermann, B. W. *Fishes of North America,* 4 vols., 1900.
Kellogg, V. L. *American Insects,* 1905.
Kingsley, J. S. *Textbook of Vertebrate Zoology,* 1899.
Knowlton, F. H. *Birds of the World,* 1909.
Korschelt, E., and Heider, K. *Textbook of the Embryology of Invertebrates,* 4 vols., 1895.
Lang, A. *Comparative Anatomy of Invertebrates.*
Lankester, E. R. *A Treatise on Zoology,* 1900–1909.
Marshall, A. M., and Hurst, C. H. *Practical Zoology,* 1905.
Matthew, W. D. *Evolution of the Horse.* American Museum Journal, Vol. III. Guide Leaflet No. 9, 1903.
Morgan, T. H. *Regeneration,* 1901.
Osborn, H. F. *The Age of Mammals,* 1910.
Parker, T. J. *Zootomy,* 1884.

Parker, T. J., and Parker, W. N. *An Elementary Course in Practical Zoology,* 1908.
—— and Haswell, W. A. *Textbook of Zoology,* 1910.
Schmeil, O. *Textbook of Zoology,* 1901.
Sedgwick, A. *Student's Textbook of Zoology,* 3 vols., 1898–1909.
Sedgwick, W. T., and Wilson, E. B. *General Biology,* 1899.
Shipley, A. E., and MacBride, E. W. *Zoology,* 1904.
Simpson, G. B. *Anatomy and Physiology of Polygyra Albolabris and Limax Maximus.* Bul. N. Y. State Mus., Vol. 8, 1901.
Stone, W., and Cram, W. E. *American Animals,* 1905.
United States Department of Agriculture. Circulars and Bulletins.
Verworn, M. *General Physiology,* 1899.
Wiedersheim, R., and Parker, W. N. *Comparative Anatomy of Vertebrates,* 1907.
Wilder, H. H. *History of the Human Body,* 1909.
Willey, A. *Amphioxus and the Ancestry of the Vertebrates,* 1894.
Williams, L. W. *Anatomy of the Common Squid.* American Museum of Natural History.
Wilson, E. B. *The Cell in Development and Inheritance,* 1900.
Zittel, K. von. *Textbook of Palæontology,* 3 vols., 1925.

In an endeavor to avoid as many errors as possible, the manuscript of most of the chapters has been read by zoologists who are authorities in the special field treated therein. It is a great pleasure to thank these gentlemen in this place for the invaluable assistance they have rendered. I am indebted to Professor A. S. Pearse for reading Chapters I–IX; to Mr. Peter Okkelberg for reading the entire manuscript; to Professor G. N. Calkins for reading Chapter II; to Professor H. V. Wilson for reading Chapter IV; to Professor Charles W. Hargitt for reading Chapters V and VI; to Professor W. C. Curtis for reading Chapters VII and IX; to Dr. G. R. La Rue for reading Chapter VII; to Dr. B. H. Ransom for reading Chapter VIII; to Dr. Hubert Lyman Clark for reading Chapter X; to Professor J. Percy Moore for reading Chapter XI; to Mr. H. B. Baker for reading Chapter XII; to Professor A. E. Ortmann for reading the part of Chapter XIII relating to the Crustacea, Onychophora, and Myriapoda; to Professor Vernon L. Kellogg for reading the part of Chapter XIII relating to Insecta; to Mr. J. H. Emerton for reading the part of

Chapter XIII relating to the Arachnida; to Professor Alexander G. Ruthven for reading Chapters XIV–XIX; to Professor B. M. Allen for reading Chapter XIV; to Mr. R. E. Richardson for reading Chapters XV–XVII; to Professor Lynds Jones for reading Chapter XX; and to Mr. Marcus W. Lyon, Jr., and Mr. N. Hollister for reading Chapter XXI. I am also indebted to Dr. A. F. Shull for reading a large part of the proof, and to my wife for her especially valuable assistance in reading proof and preparing the index.

R. W. H.

May 14, 1912.

CONTENTS

xiii

CHAPTER IV

CHAPTER V

CHAPTER VI

CHAPTER VII

CHAPTER VIII

CHAPTER IX

CHAPTER XIV

CHAPTER XV

CHAPTER XVI

CHAPTER XVII

CHAPTER XVIII

CHAPTER XIX

CHAPTER XX

CHAPTER XXI

CHAPTER XXII

SCHEME OF THE CLASSIFICATION ADOPTED IN THIS BOOK

COLLEGE ZOOLOGY

CHAPTER I

INTRODUCTION [1]

1. General Survey of the Animal Kingdom

One who is not a naturalist or who does not have access to the apparatus necessary for the examination of minute objects usually becomes acquainted with only a few of the many kinds of animals that inhabit the earth. The most familiar of these are the comparatively large four-footed beasts, the fish, the frogs, the snakes, the birds, and the insects. The majority of animals are never seen by most people, and perhaps never even heard of. This is true of the microscopic parasite which is present in the blood of malaria patients, of the coral polyp (Fig. 86) which builds up entire islands in the sea, of the *Trichinella* (Fig. 113), a parasitic worm which sometimes causes a human disease called trichinosis, and of a host of others.

Scientists have found it convenient to separate all animals into two groups, the *vertebrates* and the *invertebrates*. The vertebrates possess a backbone or vertebral column consisting of a linear series of bones called vertebræ (Fig. 419); the invertebrates have no vertebral column. The vertebrates are better known than the invertebrates, since they are usually large and include most of the domesticated animals. The invertebrates, however, are much more numerous both in regard to the number

---

[1] In this chapter the *variety of animal life* is set forth by a brief survey of the animal kingdom, with emphasis on those species that come most often within our common experience, and the *unity of animal life* by discussions of *protoplasm* and of the principle known as the *cell theory*. Brief statements regarding the origin of life, the contrasting characters of plants and animals, the principles of classification, and the divisions into which the science of zoology is separated, all serve to give an introduction to the detailed accounts in succeeding chapters. And finally a brief account is given of some of the great men who have done the most to build up the principles of zoology.

1

of kinds and the number of individuals. Thus of the eleven main groups (phyla) of animals recognized in the classification adopted in this book only part of one group, the CHORDATA (Chap. XIV), deals with the vertebrates, whereas the rest of this group and the other ten chief divisions are composed entirely of invertebrates.

It is therefore of considerable importance at the very beginning to learn something of the characteristics and habitats of the thousands of living creatures that form the basis for the study of zoology. In the following paragraphs a few facts about each main group are presented in such a way as to give a bird's-eye view of the entire animal kingdom.

(1) **The Vertebrates.** — The members of this group possess a bony axis of vertebræ called the vertebral column or backbone (Fig. 419). They are the most highly developed of all animals, and include man. The vertebrates may be subdivided into seven assemblages, each containing numbers of more or less familiar forms.

At the top of the series are placed the MAMMALIA (Chap. XXI), usually known as *animals* or *beasts*. Among the representative mammals are man, the apes, monkeys, bats, moles, rats, mice, rabbits, dogs, cats, cows, sheep, horses, whales, sloths, opossums, and the peculiar duckbill (Fig. 513) and spiny ant-eater of Australia. They are vertebrates which possess hair, and, with a few exceptions, nourish their young with milk secreted by mammary glands. They breathe air by means of lungs, and are said to be warm-blooded, since their body temperature is nearly 100° F., regardless of the temperature of the surrounding medium.

The members of the group AVES or BIRDS (Chap. XX) are characterized by the presence of feathers; no other animals possess these structures. Birds are air-breathers and warm-blooded, having a higher body temperature than any other organisms. They are all terrestrial, though many of them are adapted to life on or near the water. The majority of the birds are able to fly long distances, but some of them, like the ostrich and the auk, are flightless.

REPTILES (Chap. XIX) are remarkably diversified in form, and occupy many kinds of habitats. Most of them live on land, but the *turtles* and *alligators* spend much of their existence in the water; the *lizards* are in many cases arboreal; and the *snakes* live in almost every conceivable environment. They are all called cold-blooded vertebrates because their body temperature varies with that of the surrounding medium and may drop to the freezing point. They possess lungs, and in most cases are covered with an armor of scales or bony plates.

The most familiar AMPHIBIA (Chap. XVIII) are the *frogs, toads,* and *salamanders.* They pass the first part of their lives in the water, at which time they breathe by means of gills; but later they become air-breathers, and many of them leave the water and live on land. In form certain AMPHIBIA resemble reptiles, but they usually do not possess scales and are anatomically quite different. They are cold-blooded.

The *common fishes* are members of the group PISCES (Chap. XVII). They are cold-blooded animals, usually covered with scales, and spend their entire existence in the water. They possess gills for breathing, and swim about by means of fins. Some of them, like the sea-horse (Fig. 398), are so modified as to be hardly recognizable as fish; others, called lung-fishes, are able to breathe out of water.

Belonging to the vertebrate series, but lower in the scale of life than the common fishes, are two groups of fishlike animals that are comparatively little known. These are the ELASMO-BRANCHII, or sharks and rays (Chap. XVI), and the CYCLOSTO-MATA, or lamprey-eels and hagfishes (Chap. XV; Fig. 352).

(2) **The Arthropoda.** — The *crayfishes, centipedes, insects,* and *spiders* are among the commonest ARTHROPODA (Chap. XIII). All of these animals have jointed appendages, and their bodies are divided into a number of segments which are arranged in a single row and are modified for various purposes. An outer covering of a yellowish substance called *chitin* gives firmness to the body and also serves as a protection from mechanical injury.

The ARACHNIDA are the *spiders, scorpions, mites, ticks,* etc. They may usually be distinguished from other ARTHROPODA by the presence of eight legs. Many of them, like the scorpion, are capable of inflicting severe wounds with their stings. The curious *king-crab* is now placed by zoologists in the group ARACHNIDA.

The INSECTA are the *butterflies, bees, beetles, bugs,* etc. They have six legs, and usually possess wings.

The MYRIAPODA are long, slender, terrestrial animals with one or two pairs of legs on each body segment; they are known as *centipedes* (Fig. 233) and *millipedes* (Fig. 232).

The CRUSTACEA are mainly aquatic ARTHROPODA, and breathe with gills ; they include the *lobsters, crayfishes, crabs, barnacles, sow bugs,* and many others.

(3) **The Mollusca.** — The MOLLUSCA (Chap. XII) most often seen are the *snails* and *clams;* the *slug, oyster, squid* (Fig. 191), *nautilus* (Fig. 194), *cuttlefish,* and *octopus,* are also well known. They are of various shapes and sizes, but most of them possess a ventral muscular structure called the foot, which usually serves as an organ of locomotion. Often a heavy shell of calcium carbonate covers the body.

(4) **The Annelida.** — The ANNELIDA (Chap. XI) are known as *segmented worms,* since their bodies consist of sometimes over one hundred rings or segments and their shape is wormlike. The *earthworm* is the commonest representative of the group. There are many marine annelids, and also a number of fresh-water members, like the *leech.* The medicinal leech (Fig. 169) is famous for its use in sucking blood.

(5) **The Echinodermata.** — The *starfish* (Fig. 131) is a well-known echinoderm, and usually serves as a type of the group. Like all echinoderms, it is radially symmetrical, and has five arms extending out from a central disc. The other echinoderms are called *brittle stars, sea urchins, sea cucumbers,* and *sea lilies.* Most of these animals have a body-wall supplied with spicules of calcium carbonate ; hence their name, which means spiny-skinned. They all live in salt water, and are therefore seldom seen by people who do not visit the seacoast.

(6) **The Nemathelminthes.** — The NEMATHELMINTHES are *unsegmented round* or *thread worms.* Most of them are parasitic like the roundworm, *Ascaris* (Fig. 111), which inhabits the alimentary canal of man, the horse, and many other animals. One dangerous parasite is *Trichinella* (Fig. 113), which spends part of its life in the muscle of the hog, and may attack human beings if infected pork is eaten without being sufficiently cooked. Vinegar usually contains a number of roundworms called *vinegar eels;* they can be seen only with the aid of a microscope.

(7) **The Platyhelminthes.** — The PLATYHELMINTHES or *flatworms* are also wormlike and unsegmented. The best known members are the *tapeworms,* which are parasitic in man and other animals. The *liver fluke* is a serious pest ; it inhabits the bile ducts of sheep and causes the death of large numbers of infected

individuals in certain localities. Less widely known are the fresh-water flatworms, like *Planaria* (Fig. 97), and the terrestrial and marine forms.

(8) **The Cœlenterata.** — The Cœlenterata are mostly marine animals, and are known as *hydroids* (Fig. 73) and *jellyfishes* (Fig. 82). Their bodies are fundamentally simple sacs, although many modifications give the impression of great complexity. Some cœlenterates are famous for the rigid skeletal structures they produce ; this is true of the *coral polyps* (Fig. 86), which have even built up entire islands. There are only a few fresh-water cœlenterates ; one of these, *Hydra* (Fig. 65), is comparatively common, and is studied as a type of this group by most students of biology.

(9) **The Porifera.** — The Porifera are *sponges*. The ordinary bath sponge is the horny skeleton of an animal that lives in the sea (Fig. 63). *Venus's flower basket* (Fig. 62) is a sponge skeleton that is often seen in museums. Most of the sponges secrete a supporting framework of calcium carbonate or silica. Only a few of the sponges live in fresh water, and none lives on land.

(10) **The Protozoa.** — The Protozoa (Chap. II) are in most cases so small as to be visible only with the microscope. They are, however, of great importance, especially those which cause diseases such as malaria. Protozoa are to be found almost everywhere. If a few dead leaves are placed in a dish of water and left to decay, the scum which forms on the surface will be found to contain thousands of these minute organisms. The simplest animals belong to the Protozoa ; among these are *Amœba* (Fig. 9), *Paramecium* (Fig. 35), and *Euglena* (Fig. 22), which will be studied in some detail in Chapter II.

Few people realize the abundance and variety of animal life. Almost every part of the earth is inhabited by animals of some kind, and these animals are more or less restricted to certain kinds of habitats. For example, fishes live in the water, earthworms in the ground, the polar bear in Arctic regions, the elephant in the Tropics, the prairie dog on the prairies, the mountain goat on the mountains, and parasites upon or within the bodies of other organisms. Four principal kinds of animals may be recognized according to their mode of existence : (1) marine animals living in the salt waters of the sea, (2) fresh-water animals living in fresh-water streams, ponds, and lakes, (3) terrestrial animals living on land, and (4) parasites which live on or within the bodies of other animals.

The oceans are inhabited by millions of animals of all sizes, ranging from the whale to the microscopic floating organisms known as *plankton*. Salt-water animals are restricted to certain definite regions ; some float on or near the surface, and others live at various distances from the surface, until a depth is reached where the light never penetrates. As a rule, animals living in salt water die almost at once if transferred to fresh water ; likewise salt water is fatal to fresh-water animals.

Every pond, lake, brook, creek, and river is inhabited by a host of living animals. A pond, for example, furnishes a home for the early stages in the life history of the mosquito, whose eggs are laid in a raft-like mass on top of the water, and whose young swim about at or near the surface. Frogs and salamanders find a home amid the vegetation common to ponds. Crayfishes crawl about on the bottom ; wheel animalcules (Fig. 122) and many other extremely small animals swim about in search of food ; and almost every drop of pond water contains a number of microscopic forms.

The *terrestrial* animals are the ones best known to the average person, and every one is aware of the vast numbers of deer, wolves, field-mice, snakes, insects, and other forms that move about on the surface of the earth. Animals like the mole and the earthworm which live underground are said to be *subterrestrial*, and those like the birds and butterflies that frequent the air are called *aërial*.

Parasites are more widely spread than is generally known. Almost every animal is infested with others which prey upon it. The malarial fever germ is one of the most important, although one of the smallest, parasites. The fleas and lice are called external parasites. The internal parasites of man include the roundworm *Ascaris* (Fig. 111), the tapeworm (Fig. 107), and the *Trichinella* (Fig. 113). Frequently parasites are preyed upon by other parasites, — a condition known as hyperparasitism — and even the hyperparasites may be parasitized. Thus the following humorous lines contain a grain of truth :

> " Great fleas have little fleas
> Upon their backs to bite 'em,
> And little fleas have lesser fleas,
> And so *ad infinitum*."

The survey of the animal kingdom just concluded attempts to present a few facts about the groups of animals to be studied in the succeeding chapters. The most highly organized and most familiar animals, the *mammals*, were considered first, and the less complex were successively discussed in a descending series, until the last and simplest organisms were reached. A glance at the table of contents of this book will show that the extended studies of these groups have been arranged in a reversed order, beginning with the simplest animals, the PROTOZOA, and ending with the highest type, the *Mammal*. This method of presenting the facts of zoology has been employed with the idea of organic evolution in mind.

Practically every zoologist at the present time believes that the complex animals have *evolved* from simpler forms at some period in the world's history. How this evolution has taken place is still a moot question. According to the evolution theory the first animals that existed on the earth consisted of a single cell, and all the animals that lived at that time would now be called PROTOZOA (Chap. II). These animals gave rise in some way still unknown to organisms consisting of many cells (Chap. III). In the course of millions of years new and more complex forms were continually being evolved from older and simpler animals, so that all those now existing may be arranged in an ascending series constituting a sort of genealogical tree. Many of the connecting links between the various groups have disappeared, but in a few cases the remains preserved in the rocks as fossils give us very definite ideas of the order of evolution.

Man is no exception in the evolutionary process, but is closely allied to the anthropoid apes, and doubtless arose from an ape-like ancestor. The simpler animals living to-day probably do not represent ancestral forms, since they have become modified in many ways. It is only safe to make general statements, such as, that man has evolved from ape-like ancestors, that the birds have arisen from reptile-like ancestors, and that the insects have descended from worm-like ancestors.

2. LIVING MATTER CONTRASTED WITH NON-LIVING MATTER

All living things are either plants or animals, and have certain peculiarities which separate them from non-living things. These peculiarities do not all pertain exclusively to living organisms, but may, to a certain extent, be attributes of non-living bodies ; nevertheless, when taken together, they are sufficient to determine whether an object is living or lifeless. The most important peculiarities are as follows : —

(1) **Definite Size**. — The size of living organisms varies within definite limits. The smallest animals known are microscopic blood parasites ; the largest living animals are the whales. The difference is great but definite, and each kind of animal has a characteristic size. Non-living bodies, on the other hand, may be of any size ; for example, water may exist as a particle of vapor or as an ocean.

(2) **Definite Form**. — If animals were not constant in form, we would be unable to distinguish one from another. Non-living bodies usually have no definite form, but may, like water in a lake-bed, assume the shape temporarily forced upon them.

(3) **Definite Chemical Composition**. — The elements found in living matter are all found in non-living bodies, but in living matter certain elements are combined so as to produce a substance known as *protoplasm*. These elements are present in a typical animal in the following proportions : —

$$
\left.\begin{array}{l} \text{Carbon} \\ \text{Oxygen} \\ \text{Nitrogen} \\ \text{Hydrogen} \\ \text{Sulphur} \end{array}\right\} 99 \text{ per cent of weight ;}
$$

$$
\left.\begin{array}{l} \text{Phosphorus} \\ \text{Chlorine} \\ \text{Potassium} \\ \text{Sodium} \\ \text{Magnesium} \\ \text{Calcium} \\ \text{Iron} \end{array}\right\} 1 \text{ per cent of weight.}
$$

(4) **Definite Organization**. — The protoplasm contained in the bodies of animals is not continuous in most cases but is divided up into small units called cells (p. 12, Fig. 2). A cell is a small mass of protoplasm containing a nucleus. The bodies of some animals are composed of only a single cell (PROTOZOA, Chap. II), but all of the more highly organized animals are made up of almost

countless numbers. Non-living bodies possess no unit of structure comparable to the cell.

(5) **Metabolism.** — Animals are able to change food into protoplasm ; this process is termed *metabolism* (p. 17) ; *growth* takes place by the addition of these particles of protoplasm among the preexisting particles. This is growth by *intussusception.* Non-living bodies are not metabolic, and, if they can be said to grow at all, increase in size by the addition of particles on the outside, that is, growth is by *accretion.*

(6) **Reproduction.** — Animals are able to produce other animals like themselves. Non-living bodies cannot reproduce their kind.

(7) **Irritability or Reactiveness.** — Animals have the ability of responding to changes in their environment. The change is termed a *stimulus,* and the sum total of the animal's movements is known as its *behavior.* Non-living objects are not irritable.

3. THE PHYSICAL BASIS OF LIFE — PROTOPLASM

Protoplasm is a term used by both zoologists and botanists to designate the essential substance of which plants and animals are composed. All living organisms are built up of protoplasm, but no non-living object possesses any of this compound. Protoplasm has been called by Huxley " the physical basis of life," since all vital phenomena are due to its presence.

There are several theories regarding its structure : A, the *alveolar* theory, B, the *reticular* theory, and C, the *granular* theory. According to the alveolar theory (Fig. 1, A), protoplasm consists of two substances, one of which is in the shape of spheres embedded in the other. The reticular theory (Fig. 1, B) considers protoplasm a network of living anastomosing fibers among which are non-living substances such as water and fat. The third theory maintains that protoplasm is composed of innumerable living granules variously arranged. It is still uncertain which of these theories, if any, is correct.

Ninety-seven per cent of protoplasm consists of the following four elements : —

Oxygen	65.0 per cent
Carbon	18.5 per cent
Hydrogen	11.0 per cent
Nitrogen	2.5 per cent

These and other elements form rather definite compounds. The principal *inorganic constituents* of protoplasm are (1) *water*, which comprises more than 50 per cent of the weight of most animals, (2) *salts*, such as the chlorides, carbonates, and phosphates, and (3) *gases*, such as oxygen and carbon dioxide.

The *organic compounds* found in protoplasm comprise the proteids, carbohydrates, and fats. *Proteids* consist of large molecules which always contain carbon, oxygen, hydrogen, and nitrogen. They do not dissolve in water, but absorb quantities of this

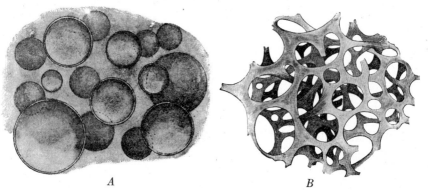

A   B

FIG. 1. — Diagrams to illustrate, A, the alveolar and B, the reticular theories of protoplasmic structure. (From Dahlgren and Kepner.)

fluid, swelling up like a sponge. Other peculiarities are their inability to pass through animal membranes and their property of coagulation or clotting. *Carbohydrates* are compounds of carbon, hydrogen, and oxygen, the last two nearly always occurring in the same proportion in which they are found in water (H_2O). Starches and sugars are common carbohydrates. Some living substances apparently do not contain this compound. *Fats* are likewise not invariable constituents of protoplasm. The protoplasm of each species of animal differs from that of every other species, but in all it has similar characteristics.

4. THE ORIGIN OF LIFE

No one knows when and where life originated on the earth. Many of the ancients believed that animals were created by divine providence, but this theory of *special creation* is not accepted by present-day zoologists. Historically the special creation theory was followed by that of *spontaneous generation*. According to this theory animals were supposed to originate directly from inorganic substances ; for example, frogs and toads from the muddy bottom of ponds under the influence of the sun, and insects from dew. The brilliant experiments of Redi (1668), Pasteur (1864), and Tyndall (1876) overthrew this theory completely, and scientists now believe that *living organisms originate only from preexisting organisms*. Where life first began is still unknown, but the meeting point of sea and land is the most probable place of origin. From here the fresh water, deep sea, and land were gradually peopled.

5. THE CELL AND THE CELL THEORY

(1) **Structure**. — It has already been noted that the body of an animal is divided up into microscopic units called *cells*, and that each cell is *a small mass of protoplasm containing a nucleus*. Cells vary in *size* and *form;* some are extremely small, *e.g.* blood parasites, whereas others, like the egg of a bird, are very large. They have no definite shape, but may be columnar, flat, spherical, or long and thin (Fig. 46). The *number* of cells in a complex animal is enormous ; there are about 9,200,000,000 in the gray matter of the human brain. On the other hand, certain animals (PROTOZOA) consist of but a single cell. The size of the animal does not depend upon the size of its cells, but upon their number.

Figure 2 shows the essential structure of a cell. The largest part of the contents is the *cytoplasm*, which may be separated into an outer layer of *ectoplasm* and an inner mass of *endoplasm*. Within this substance is embedded a *nucleus*. At certain stages in the life activities of the cell an *attraction-sphere* enclosing one or two *centrosomes* is visible. *Vacuoles, plastids, mitochondria, chromidia*, and non-living bodies (*metaplasm*) may also be present. The entire cell may or may not be surrounded by a *membrane*.

The cell *nucleus* contains a fluid through which runs a network of thin *linin fibers*. Scattered about on these fibers are granules of *chromatin*, a substance that has a strong affinity for certain dyes. Frequently several granules of chromatin unite to form a net-knot or *karyosome*. In addition to these regular constituents of the nucleus, one or more bodies, known as *nucleoli* or *plasmosomes*, may be present. In certain cases a cell may possess more than one nucleus, and a few cells have no definite nucleus, but contain chromatin granules which are scattered about in the cytoplasm.

(2) **Physiology**. — There is a definite division of labor among the parts of a cell. The particular function of the *nucleus*, aside from its important relation to cell division, to be described later, seems to be the control of the activities by which the protoplasm is elaborated.

The *cytoplasm*, from its direct relation to the outside world, is the seat of such functions as irritability, absorption, digestion,

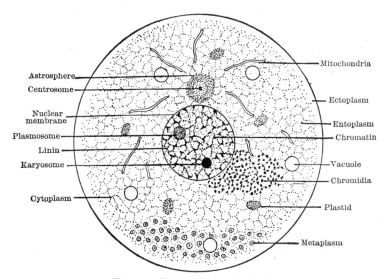

Fig. 2. — Diagram of a typical cell.

excretion, and respiration. The *centrosome* is of importance during cell division. The *cell covering* may serve for protection or support, or may be extremely delicate and have significance only as it helps to control the absorption of certain fluids. *Plastids* may represent stored food or waste products ; some of them, however, have other functions, *e.g.* the chloroplasts, which carry on photosynthesis in many plants and a few animal cells.

(3) **Cell Division**. — Cells multiply either by direct division (amitosis) or indirect division (mitosis). In amitosis (Fig. 3) the nucleus is either pinched in two in the middle, or a plate is formed in the plane of division, which later becomes double, and then the two plates separate, or two nuclear membranes are built

up inside of the old membrane. The cell body then divides, though in many cases this process does not occur (Fig. 3). Amitosis is characteristic of senescent cells.

Mitosis is the usual method of nuclear division. It consists of a series of complex processes that may be arranged into four phases. Constant reference to Figure 4 will make clear the following brief account.

(*a*) During the *prophase* the chromatin granules that are scattered through the nucleus in the resting cell (A) become arranged in the form of a long thread or *spireme* (B). At the same time the centrosomes move apart (A, *c;* B, *a*). The radiating lines that appear about them (B) later give rise to a spindle (C). While this is going on the nuclear membrane generally disintegrates

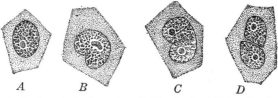

A B C D

Fig. 3. — **Amitosis**. Amitotic nuclear division in the follicle cells of a cricket's egg. (From Dahlgren and Kepner.)

and the spireme segments into a number of bodies called *chromosomes* (C) ; these take a position at the equator of the spindle, halfway between the centrosomes (D, *ep*). The stage shown in Figure 4, D, is known as the *amphiaster;* at this time all of the machinery concerned in mitosis is present. There are two *asters*, each consisting of a centrosome surrounded by a number of radiating astral rays, and a spindle which lies between them. The chromosomes lie in the equatorial plate (*ep*).

(*b*) During the second stage, the *metaphase*, the chromosomes split in such a way that each of their parts contains an equal amount of chromatin (E, *ep*). As we shall see later, this is one of the most significant events that takes place during mitosis.

(*c*) During the *anaphase* (F) the chromosomes formed by splitting move along the spindle fibers to the centrosomes. As a result every chromosome present at the end of the prophase (D) sends half of its chromatin to either end of the spindle. The mechanism that brings about this migration is as yet somewhat in question. Fibers are usually left between the separating chromosomes ; these are known as interzonal fibers (F, *if*).

(*d*) The *telephase* (G, H) is a stage of reconstruction from which the nuclei emerge in a resting condition ; the chromatin becomes scattered throughout the nucleus, which is again enveloped by a definite membrane (H) ; the centrosome divides and, with the

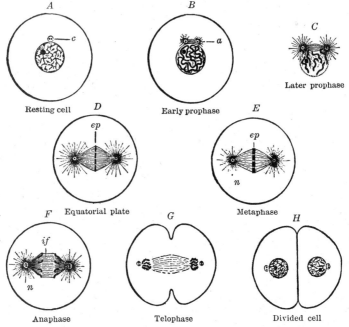

FIG. 4. — **Mitosis.** Diagrams illustrating mitotic cell division. (From Wilson.) **A**, resting cell (*c* = astrosphere) ; **B**, prophase showing spireme and nucleolus within the nucleus and the formation of spindle and asters (*a*) ; **C**, later prophase showing disintegration of nuclear membrane, and breaking up of spireme into chromosomes ; **D**, end of prophases, showing complete spindle and asters with chromosomes in equatorial plate (*ep*) ; **E**, metaphase — each chromosome splits in two ; **F**, anaphase — the chromosomes are drawn toward the asters, *if* = interzonal fibers ; **G**, telophase, showing reconstruction of nuclei ; **H**, later telophase, showing division of the cell into two.

centrosphere, takes a position near the nucleus. Finally the cycle is completed by the constriction of the cell into two daughter cells.

Chromosomes. — Every species of animal has a definite number of chromosomes that appear when the cells of its body undergo mitosis. Thus there are 48 in man ; 4 in the nematode worm,

Ascaris megalocephala; 8 in the fruit fly, *Drosophila melanogaster;* and the brine shrimp (*Artemia*) may possess one hundred and sixty-eight. An even number of chromosomes is characteristic of most animals, but recent researches have demonstrated that some forms, particularly the males of insects, have an odd number. The chromosomes are considered by most zoologists to be the bearers of hereditary materials, called determiners or *genes*, from parent to offspring.

In concluding this account of cell division two points are worthy of special emphasis. First, with regard to the *continuity of the chromatin*, it may be said that the chromatin is continuous from one cell generation to another. The cells resulting from mitosis may differ greatly in size, but the chromatin seems to be divided equally between them with great exactness. Second, *cells are never known to arise except from preexisting cells*. These two facts are perhaps the most important for us to keep in mind as we go on to study the more complex problems of fertilization and cell division in the many-celled animals.

(4) **The Cell Theory.** — Cells were first described by Hooke, an Englishman, in 1665. The regular arrangement of the compartments in cork (Fig. 5) reminded him of the cells of the monks

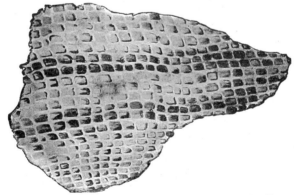

FIG. 5. — Cells of cork. Facsimile of a figure by Hooke. (From Farmer in Lankester's Zoology.)

in a monastery and suggested the term. In 1833 Brown described the nucleus as a constant cell element, and a few years later Schleiden (1838) and Schwann (1839) advanced the idea that all plants and animals are composed of cells. For many years the cell-wall was considered the important part of the structure, but later the protoplasm within it was recognized as the principal constituent, and the cell was then defined as *a mass of protoplasm containing a nucleus* (Max Schultze, 1861).

The importance attached to the cell theory may be judged from the following quotation from E. B. Wilson, the foremost investigator of cellular phenomena in this country.

" During the half-century that has elapsed since the enunciation of the cell-theory by Schleiden and Schwann, in 1838–1839, it has become ever more clearly apparent that the key to all ultimate biological problems must, in the last analysis, be sought in the cell. It was the cell-theory that first brought the structure of plants and animals under one point of view, by revealing their common plan of organization. It was through the cell-theory that Kölliker, Remak, Nägeli, and Hofmeister opened the way to an understanding of the nature of embryological development, and the law of genetic continuity lying at the basis of inheritance. It was the cell-theory again which, in the hands of Goodsir, Virchow, and Max Schultze, inaugurated a new era in the history of physiology and pathology, by showing that all the various functions of the body in health and in disease are but the outward expressions of cell activities. And at a still later day it was through the cell-theory that Hertwig, Fol, Van Beneden, and Strasburger solved the long-standing riddle of the fertilization of the egg and the mechanism of hereditary transmission. No other biological generalization, save only the theory of organic evolution, has brought so many apparently diverse phenomena under a common point of view, or has accomplished more for the unification of knowledge. The cell-theory must therefore be placed beside the evolution-theory as one of the foundation stones of modern biology."

6. Plants contrasted with Animals

It is easy to choose characteristics that will serve to distinguish a tree from a man, but the separation of the simplest animals from the simplest plants is a more difficult problem. In fact, there are at the present time a number of organisms that are claimed by both botanists and zoologists. There is no single peculiarity which can be used in all cases to discriminate between these groups of organisms. The view now generally accepted is that plants and animals originated together but have developed along divergent lines. However, certain general features can be indicated in which the two kingdoms differ. These are given in Table I ; but the reader should bear in mind that there are exceptions to every one of these criteria.

TABLE I

THE CHARACTERISTICS OF PLANTS CONTRASTED WITH THOSE OF ANIMALS

	PLANTS	ANIMALS
1. STRUCTURE	Form of body rather variable; new organs added externally.	Form of body usually invariable; organs compact and mostly internal.
2. LOCOMOTION	Usually none in adult condition.	Usually well developed.
3. IRRITABILITY	Respond to stimuli slowly; no nervous system.	Respond to stimuli quickly; nervous system present in higher forms.
4. METABOLISM	Possess chlorophyll; manufacture organic food from CO_2 and H_2O in the presence of light.	No chlorophyll; require organic food.
5. WASTE PRODUCTS	Oxygen, carbon dioxide, water.	Carbon dioxide, water, urea, fæces.

One of the principal differences between plants and animals is in their method of obtaining food and changing it into protoplasm. The processes involved are included under the term *metabolism.* Those processes which use energy to build up compounds are said to be *anabolic;* those which destroy substances to produce energy are *katabolic.* Animals, as shown in Figure 6, take in food which is digested and assimilated, that is, dissolved, absorbed, and changed into protoplasm. Oxygen is also taken in during respiration ; this unites with protoplasm (oxidation), furnishing energy and producing waste products or excretions. Animals are primarily katabolic organisms, being unable to manufacture organic compounds from simple inorganic substances.

Plants or other animals are therefore absolutely necessary for their existence.

Plants, on the other hand, are able to manufacture food from inorganic matter by a process known as *photosynthesis* (Fig. 7). Carbon dioxide and water are taken into the plant and are changed

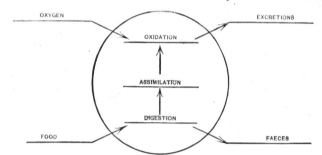

Fig. 6. — **Metabolism.**   Diagram showing the various metabolic activities of animals.

into starch by means of a green substance known as chlorophyll. Light is necessary for this process.   A by-product of photosynthesis is oxygen.

The qualities that are usually cited as being peculiarly characteristic of animals are locomotion and nervous activity.   With the exception of a few extremely sensitive species of which the

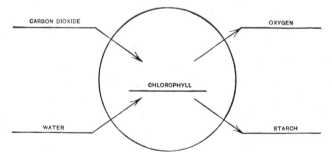

Fig. 7. — **Metabolism.**   Diagram showing the manufacture of food by plants (photosynthesis).

common sensitive plant, *Mimosa pudica,* is the most familiar example, plants respond very slowly to external stimuli, and their power of transmitting impulses is poorly developed.   Locomotion is impossible except in a few simple forms and free swimming reproductive cells.

7. Classification

It is natural when a large number of dissimilar objects are collected to attempt to place them in groups according to the presence or absence of certain characteristics. This is known as *classification*. Animals are not infinitely variable, since only about five hundred thousand species have been described, and they may be classified in several ways.

By *artificial classification* we mean the grouping of animals according to some resemblance in structure, color, habitat, etc. For example, certain animals may be said to be aquatic because they live in the water ; others terrestrial, because they live on land. Or certain animals are said to be carnivorous because they eat flesh, others herbivorous because they live on vegetable food, and still others omnivorous because they devour both animal and vegetable matter.

It is often convenient to use an artificial classification, but for all scientific work the *natural classification* is employed. This is an attempt to seek out the relationships of animals and to group them, not because of superficial resemblances, but on a basis of their similarity in structure and probable kinship. A number of large divisions, known as PHYLA, are recognized by zoologists. Each phylum is again divided into CLASSES, each class into ORDERS, each order into FAMILIES, each family into GENERA, and each genus into SPECIES.

The gray wolf, for example, belongs to the species *lycaon* of the genus *Canis*. This genus, along with others, such as the genus *Vulpes*, which contains the red fox, constitute the family CANIDÆ. The CANIDÆ are included with the bears (family URSIDÆ), the seals (family PHOCIDÆ), and a number of other groups of flesh-eating animals in the order CARNIVORA. Fifteen related orders, of which the CARNIVORA forms one, are placed in the class MAMMALIA. Mammals possess hair and mammary glands ; these characteristics distinguish them from the five other classes that make up the SUBPHYLUM VERTEBRATA, or animals possessing vertebral columns. The SUBPHYLUM VERTEBRATA, together with three other SUBPHYLA, usually called primitive vertebrates, are grouped under the PHYLUM CHORDATA, which contains animals possessing at some time in their existence an internal rod-like support known as the *notochord*.

The scientific name of any animal consists of the terms used to designate the genus and species ; this is commonly followed by the name of the zoologist who wrote the first authoritative description of that particular species. The scientific name of the gray wolf is therefore written *Canis lycaon* Schreber.

The complete classification of the gray wolf may be shown in outline in the following manner : —

Phylum CHORDATA
  Subphylum VERTEBRATA
    Class MAMMALIA
      Order CARNIVORA
        Family CANIDÆ
          Genus CANIS
            Species LYCAON Schreber.

Intermediate terms such as SUBORDER, SUBFAMILY, SUBGENUS, and SUBSPECIES are also in use. The typical grizzly bear, for example, bears the name *Ursus horribilis,* but large specimens with long ears occur in central California that belong to the SUBSPECIES *Ursus horribilis californicus.*

Zoologists do not agree as to the exact meaning of the term *species.* One authority gives the following definition : " A species may be defined as a group of interbreeding individuals which, while they may differ markedly among themselves, yet resemble each other more closely than they do those of any other group ; the characters that distinguish the group being considerable, not obliterated by intermediate forms, and inherited from generation to generation."

8. THE PRINCIPAL PHYLA OF THE ANIMAL KINGDOM

The principal phyla of the animal kingdom as outlined in the following paragraphs are presented in this place since they will be of value for reference purposes during the perusal of the more detailed accounts in the succeeding chapters. The numbers after each phylum indicate approximately the number of living species known at the present time.[1] The groups of animals of more or less uncertain systematic position have been omitted from this outline (see Chap. IX).

[1] I am indebted to Professor Henry S. Pratt for the numbers given.

(1) **Protozoa.** — Single-celled animals ; often colonial ; sperm and egg cells usually wanting. 8500.

(2) **Porifera.** — Sponges. Diploblastic (?) ; radially symmetrical, number of antimeres variable ; body-wall permeated by many pores and usually supported by a skeleton of spicules or spongin. 2500.

(3) **Cœlenterata.** — Jellyfishes, Polyps, and Corals. Diploblastic; radially symmetrical, with usually four or six antimeres; single gastro-vascular cavity; no anus; body-wall contains peculiar structures known as nematocysts or stinging cells. 4200.

(4) **Ctenophora.** — Sea Walnuts or Comb Jellies. Triploblastic; radial combined with bilateral symmetry; eight radially arranged rows of paddle plates. 100.

(5) **Platyhelminthes.** — Flatworms. Triploblastic; bilaterally symmetrical; single gastro-vascular cavity; no anus; presence of cœlom doubtful. 4600.

(6) **Nemathelminthes.** — Thread Worms. Triploblastic; bilaterally symmetrical; possess a tubular digestive system with an anus; cœlom present. 1500.

(7) **Echinodermata.** — Starfishes, Sea Cucumbers, Sea Urchins, Sea Lilies. Triploblastic; radially symmetrical; usually five antimeres; cœlom well developed; anus usually present; locomotion in many species accomplished by characteristic organs known as tube feet; a spiny skeleton of calcareous plates generally covers the body. 3000.

(8) **Annelida.** — Jointed Worms. Triploblastic; bilaterally symmetrical; cœlom well developed; anus present; segmented, somites similar. 4000.

(9) **Mollusca.** — Clams, Snails, Devilfishes. Triploblastic; bilaterally symmetrical; anus and cœlom present; no segmentation; shell usually present; the characteristic organ is a ventral muscular foot. 60,000.

(10) **Arthropoda.** — Crabs, Insects, Spiders, Centipedes, Scorpions, Ticks. Triploblastic; bilaterally symmetrical; anus present; cœlom poorly developed; segmented, somites usually more or less dissimilar; paired, jointed appendages present on all or a part of the somites; chitinous exoskeleton. 400,000.

(11) **Chordata.** — Amphioxus, Sea Squirts, Vertebrates. Triploblastic; bilaterally symmetrical; anus and cœlom present;

segmented; gill slits and a rod called the notochord present in some stage of life history ; central nervous system on dorsal side of alimentary canal. 30,000.

Zoologists do not agree as to the number of phyla into which the animal kingdom should be divided. Some authorities recognize only eight, while others maintain that there should be as many as twenty, or even more. Two sub-kingdoms are generally recognized, Protozoa (Phylum 1) and Metazoa (Phyla 2–11). Recently many zoologists have come to believe that the sponges (Phylum 2) should be separated from other Metazoa and called the Parazoa.

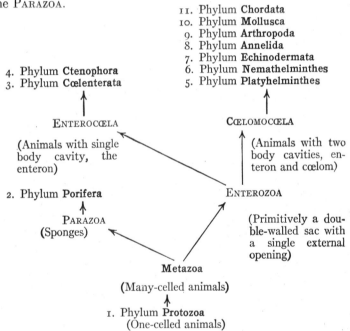

11. Phylum **Chordata**
10. Phylum **Mollusca**
9. Phylum **Arthropoda**
8. Phylum **Annelida**
7. Phylum **Echinodermata**
6. Phylum **Nemathelminthes**
5. Phylum **Platyhelminthes**

4. Phylum **Ctenophora**
3. Phylum **Cœlenterata**

ENTEROCŒLA

(Animals with single body cavity, the enteron)

2. Phylum **Porifera**

PARAZOA
(Sponges)

CŒLOMOCŒLA

(Animals with two body cavities, enteron and cœlom)

ENTEROZOA

(Primitively a double-walled sac with a single external opening)

Metazoa
(Many-celled animals)

1. Phylum **Protozoa**
(One-celled animals)

Fig. 8. — **Classification.** Diagram showing one way of classifying animals.

Figure 8 shows by a diagram one method of classification; this is modified from Lankester's " Treatise on Zoology," Part II, p. 2.

9. Zoology and its Subsciences

Zoology is the science of animals, but the facts about animals and the methods of studying them have become so numerous that one man in his lifetime can master and become an authority on only one, or at most a few phases of the subject. It has, therefore, been found necessary and convenient to divide Zoology into subsciences. The principal subsciences are named and very briefly defined in Table II.

TABLE II

ZOOLOGY AND ITS SUBSCIENCES

Zoology (Gr. *zoön*, animal; *logos*, discourse). The scientific study of animals.

Morphology (Gr. *morphe*, form; *logos*, discourse). The study of form and structure.

Anatomy (Gr. *anatemno*, cut up).
The study of the structure of organisms as made out by dissection.

Histology (Gr. *histos*, tissue; *logos*, discourse).
The study of the microscopic structure of tissues.

Taxonomy (Gr. *taxis*, arrangement; *nomos*, law).
The study of the laws and principles of classification.

Zoogeography (Gr. *zoön*, animal; geography).
The study of the geographical distribution of animals.

Paleontology (Gr. *palaios*, ancient; *onta*, beings; *logos*, discourse).
The study of fossil organisms.

Teratology (Gr. *teras*, wonder; *logos*, discourse).
The study of malformations and monstrosities in organisms.

Phylogeny (Gr. *phylon*, tribe; *gennao*, produce).
The study of the ancestral history of organisms.

Physiology (Gr. *phusis*, nature; *logos*, discourse). The study of functions.

Embryology (Gr. *em*, in; *bruo*, bud).
The study of the early developmental stages of animals.

Pathology (Gr. *pathos*, suffering; *logos*, discourse).
The study of the nature of diseases, and their causes and symptoms.

Physiology (Gr. *phusis*, nature; *logos*, discourse).
The study of the functions of organisms.

Ecology (Gr. *oikos*, house; *logos*, discourse).
The study of the relations of organisms to their environment.

Psychology (Gr. *psuche*, mind; *logos*, discourse).
The study of the mind.

Sociology (L. *socius*, companion; *logos*, discourse).
The study of animal societies.

10. THE HISTORY OF ZOOLOGY

Very little of our knowledge of zoology is due to the efforts of men of the present generation, but has been accumulating for hundreds of years as a result of the investigations of many thousands of scientists who devoted their lives to the study of animals (Plate I).

Aristotle (384–322 B.C.). — The first great historical work of zoological nature is that of Aristotle, a Greek scientist whose greatest works were on the natural history and development of animals. He was a critical compiler and in his work reveals a remarkable knowledge of *comparative anatomy, physiology,* and *embryology.*

Linnæus (1707–1778). — Aristotle's work was considered authoritative for twenty centuries, and, since the Middle Ages are a blank so far as zoological progress is concerned, we may pass on to the time of the great Swedish scientist, Linnæus. The contribution of this eminent biologist was to place systematic zoology on a firm basis. He succeeded in listing 4,378 different species of animals and plants and stimulated activity in this field.

Cuvier (1769–1832). — The comparison of the structures of animals brought about by the systematic work of Linnæus lead to the development of the subject of *comparative anatomy.* Cuvier of France was one of the foremost students of this branch of zoology. He studied fossil as well as living animals and founded the science of vertebrate *paleontology.*

Johannes Müller (1801–1858). — Following the work of Harvey, who discovered the circulation of the blood in 1621, and of other early physiologists, came Müller, the founder of modern *comparative physiology.* Müller used the microscope in his work and brought to the study of his subject a knowledge of physics and chemistry which are of the greatest importance in the study of physiological processes.

Charles Darwin (1809–1882). The theory of special creation was largely replaced during the past century by that of organic evolution through the appearance in 1859 of Darwin's Book, *The Origin of Species by Means of Natural Selection.* Arguments in favor of this theory have been derived particularly from the study of comparative anatomy, phylogeny, embryology, classification, geographical distribution and paleontology. At the present time zoologists accept organic evolution as a fact, but are actively engaged in efforts to discover how it has taken place.

Gregor Mendel (1822–1884). We have to thank an Austrian Monk, Mendel, for pointing the way to our modern methods of

PLATE I. A, Linnæus (1707–1778). B, Darwin (1809–1882). C, Mendel (1822–1884). D, Pasteur (1822–1895). (A and C from Newman; B, from Davenport; D, from Peabody and Hunt.)

studying *heredity* and *genetics*. Mendel crossed different kinds of peas and found that the offspring all resembled one of the parents. When these offspring were inter-bred, however, three-fourths of their offspring resembled one grandparent and one-fourth resembled the other grandparent. This and other facts published by Mendel in 1865 and 1866 were rediscovered in 1900 and have led to the principal advances in our knowledge of heredity and genetics during the past twenty-five years. Certain of these facts comprise what is known as Mendel's Law.

Pasteur (1822–1895). Pasteur was a chemist but is most famous because of his discoveries in the realms of *microbiology*. He was particularly fortunate in combining pure science and applied science. Thus he proved that living microorganisms cause fermentation and suggested that various substances could be preserved by heating them to a temperature high enough to kill these germs (*pasteurization*). He saved the silkworm industry of France and Italy by discovering the microorganism that was killing the insects. His scientific work with microorganisms paved the way for many later discoveries that have been of enormous benefit to mankind.

The work of such men as mentioned above and thousands of others who have made notable contributions to zoology is being continued by the zoologists of the present day in the laboratories of our colleges and universities, biological stations, research institutions, zoological museums, and state and national institutions. Perhaps the work of some of these men will in the future be ranked with that of the great zoologists of the past.

CHAPTER II

PHYLUM PROTOZOA [1]

THE PROTOZOA (Gr. *prōtos*, first ; *zoön*, an animal) are mostly microscopic animals, although some of the commonest species, like *Paramœcium* (Fig. 35), are visible to the naked eye. They are the simplest of all animals, consisting of but a single cell. Nevertheless, most of the activities characteristic of the many-celled, complex animals are exhibited by them, usually in a simpler form. In many cases PROTOZOA are colonial ; that is, a number of individuals of one species are more or less intimately associated into a colony (Fig. 25).

The PROTOZOA are separated into classes according to the presence or absence of locomotor organs and the character of these when present. Four classes are usually recognized :

Class I. SARCODINA (Gr. *sarx*, flesh), with pseudopodia (Fig. 9) ;

Class II. MASTIGOPHORA (Gr. *mastix*, whip ; *phero*, bear), with flagella (Fig. 22) ;

Class III. SPOROZOA (Gr. *spora*, seed ; *zoön*, animal), without locomotor organs in adult stage (Fig. 34) ; and

Class IV. INFUSORIA (Lat. *infusus*, poured into, crowded in); with cilia (Fig. 35).

---

[1] The PROTOZOA are the simplest of all animals and only under exceptional circumstances can they be seen with the naked eye. Nevertheless these minute organisms exhibit all of the essential biological characteristics attributed to the most complex animals. *Amœba proteus* and *Paramœcium caudatum* are among the commonest of all PROTOZOA and should be studied in detail in order to obtain a satisfactory knowledge of the principles of morphology and physiology in this phylum. Here we find illustrated the characteristics of living matter as described in general in Chapter I, and learn how these minute organisms maintain themselves and their race in their complex environment. These two species are especially favorable for the demonstration of such phenomena as protoplasmic movement, animal behavior, types of metabolism and methods of reproduction. If time allows, the flagellate, *Euglena*, and the SPOROZOA, *Monocystis* and *Plasmodium*, offer interesting variations for study. The SPOROZOA are especially important, since they introduce us to animals that are parasitic and to the great subject of animal associations, as well as to pathogenic organisms. The sections on *Sarcodina in General*, *Mastigophora in General*, *Sporozoa in General*, and *Infusoria in General* are included for reference purposes, although the examples mentioned and figured are frequently met with in material usually available for laboratory study.

1. Class I. Sarcodina

a. *Amœba proteus*

The fresh-water Protozoon, *Amœba proteus* (Fig. 9), is usually selected as a type of the class Sarcodina. It is only about $\frac{1}{100}$ inch in diameter, and is therefore invisible to the naked eye. Under the compound microscope *Amœba* looks like an irregular colorless particle of animated jelly. The best way to obtain specimens for laboratory use is to collect a mass of pond weed

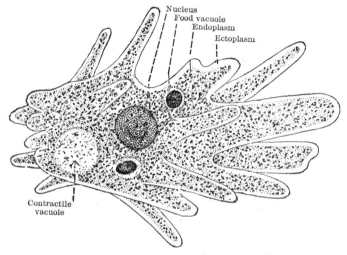

Nucleus
Food vacuole
Endoplasm
Ectoplasm

Contractile vacuole

Fig. 9. — *Amœba proteus*.   (From Kepner.)

(preferably *Ceratophyllum*), place it in a flat dish, and immerse in water. The brown scum which appears on the surface in a few days generally contains many *Amœbæ*.

Anatomy. — Two regions are distinguishable in the body of *Amœba*, the ectosarc and the endosarc. The *ectosarc* (Fig. 9), which consists of *ectoplasm*, is the outer colorless layer. It is firmer than the endosarc and is free from granules. The *endosarc* is the large central mass of granular protoplasm. Within it lies the *nucleus* (Fig. 9), which is difficult to find in living *Amœbæ*, but can easily be made out in animals that have been properly killed and stained. The nucleus is necessary for the life of the animal, since if an individual is cut in two the part with the nucleus survives, whereas the enucleated fragment dies.

It probably plays an important rôle in the metabolic activity of the cell.

A clear space filled with a fluid less dense than the surrounding protoplasm may be seen in favorable specimens. It is called the *contractile vacuole* (Fig. 9), since its walls contract at more or less regular intervals and force the fluid contents out of the body. It serves to get rid of the water taken in through the surface of the body, thus regulating the tension between the protoplasm and the surrounding medium. It is also considered a primitive excretory organ.

The solid particles of food engulfed by *Amœba* cause the formation of *food vacuoles*, which are temporary structures for the digestion of organic material. Besides the nucleus, contractile vacuole, and usually one or more food vacuoles, there are small granules or micromeres and sometimes crystals, as well as undigested particles, and foreign substances, like grains of sand, embedded in the endoplasm.

Metabolism. — Metabolism is the term applied to the series of processes concerned with the manufacture and breaking down of protoplasm. The term *anabolism* is used for the constructive processes such as the ingestion, digestion, absorption, and assimilation of food. The term *katabolism* means the breaking down of protoplasm into simpler products, and includes the processes of secretion, excretion, and respiration.

Food. — The food of *Amœba* consists of very small aquatic plants, such as *Oscillaria* and diatoms, PROTOZOA, BACTERIA, and other animal and vegetable matter. A certain amount of choice of food is exercised, or the *Amœba's* body would become overloaded with particles of sand and other indigestible material among which it lives.

Ingestion (Fig. 10). — The ingestion or taking in of food occurs without the aid of a mouth. Food may be engulfed at any point on the surface of the body, but it is usually taken in at what may be called the temporary anterior end, that is, the part of the body toward the direction of locomotion. A small amount of water is taken in with the food, so that there is formed a vacuole whose contents consist of a particle of nutritive material suspended in water. The whole process of food-taking occupies one or more minutes, depending on the character of the food. No doubt the reactions in food-taking depend upon both mechanical and chemical stimuli.

Imitations of the engulfing of food by *Amœba* have been devised, based on the theory that ingestion depends on the physical adhesion between the liquid protoplasm and the solid food.   Drops of water, glycerin, white of egg, etc., will draw into contact and engulf solid particles of various kinds.

Digestion. — Digestion takes place without the aid of a stomach. After a food vacuole has become embedded in the endoplasm, a secretion of some mineral acid, probably HCl, enters through the walls of the vacuole.   This digestive fluid seems to dissolve only proteid substances, having no effect upon fats and carbohydrates.

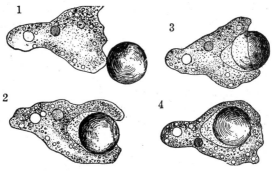

Fig. 10. — *Amœba* ingesting a *Euglena* cyst.   1, 2, 3, 4, successive stages in the process.   (From Jennings.)

Egestion. — Undigested particles, the fæces, are egested at any point on the surface of the *Amœba*, there being no special opening to the exterior for this waste matter.   Usually such particles are heavier than the protoplasm, and, as the animal moves forward, they lag behind, finally passing out at the end away from the direction of movement ; that is, *Amœba* flows away, leaving the undigested solids behind.

Assimilation. — The peptones, derived from the digestion of proteid substances, together with the water and mineral matter taken in when the food vacuole was formed, are absorbed by the surrounding protoplasm, and pass into the body substance of the animal, no circulatory system being present, so far as we know. These particles of organic and inorganic matter are then assimilated ; that is, they are rearranged to form new particles of living protoplasm, which are deposited among the previously existing particles.   The ability to thus manufacture protoplasm from unorganized matter, it will be remembered, is one of the fundamental properties of living substance (p. 9).

Katabolism. — The energy for the work done by *Amœba* comes from the breaking down of complex molecules of protoplasm by oxidation or " physiological burning." This is known as *katabolism* or *dissimilation.* The products of this slow combustion are the energy of movement, heat, and residual matter. This residual matter ordinarily consists of solids and fluids, mainly water, some mineral substances, urea and carbon dioxide. Secretions, excretions, and the products of respiration are included in this list.

Secretion. — We have already noted that an acid is poured into the gastric vacuole by the surrounding protoplasm. Such a product of dissimilation, which is of use in the economy of the animal, is known as a *secretion.*

Excretion. — Materials representing the final reduction of substances in the process of katabolism are called *excretions.* These are deposited either within or outside of the body. A large part of the excretory matter, including urea and carbon dioxide, passes through the general surface of the body. The fluid contents of the contractile vacuole are known to contain urea, therefore this organ is excretory in function.

Respiration. — The contractile vacuole is also *respiratory,* since carbon dioxide probably makes its way to the exterior by way of this organ. Oxygen dissolved in water is taken in through the surface of the body. This gas is necessary for the life of the animal ; if replaced by hydrogen, movements cease after twenty-four hours ; if air is then introduced, movements begin again ; if not, death ensues.

Growth. — If food is plentiful, more substance is added to the living protoplasm of the *Amœba* than is used up in its various physical activities. The result is an increase in the volume of the animal. This is growth, and, as in all other living organisms, growth by the addition of new particles among the preexisting particles, *i.e. growth by intussusception.*

Reproduction. — There is, however, a limit with regard to the size that may be attained by *Amœba proteus,* as it rarely exceeds .25 mm. ($\frac{1}{100}$ inch) in diameter. When this limit is reached the animal divides into two parts. Why should there be such a limit? The following explanation is given by Herbert Spencer and others. The volume of an organism varies as the cube of its diameter, the surface as the square. Thus, as an animal grows, the ratio between surface and volume decreases ; and, since *Amœba* takes in food, gives off waste material, and carries on respiration through its surface, the activities of the cell must decrease with increase in size until further growth is impossible. The solution of the problem is the division of the animal into two, whereby the ratio of surface to volume is increased. Reproduction by *binary division*, therefore, takes place when growth

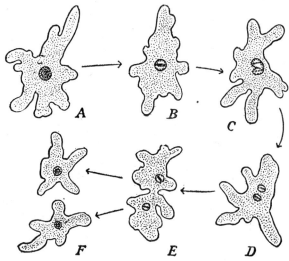

Fig. 11. — Fission of *Amœba*. **A**, *Amœba* before the onset of fission ; **B**, most of the chromatin has become concentrated in chromosomes about the equator of the nucleus ; **C**, each chromosome has divided into two, the two sets of daughter chromosomes are moving apart and the boundary of the nucleus is becoming indented between them ; **D**, the nucleus has become completely divided into two daughter nuclei ; **E**, the two nuclei have moved apart and the cytoplasmic body of the *Amœba* is undergoing constriction ; **F**, the process has been completed. (From Kerr.)

is no longer possible. It is supposed that this division is inaugurated through some unknown change in the relations between the nucleus and cytoplasm.

There are at least two kinds of reproduction in *Amœba proteus*, but neither has ever been satisfactorily worked out in detail.

They are (1) binary division and (2) sporulation.

(1) During *binary division* (Fig. 11) the nucleus divides by a primitive sort of mitosis. Then the animal elongates, a constric-

tion appears near the center, and division into two daughter cells finally takes place.

(2) *Sporulation* is apparently a rare process of multiplication in *Amœba*, and its details are not well known. First the pseudopodia are drawn in and the animal becomes spherical ; a three-layered cyst is then secreted. By successive divisions of the nucleus from five hundred to six hundred daughter nuclei are produced. Cell walls then appear, dividing the *Amœba* into as many cells as there are nuclei. These *Amœbulæ*, or *pseudopodiospores*, as they are sometimes called, break out through the cyst and become recognizable as *Amœba proteus* in about three weeks.

The Behavior of Amœba. — The sum total of all the movements of an animal constitute what is known as its *behavior*. In *Amœba* these movements may be separated into those connected with *locomotion* and those resulting from *external* and *internal stimuli*.

Locomotion. — *Amœba* moves from place to place by means of finger-like protrusions of the body, known as *pseudopodia* (Fig. 9). A pseudopodium is formed in the following manner. The ectoplasm bulges out and enlarges until a blunt projection is produced ; the endoplasm then flows into it. The result is a movement of the entire animal in the direction of the pseudopodium. If more than one are formed at the same time, there occurs a struggle for supremacy until finally one survives while the others flow back and gradually disappear. *Amœba* moves, therefore, by thrusting out pseudopodia and then flowing into them.

There are three principal theories which attempt to explain the formation of pseudopodia. (1) The *adherence theory* holds that the pseudopodium adheres on one side more strongly than on the others, and that the entire animal, therefore, moves toward the adhering side. (2) The *surface tension theory* maintains that local changes in the surface tension cause the currents which initiate movement. (3) According to the *contractile theory*, *Amœba* moves by means of a contractile substance in the following manner. In advancing the *Amœbæ* " extend the anterior end free in the water and attach it at or near the tip and then contract. At the same time the posterior end is contracting and the substance thus pushed and pulled forward goes to form the new anterior end. . . . In other cases the anterior end is lifted free (Fig. 12, I, a) and then curves down to the substratum and attaches (II, b), forming a long loop. The posterior end is then released, and the substance flows over to the anterior end. At the same time another anterior end is extended.

Amœba no doubt consists of a complex series of colloidal substances, and recent investigations indicate that the formation of pseudopodia is probably concerned with such phenomena as solation and gelation.

The most recent work seems to indicate that the body of an *amœba* is divided into three parts : (1) the *plasmasol* which is a

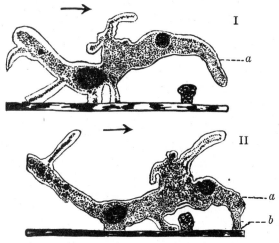

FIG. 12. — Locomotion of *Amœba proteus.* Two positions of an *Amœba* advancing in the direction indicated by the arrows. I shows a pseudopod, *a,* being thrown over and beyond an inert object. In II pseudopod, *a,* has been fixed to substratum at *b,* and the body-proper has been dragged forward by the contraction of *a.* (From Kepner, after Dellinger.)

central elongated portion, (2) the *plasmagel* which is a solid layer surrounding the plasmasol and which is divided into an outer hyaline and an inner granular portion, and (3) the *plasmalemma* which is a very thin elastic surface layer or membrane. The plasmasol and the granular portion of the plasmagel constitute the endoplasm, and the hyaline portion of the plasmagel and the plasmalemma constitute the ectoplasm. During locomotion the plasmasol continuously flows forward and at the anterior end changes into plasmagel, while at the posterior end the reverse process takes place. The plasmalemma, which is a fairly permanent structure, is sufficiently distinct to move freely over the plasmagel, and during locomotion slides forward over the plasmagel and turns down at the anterior end, where it comes in contact with the substratum. Here it adheres and remains stationary until, due to the forward movement of the *Amœba*, it is located at the posterior end, when it moves upward and forward again. The attachment of the plasmalemma to the substratum makes forward movement possible. The energy involved in forward movement is derived from several processes. 1. The plasmasol is hypertonic and the plasmagel and plasmalemma are semi-permeable, both of which result in an excess inflow of water that stretches the two outer layers until their elasticity equals the diffusion pressure. 2. There is a local swelling of the plasmagel accompanied by a decrease in its elasticity at the tip of the forming or advancing pseudopodium. 3. During the last process, there is a contraction of the remainder of the plasmagel, and a liquefaction at the inner surface of the posterior end of the plasmagel giving rise to an increase in volume in the plasmasol at this point ; both the contraction and the lique-faction tend to drive the plasmasol forward. 4. The forward flow of the plasmasol is also aided by the gelation of the plasmasol at the anterior end resulting, in a decrease in volume. When the true explanation of amœboid movement is found, it will probably give a key not only to the formation of pseudopodia but to the movement of flagella, cilia, and even muscular contraction. (From Taliaferro, after Mast in Hegner and Taliaferro's *Human Proto-zoology*.)

Reactions to Stimuli . — A turning of an animal resulting from a change in its environment, for example an increase in the intensity of the light, is known as a *"tropism"* or *"taxis."* The term " tropism " means " a turning " ; it is used for purely descriptive purposes. Nothing is known of the psychic phe-nomena of the lower animals, and one must be cautious in at-tributing to them his own mental states. The term " tropism " merely describes an animal's behavior in response to stimuli. The kind of stimulus employed is indicated by a prefix. The principal kinds of tropisms are as follows : —

(1) Thigmotropism = reaction to contact.
(2) Chemotropism = reaction to a chemical.
(3) Thermotropism = reaction to heat.
(4) Phototropism = reaction to light.

(5) Galvanotropism = reaction to electric current.

(6) Geotropism = reaction to gravity.

(7) Rheotropism = reaction to current.

" Taxis " is often employed instead of " tropism," when the terms read " thigmotaxis," " chemotaxis," etc. If the animal reacts by a movement toward the stimulus, such as light, it is said to be *positively* phototropic or phototactic, etc. ; if away from the stimulus, *negatively* phototropic or phototactic, etc. *Amœba* has been found to respond to contact with solids, to chemicals, to heat, to light, and to electricity.

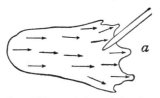 

FIG. 13. — Thigmotropism of *Amœba*. The animal moves away when stimulated by a glass rod. (From Jennings.)

Amœba exhibits negative *thigmotropism* when touched at any point with a solid object ; the part affected contracts and the animal moves away (Fig. 13). When, however, an *Amœba* is floating freely in the water and a pseudopodium comes in contact with the substratum, the animal moves in the direction of that pseudopodium until the normal creeping position has

FIG. 14. — Chemotropism of *Amœba*. The animal moves away when a little methyl green diffuses against the advancing end. (From Jennings.)

been attained. Contact with food also results in positive reactions. *Amœba*, therefore, reacts negatively to a strong mechanical stimulus and positively to a weak one.

Chemotropic reactions prove that *Amœba* is sensitive to changes in the chemical composition of the water surrounding it. " It has been shown to react negatively when the following substances come in contact with one side of its body ; methylene blue, methyl green (Fig. 14), sodium chloride, sodium carbonate, potassium nitrate, potassium hydroxide, acetic acid, hydrochloric acid, cane sugar, distilled water, tap water, and water from other cultures than that in which the *Amœba* under experimentation lives."

Negatively *thermotropic* reactions result if *Amœba* is locally affected by heat, since the animal will move away from heat stimuli. Cold and excessive heat retard its activities, which cease altogether between 30° and 35° C.

Amœba is negatively *photo-tropic*, since it will orient itself in the direction of the rays of a strong light and move away from it (Fig. 15).

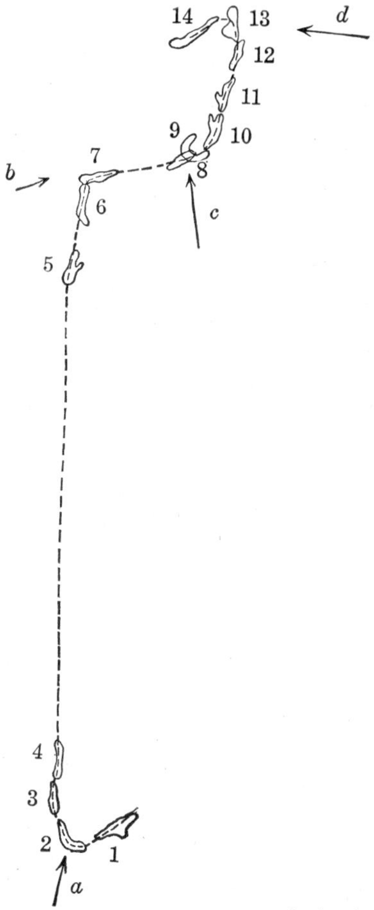

In *Amœba* there are no organs that can be compared with what we call sense organs in higher animals, and we must attribute its reactions to stimuli to that fundamental property of proto-plasm called irritability. The superficial layer of cytoplasm receives the stimulus and trans-fers the effects to some other part of the body ; thus may be shown the phenomenon of *inter-nal irritability* or *conductivity*. The stimulus causing a reaction seems to be in most cases *a change in the environment*. The behavior of *Amœba* in the ab-sence of external stimuli, for example when it is suspended freely in the water (p. 36), shows that some of its activi-ties are initiated by internal causes.

Fig. 15. — Phototropism of *Amœba*. The arrows indicate the direction of the light rays and the numbers the successive positions assumed by the animal. The *Amœba* always moves away from the source of light. (From Jennings, after Davenport.)

The reactions of *Amœba* to stimuli are of undoubted value to the individual and to the preservation of the race, for the negative reaction is in most cases produced by injurious agents such as strong chemicals, heat, and mechanical impacts, whereas positive reactions are produced usually by beneficial agents. The responses, therefore, in the former cases carry the animal out of danger, in the latter, to safety.

Amœba is of fundamental interest to animal psychologists, since it represents the " *animal mind* " in its most primitive form. Whether or not the animal is in any degree *conscious* is a question still unanswered. If *Amœba* has recognizable sensations, they must be infinitely less in both quality and quantity than those of higher organisms. Furthermore, it is unable to learn from the few kinds of experiences it does pass through, and is therefore lacking in memory images.

A review of the facts thus far obtained seems to show that factors are present in the behavior of *Amœba* " comparable to the habits, reflexes, and automatic activities of higher organisms," and " if *Amœba* were a large animal, so as to come within the everyday experience of human beings, its behavior would at once call forth the attribution to it of states of pleasure and pain, of hunger, desire, and the like, on precisely the same basis as we attribute these things to the dog."

b. *Sarcodina in General*

The PROTOZOA which are included in the class SARCODINA have been grouped into two subclasses and six principal orders according to the character of their pseudopodia and the structure of their shells, if these are present.

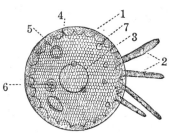

FIG. 16. — *Arcella discoides* (order LOBOSA) as seen from above, *1*, shell; *2*, pseudopodia; *3*, edge of opening into shell; *4*, thread attaching animal to interior of shell; *5*, nucleus; *6*, food vacuole; *7*, gas vacuole. (From Leidy.)

Subclass I. Rhizopoda. Typically creeping forms with lobose (branched, rootlike or fingerlike) or reticulose (anastomosing) pseudopodia.

Order 1. Lobosa. RHIZOPODA with fingerlike (lobose) pseudopodia. Most of the LOBOSA occur in fresh water, a few in moist earth, and some are parasites. Examples: *Amœba* (Fig. 9), *Arcella* (Fig. 16), and *Difflugia* (Fig. 17).

Arcella (Fig. 16) is common in the ooze on vegetation in freshwater ponds and ditches. It has a dome-shaped brownish shell of chitin which it secretes. The lobose pseudopodia protrude from a circular opening in the center of the flattened surface.

Difflugia (Fig. 17) is another common member of the order LOBOSA, and is found in the ooze of ponds. Its shell consists of minute particles of sand and other foreign objects held together by chitin.

Order 2. Proteomyxa. Rhizopoda with filose or reticulose pseudopodia and without shells. An example

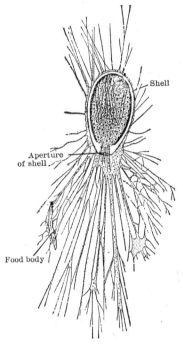

FIG. 18. — *Allogromia* (order FORAMINIFERA). (From the Cambridge Natural History.)

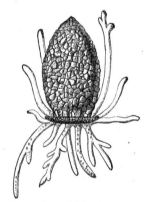

FIG. 17. — *Difflugia urceolata* (order LOBOSA) as seen from the side. The shell is composed of minute particles of sand. (From Leidy.)

of this order is *Pseudospora volvocis*, a parasite on *Volvox* (Fig. 31).

Order 3. Foraminifera. — RHIZOPODA, mostly marine, with fine, branching pseudopodia which fuse, forming a protoplasmic network. Examples : *Allogromia* (Fig. 18), *Globigerina, Discorbina.*

Allogromia (Fig. 18) lives in fresh water and has a chitinous shell. The shells of many FORAMINIFERA consist of numerous chambers connected by openings (foramina), and are composed of calcium carbonate. When these shells sink to the sea-bottom, they become Globigerina ooze, which solidifies, forming gray chalk (Fig. 19).

Order 4. Mycetozoa. Rhizopoda, semi-terrestrial in habit, reproducing by resistant spores and formation of plasmodia. These live on decaying vegetable matter and the plasmodia may

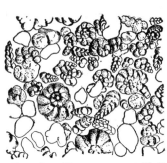

FIG. 19. — FORAMINIFERA. Shells as they exist in gray chalk. (From Scott, after a photograph by the Geological Survey of Iowa.)

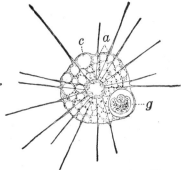

FIG. 20. — *Actinophrys sol*, a HELIOZOON. *a*, axial filaments; *c*, contractile vacuole; *g*, food vacuole. (From Calkins, after Greenacher.)

contain thousands of nuclei and contractile vacuoles. They may become several inches in diameter and are often brightly colored.

Subclass II. Actinopoda. Typically floating forms with radiating, unbranched pseudopodia.

Order 5. Heliozoa. — ACTINOPODA with thin, radially arranged pseudopodia, which are usually supported by axial threads (Fig. 20, *a*). Examples : *Actinosphærium, Actinophrys* (Fig. 20).

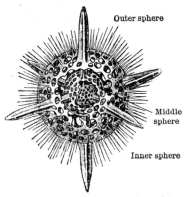

Outer sphere

Middle sphere

Inner sphere

FIG. 21. — *Actinomma asteracanthion*, a RADIOLARIAN. The shell is broken away so as to show the outer, middle, and inner spheres. (From Weysse, after Haeckel and Hertwig.)

Actinophrys (Fig. 20), the sun animalcule, lives among the aquatic plants in fresh-water ponds and ditches. The body appears vesicular, being crowded with vacuoles (*c*). The small organisms which serve as food strike the pseudopodia, pass down to the body, and are engulfed ; larger organisms (*g*) are drawn in by several neighboring pseudopodia acting together.

Order 6. Radiolaria. — Marine ACTINOPODA with raylike pseudopodia, a central perforated capsule of chitin (Fig. 21),

and usually a larger enclosing skeleton of silica. Examples :
Actinomma (Fig. 21), *Thalassicolla, Heliosphœra.*

The shells of the radiolarians, upon sinking to the sea bottom,
form radiolarian ooze ; this becomes hardened, producing rock
strata as much as 1000 feet thick. These rocks may take the form
of quartzites, flint, or chert concretions.

2. CLASS II. MASTIGOPHORA

a. *Euglena viridis*

Euglena viridis (Fig. 22) is a small greenish PROTOZOON which
will serve to point out the characteristics of the MASTIGOPHORA.
It lives in small bodies of fresh water, and may appear in amœba
cultures.

Anatomy. — *Euglena* (Fig. 22) is a simple elongated cell, and,
although somewhat *elastic*, maintains a more or less constant
shape. It possesses, in addition to *ectosarc* and *endosarc*, a thin
outer membrane, the *cuticle*, which is striated, as shown in Figure
22, *B.* Near the center of the anterior end is a long slender
whiplike process, the *flagellum*, which extends out from an opening called the *mouth* (Fig. 22, *A.*) From the mouth a tubular
" *gullet* " leads to a permanent vesicle, the *reservoir* (*A*) ; into
this reservoir several *contractile vacuoles* (*A*) discharge their contents. Close to the reservoir is a protoplasmic mass containing
granules of a red coloring matter, *hæmatochrome;* this is called
the *stigma* or *eye-spot* (*A*) because it is supposed to be especially
sensitive to light. Near the center of the body is a *nucleus* (*A*),
and scattered about in the protoplasm are many oval bodies,
greenish in color, called *chromatophores* (*A*).

Physiology. — *Nutrition.* — *Euglena* probably does not ingest
solid particles by means of the mouth and gullet, but *manufactures
its own food by the aid of the chlorophyll contained in the chromatophores.* As in plants, this chlorophyll is able, in the presence
of light, to break down the carbon dioxide (CO_2), thus setting
free the oxygen, and to unite the carbon with water, forming a
substance allied to starch, called *paramylum* (Fig. 22, *A* and *B*).
This mode of nutrition is known as *holophytic.* Some organic
substances are probably absorbed through the surface of the body,
that is, *saprophytic* nutrition supplements the holophytic.
Euglena differs from most animals in its method of nutrition, since

the majority of them ingest solid particles and are said to be *holozoic.*

Behavior. — *Locomotion*. — *Euglena* because of its elasticity is able to squirm through small openings, but its chief method of

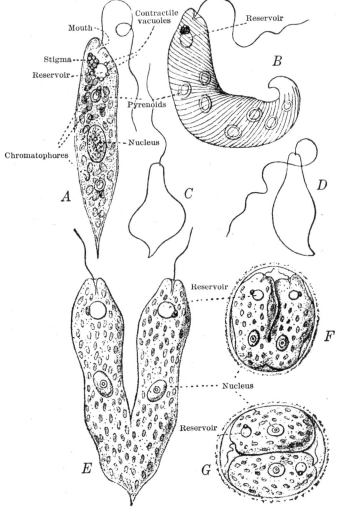

Fig. 22. — *Euglena viridis.* **A**, view of free-swimming specimen showing details of structure; **B**, another animal showing change of shape and striations; **C** and **D**, outlines showing stages of contraction; **E**, reproduction by longitudinal fission; **F** and **G**, division within a cyst. (A–D, from Bourne; E–G, from Bourne, after Stein.)

locomotion is *swimming.* The flagellum, consisting of an external layer of elastic substance enclosing a number of fibrils called myonemes, bends to and fro, drawing the animal along.

Reactions to Stimuli. — *Euglena* is very sensitive to light, and is a favorable object for the study of *phototropism.* It swims toward an ordinary light such as that from a window, and if a culture containing *Euglenæ* is examined, most of the animals will be found on the brightest side. This is of distinct advantage to the animal, since light is necessary for the assimilation of carbon dioxide by means of its chlorophyll. If a drop of water containing *Euglenæ* is placed in the direct sunlight and then one half of it is shaded, the animals will avoid the shady part and also the direct sunlight, both of which are injurious to them, and will remain in a small band between the two in the light best suited for them, that is, their *optimum* (Fig. 23). By shading various portions of the body of a *Euglena* it has been found that the region in front of the eyespot is more sensitive than any other part. It should be noted that when *Euglenæ* are swimming through the water it is this anterior end which first reaches an injurious environment; the animals give the avoiding reaction at once, and are thus carried out of danger.

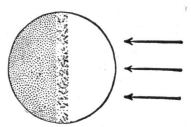

Fig. 23. — Phototropism of *Euglena.* Diagram showing the reaction of *Euglenæ* to light. The light comes from the directions indicated by the arrows, while the opposite side of the vessel is shaded, as indicated by the dots. The *Euglenæ* gather in the intermediate region across the middle. (From Jennings.)

Reproduction. — Reproduction in *Euglena* takes place by *binary longitudinal division* (Fig. 22, *E*). The nucleus divides by a primitive sort of mitosis. The body begins to divide at the anterior end. The old flagellum is retained by one half, while a new flagellum is developed by the other. Frequently *Euglenæ* become spherical and secrete a gelatinous covering, called a *cyst.* Periods of drought are successfully passed while in the encysted condition, the animals becoming active when water is again encountered. Sometimes division takes place during encystment (Fig. 22 *F, G*). One cyst usually produces two *Euglenæ*, although these may divide while still within the old cyst wall, making four in all. Thirty-two young flagellated *Euglenæ* may escape from a single cyst.

FIG. 24. — *Mastigamœba reptans*, a FLAGELLATE.

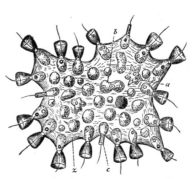

FIG. 25. — *Proterospongia haeckeli*, a colonial CHOANOFLAGELLATE. *a*, ameboid cell ; *b*, a cell dividing ; *c*, cell with small collar ; *z*, jelly. (From the Cambridge Natural History, after Kent.)

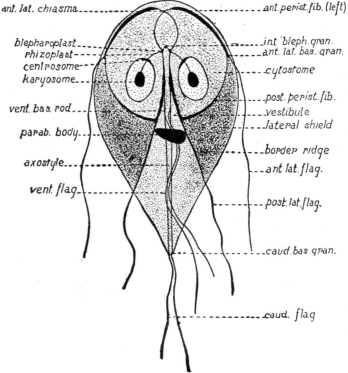

ant. lat. chiasma

ant. perist. fib. (left)

blepharoplast
rhizoplast
centrosome
karyosome

int. bleph. gran.
ant. lat. bas. gran.

cytostome

vent. bas. rod

post. perist. fib.
vestibule
lateral shield

parab. body

axostyle

border ridge
ant. lat. flag.

vent. flag.

post. lat. flag.

caud. bas. gran.

caud. flag

FIG. 26. — *Giardia lamblia*. Motile flagellate showing details of structure. (After Simon.)

44

b. *Mastigophora in General*

The MASTIGOPHORA may easily be distinguished from other PROTOZOA by the presence of one or more flagella. Two subclasses and nine orders may be recognized as follows :

SUBCLASS I. ZOOMASTIGINA. Animal-like flagellates.

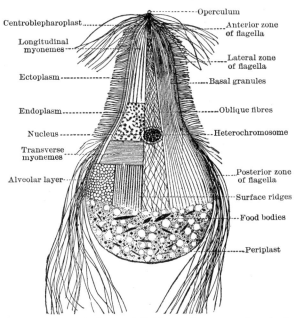

FIG. 27. — Diagrammatic figure of *Trichonympha campanula*. Sections of the body show the structures found at different levels. Surface ridges form the outer layer with their rows of flagella ; beneath are successively the oblique fibers, alveolar layer and transverse myonemes. In the endoplasm are the longitudinal myonemes. × 300. (From Kofoid and Swezy.)

Order 1. Pantastomina. Holozoic ; no mouth opening ; food ingested by means of pseudopodia anywhere on body surface. Example, *Mastigamœba* (Fig. 24).

Order 2. Protomonadina. Holozoic, saprophytic, or entozoic. These are mostly small flagellates including a number that inhabit the intestinal tract and blood stream of man. Here also belong certain species with peculiar collar-like structures, the so-called choanoflagellates. An interesting species of this group is the colonial form, *Proterospongia* (Fig. 25).

Order 3. Distomatina. Mostly entozoic; body bilaterally symmetrical ; 4 to 8 flagella arranged in pairs. A typical example of this order is *Giardia lamblia* (Fig. 26) that lives in the duodenum of man.

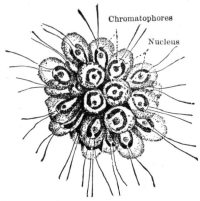

FIG. 28. — *Synura uvella*, a colonial flagellate. (From Calkins.)

Order 4. Hypermastigina. All entozoic in the intestine of insects. These possess many flagella, as illustrated in *Trichonympha campanula* which lives in termites (Fig. 27).

SUBCLASS II. PHYTOMASTIGINA. Plant-like flagellates.

Order 5. Chrysomonadina. Holozoic or holophytic with one or two yellowish chromatophores and one or two flagella. Some of the members of this order form colonies, such as *Synura uvella* (Fig. 28) which causes the " oily odor ". in certain reservoirs of drinking water.

Order 6. Cryptomonadina. Holophytic or saprophytic, with two flagella associated with œsophagous-like canal and contractile vacuole. *Chilomonas* (Fig. 29) is a very common member of this order.

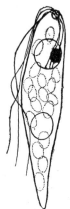

FIG. 30. — *Euglenamorpha hegneri.* An entozoic euglenoid with three flagella living in the intestine and rectum of tadpoles. From a living specimen. × 1600. (After Hegner.)

Order 7. Euglenoidina. Holozoic, holophytic or saprophytic, with one or two flagella. *Euglena* (Fig. 22) is a common representative of this order. A species recently described as *Euglenamorpha hegneri* (Fig. 30) has from three to six flagella; it lives in the intestine of tadpoles.

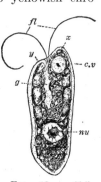

FIG. 29. — *Chilomonas*, a FLAGELLATE. *c.v*, contractile vacuole ; *fl*, flagella ; *g*, gullet ; *nu*, nucleus ; *x*, dorsal or upper lip ; *y*, ventral or lower lip. (From Jennings.)

Order 8. Phytomonadina. Holophytic, with body covered with cellulose wall and without mouth opening. Colony formation is of frequent occurrence in this group and is especially complex in *Volvox globator* (Fig. 31). This species lives in fresh-water ponds and may consist of as many as twelve thousand cells. Protoplasmic strands connect each cell with those that surround it (Fig. 31 *B*); physiological

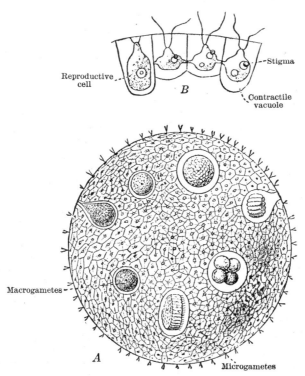

Fig. 31. — *Volvox globator;* a large colonial FLAGELLATE. **A**, a sexually ripe colony, showing microgametes and macrogametes in various stages of development. **B**, a portion of the edge of the colony highly magnified, showing three flagellate cells united by protoplasmic threads, and a single reproductive cell. (From Bourne, after Kölliker.)

continuity is thus established. All of the cells are not alike, since some of them, the germ cells, are able to produce new colonies, but others, called somatic or body cells, have no reproductive power.

Some of the germ cells, the parthenogonidia, grow large, divide into many cells, drop into the center of the mother colony, and finally escape through a break in the wall. Other germ cells pro-

duce by division a great number of minute microgametes or spermatozoa, and still others grow large, becoming macrogametes
or eggs.   The eggs are fertilized by the spermatozoa, and, after
a resting stage, develop into
new colonies.

Order 9.   Dinoflagellata.

Holozoic or holophytic, with
two flagella, one at the anterior end, the other passing

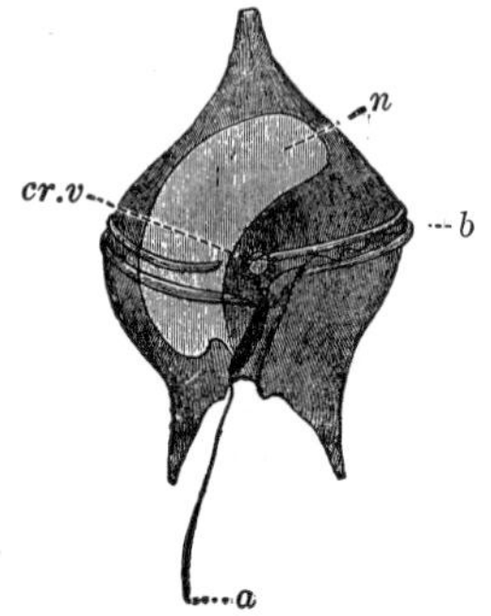

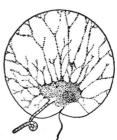

FIG. 32. — *Peridinium di-
vergens*, a DINOFLAGELLATE.
a, flagellum of longitudinal
groove;   *b*,   flagellum   of
transverse groove ; *cr. v*, contractile vacuole surrounded
by   formative   vacuoles;
n, nucleus. (From the Cambridge   Natural   History,
after Schütt.)

FIG. 33. — *Noctiluca
miliaris*, a DINOFLAGEL-
LATE.   (From Weysse,
after Cienkowski.)

around the body, often in a groove.   Examples: *Peridinium*
(Fig. 32), *Noctiluca* (Fig. 33).

Enormous numbers of *Noctiluca* are often found floating near
the surface of the sea, giving it the appearance, as Haeckel says,
of " tomato soup."   At night they are phosphorescent, emitting
a bluish or greenish light.

3. CLASS III.   SPOROZOA

a. *Monocystis*

Monocystis (Fig. 34) is a SPOROZOON easily obtained for study
in the laboratory, since it is a parasite in the seminal vesicles of
the   common   earthworm.   It   is   about $\frac{1}{100}$ inch   long.   No
locomotor organs of any kind are present.   The life history of
Monocystis is shown in Figure 34, and may be described briefly
as follows.

The animals are in some unknown way transferred from one
earthworm to another as *spores* (Fig. 34, *K*), each containing

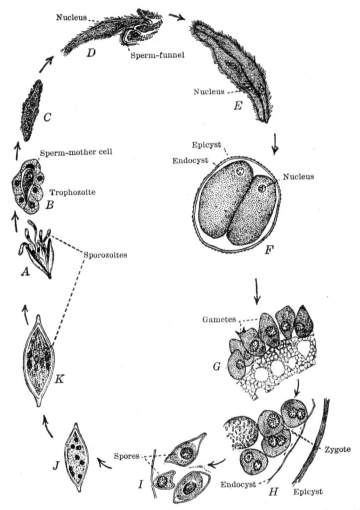

Fig. 34. — *Monocystis*, a gregarine parasitic in the seminal vesicle of the earthworm. *A*, the eight sporozoites escaping from the sporocyst. *B*, young trophozoite among sperm-mother cells. *C*, a free individual with a few withered sperm cells adhering to it. *D*, a mature individual attached to the sperm-funnel of the earthworm. *E*, two mature individuals joined side by side. *F*, two individuals have formed a cyst. *G*, gametes formed within the cyst. *H*, conjugation of gametes to form zygotes. *I*, zygotes that have become spores. *J*, a single spore containing eight nuclei. *K*, a fully developed spore containing eight sporozoites. (From Hegner, after Cuénot and Bourne.)

eight elongated bodies called *sporozoites* (K, A). Each sporozoite penetrates a bundle of sperm mother cells (B) of the earthworm, and is then termed a *trophozoite* (B). Here it lives at the expense of the cells among which it lies. The spermatozoa of the earthworm, which are deprived of nourishment by the parasite, slowly shrivel up (C), finally becoming tiny filaments on the surface of the trophozoite (D).

When this stage is reached, two trophozoites come together (E) and are surrounded by a common two-layered *cyst wall* (F). Each then divides, producing a number of small cells called *gametes* (G). The gametes unite in pairs (H) to form *zygotes*. It is probable that the gametes produced by one of the trophozoites do not fuse with each other, but with gametes produced by the other trophozoite enclosed in the cyst. Each zygote becomes lemon-shaped, and secretes a thin hard wall about itself. It is now known as a *sporoblast* (I). The nucleus of the sporoblast divides successively into two, four, and finally eight daughter nuclei (J); each of these, together with a portion of the cytoplasm, becomes a *sporozoite* (K, A).

b. *Plasmodium vivax*

One of the best known of all the SPOROZOA is *Plasmodium vivax*, which causes tertian malarial fever. This minute animal was discovered in 1880 in the blood of malaria patients by a French military doctor, Laveran. It was suggested by this investigator, in 1891, that the parasite is probably transmitted from man to man by some blood-sucking insects, and this hypothesis was proved to be correct by the work of Sir Ronald Ross in 1899. Not only was it demonstrated that malaria is spread by insects, but it was proved that human beings can only become infected by the bite of a diseased mosquito belonging to the genus *Anopheles*. The two most common genera of mosquitoes are *Culex* and *Anopheles*. One of the easiest methods of distinguishing one from the other is by observing their position when at rest. It will be found that the harmless *Culex* holds its abdomen approximately parallel to the surface on which it alights, whereas the abdomen of *Anopheles* is held at an angle.

There are three well known types of malaria ; these may be recognized by the intervals between successive chills. (1) *Tertian fever*, caused by *Plasmodium vivax*, is characterized by an attack every forty-eight hours ; (2) *quartan fever,* caused by *Plasmodium malariæ,* with an attack every seventy-two hours, and (3) *estivo-autumnal* or *subtertian fever,* caused by *Plasmodium falciparum,* produces attacks daily, or more or less constant fever. The life histories of these three species of *Plasmodium* differ very slightly one from another.

Malarial fever is transmitted by diseased female mosquitoes only. The mouth parts of these insects are adapted for piercing. When they have been thrust into the skin of the victim, a little saliva is forced into the wound. This saliva contains a weak poison, which is supposed to prevent the coagulation of the blood and thus the clogging of the puncture. Blood is sucked up by the mouth parts into the alimentary canal of the mosquito; this process occupies from two to three and a half minutes. With the saliva a number of parasites, which were stored in the salivary glands of the insect, find their way into the wound. The human blood corpuscles are immediately entered by the parasites, and their contents slowly consumed. Finally the blood corpuscle breaks down, and the spores, which were formed within it by the parasite, escape.

The malaria parasite multiplies very rapidly, and the " chill " so characteristic of the disease results either from the simultaneous destruction of great numbers of blood corpuscles or from the liberation of a poison produced by the parasites. When a mosquito bites a malaria patient, it sucks up some of the parasites with the blood. These parasites pass through part of their life history within the alimentary canal and body cavities of the insect, and, after a period of multiplication, make their way into the salivary glands. They are then ready to be injected into the next human being the mosquito bites. Quinine is the remedy commonly used against the malarial parasite. It acts directly upon the younger stages of the organism, causing their death.

c. *Sporozoa in General*

The SPOROZOA are PROTOZOA without motile organs. They are parasitic in METAZOA. Reproduction is mainly by spore formation. The following classification is simplified from Minchin's account in Lankester's *Treatise on Zoology,* Part I.

SUBCLASS I. TELOSPORIDIA .— SPOROZOA in which the life of the individual ends in spore formation.

Order 1. Gregarinæ. — TELOSPORIDIA possessing a firm pellicle and complex ectosarc; intracellular during the early stages of the life cycle, later free in the body cavities of invertebrates. Examples: *Monocystis* (Fig. 34), *Porospora, Gregarina.*

Monocystis (Fig. 34) may be found in the seminal vesicles of almost every earthworm; *Gregarina* is a common parasite of the cockroach; and *Porospora gigantea*, which reaches a length of two-thirds of an inch, inhabits the alimentary canal of the lobster.

Order 2. Coccidia. — TELOSPORIDIA simple in structure ; trophozoite is a minute intracellular parasite. Example: *Coccidium.*

Members of this order are sometimes found in the liver and intestine of man and other vertebrates, and in ARTHROPODA and MOLLUSCA.

Order 3. Hæmosporidia. — TELOSPORIDIA parasitic in the blood of vertebrates. Example: *Plasmodium* (p. 50).

SUBCLASS II. NEOSPORIDIA. — SPOROZOA which give rise to spores at intervals during active life.

Order 1. Myxosporidia. — NEOSPORIDIA with ameboid intercellular trophozoite. Example: *Myxidium.*

The MYXOSPORIDIA are parasitic especially in fish, frequently causing serious epidemics in aquaria.

Order 2. Microsporidia. — NEOSPORIDIA with small spores usually with one polar capsule.

Example: *Nosema.*

The MICROSPORIDIA are principally parasitic on insects. *Nosema bombycis* produces the silkworm disease, pébrine. Pasteur discovered that the infective stages of this parasite penetrate into the eggs of the silkworm moth before they are laid. The caterpillars that hatch from these eggs are infected. By selecting eggs from healthy moths healthy caterpillars may be obtained.

Order 3. Sarcosporidia. — NEOSPORIDIA usually parasitic in the muscles of vertebrates. Example: *Sarcocystis.*

The most common SARCOSPORIDIA are *Sarcocystis miescheriana* in the muscle of the pig, *S. muris* in that of the mouse, *S. lindemanni*, rarely occurring in the muscles of human beings.

Order 4. Haplosporidia. — NEOSPORIDIA with simple spores without polar capsules.

The HAPLOSPORIDIA are mostly parasites of fish and invertebrates.

4. Class IV. Infusoria

a. *Paramecium caudatum*

Paramecia are unicellular animals visible to the naked eye if a proper background is provided. They are found in fresh water, and usually appear in cultures prepared for *Amœba* as described on page 28.

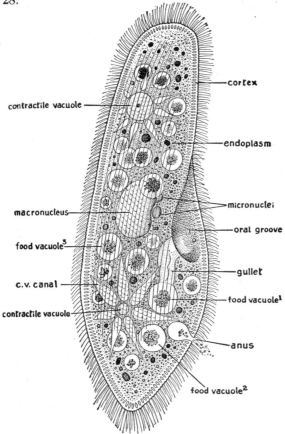

Fig. 35. — *Paramecium* viewed from the side. This is the species *P. aurelia* which has two micronuclei. (From Newman after Pfurtscheller wall chart.)

Anatomy. — *Paramecium* (Fig. 35) is a cigar-shaped animal with a depression called the *oral groove* extending from the forward end obliquely backward, ending just posterior to the middle of the body. The *mouth* is situated near the end of the oral groove.

Endosarc and *ectosarc* occur in *Paramecium* as in *Amœba*. Covering the surface is an additional membrane, the *pellicle* or *cuticle;* this can easily be seen if a drop or two of 35 per cent alcohol is added to a drop of water containing specimens. The pellicle will then be raised as a blister, and will be seen to consist of many hexagonal areas which produce *striations* on the surface.

The motile organs are thin thread-like *cilia*, one of which projects from the center of each hexagonal area of the cuticle. The beating of the cilia propels the animal forward or backward, and draws food particles into the mouth.

Just beneath the pellicle is a layer of spindle-shaped cavities in the ectoplasm filled with a semi-fluid substance. These are called *trichocysts*, and are probably weapons of offense and defense. Under certain conditions the trichocysts may be exploded, for example when a little acetic acid is added to the water, and long threads are discharged.

Two *contractile vacuoles* are present, one near either end of the body. Each communicates with a large portion of the body by means of a system of *radiating canals*, six to ten in number. These canals collect fluid from the surrounding protoplasm and pour it into the vacuole. The vacuoles contract alternately at intervals of about ten to twenty seconds. Their fluid contents are discharged to the outside. As in *Amœba*, they act as organs of *excretion* and *respiration*.

Metabolism. — The *food* of *Paramecium* consists principally of Bacteria and minute Protozoa. The cilia in the oral groove (Fig. 35) create a current of water toward the mouth. Food particles are forced down the gullet by a row of cilia which have fused side by side, forming an *undulating membrane*. At the end of the gullet a *food vacuole* is produced ; this when fully formed separates from the gullet and is swept away by the rotary streaming movement of the endoplasm, known as *cyclosis*. This carries the food vacuole around a definite course. *Digestion* occurs within the food vacuole. Undigested particles are cast out at a definite *anal spot*, which can only be seen when the *fæces* are voided. The processes of digestion, absorption, assimilation, excretion, and respiration are similar to those described for *Amœba*.

Behavior. — *Locomotion*. — If confined in close quarters, *Paramecium* exhibits *elasticity*, and can squirm through small openings; but when in a free field it *swims* by means of its cilia. These are inclined backward and obliquely, so that the body is rotated in its long axis over to the left as well as propelled forward (Fig. 36).

" The cilia in the oral groove beat more effectively than those elsewhere. The result is to turn the anterior end continually away from the oral side, just as happens in a boat that is rowed on one side more strongly than on the other. As a result the animal would swim in circles, turning continually toward the aboral side, but for the fact that it rotates on its long axis. Through the rotation the forward movement and the swerving to one side are combined to produce a spiral course. The swerving when the oral side is to the left, is to the right; when the oral side is above, the body swerves downward; when the oral side is to the right, the body swerves to the left, etc. Hence the swerving in any given direction is compensated by an equal swerving in the opposite direction; the resultant is a spiral path having a straight axis " (Fig. 36).

Rotation is thus effective in enabling an unsymmetrical animal to swim in a straight course through a medium which allows deviations to right or left, and up or down.

Reactions to Stimuli. — *Paramecium* responds to stimuli either *negatively* or *positively*. The negative *response* is known as the " *avoiding reaction* " (Fig. 37); it takes place in the following manner. When a *Paramecium* receives an injurious stimulus at its anterior end, it reverses its cilia and swims backward for a short distance out of the region of stimulation; then its rotation decreases in rapidity and it swerves toward the aboral side more strongly than under normal conditions. Its posterior end then becomes a sort of pivot upon which the animal swings about in a circle (Fig. 37, *3–5*).

Fig. 36. — Spiral path of *Paramecium*. 1, 2, 3, 4, successive positions occupied. The dotted areas with small arrows show the currents of water drawn from in front. (From Jennings.)

During this revolution samples of the surrounding medium are brought into the oral groove. When a sample no longer contains the stimulus, the cilia resume their normal beating, and the animal moves forward again. If this once more brings it into the

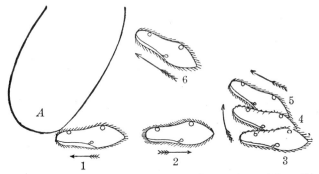

FIG. 37. — Diagram of the avoiding reaction of *Paramecium*. A is a solid object or other source of stimulation. 1–6, successive positions occupied by the animal. (The rotation on the long axis is not shown.) (From Jennings.)

region of the stimulus, the avoiding reaction is repeated ; this goes on as long as the animal receives the stimulus. The repetition of the avoiding reaction is very well shown when *Paramecium* enters a drop of $\frac{1}{35}$ per cent acetic acid. In attempting to get out of the drop the surrounding water is encountered; to this the avoiding

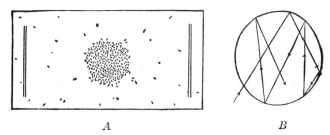

A   B

FIG. 38. — The positive reaction of *Paramecium* to acids. A, collection of *Paramecia* in a drop of $\frac{1}{50}$ per cent acetic acid. B, path followed by a single *Paramecium* in a drop of acid showing mechanism of the collection shown in A. Each time the organism comes to the boundary of the acid it gives an avoiding reaction. (From Jennings.)

reaction is given and a new direction is taken within the acid, which of course leads to the water and another negative reaction. The accompanying Figure 38 shows part of the pathway made by a single *Paramecium* under these conditions.

Paramecium responds *positively* under certain conditions. Often it comes to rest against an object, positive *thigmotropism.* When subjected to *chemical substances* or heat, it swims about in all directions, giving the avoiding reaction until it succeeds in getting into a suitable environment. This is the *method of trial and error*, that is, the animal tries all directions until the one is discovered which allows it to escape from the region of unfavorable stimulation. " For each chemical there is a certain *optimum concentration* in which the *Paramecia* are not caused to react." There is also an *optimum temperature*, which lies, under ordinary conditions, between 24° and 28° C.

Gravity stimulates *Paramecium* in some unknown way to orient itself with the forward end pointing upward, so that if a number are equally distributed in a test tube of water, they will gradually find their way to the top. In *running water, Paramecia* swim upstream, probably because the current would interfere with the beating of the cilia if any other direction were taken. The *electric current* also affects the beating of the cilia and causes certain definite movements.

Frequently *Paramecium* may be stimulated in more than one way at the same time. For example, a specimen which is in contact with a solid is acted upon by gravity, and may be acted upon by chemicals, heat, currents of water, and other stimuli. It has been found that gravity always gives way to other stimuli, and that if more than one other factor is at work the one first in the field exerts the greater influence.

Both the spontaneous activities, such as swimming, and reactions due to external stimuli, are due to *changes in the internal condition of the animal.* The physiological condition of *Paramecium*, therefore, determines the character of its response. This physiological state is a dynamic condition, changing continually with the processes of metabolism going on within the living substance of the animal. Thus one physiological state resolves itself into another ; this " becomes easier and more rapid after it has taken place a number of times," giving us grounds for the belief that stimuli and reactions have a distinct effect upon succeeding responses.

" We may sum up the external factors that produce or determine reactions as follows : (1) The organism may react to a change, even though neither beneficial nor injurious. (2) Anything that tends to interfere with the normal current of life activities produces reactions of a certain sort (' negative '). (3) Any change that tends to restore or favor the normal life processes may produce reactions of a different sort (' positive '). (4) Changes that in themselves neither interfere with nor assist the normal stream of life processes may produce negative or positive reactions, according as they are usually followed by

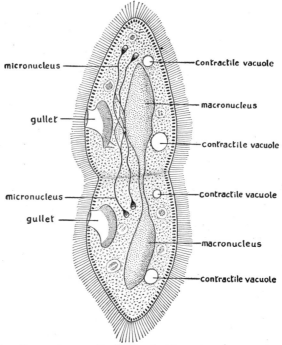

micronucleus — — contractile vacuole

gullet — — macronucleus

— contractile vacuole

micronucleus — — contractile vacuole

gullet — — macronucleus

— contractile vacuole

Fig. 39. — *Paramecium aurelia* dividing by binary fission. (From Newman after Lang.)

changes that are injurious or beneficial. (5) Whether a given change shall produce reaction or not often depends on the completeness or incompleteness of the performance of the metabolic processes of the organism under the existing conditions. This makes the behavior fundamentally regulatory."

Reproduction. — *Paramecium* reproduces only by simple *binary division*. This process is interrupted occasionally by a temporary union (*conjugation*) of two individuals and a subsequent mutual *fertilization*.

Binary fission. — In binary fission the animal divides transversely (Fig. 39). Both the macronucleus and micronucleus divide, forming daughter nuclei. A new gullet is budded off from the old gullet, and two new contractile vacuoles arise. The animal is then divided into two by a constriction. The entire process occupies from about half an hour to two hours. The daughter *Paramecia* grow rapidly and divide again at the end of twenty-four hours or even sooner, depending on the temperature, food, and other external conditions. It has been estimated that one *Paramecium* may be responsible for the production of 268,000,000 offspring in one month.

Conjugation. — The conditions that initiate conjugation are not yet known, but the complicated stages have been quite fully worked out. When two Paramecia, which are ready to conjugate, come together, they remain attached to each other because of the adhesive state of the external protoplasm. The ventral surfaces of the two animals are opposed, and a protoplasmic bridge is constructed between them. As soon as this union is effected, the nuclei pass through a series of stages which have been likened to the maturation processes of metazoan eggs (Chap. III, p. 79). Reference to Figure 40 will help to make clear the following description. The micronucleus moves from its normal position in a concavity of the macronucleus (Fig. 35), grows larger, then lengthens, forming a spindle (Fig. 40, *a*), and subsequently divides into two (*b*). These immediately divide again without the intervention of a resting stage. The resultant four nuclei (*c*) have been compared to the four spermatozoa produced by a primary spermatocyte or to an egg with its polar bodies, and the divisions are considered as the first and second maturation mitoses (see p. 80). Three of the four nuclei degenerate (*d*), the fourth divides again. During this division the granules of chromatin contained in the nuclei separate into two groups, one smaller (Fig. 41, *A*) than the other (Fig. 41). The smaller nucleus might be considered comparable to the male nucleus, the other to the female. The male nucleus migrates across the protoplasmic bridge between the two animals (Fig. 40, *f*) and unites with the female nucleus of the other conjugant (Fig. 40, *g* ; Fig. 41, *B*), forming a fusion nucleus (Fig. 40, *h*). Thus is fertilization effected.

The conjugants separate soon after fertilization (Fig. 40, *g*). The macronucleus, which up to this time has remained at rest, now assumes a vermiform shape, breaks up into small segments, and then dissolves. Shortly after separation the fusion nucleus of each conjugant divides by mitosis into two (*i*), these two into

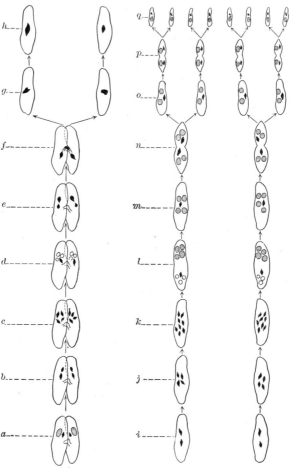

Fig. 40. — *Paramecia* conjugating. *a–q*, stages in the nuclei during conjugation and the subsequent divisions of the conjugants during the period of nuclear reconstruction. The original macronuclei have been omitted except in stage *a*. (After Calkins and Cull.)

four (*j*), and these four into eight nuclei equal in size (*k*). Four of these increase in size and develop into macronuclei (*l*) ; the other four remain micronuclei. The whole animal then divides by binary fission (*m*, *n*), each daughter cell securing two of the macronuclei and two micronuclei (*o*). Another binary division (*p*) results in four cells each with one macronucleus and one micronucleus (*q*). An indefinite number of generations are produced by the transverse division of the four daughter cells resulting from each conjugant.

The significance of conjugation cannot be definitely stated. Some investigators believe that *Paramecium* passes through a life cycle containing three distinct stages. The period of (1) *youth* is characterized by rapid cell multiplication and growth ; (2) *maturity* by less frequent cell division, sexual maturity, and the cessation of growth; and (3) *old age* by degeneration and natural death. Death is avoided by conjugation, which rejuvenates the senescent animals.

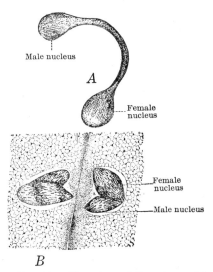

Jennings has shown that some *Paramecia* conjugate more often than others, and Woodruff has succeeded in carrying a culture through a period of over ten years without conjugation. During this time there were over twelve thousand generations. These facts " weaken the theory that conjugation is to

FIG. 41. — Two views of the micronuclei during the conjugation of *Paramecium*. A, the spindle formed during the division of the micronucleus which results in the production of a large female nucleus and a smaller male nucleus. B, the fusion of the male nucleus of one conjugant with the female nucleus of the other conjugant. (From Calkins and Cull in *Archiv f. Protist.*)

be considered the result of senile degeneration at the end of the life cycle," and show that this Protozoon " has unlimited power of reproduction without conjugation or artificial stimulation " if given a favorable environment.

A very interesting phenomenon that occurs in *Paramecium* is termed *endomixis*. In *Paramecium aurelia* (Fig. 35), a species which possesses two micronuclei, definite rhythms in division rate have been noted and the organisms regularly every 40 or 50 generations replace their old macronucleus with a new one derived

from the micronucleus. In other words, the active vegetative
macronucleus is regularly replaced by chromatin from the reserve
micronucleus just as in conjugation except that there is no admix-
ture of any foreign chromatin. During this process the macronucleus breaks down (Fig. 42, *B*) and the micronuclei undergo

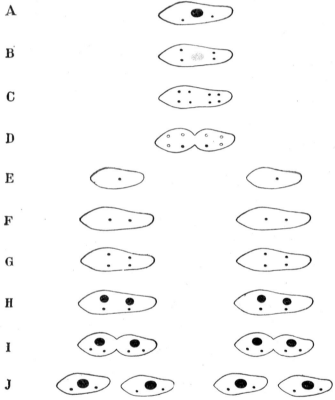

Fig. 42. — Diagram of the nuclear changes during endomixis in *Paramecium
aurelia*. **A**, typical nuclear condition; **B**, degeneration of macronucleus and first
division of micronuclei; **C**, second division of micronuclei; **D**, degeneration of six
of the eight micronuclei; **E**, division of the cell; **F**, first reconstruction micronuclear
division; **G**, second reconstruction micronuclear division; **H**, transformation of two
micronuclei into macronuclei; **I**, micronuclear and cell division; **J**, typical nuclear
condition restored. (From Woodruff.)

two divisions (Fig. 42, *B, C*). Six of these disintegrate (*D*) and
the *Paramecium* then divides, each daughter receiving one micronucleus (*E*). This micronucleus then divides twice (*F, G*) and
two of the resultant four micronuclei develops into macronuclei

(*H*).   The micronuclei divide again and the entire *Paramecium*
then divides, resulting in two daughters each with one macronucleus and two micronuclei.   Endomixis occurs also in *Paramecium
caudatum* and in certain other ciliates.   Endomixis apparently
brings about a physiological stimulation in the organism similar
to that following conjugation.

b. *Infusoria in General*

The INFUSORIA are PROTOZOA with cilia which serve as locomotor organs and for procuring food.   *Paramecium* is a typical
member of the class.   There are two subclasses, (1) CILIATA and
(2) ACINETARIA.

SUBCLASS I.   CILIATA. — INFUSORIA with cilia in the adult
stage, a mouth, and usually undulating membranes or cirri.
Many ciliates are confined to fresh water, others occur either in

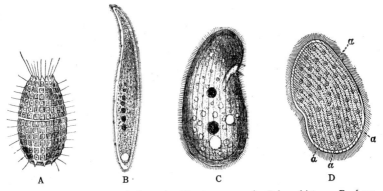

FIG. 43. — INFUSORIA of the order HOLOTRICHA. **A,** *Coleps hirtus.* **B,** *Loxo-phyllum rostratum.* **C,** *Colpoda cucullulus.* **D,** *Opalina ranarum* ; *a,* macronuclei.
(A, B, C, from Conn ; D from Lankester, after Zeller.)

fresh or salt water, and still others are parasitic in METAZOA.
There are four orders: (1) HOLOTRICHA, (2) HETEROTRICHA,
(3) HYPOTRICHA, (4) PERITRICHA.

Order 1.   Holotricha (Figs. 35 and 43). — CILIATA with cilia
all over the body and of approximately equal length and thickness.   Examples: *Paramecium* (Fig. 35), *Coleps* (Fig. 43, *A*),
Loxophyllum (Fig. 43, *B*), *Colpoda* (Fig. 43, *C*), *Opalina* (Fig. 43,
D).

The HOLOTRICHA are probably the most primitive INFUSORIA.
Paramecium caudatum is the best known species.   The species

shown in Figure 43 are frequently found in fresh-water cultures except *Opalina ranarum* (Fig. 43, *D*), which is a large multinucleate species living in the intestine of the frog. It has no mouth, but absorbs digested foods through the surface.

Order 2. Heterotricha (Fig. 44, *A*). — CILIATA whose cilia cover the entire body, but are larger and stronger about the

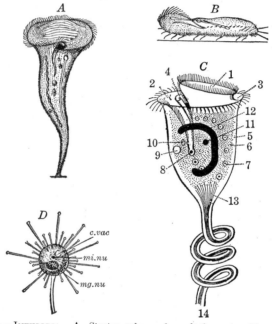

FIG. 44. — INFUSORIA. **A**, *Stentor polymorphus* of the order HETEROTRICHA. **B**, *Stylonychia mytilus* of the order HYPOTRICHA. **C**, *Vorticella* of the order PERITRICHA. **D**, *Podophrya* of the subclass SUCTORIA. *c.vac*, contractile vacuole; *mg.nu*, macronucleus; *mi.nu*, micronucleus; *1*, disc; *2*, mouth; *3*, peristomial groove; *4*, vibratile membrane in mouth; *5*, ectoplasm; *6*, endoplasm; *7*, food vacuoles; *8*, pharynx showing formation of food vacuoles; *9*, contractile vacuoles; *10*, permanent receptacle into which contractile vacuole opens; *11*, micronucleus; *12*, nucleus; *13*, contractile fibrils running into muscle in stalk; *14*, stalk contracted (the axial fiber should touch the cuticle in places). (A and B, from Weysse, after Kent; C, from Shipley and MacBride; D, from Parker and Haswell.)

mouth opening than elsewhere. This adoral ciliated spiral consists of rows of cilia fused into membranelles and leads into the mouth. Examples: *Spirostomum, Bursaria,* and *Stentor* (Fig. 44, *A*).

Stentor (Fig. 44, *A*) may be either fixed or free swimming. It is trumpet-shaped when attached and pear-shaped when swimming. The cuticle is striated and just beneath it are muscle fibers (myonemes). The nucleus is ellipsoidal, or like a row of beads.

Order 3. Hypotricha (Fig. 44, *B*). — CILIATA with a flattened body and dorsal and ventral surfaces. The dorsal surface is free from cilia, but spines may be present. The ventral surface is provided with longitudinal rows of cilia and also spines and hooked cirri, which are used as locomotor organs in creeping about. The cilia around the oral groove aid in swimming as well as in food taking. There is a macronucleus, often divided, and two or four micronuclei. Examples: *Oxytricha, Stylonychia.* A side view of a creeping *Stylonychia* is shown in Figure 44, *B*.

Order 4. Peritricha (Fig. 44, *C*). — CILIATA with an adoral ciliated spiral, the rest of the body is without cilia, except in a few species where a circlet of cilia occurs near the aboral end. Examples: *Vorticella* (Fig. 44, *C*), *Carchesium, Zoothamnium.*

The common members of this order are bell-shaped and attached by a contractile stalk. Certain species are solitary (*Vorticella*, Fig. 44, *C*), others form tree-like colonies (*Carchesium*), and still others are colonial but with an enveloping mass of jelly (*Zoothamnium*). The anatomy of *Vorticella* is shown in Figure 44, *C*. The stalk contains a winding fiber composed of myoneme fibrils; this fiber, on contracting, draws the stalk into a shape like a coil spring.

SUBCLASS II. ACINETARIA. — INFUSORIA without cilia in the adult stage. No locomotor organs are present and the animals are attached either directly or by a stalk. No oral groove nor mouth occurs, but a number of tubelike tentacles extend out through the cuticle. Examples: *Podophrya* (Fig. 44, *D*), *Sphærophrya.*

Ciliates are captured by these tentacles and their substance is sucked by them into the body. Both fresh-water and marine species are known. *Podophrya* (Fig. 44, *D*) is a well-known fresh-water form. *Sphærophrya* is parasitic in other INFUSORIA.

5. PROTOZOA IN GENERAL

PROTOZOA may be defined as unicellular animals which in many cases form colonies. An examination of the types discussed in the preceding pages will show that the PROTOZOA differ one from another in structure, physiology, and reproduction. These differences are briefly reviewed in the following paragraphs.

Morphology. — PROTOZOA vary in size from the minute blood parasites, such as *Plasmodium*, which causes malaria, to the huge gregarine, *Porospora gigantea*, which lives in the alimentary canal of the lobster and may be two-thirds of an inch long. Most of them are invisible to the naked eye.

The shapes of PROTOZOA are likewise extremely varied. *Amœba* has no fixed shape; many species are globular with radiating projections (HELIOZOA, Fig. 20; RADIOLARIA, Fig. 21); *Euglena* (Fig. 22) is spindle-shaped; *Paramecium* (Fig. 35) resembles a slipper; *Vorticella* (Fig. 44, *C*), a bell; *Stentor* (Fig. 44, *A*), a trumpet; some like *Stylonychia* (Fig. 44, *B*) have definite dorsal and ventral surfaces; in fact, almost every conceivable shape seems to occur in this group.

Most of the PROTOZOA are either faintly colored or entirely without pigment. When coloring-matter is present it often consists of chlorophyll, or some allied substance, which is contained in chromatophores, *e.g. Euglena* (Fig. 22, *A*). Drinking water is often colored red by *Euglena sanguinea*, or yellow by *Uroglena;* the surface of the sea is sometimes colored orange by vast numbers of *Noctiluca* (Fig. 33), or red by a DINOFLAGELLATE, *Peridinium* (Fig. 32).

The simplest kind of locomotor organs are *pseudopodia* like those of *Amœba* (Fig. 9). The pseudopodia of some species have a firm axial rod (HELIOZOA, Fig. 20), and those of others may branch and fuse with one another (FORAMINIFERA, Fig. 18). *Flagella* may be likened to very thin pseudopodia that have become permanent. They seem to be composed of long fibrils that are spirally wound. *Cilia* are smaller and more numerous than flagella; often they are fused together in groups forming large *cirri* (*Stylonychia*, Fig. 44, *B*), or side by side, forming *membranelles* as in the gullet of *Paramecium*.

An external covering may be absent from the body of PROTOZOA (*Amœba*) or may be present as a distinct *cuticle* (*Paramecium*). *Shells* may also occur; these consist of material secreted by the animal, *e.g.* chitin by *Arcella* (Fig. 16), calcium carbonate by FORAMINIFERA (Fig. 19), and silica by RADIOLARIA (Fig. 21), or are made up of foreign particles such as grains of sand (*Difflugia*, Fig. 17).

The *cytoplasm* of PROTOZOA is probably alveolar in structure. It can usually be separated into a firm, clear, outer layer, the *ectosarc*, and a more fluid, granular, inner mass, the *endosarc*. Within the cytoplasm are embedded one or more *nuclei, vacuoles* of several kinds, and frequently *plastids*.

A *nucleus* is always present, although in some cases its essential substance, chromatin, is scattered throughout the cells, forming a " distributed nucleus." Some PROTOZOA have two kinds of nuclei, a *macronucleus* (*Paramecium*, Fig. 35), which is supposed to have charge of the metabolic processes, and a *micronucleus*, which functions only in reproduction. During binary division the chromatin of the nucleus may form distinct chromosomes, but in many cases chromosomes have not been observed.

Vacuoles are of several kinds: (1) *permanent globules* of liquid (*Actinophrys*, Fig. 20), (2) *contractile vacuoles* (*Amœba*, Fig. 9), and (3) *food vacuoles* (*Paramecium*, Fig. 35).

Many PROTOZOA possess *plastids;* these are usually bodies of starchy food material, or colored bodies called *chromatophores*, such as occur in *Euglena*. Besides these, many other substances may be present, such as food material, indigestible matter, oil drops, grains of sand, etc.

Physiology. — *Metabolism.* — The *food* of PROTOZOA consists of organic matter both vegetable and animal. BACTERIA, diatoms, and other PROTOZOA form a large part of the bill of fare. Such species as *Euglena* do not ingest solid food, but manufacture it by means of chlorophyll.

Usually some structure is present which aids in the *ingestion* of food, but in the RHIZOPODA, like *Amœba*, there is no mouth, and food is engulfed at any point on the surface. The flagella of many flagellates and the cilia of ciliates draw or drive food particles toward the mouth and down into the gullet at the end of which a food vacuole is formed (*Paramecium*, Fig. 35). The ACINETARIA (Fig. 44, *D*) capture their prey with their tentacles and suck the contents into the body. Parasitic PROTOZOA take food directly through the surface of the body.

Digestion takes place in the food vacuoles, which are really temporary stomachs. The surrounding protoplasm secretes ferments which enter the vacuoles and dissolve certain food substances. Undigested matter is cast out at any point (*Amœba*), or at a particular spot (*Paramecium*), or through a definite anal opening (*Stentor*). Digested food passes out into the cytoplasm and is *assimilated, i.e.* is transformed into protoplasm. Figure 6 indicates that oxygen is necessary before life activities can be carried on, and carbon dioxide is given off. This is *respiration*. The oxygen is taken in through the body-wall. It combines with protoplasm, *i.e.* oxidation takes place. Free energy is a result of this oxidation, and carbon dioxide and other waste matter in solution are by-products. These by-products pass out through the body-wall, and probably by way of the contractile vacuole. The contractile vacuole may therefore be called a primitive *excretory organ*.

From the above discussion it may be concluded that the PRO-TOZOA carry on many of the activities characteristic of the higher organisms without the aid of the systems of organs we usually associate with these functions.

Behavior. — *Locomotion.* — Protozoa move from place to place either by creeping over the surface of objects (*Amœba*, Fig. 9; *Stylonychia*, Fig. 44, *B*), or by free swimming. The locomotor organs are pseudopodia, flagella, and cilia. In some PROTOZOA muscle fibrils (myonemes) are present just beneath the cuticle (*Stentor*, Fig. 44, *A*; *Vorticella*, Fig. 44, *C*); these are capable of contraction and can change the shape of the animal. In the stalk of *Vorticella* the muscle fibrils are agents for moving the bell from place to place.

Reactions to Stimuli. — Brief accounts have been given of the reactions of *Amœba* (p. 35), *Euglena* (p. 43), and *Paramecium* (p. 55) to stimuli. It has been shown that these minute organisms are capable of *spontaneous activities* and respond to a number of different *external stimuli*, which are changes in their environment. These responses are carried on without the help of a nervous system. The study of the behavior of the lower organisms has become quite prominent within the past decade and has led a prominent investigator in this field to the following conclusion. " All together, there is no evidence of the existence of differences of fundamental character between the behavior of the Protozoa and that of the lower Metazoa. The study of behavior lends no support to the view that the life activities are of an essentially different character in the Protozoa and the Metazoa. The behavior of the Protozoa appears to be no more and no less machine-like than that of the Metazoa; similar principles govern both." (Jennings, *Behavior of the Lower Organisms,* p. 263.)

Reproduction. — The usual method of reproduction in the PROTOZOA is that of *binary division.* This occurs in most of the types discussed in the preceding pages (*Amœba, Euglena, Paramecium,* etc.). During binary division the body of the PROTOZOON divides into two approximately equal parts, the daughtercells. Binary division is frequently interrupted by *conjugation* or endomixis as in *Paramecium* (p. 61). When the division of the PROTOZOON is unequal, the process is spoken of as *budding* or *gemmation.* A third method of reproduction is by the formation of *spores* (*Amœba,* p. 33; *Monocystis,* p. 48, Fig. 34).

6. PURE LINES AND SELECTION IN PROTOZOA

Protozoa were among the first animals studied by modern genetic methods after the rediscovery of Mendel's Law (see p. 26). In these animals it is possible to obtain, by asexual reproduction (binary division) from a single parent, large numbers of specimens. Such an assemblage of individuals derived from a single parent by asexual reproduction is often called a pure line. It has been demonstrated in the case of *Paramecium* and other species that a large number of different pure lines exist in nature. That is, if a number of specimens are selected at random from cultures and pure lines derived from them the members of one pure line will be found to differ in size from those of another and these size differences are inherited during asexual reproduction. There are slight differences in size within a pure line but all attempts to obtain new pure lines in *Paramecium* by selecting the largest or smallest members of a single pure line have proved futile.

Different results, however, occurred when selection was attempted with the rhizopods, *Difflugia* (Fig. 17) and *Arcella* (16). By selecting the largest and smallest individuals from a single pure line of these species for many generations it has been possible to obtain new pure lines, that is, lines that are heritably different from the original line in such characteristics as size, number of spines, and division rate. Changes such as these, that are inherited, are required for the evolution of new species, and it seems probable that the investigators who have observed heritably diverse pure lines arise from a single pure line have actually followed a process that is in part responsible for the origin of species.

7. PATHOGENIC PROTOZOA

The PROTOZOA that cause diseases are said to be pathogenic. One of the best known of these is the malarial fever parasite, *Plasmodium*. This species belongs, with many other important

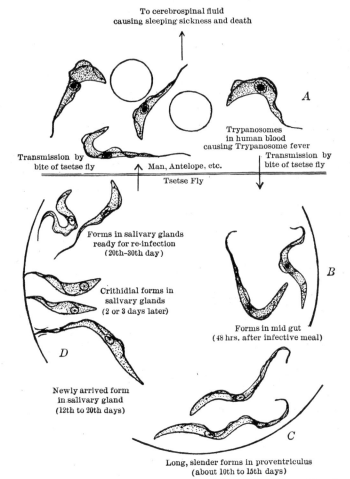

FIG. 45. — Life cycle of *Trypanosoma gambiense*. × 1500. (From Chandler, after Robertson.)

parasites, to the class SPOROZOA, but all protozoan parasites do not belong to this class. There are many injurious parasites in each of the other classes, and these affect both man and other animals. The importance of pathogenic Protozoa has but recently been recognized, and, although a vast amount of work has been done in this field, still comparatively little is known about them. A few examples of those affecting man are described in the following paragraphs.

Rhizopoda. — Minute amœba-like organisms, named *Endamœba histolytica*, are the cause of amebic dysentery, and are always found in the alimentary canal of patients suffering from this disease. They cause ulcers and other lesions.

Mastigophora. — *Trypanosoma* is at the present time the most widely studied of all parasitic Mastigophora that affect man. In certain parts of tropical Africa they cause the disease called *trypanosomiasis*, commonly known as *sleeping sickness*. Trypanosomes are also parasitic in rats and other animals. One of the species affecting man is named *Trypanosoma gambiense* (Fig. 45). It is carried from one person to another by certain species of tsetse-flies. The parasite, after gaining access to the blood of a human being, multiplies with remarkable rapidity. The nervous system of the patient is affected either directly or by a poison secreted by the parasites. The disease may last several months or even years. Irregular fever soon follows infection, and later general debility sets in. The victim exhibits an increasing tendency to sleep, gradually wastes away, and finally dies.

Sporozoa. — Of the Sporozoa which affect man, the malarial fever parasite is the most important (pp. 50–52).

Infusoria. — *Balantidium coli* is the only pathogenic ciliate of man. It causes balantidial dysentery, which sometimes ends fatally but is very rare except in certain parts of the tropics.

CHAPTER III

AN INTRODUCTION TO THE METAZOA [1]

THE METAZOA (Gr. *meta*, beyond; *zoön*, animal) are animals consisting of many cells. These cells are not all alike, as in the colonial PROTOZOA, but are separated into groups according to their structure and functions. Although every METAZOON begins its existence as a single cell, in the adult stage there are many cells, and one kind of cell cannot exist without the presence of the other kinds of cells; that is, the cells are not independent as in the PROTOZOA, but are dependent upon one another. This is the result of the *division of labor* among the cells.

There is no sharp line between the METAZOA and the PROTOZOA. The colonial PROTOZOA are many-celled animals, and, as we have seen (p. 46), *Volvox* (Fig. 31) consists of cells which are made interdependent by protoplasmic connections. There are a considerable number of animals which are intermediate between the PROTOZOA and the METAZOA, but, on the whole, the two groups are fairly well defined.

---

[1] Chapter III introduces a number of principles of great value as we proceed to the study of the METAZOA. *Division of labor among cells*, which is the fundamental characteristic of the METAZOA, results in the differentiation between germ cells and somatic or tissue cells, and in the further differentiation of the former into eggs and spermatozoa, and of the latter into various types of tissues. The grouping of these according to functions gives rise to organs and systems of organs. The general principles of reproduction serve to introduce such phenomena as fission, budding, sporulation, metagenesis, parthenogenesis, pædogenesis, the behavior of the chromosomes in the origin of eggs and spermatozoa (oogenesis and spermatogenesis), and fertilization; various types of sexuality, such as the diœcious and monœcious (hermaphroditic) conditions; self-fertilization and cross-fertilization; and oviparous and viviparous animals. An introductory discussion of the development of the individual from the egg (embryology), including cleavage, the formation of the blastual, gastrula, germ-layers and the cœlom, leads to an account of symmetry, metamerism and the adaptations of homologous and analogous appendages. These various principles are referred to frequently in succeeding chapters where abundant illustrative material is furnished. It is advisable to become well acquainted with the elements, however, as presented in this chapter, referring to the indicated figures, before proceeding to the study of the phyla of METAZOA.

72

1. Germ-cells and Somatic Cells

There are two chief kinds of cells in all the Metazoa, *germ-cells* (Fig. 46, *A, B*) and *somatic cells* (Fig. 46, *C–G*). The germ-cells, like those in *Volvox* (Fig. 31, ♂ , ♀), are set aside for *reproductive purposes only;* the somatic cells form a distinct body, which carries on all the functions characteristic of animals except reproduction. The detailed study of these two kinds of cells in all groups of the Metazoa has led to the idea that the somatic cells constitute a sort of vehicle for the transportation of the germ-cells, and that when the germ-cells become mature they separate from the body, giving rise to a new generation, whereas the somatic cells die.

2. Tissues

The somatic or body cells of the Metazoa are of various kinds, and are grouped together into *tissues.* A tissue is an association of similar cells originating from a particular part of the embryo and with special functions to perform. Some of the simple Metazoa possess only two kinds of tissue; others are made up of a great number. The many different kinds of tissues may be classified according to their structure and functions into four groups.

(1) **Epithelial tissue** (Fig. 46, *C*) consists of cells which cover all the surfaces of the body both without and within. In the simpler animals this is the only kind of tissue present. In the more complex animals epithelial cells become variously modified because they are the means of communication between the organism and its environment; nutritive material passes through them into the body, and excretory products pass through them on their way out of the body; they also contain the end organs of the sensory apparatus, and protect the body from physical contact with the outside world. In man the cuticle and the lining of the alimentary canal are examples of epithelium.

(2) **Supporting and Connective Tissues** (Fig. 46, *D*) may be encountered in almost any part of the body. Their chief functions are (*a*) to bind together various parts of the body, and (*b*) to form rigid structures capable of resisting shocks and pressures of all kinds. These tissues consist largely of non-living substances, fibers, plates, and masses produced by the cells either within the cell wall or outside of it. The tendons which unite

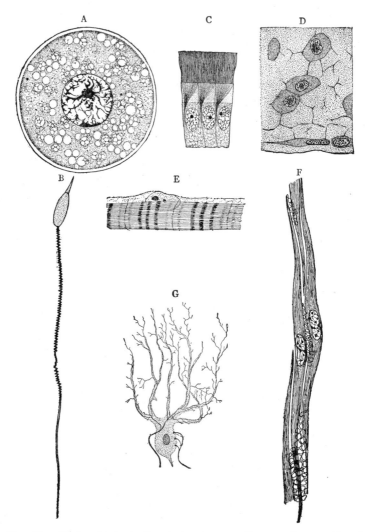

Fig. 46. — Various kinds of cells. **A**, female germ cell, ovum of a cat. **B**, male germ cell, spermatozoon of a snake, *Coluber*. **C**, ciliated epithelium from the digestive tract of a mollusk, *Cyclas*. **D**, cartilage of a squid. **E**, striated muscle fiber from an insect larva, *Corydalis cornutus*. **F**, smooth muscle fibers from the bladder of a calf. **G**, a nerve cell from the cerebellum of man. (From Dahlgren and Kepner.)

muscles to bones, and the bones and cartilage, illustrate the two kinds of tissue in this group.

(3) **Muscular tissues** (Fig. 46, *E*, *F*) are the agents of active movement. In certain PROTOZOA there are contractile fibrils called myonemes in the membranous coverings (p. 68). In most of the higher organisms special muscle cells are differentiated for performing the various movements of the body. These cells possess muscle fibrils which are able to contract with great force and in quick succession. The fibrils are usually of two kinds: (*a*) cross-striated (*E*), and (*b*) smooth non-striated (*F*). The latter form a less highly developed tissue than the former and are found in the simpler inactive animals, and in those internal organs of higher organisms not subject to the will of the animal.

(4) **Nervous tissue** (Fig. 46, *G*) is composed of cells which are so acted upon by external physical and chemical agents that they are able to perceive a stimulus, to conduct it to some other cell or cells of the body, and to stimulate still other cells to activity. All protoplasm is irritable; animals without nervous systems, *e.g.* Amœba, are capable of reacting to a stimulus, but in more complex organisms certain cells are specialized for the sole purpose of performing the functions described above as characteristic of nervous tissue.

3. Organs and Systems of Organs

An *organ* is an association of tissues which act together in the performance of certain functions. For example, the legs of human beings are organs of locomotion; they consist of a variety of tissues, including epithelial (skin), muscular (muscles), nervous (nerves), and supporting (bones) tissues.

The organs of different animals which occupy the same relative position and have a similar origin, *i.e.* are morphologically equivalent, are said to be *homologous*. Homologous organs may have similar functions, *e.g.* the legs of man and the hind legs of the horse, or they may have different functions, *e.g.* the arms of man and the wings of a bird. When the organs of different animals perform the same functions they are said to be *analogous*, *e.g.* the wing of a bird and the wing of a butterfly. In many cases homologous organs are also analogous, being morphologically equivalent and having the same functions, *e.g.* the legs of man and the legs of a bird.

Many organs are usually necessary for the performance of a single function; for example, the proper digestion of food in a complex animal requires a large number of organs collectively known as the alimentary canal and its appendages. These organs constitute the digestive system. Similarly, other sets of organs are associated for carrying on other functions. The principal systems of organs and their chief functions are as follows: —

(1) Digestive system — Digestion and absorption of food.

(2) Circulatory system — Transportation of food, oxygen, and waste products.

(3) Respiratory system — Taking in oxygen and giving off carbon dioxide.

(4) Excretory system — Elimination of waste products of metabolism.

(5) Muscular system — Motion and locomotion.

(6) Skeletal system — Protection and support.

(7) Nervous system — Sensation and correlation.

(8) Reproductive system — Reproduction.

It has been shown in Chapter II that the PROTOZOA carry on the processes of digestion, respiration, excretion, etc., without the presence of definite organs. Likewise many of the simpler METAZOA do not have special organs for the performance of certain functions, but the more complex animals are provided with well-developed systems of organs. The following paragraphs give a general account of the systems of organs and their functions in complex animals.

(1) The **digestive system** has for its functions the changing of solid food into liquids and the absorption of these liquids into the blood. This system consists usually of a tube, the *alimentary canal*, with an opening at either end of the body. Connected with this tube are a number of *glands*. Solids taken in as food are usually broken up in the mouth, where they are mixed with juices from the *salivary glands;* the mixture then passes through the *œsophagus* into the *stomach,* where chemical digestion, aided by secretions from the *gastric glands,* takes place; it then enters the *intestine,* which absorbs the dissolved material through its walls. Undigested solids travel onward into the *rectum* and are cast out through the *anus* as fæces.

(2) The **circulatory system** transports the absorbed food to all parts of the body. It also carries oxygen to the tissues and

carbon dioxide and other waste products away from the tissues. These substances are transported by fluids called *blood* and *lymph*, which are usually confined in tubes, the *blood-vessels*, and in irregular spaces known as *sinuses*. The blood consists of a plasma and corpuscles. It is forced to the various parts of the body by the contractions of muscular organs called *hearts*.

(3) The **respiratory system** takes in oxygen (inspiration) and gives off carbon dioxide (expiration). In many animals, like the earthworm, the oxygen and carbon dioxide pass through the moist surface of the body, but in higher animals there is a special system of organs for this purpose. Aquatic animals usually possess *gills* which take oxygen from the water. Terrestrial animals generally take air into cavities in the body, such as the *lungs* of vertebrates and the *tracheæ* of insects.

(4) The **excretory system** is necessary for the elimination of the waste products of metabolism which are injurious to the body. These waste products result from the oxidation of the protoplasm. Various names are applied to the organs of excretion such as *nephridia* (Fig. 153) and *kidneys* (Fig. 418).

(5) The **muscular system** enables animals to move about in search of food and to escape from their enemies. Many animals, like the oyster, have the power of *motion*, but not of *locomotion*. The muscles would be of slight efficiency were it not for the hard skeletal parts to which they are attached and which serve as levers.

(6) The **skeletal system** is either external (*exoskeleton*) or internal (*endoskeleton*). The hard shell of the crayfish is an example of an exoskeleton; the bones of man form an endoskeleton. In either case the skeleton not only supports and protects the soft parts of the body but also provides places for the attachment muscles.

(7) The **nervous system** in higher METAZOA consists of two parts, (a) *central* and (b) *peripheral*. The *brain* and *spinal cord* constitute the central nervous system. The *organs of special sense*, such as sight, smell, taste, hearing, touch, temperature, and equilibrium, and the nerves connected with them, and all other nerves connecting the central nervous system with various parts of the body, constitute the peripheral nervous system. *Afferent* (sensory) nerve fibers conduct impulses from end organs of sense, like the eye, to the brain or spinal cord.

Efferent (motor) nerve fibers conduct impulses from the brain and nerve cord to an active organ like a muscle or gland.

(8) The **reproductive system** consists of the *germ-cells*, and the organs necessary for furnishing yolk and protective envelopes, and for insuring the union of the *eggs* and *spermatozoa*. The essential reproductive organs in complex animals are usually the *ovaries*, which contain the eggs, and the *testes*, in which the spermatozoa ripen. The *accessory organs* are generally *ducts* leading to the exterior, *glands* connected with these ducts, and *copulatory organs*.

4. REPRODUCTION

(1) **Methods of Reproduction.** — In the PROTOZOA reproduction is usually by *binary fission, budding,* or *sporulation* (see pp. 32 and 48); these processes may be preceded by *conjugation*, which is a temporary or permanent union of two cells (see pp. 59–63). In the METAZOA reproduction is usually *sexual*, although *asexual* processes are normal in some species.

Sexual Reproduction. — Reproduction is said to be *sexual* when the individual develops from a mature egg which usually fuses with a spermatozoon (pp. 82–83). In many cases the egg does not unite with a spermatozoon before development; when this occurs, the term *parthenogenesis* is applied to the process. For example, certain eggs of plant lice (*Aphids*) and water fleas (*Daphnia*) normally develop parthenogenetically. In a few cases animals which have not reached maturity produce eggs which develop without being fertilized; this sort of parthenogenesis is called *pædogenesis*. For example, the larvæ of a gall-gnat, and the pupæ of a midge, produce eggs which develop without fertilization.

A species of animal in which each individual possesses only one kind of reproductive organs, either male or female, is *diœcious*. A species with both male and female reproductive organs in the same individual is *monœcious*, or *hermaphroditic*. *Hydra* (Figs. 65–72) and the earth worm (Figs. 153–159) are examples of monœcious animals; the crayfish (Figs. 200–208) is a diœcious species.

If the eggs of a monœcious animal are fertilized by the same individual, *self-fertilization* occurs; whereas, if the egg of one individual unites with the spermatozoon of another, *cross-fertilization* results.

Animals which lay eggs, like a bird or crayfish, are *oviparous;* those which bring forth young from eggs developed within the body, like mammals and certain snakes, *viviparous.*

Asexual Reproduction. — This term is applied to reproduction by means of *budding* or *fission,* and not by the production of eggs. By *fission* is meant the division of the parent into two or more equivalent parts, the daughters. This occurs frequently in PROTOZOA (*Amœba,* p. 32, *Paramecium,* p. 59, *Euglena,* p. 43), and less often in METAZOA. The fresh-water flatworm, *Planaria* (Figs. 97–102), and the annelid, *Dero,* often divide by fission. The offspring produced by *budding* are smaller than their parent. *Hydra* (Fig. 65) affords an excellent example of an organism that reproduces in this way.

Metagenesis. — Some animals reproduce by budding and do not develop eggs nor spermatozoa. Certain of the buds, however, separate from the parent and produce reproductive cells which, after fertilization, grow into budding individuals. There is here an alternation of an *asexual budding generation* with a *sexual generation.* *Obelia,* as will be explained later (Fig. 73), develops metagenetically.

(2) **The Origin of the Egg and Spermatozoon.** — *Spermatogenesis.* — The origin of the male germ-cell or spermatozoon is termed *spermatogenesis.* This process may be divided into three periods: (*a*) the *multiplication* of the primordial germ-cells or *spermatogonia,* (*b*) the *growth* of these cells, and (*c*) their *ripening* or *maturation.* These stages occur in all METAZOA from the lowest to man.

No one knows how many cells are produced during the period of multiplication. The last generation of spermatogonia (Fig. 47) gives rise by division to the *primary spermatocytes.* The latter increase greatly in size during the long growth period, and in each of them the chromosomes unite or conjugate in synapsis. Each primary spermatocyte gives rise by division to two *secondary spermatocytes.* The secondary spermatocytes immediately divide, each forming two *spermatids.* In one of these divisions the chromosomes, which united to form the bivalent chromosomes, separate, one single chromosome going to each daughter cell. This is the only known case in cell division where entire chromosomes are separated from one another, except the corresponding stage in oogenesis. It is known as a *reduction division* because it results

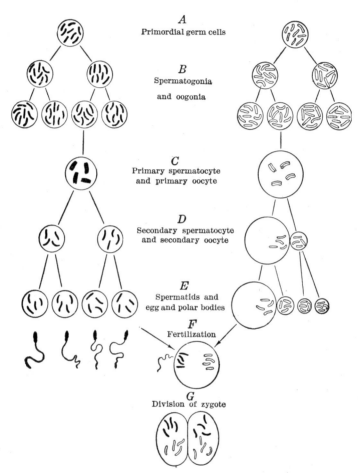

A
Primordial germ cells

B
Spermatogonia
and oogonia

C
Primary spermatocyte
and primary oocyte

D
Secondary spermatocyte
and secondary oocyte

E
Spermatids and
egg and polar bodies

F
Fertilization

G
Division of zygote

Fig. 47. — Diagram of the general plan of spermatogenesis and oogenesis in animals. The somatic, or diploid, number of chromosomes (duplex group) is assumed to be eight. Male, to the left; female, to the right. *A*, primordial germ cells; *B*, spermatogonia and oogonia, many of which arise during the period of multiplication; *C*, primary spermatocyte and oocyte, with haploid number (simplex group) of chromosomes, which have arisen by the first maturation (reduction) division; *E*, spermatids (which become transformed into sperm) and egg and three polar bodies which have arisen by the second maturation (equation) division; *F*, union of sperm and egg (fertilization) to form zygote with diploid number (duplex group) of chromosomes; *G*, chromosome complex of cells after first division of the zygote, and of all subsequent somatic cells, and germ cells until maturation. (From Woodruff.)

in a reduction in the number of chromosomes to one half in the daughter cells. After these two *maturation* divisions, as they are called, the spermatids are metamorphosed into spermatozoa.

The *spermatozoa* of various animals are usually easily distinguished one from another, but are mostly constructed on the same plan. They resemble an elongated tadpole (Fig. 46), having a head filled almost entirely with nuclear material and a long flagellum-like tail which is the organ of locomotion; a middle piece joins these two. The spermatozoa are the active germ-cells. It is their function to seek out and fertilize the larger stationary egg cells. Frequently they are only $\frac{1}{100000}$ the size of the egg, and in the sea-urchin, *Toxopneustes*, their bulk is about $\frac{1}{500000}$ the volume of the ovum.

Oogenesis. — The origin of the female germ cell or egg is called *oogenesis* (Fig. 48). Stages are passed through by the germ cells corresponding almost exactly to those described under spermatogenesis (Fig. 47). Before the growth period the germ-cells which will produce eggs are known as *oogonia* (Fig. 46; Fig. 47; Fig. 48, *a*). At the completion of the growth period they are termed *primary oocytes* (Fig. 48, *b*). The primary oocytes contain only one-half the number of chromosomes characteristic of the somatic cells and oogonia. As in the primary spermatocytes, these chromosomes are bivalent, resulting from the union two by two of the univalent chromosomes of the oogonia. The primary oocyte divides in the following manner. Its nucleus, called the germinal vesicle (Fig. 48, *a*), moves to the periphery (*b*), where a mitotic figure is formed perpendicular to the surface of the egg (*c*). A small bud-like protrusion is now formed into which pass one univalent chromosome from each of the bivalent chromosomes present in the primary oocyte (*d*). The bud is then pinched off. Two *secondary oocytes* are produced by this division, each containing an equal amount of chromatin, but one with a great deal more cytoplasm and yolk than the other (*e*). The small one is known as the *first polar body* (*e*) and is not functional; the larger is the *egg*. Each secondary oocyte now prepares for division (*e*). The first polar body in some cases does not divide; when it does, the division is equal (*g*). The egg throws off a *second polar body* (*g*), which contains one half of each chromosome. This second polar body disintegrates, as does the first.

(3) **Fertilization**. — The mature ovum now becomes the center of the interesting process of *fertilization*. The spermatozoon sometimes enters the egg before the polar bodies are formed, and sometimes afterward. In the illustration (Fig. 48, *e*) the sperm

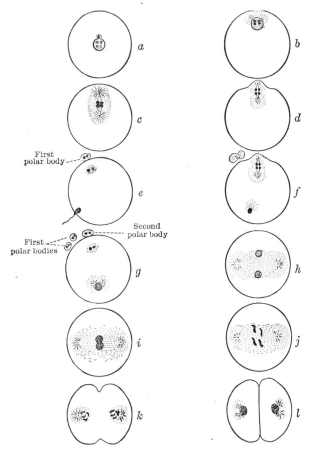

FIG. 48. — Diagrams illustrating the maturation, fertilization, and cleavage of an egg. The primordial germ-cell is represented as possessing four chromosomes.

is shown entering the egg at the end of the first oocyte division. The sperm brings into the egg a nucleus, a centrosome, and a very small amount of cytoplasm. The sperm nucleus soon grows larger by the absorption of material from the cytoplasm of the egg, and the centrosome begins its activity. A mitotic figure soon grows up (*g*) and moves toward the center of the egg. The egg nucleus also moves in this direction (*h*), and finally both the male and female nuclei are brought together in the midst of the spindle produced about the sperm nucleus (*i*). This completes the process usually known as fertilization. In this process the chief aim so far seems to be *the union of two nuclei, one of maternal origin, the other of paternal origin.* We shall see later that fertilization is really not consummated until the animal which develops from the egg has become sexually mature.

Chromosome Reduction. — It is now possible to point out the result of the reduction in the number of chromosomes which takes place during maturation. It has already been stated (p. 14) that every species of animal has a definite, even number of chromosomes in its somatic cells. This number remains constant, generation after generation. Now if the mature egg contained this somatic number of chromosomes and the sperm brought into it a like number, the animal which developed from the fertilized egg would possess in its somatic cells twice as many as its parents. The number is kept constant by reduction during the maturation divisions (Fig. 47), so that both egg and sperm contain only one half the number in the somatic cells. The union of egg and sperm again establishes the normal number of chromosomes possessed by the parents.

Union of Chromosomes in Fertilization. — If we return for a moment to the subject of maturation, the final process in fertilization may be understood. It appears that chance has very little to do with the union of chromosomes in pairs during the early history of the germ-cells (pp. 79–83, Figs. 47, 48); but that one chromosome of each pair came originally from the egg and is therefore *maternal,* while the other was derived from the sperm, and is *paternal.* Since the chromosomes are recognized as the bearers of hereditary qualities, it follows that the blending of the characteristics of the mother and the father in the germ-cells does not occur when the sperm enters the egg, but when the individual developing from the zygote becomes sexually mature.

(4) **Embryology.** — *Cleavage.* — The division of the fertilized egg is known as *cleavage.* The chromatin of the united germ nuclei condenses into chromosomes, which are so arranged on the first cleavage spindle (Fig. 48, *j*) that each daughter nucleus receives half of each. This means that each daughter

cell will contain half of each chromosome of paternal origin and half of each chromosome of maternal origin. Further mitotic divisions insure a like distribution to every cell in the body. After nuclear division comes the division of the entire cells into two (*k* and *l*).

Typically the fertilized egg divides into two cells, these two into four, these four into eight, etc., each cleavage plane being perpendicular to the last preceding plane (Fig. 50). This is known as *total cleavage*, and is characteristic of *holoblastic* eggs. Other eggs are said to be *meroblastic* and exhibit *partial cleavage;* that is, only a small part of the egg enters into cell division, the remainder serving as nutritive material for the cleavage cells. In all we can recognize four distinct types of cleavage: (1) *equal cleavage,* where the egg divides into two equal halves (Fig. 49, *A*); (2) *unequal cleavage,* where the first division of the egg results in one large and one small cell (Fig. 49, *B*); (3) *discoidal cleavage,* where the entire egg does not divide, but small cells are cut off at the surface and form a disc-shaped region (Fig. 49, *C*); and (4) *superficial cleavage,* where the nucleus of the egg divides rapidly; the daughter nuclei migrate to the periphery and form a single layer of cells at the surface (Fig. 49, *D*).

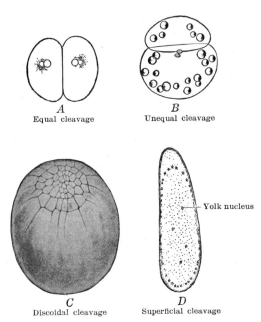

A
Equal cleavage

B
Unequal cleavage

C
Discoidal cleavage

D
Superficial cleavage

Yolk nucleus

Fig. 49. — Figures illustrating four different kinds of cleavage. **A,** equal cleavage of the sea-urchin egg. **B,** unequal cleavage of the egg of a marine worm. **C,** discoidal cleavage of the egg of a squid. **D,** superficial cleavage of an insect's egg. (A–B, from Wilson; C, from Wilson, after Watase; D, from Korschelt and Heider.)

That part of ontogeny which concerns the development of an

animal from the egg to maturity is known as *embryogeny*. Certain stages in this development have been recognized as common to all higher animals, and have been given names. The stages occur in a certain regular order, as follows: (1) cleavage, (2) the

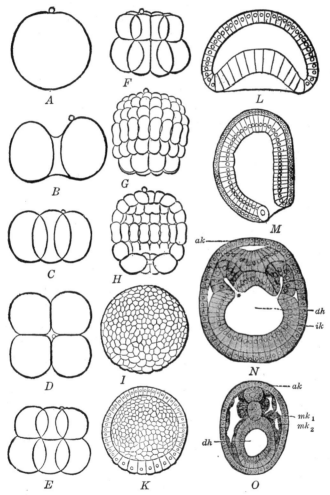

Fig. 50. — Figures illustrating the cleavage of the holoblastic egg of *Amphioxus*, and the formation of germ layers. **A–K**, cleavage and formation of the blastula. **L–M**, gastrulation. **N**, production of the mesoderm and cœlomic cavities. **O**, cœlom further developed. *ak*, ectoderm; *dh*, primitive alimentary canal; *ik*, entoderm; *mk₁*, somatic layer of mesoderm; *mk₂*, splanchnic layer of mesoderm. (From Korschelt and Heider, after Hatschek.)

morula, (3) the blastula, (4) the gastrula, (5) the formation of germ-layers, and (6) organogeny.

Cleavage in a holoblastic egg (Fig. 50, *A*) results in the production of two (*B*), four (*C*, *D*), eight (*E*), sixteen (*F*), etc. cells approximately equal to one another and growing smaller as their number increases. Each of these cells is known as a *blastomere*. The blastomeres do not separate as do the daughter cells produced by the binasy division of *Paramecium* (Fig. 40, *o — q*), but remain attached to one another. The resemblance of the group of blastomeres to a mulberry suggested the term *morula*, which is often used in describing the egg during the early cleavage stages.

Blastula. — As cleavage advances, a cavity becomes noticeable in the center of the egg (Fig. 50, *H*), enlarging as development proceeds until the whole resembles a hollow rubber ball, the rubber being represented by a single layer of cells. At this stage the egg is called a *blastula*, the cavity the *cleavage* or *segmentation cavity*, and the cellular layer the *blastoderm*. The blastula resembles somewhat a single colony of *Volvox* (Fig. 31).

Gastrula. — The cells on one side of the blastula are seen to be thicker than elsewhere (Fig. 50, *K*) and begin to invaginate (Fig. 50, *L*). This process results in a cup-shaped structure with a wall of two layers, an outer layer of small cells and an inner layer of larger cells. The embryo may now be called a *gastrula* (*M*), and the process by which it developed from the blastula is termed *gastrulation*. The cleavage cavity is almost obliterated during the invagination, while a new cavity, the *primitive digestive tract* or *archenteron*, is established.

Germ-layers. — The cells of one layer of the gastrula resemble one another, but differ in appearance from the cells of the other layer. Each layer gives rise to certain definite parts of the body, and is therefore termed a *germ-layer;* the outer is the *ectoderm* (Fig. 50, *N*,) the inner, the *entoderm* (*N*). Animals with only these two layers are said to be *diploblastic;* but the majority of the higher animals have a third layer which usually appears between the first two after the gastrula has been formed. This is the middle layer or *mesoderm.* It originates either from the proliferation of a few special cells which may be recognized in the early cleavage stages, or from cells budded off from the inner surface of both the ectoderm and entoderm, or from pouches arising from the walls of the entoderm (Fig. 50, *N*). Animals with three germ-layers are said to be *triploblastic*.

The tissues developing from the germ-layers are, in part, as follows. From the *ectoderm* arise the epidermis, epithelium of various organs, and the nervous system; from the *mesoderm* come the muscles, connective and supporting tissues, and blood and blood-vessels; the *entoderm* becomes the epithelium of the digestive tract, pharynx, and respiratory tract.

Cœlom. — The *cœlom* is a cavity in the mesoderm lined by an epithelium; into it the excretory organs open, and from its walls the reproductive cells originate. There is no cœlom in the lower METAZOA, but one is present in all the more complex animals. As shown in Figure 50, *N*, *O*, it arises in a typical animal as cavities of the mesodermal pouches which form from the primitive alimentary canal (*N*). The outer mesodermal lining of the cœlomic cavities is called the *somatic epithelium* (*O*) and the inner the *splanchnic epithelium* (*O*). The importance of the cœlom both morphologically and physiologically will be discussed later.

5. THE FORMS OF ANIMALS

Although most animals pass through similar stages in their development from the egg, the adult organisms differ widely in the form of their bodies. This is a result of two factors: (1) the initial structure of the germ, and (2) the influence of the environment. Differences in the form of animals are due principally to *symmetry, metamerism,* and the *character of the appendages*.

Symmetry. — Animals are either *symmetrical* or *asymmetrical*. The symmetrical animals may be divided into two types: (1) *radially symmetrical,* and (2) *bilaterally symmetrical*.

A *radially symmetrical* animal possesses a number of similar parts, called *antimeres*, which radiate out from a central axis. The adult starfish (Fig. 131) is a good example; its arms are similar and radiate out from the central disc. Some simple sponges (Fig. 55), the majority of the CŒLENTERATA (Fig. 79), and most adult ECHINODERMATA are radially symmetrical. Radial symmetry is best suited to sessile animals, since the similarity of the antimeres enables them to obtain food or repel enemies from all sides.

The bodies of *bilaterally symmetrical* animals are so constructed that the chief organs are arranged in pairs on either side of an axis passing from the head or anterior end to the tail or posterior end. There is only one plane through which their bodies can be divided into two similar parts. An upper or *dorsal surface* and a lower or *ventral surface* are recognizable, as well as *right* and *left sides*. Bilateral symmetry is characteristic of the most successful animals living at the present time, including all of the vertebrates and most of the invertebrates.

Metamerism. — Metameric animals have bodies composed of more or less similar parts or organs arranged in a linear series along the main axis. Each part is called a *metamere, somite,* or *segment*. In many animals metamerism is not shown by the external structures, but is exhibited by the internal organs; this is true of the vertebrates, which have the vertebræ of the backbone, the ribs, and nerves metamerically arranged. The earthworm (Fig. 154) is a good illustration of both external and internal metamerism; the body consists of a great number of similar segments, and the ganglia of the nerve cord, the chambers of the body cavity and the excretory organs are segmentally arranged.

The earthworm may serve also as an example of an animal with *homonomous segmentation*, since the metameres are similar. The crayfish (Fig. 202), on the other hand, is a *heteronomous* animal, since division of labor has resulted in the dissimilarity of the metameres of different regions of the body. The vertebrates, including man, are all heteronomous.

Appendages. — The *external appendages* of animals are outgrowths of the body, which are used for locomotion, obtaining food, protection, respiration, and many other purposes. They are greatly modified for their various functions, and these modifications furnish excellent material for the study of homologous and analogous organs. For example, the fins of fishes, the wings of birds, and the arms of man serve to distinguish their bearers from one another; nevertheless, these structures are homologous, since they are morphologically equivalent.

CHAPTER IV

PHYLUM PORIFERA [1]

THE members of the Phylum PORIFERA (Lat. *porus*, a pore; *ferre*, to bear) are commonly called sponges. The ordinary bath sponge of commerce is the skeleton of one of these animals. Most sponges live only in salt water but there are about ten genera and fifty species that inhabit fresh water, the commonest genus being *Spongilla* (Fig. 51). Formerly they were considered plants because of their irregular and plantlike habits of growth. When their animal nature was finally established (about 1857), the problem of their position in the animal series arose. By many authorities they were considered colonial PROTOZOA allied with the CHOANOFLAGELLATA (p. 45), but they are now generally classed with the many-celled animals, and placed in a separate group, the PARAZOA, as explained on page 22.

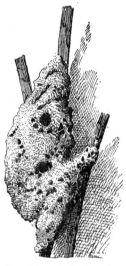

FIG. 51. — A fresh-water sponge, *Spongilla*.

Sponges may be grouped into three classes according to the composition and shape of their skeletal elements (spicules): —

CLASS I. CALCAREA (Lat. *calcarius*, lime) with spicules of carbonate of lime (Fig. 53);

[1] The sponges constitute a group of animals apparently outside of the main course of evolution, although their relations to the PROTOZOA through the choanoflagellates seems probable. Of particular interest are the reversal of the germ layers, the complicated systems of canals, and the formation of spongin and various types of spicules. The probable origin of sponges from the PROTOZOA leads us to look for the beginning of division of labor among the cells in this group and we may hope to discover the genesis of neuromuscular and other organs in these peculiar lowly organisms. If time is limited the PORIFERA may be referred to briefly and more time allotted to the comparatively more important phyla described in later chapters.

CLASS II. HEXACTINELLIDA (Gr. *hex*, six; *aktin*, a ray) with triaxon spicules of silicon (Fig. 60, *e*); and

CLASS III. DEMOSPONGIÆ (Gr. *demos*, people; *spongos*, sponge) usually with spicules of silicon, not triaxon, or with spongin (Fig. 61), or with both spicules and spongin.

1. STRUCTURE OF A SIMPLE SPONGE — LEUCOSOLENIA

Leucosolenia (Fig. 52) is a sponge which will serve to illustrate the structure of the most simple members of the phylum. It is found growing on the rocks near the sea-shore just below

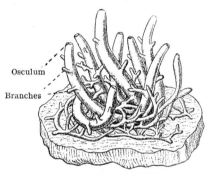

low-tide mark, and consists of a number of horizontal tubes from which branches extend up into the water. These branches have an opening, the *osculum*, at the distal end, and *buds* and *branches* projecting from their sides. The buds and branches are hollow, possessing a single *gastral cavity* (Fig. 59, A) which communicates with the horizontal tubes. The entire

FIG. 52. — A small colony of *Leucosolenia*, a simple sponge. (From Lankester's Treatise on Zoology.)

mass is a colony of animals, and the tissues connected with a single osculum may be considered an individual sponge.

If a branch is examined under a microscope, it will be found to contain a large number of three-pronged (triradiate) *spicules*, which are embedded in the soft tissue of the body-wall (Fig. 53); these serve to strengthen the body and hold it upright. The application of acid results in the dissolution of these spicules and the production of an effervescence, thus proving them to be composed of calcium carbonate. The body-wall is so flimsy that it is difficult to study even under the best conditions. It is made up of two layers of cells: an outer layer, the *dermal epithelium*, and an inner layer, the *gastral epithelium*. These layers, as will be shown later (p. 99), are not comparable to the ectoderm and entoderm of the CŒLENTERATA and other METAZOA. Between these two layers is a jelly-like substance similar to the mesoglea of *Hydra* (p. 105) in which are many *ameba-like wandering cells*.

The gastral epithelium is peculiar, since it consists of a single layer of *collar cells*, the *choanocytes* (Fig. 54), which resemble the similar cells of the choanoflagellate PROTOZOA (Fig. 25). The flagella of these collar cells beat constantly, creating a current of water. If a little coloring matter is placed in the water, it will be drawn into the animal through minute *incurrent pores*, the *ostia* (Fig. 59, A), in the body-wall and will pass out through the openings in a sieve-like membrane stretched across the osculum (Fig. 53).

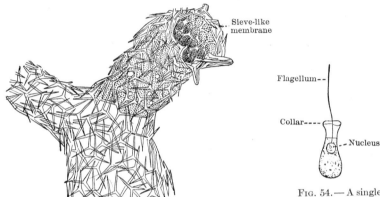

Sieve-like membrane

Flagellum--

Collar----

--Nucleus

FIG. 54.— A single collar cell of *Leucosolenia*. (From the Cambridge Natural History after Bidder.)

FIG. 53. — *Leucosolenia*, a simple sponge. View of a branch showing the sieve-like membrane which stretches across the osculum. The lower part shows spicules only. (From Shipley and MacBride, after Minchin.)

The osculum is therefore the *exhalant opening*, and not the mouth, as a casual examination might lead one to believe. The course of the current of water in such a sponge is shown by arrows in Figure 59, A. The presence of the incurrent pores suggested the name PORIFERA for members of this phylum.

2. ANATOMY AND PHYSIOLOGY OF GRANTIA

Grantia (Fig. 55) is also known as a simple sponge, though it is more complex than *Leucosolenia*. It lives in the salt water along the sea-coast and is permanently attached to the rocks and piles just below the low-tide mark. It is shaped like a vase that bulges in the middle, and is about three-fourths of an inch long. Frequently *buds* occur near the base, and a small colony is formed.

Structure. — A longitudinal section of *Grantia* (Fig. 56) shows that the body possesses a single cavity as in *Leucosolenia*, but the body wall is much thicker. This condition has been brought about by the folding of the wall of a larval stage which resembles *Leucosolenia*, resulting in the production of a series of *parallel canals*. Part of these are *incurrent canals* and open to the outside (Fig. 59, B); the rest open into the gastral cavity, are lined with choanocytes (Fig. 54), and are called *flagellated chambers* or *radial canals* (Fig. 59, B). The area covered by collar cells is enormously increased in this way (compare the black

Fig. 55. — A simple sponge. (After Minchin.)

layers in Fig. 59, A and B). Water enters the body of *Grantia* as shown by arrows in Figure 59, B, by way of the incurrent canals; from these it passes through pores, called *prosopyles*, into the radial canals, then through the *apopyles* into the gastral cavity, and finally out of the osculum.

As in *Leucosolenia*, *Grantia* possesses an outer *dermal layer* of cells, an inner *gastral epithelium* made up of collar cells which line the radial canals, and a *middle jelly-like substance* in which are a number of *wandering ameboid cells*. The last-named cells are considered by some authorities equivalent to the mesoderm of higher animals, but this is probably not the case.

The *skeleton* of *Grantia* consists of *calcareous spicules*, of which there are four varieties: (1) long, straight *monaxon* rods guarding the osculum, (2) short, straight monaxon rods surrounding the incurrent pores, (3) *triradiate* spicules always found embedded in the body-wall, and (4) *T-shaped* spicules lining the gastral cavity; four- and five-rayed spicules may also be found. Spicules are built up within cells called *scleroblasts*, which form part of the inner stratum of the dermal layer.

Physiology. — *Grantia* lives upon the minute organisms and small particles of organic matter that are drawn into the incurrent canals by the current of water produced by the beating of the collar-cell flagella. The majority of the food particles are engulfed by the collar cells. *Digestion*, as in the PROTOZOA, is *intracellular*, food vacuoles being formed. The distribution of the nutriment is accomplished by the passage of digested food from cell to cell, aided by the ameboid wandering cells of the middle layer.

Excretory matter is discharged through the general body surface, assisted probably by the ameboid wandering cells, and possibly by the collar cells, also. *Respiration* likewise takes place, in the absence of special organs, through the cells of the body-wall.

Reproduction. — Reproduction in *Grantia* takes place by both *sexual* and *asexual* methods. In the latter case, a *bud* arises near the point of attachment, finally becomes free, and takes up a separate existence.

The *sexual* reproductive cells lie in the jelly-like layer of the body-wall. Both eggs and sperms occur in a single individual; *i.e. Grantia* is *monœcious* or *hermaphroditic.* The development of the fertilized egg has been observed in *Sycon* (Fig. 57) and is probably similar to what occurs in *Grantia.* The egg segments by three vertical divisions into a pyramidal plate of eight cells. A horizontal division now

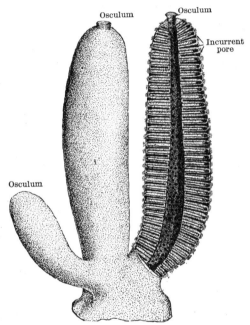

FIG. 56. — A simple sponge, *Sycon.* The right-hand member of the colony is shown in longitudinal section. (From Parker and Haswell.)

cuts off a small cell from the top of each of the eight, the result being a layer of eight large cells crowned by a layer of eight small cells. The cells now become arranged about a central cavity, producing a blastula-like sphere. The small cells multiply rapidly and develop flagella, while the large cells become granular. The small cells are now partially grown over by the others, forming a structure called the *amphiblastula.* The mass of cells then becomes disc-shaped by the pushing in of the flagellated cells. Two layers are thus formed between which the jelly-like middle layer arises. The invaginated side soon becomes attached, and the embryo lengthens into a cylinder, at the distal end of which an opening, the osculum, appears. In the meantime, spicules arise in the body-wall.

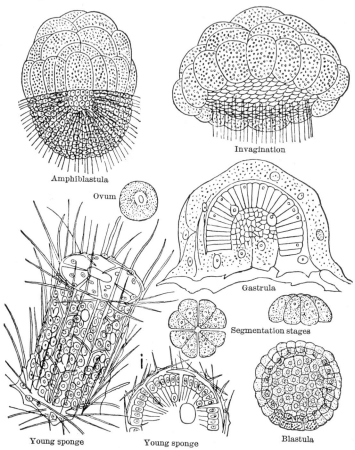

FIG. 57. — Development of a simple sponge, *Sycon*. (From Parker and Haswell, after Schulze.)

3. THE FRESH-WATER SPONGE — SPONGILLA

The fresh-water sponge (Fig. 51) lives in ponds and streams and may be found attached to the under surface of rocks, dead leaves, or sticks. It forms incrustations a fraction of an inch thick or compact masses, and is gray or green in color. The structure of *Spongilla* is shown in Figure 59, C. The canal system is more complicated than that of either *Leucosolenia* or *Grantia*. The choanocytes are restricted to flagellated chambers. This is the *rhagon* type, and there are three distinct parts to this system: (1) the water passes through the dermal ostia, and, by way of incurrent canals, reaches (2) a number of small chambers lined with choanocytes, thence it is carried through (3) an excurrent canal to the gastral cavity, and finally out of the osculum.

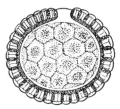

Fig. 58. — *Spongilla.* A single gemmule, seen in section, showing the thick wall with its opening, and the central mass of germinal cells. (From Weysse, after a Leuckart-Nitsche wall-chart.)

Spongilla and several marine sponges have a peculiar method of reproduction by the formation of *gemmules*. A number of germinal cells in the middle layer of the body-wall gather into a ball and become surrounded by protecting spicules. These gemmules (Fig. 58) are formed in the autumn just before the death of the adult sponge. In the spring they develop into new sponges. They are of value in carrying the race through a period of adverse conditions, such as the winter season.

4. Sponges in General

(1) **Morphology**. — *External Features*. — *Leucosolenia*, *Grantia*, and *Spongilla* have served as types of the Phylum Porifera, but other sponges vary markedly from these both in form and in structure. In many cases the character of the object to which sponges are attached causes them to assume exceedingly irregular shapes, the rocks being frequently incrusted by indefinite masses of spongy tissue. The habit of growth of many sponges is responsible for their shape. Some are branched like trees, or form a network; others are fan-shaped, cup-shaped, or dome-shaped. Some sponges are no larger than a pinhead; others are over five feet high. Most calcareous sponges are white or gray, but others may be brilliantly colored and even iridescent, exhibiting all the hues of the rainbow.

Canal Systems. — There are three principal types of canal systems exhibited by sponges: (1) *ascon*, (2) *sycon*, and (3) *rhagon*. That of *Leucosolenia* (p. 90, and Fig. 59, A) is of the ascon type, and that of *Grantia* (page 93, and Fig. 59, B) is of the sycon type. Some sponges, like *Spongilla*, have a very complicated canal system; this, the *rhagon* type, is diagrammatically shown in Figure 59, C, and described on page 95.

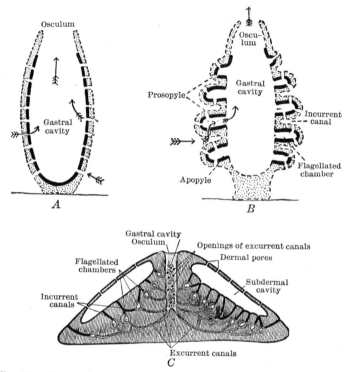

FIG. 59. — Types of canal systems of sponges. **A**, ascon type. **B**, sycon type. **C**, rhagon type (*Spongilla*). The arrows indicate the direction of the current of water. The thick black line in A and B represent the gastral layer; the dotted portion, the dermal layer. (A and B, from Minchin; C, from Parker and Haswell.)

Skeletal Systems. — The skeletons of sponges are composed of *spicules* of carbonate of lime or silicon, or of fibers of *spongin*. A few small species have no skeletons. Some of the more common types of spicules are shown in Figure 60; they are (1) *monaxon* (a, b), (2) *tetraxon* (c, d), (3) *triaxon* (e), and (4) *polyaxon* (f). Spicules with three rays like most of those in *Leucosolenia* and *Grantia* are called *triradiate*. The skeletons of the horny sponges, of which the common bath sponge is an example, are made up largely of fibers of *spongin* (Fig. 61). This substance, which is chemically allied to silk, is secreted by cells of the dermal layer called *spongoblasts*.

Histology. — The sponges are among the simplest of the METAZOA with regard to the differentiation of their cells, but they seem quite complex when compared with the PROTOZOA.

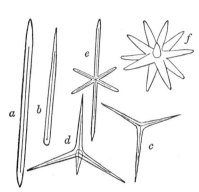

FIG. 60. — Types of sponge spicules. *a*, *b*, monaxon; *c*, *d*, tetraxon; *e*, triaxon; *f*, polyaxon. (From the Cambridge Natural History.)

FIG. 61. — Piece of network of horny fibers from the bath sponge, *Euspongia*. (From Sedgwick.)

The cells of sponges may be separated into three groups: (1) those of the dermal layer, (2) those of the gastral layer, and (3) the ameboid cells in the jelly between the dermal and gastral layers. The classes of cells and the layers to which they belong are shown in Table III.

TABLE III

CLASSES OF CELLS FOUND IN SPONGES

A. Dermal Layer	I. Epithelial stratum	1. Epithelial cells 2. Contractile cells 3. Gland cells 4. Spongoblasts
	II. Porocytes	5. Pore cells
	III. Skeletogenous stratum	6. Scleroblasts 7. Fiber cells
B. Gastral Layer	IV. Gastral epithelium	8. Choanocytes
C. Middle Region	V. Wandering cells	9. Ingestive cells 10. Nutritive cells 11. Storage cells
	VI. Reproductive cells	12. Gemmule cells 13. Sexual cells

(2) **Physiology.** — *Metabolism.* — The metabolic processes in all sponges are essentially similar to those of *Grantia* (p. 91). The current created by the beating of the flagella of the choanocytes brings organic food particles and fresh water into the canals. Most of the food particles are engulfed by the choanocytes and digested within the cells, as in PROTOZOA. The processes of excretion and respiration are carried on by the cells of the body-wall. There is, on the whole, not much difference between the metabolic activities of sponges and those of PROTOZOA.

Behavior. — Very little is known about the behavior of sponges. The larvæ, as stated before, are ciliated and swim through the water, but the adults are all attached to the sea-bottom, to rocks, or to piles, etc. Parker has shown that *Stylotella heliophila*, of the order MONAXONIDA, responds in a primitive way to certain stimuli. Among the reacting elements are fiber-like cells, *myocytes*, arranged about the osculum, and contractile cells lining certain internal cavities. The choanocytes are able to extend and contract their collars and to beat the water with their flagella. No nervous elements have been discovered.

The reactions of *Stylotella* may be stated briefly as follows: —

The *oscula* close in quiet sea-water, on exposure to air, on injury to neighboring parts, and in weak solutions of ether and cocaine; they open in currents of sea-water, in fresh water, and in weak solutions of atropine.

The *ostia* close on injury to neighboring parts and in weak solutions of ether and cocaine; they open in dilute sea-water, and in weak solutions of atropine. The choanocyte currents cease in dilute sea-water, at high temperatures, and in weak solutions of ether and chloroform. There is very little, if any, transmission of stimuli, and the reactive organs respond only to direct stimulation.

Investigators look to the lowly organized, many-celled animals for the key to the origin of the nervous system, and the condition in sponges seems to show that muscles, " as represented by the sphincters of sponges, were the first of the neuromuscular organs to appear." Sense cells are supposed to have developed next as we find them in cœlenterates (p. 107), and finally a central organ was added, completing the neuromuscular mechanism as it exists in higher METAZOA.

(3) **Reproduction.** — Reproduction is either *asexual* or *sexual.* By the asexual method there are produced *buds* and *gemmules.*

Buds may be set free to take up a separate existence, or may remain attached to the parent sponge, aiding in the formation of a complex assemblage of individuals. Gemmules are formed as described in *Spongilla* (p. 95).

In *sexual reproduction* the eggs and spermatozoa are derived as in *Sycon* (p. 93) from ameboid wandering cells in the middle layer. A *ciliated larva* is produced from a holoblastic egg. This larva swims about for a while, thus effecting the dispersal of the species, then becomes fixed and passes through many changes, finally developing ostia and an osculum which are necessary for the nutritive processes and growth.

One very important peculiarity in sponge embryology is this (Fig. 64): the flagellated cells of the larva do not become the outer (dermal) epithelium as do the flagellated cells of the larval cœlenterate (planula, Fig. 73, C, Fig. 81), but produce the gastral layer of choanocytes; and the inner cells do not become the inner (gastral) epithelium, as do the similarly situated cells in the cœlenterate planula, but produce the dermal layer. This is shown in Table IV.

TABLE IV

THE DEVELOPMENT OF A SPONGE (CLATHRINA)

Ovum-Blastomeres
{
Flagellated cells . . . Gastral layer
Ameboid inner cells . . Dermal layer
Posterior granular cells { Wandering cells
(Fig. 64, *p.g.c.*) { Sexual cells
}

It therefore seems impossible to homologize the ectoderm and entoderm of cœlenterates and other METAZOA with the layers in the sponge larva, since the outer layer (ectoderm?) of the latter becomes the inner layer (entoderm?) of the adult sponge. The outer layer is consequently termed " dermal epithelium " instead of " ectoderm," and the inner, the " gastral epithelium " instead of " entoderm."

(4) **Classification.** — PORIFERA. — SPONGES. — Diploblastic, radially symmetrical animals; number of antimeres variable; body-wall permeated by many pores, and usually supported by a skeleton of spicules or spongin.

CLASS I. CALCAREA. Marine species, mostly white or gray, living in shallow water; spicules of carbonate of lime, either monaxon (Fig. 60, a, b) or tetraxon (Fig. 60, c, d); flagellated chambers large.

Order 1. Homocœla. Gastral layer continuous. Example: *Leucosolenia* (Fig. 52, Fig. 59, A).

Order 2. Heterocœla. Gastral layer discontinuous and restricted to flagellated chambers. Example: *Grantia* (Fig. 55, Fig. 59, B).

CLASS II. HEXACTINELLIDA. Deep-sea sponges; spicules triaxon (Fig. 60, e), of silicon; canal system with thimble-shaped chambers. Example: *Euplectella aspergillum*, Venus' flower-basket (Fig. 62).

CLASS III. DEMOSPONGIÆ. Skeleton of silicious spicules, not triaxon, or with spongin, or with both spicules and spongin, canal system derived from rhagon type (Fig. 59, C); most highly organized of phylum; majority of existing sponges.

Order 1. Tetraxonida. Typically with tetraxon spicules. Example: *Geodia*.

Order 2. Monaxonida. With monaxon (Fig. 60, a, b), but no tetraxon spicules (c, d). Example: *Spongilla* (Fig. 59, C).

Order 3. Keratosa. Main skeleton of spongin. Example: *Euspongia*, the bath sponge (Fig. 63).

(5) **The Position of Sponges in the Animal Kingdom.** — As stated at the beginning of this chapter, sponges are considered many-celled animals. They were formerly, and are even now, placed by some authors in a phylum with the cœlenterates (Chapter V). They differ from the cœlenterates and other METAZOA so widely in certain important characteristics that most zoologists are inclined to separate them from the METAZOA and call them PARAZOA (see diagram, p. 22).

Sponges differ from cœlenterates in the presence of choanocytes, ostia, and oscula, in their unique method of feeding, in the germ-layers, which are apparently reversed in position (p. 199), and in the absence of a mouth and nematocysts (Fig. 66). The choanocytes of sponges recall the choanoflagellate PROTOZOA (p. 45), and it is not improbable that they may have evolved from this group. Certain colonial choanoflagellates, *e.g. Proterospongia* (Fig. 25) resemble what we might imagine to have been the ancestor of the sponges.

(6) **The Relations of Sponges to Other Organisms and to Man.** — Sponges are used as food by very few animals, since they are protected by spicules and by excretions of poisonous ferments making them distasteful. Nudibranch mollusks (Chap. XII) feed

on them to a certain extent. The cavities of sponges offer shelter to many animals, especially CRUSTACEA and cœlenterates; this may lead to a sort of partnership called *commensalism*. For

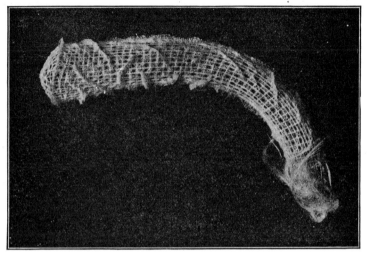

FIG. 62. — Venus's flower-basket. The skeleton of a sponge, *Euplectella*. (From Weysse.)

example, certain hermit crabs protect themselves from attack by surrounding their shells with obnoxious sponges. Oysters and other bivalves are often starved by sponges which cover their shells and take away their food supply, and oyster culturists often prevent this by growing the bivalves in frames which are pulled up during a rain, thus killing the sponges with fresh water.

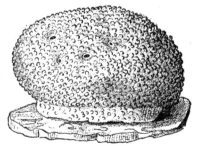

FIG. 63. — The bath sponge, *Euspongia officinalis*. (From Lankester, after Schulze.)

The origin of flint is in part due to the activities of sponges. It has been estimated that to extract one ounce of silicious spicules at least a ton of sea water must pass through the canal system of the sponge. The spicules aid in the formation of flint, this substance being always associated with the remains of sponges, RADIOLARIA (p. 40), and other organisms having silicious skeletons.

Of the commercial sponges may be mentioned the beautiful skeleton of Venus' flower-basket, *Euplectella* (Fig. 62), which is obtained chiefly in the Philippine Islands, and the common bath sponge, *Euspongia* (Fig. 63), and others, which are especially grown for market in some localities. The best bath sponges come from the Mediterranean coast, Australia, the Bahamas, Florida, and the north coast of Cuba. They are gathered by means of long hooks, by divers, or by dredging. They are allowed to decay, are washed, dried, and then sent to market. The depletion of the sponge supply by unwise fishing has resulted in an attempt to regulate the industry by governmental control. Sponge culture is now carried on successfully in Italy and Florida. Perfect specimens are cut into pieces about one inch square, and " planted " on stakes on clean, rocky bottoms free from cold currents. These grow into marketable size in five or six years.

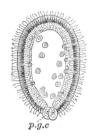

p.g.c

Fig. 64.— Section of the larva of a sponge, *Clathrina blanca.   p.g.c,* posterior granular cells. (From Lankester's Treatise.)

CHAPTER V

PHYLUM CŒLENTERATA [1]

THE Phylum CŒLENTERATA (Gr. *koĩlos*, hollow; *enteron*, intestine) includes a great number of aquatic animals, mostly marine, very few of which ever come to the notice of persons who do not visit the seashore or are not especially interested in natural history. As in the case of the sponges, many species of cœlenterates, the corals, are known because of the beautiful skeletons they construct.

The three classes of cœlenterates are as follows: —

CLASS I. HYDROZOA (Gr. *hudra*, a water serpent; *zoön*, an animal), fresh-water polyps, hydroid zoophytes, many of the small medusæ or jellyfishes, and a few stony corals;

CLASS II. SCYPHOZOA (Gr. *skuphos*, cup; *zoön*, animal), most of the large jellyfishes; and

CLASS III. ANTHOZOA (Gr. *anthos*, a flower; *zoön*, animal), (Actinozoa), sea-anemones, most stony corals, sea-fans, sea-pens, and precious corals.

A simple member of the CŒLENTERATA and one that is common in fresh water is the polyp known as *Hydra*. A study of this little animal will serve to illustrate cœlenterate characteristics and will enable one to understand the more complex species belonging to this phylum.

---

[1] The Phylum CŒLENTERATA contains simple diploblastic animals of which *Hydra* is among the most primitive and exhibits the characteristics of the lower METAZOA to the best advantage. The sections devoted to the colonial HYDROZOA, the SCYPHOZOA and the ANTHOZOA are intended for careful study only when considerable time is available; and the sections on *Classification* are for reference purposes only. However, the cœlenterates as a whole serve to illustrate a number of phenomena, such as budding in a metazoon; the principles of animal behavior as illustrated by various types of stimulation, trial and error, optimum environmental conditions, and physiological states; the phenomena of regeneration and grafting; and colony formation, metagenesis and polymorphism. Since these are all exhibited within the class HYDROZOA, it is suggested that this group be studied in more detail than the SCYPHOZOA and ANTHOZOA which may be more briefly considered in order to obtain a general idea of sea anemones, corals and coral reefs.

1. THE FRESH-WATER POLYP — HYDRA

Hydra fusca is abundant in ponds and streams, where it may be found attached by one end to aquatic vegetation. Hydras are easily seen with the naked eye, being from 2 to 20 mm. in length.

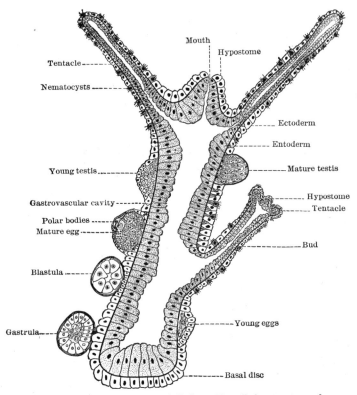

FIG. 65. — A longitudinal section of *Hydra*. Not all the structures shown occur on one animal at the same time.

They may be likened to a short, thick thread unraveled at the unattached, distal end.

Morphology. — *External Features.* — The body of *Hydra* is really a tube usually attached by a *basal disc* at one end, and with a *mouth* opening at the distal or free end. Around the mouth are arranged from six to ten smaller tubes, closed at their outer end, called *tentacles* (Fig. 65). Both the body and tentacles vary at different times in length and thickness. One or more *buds* are often found extending out from the body, and in September and October *reproductive organs* may also appear. The male organs (*testes*) are conical elevations on the distal third of the body; the female organs (*ovaries*) are knoblike projections near the basal disc.

Structure (Fig. 65). — *Hydra* is a *diploblastic* animal consisting of two cellular layers, an outer thin, colorless layer, the *ectoderm* and an inner layer, the *entoderm*, twice as thick as the outer, and containing the brown bodies which give *Hydra fusca* its characteristic color. Both layers are composed of *epithelial cells*. A thin space containing a non-cellular jelly-like substance, the *mesoglea*, separates ectoderm from entoderm. Not only the body-wall, but also the tentacles, possess these three definite regions. The body, with the exception of the basal disc, is covered by a thin, transparent *cuticle*. Both body and tentacles are hollow, the single central space being known as the *gastrovascular cavity*.

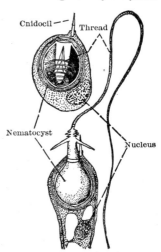

FIG. 66. — Nematocysts of *Hydra* before and after discharge. (From Dahlgren and Kepner after Schneider.)

The *ectoderm* is primarily *protective* and *sensory*, and is made up of two principal kinds of cells: (1) *epithelio-muscular*, and (2) *interstitial*. The former are shaped like inverted cones, and possess long (up to .38 mm.), unstriped *contractile fibrils* at their inner ends; these enable the animal to expand and contract.

The *interstitial cells* lie among the bases of the epitheliomuscular cells; they give rise to three kinds of *nematocysts* or stinging cells (Fig. 65; Fig. 66). Nematocysts are present on all parts of the body except the basal disc, being most numerous on the tentacles. The interstitial cell in which the nematocyst develops is called a cnidoblast (Fig. 66); it contains a nucleus and develops a trigger-like process, the cnidocil, at its outer end, but is almost completely filled by the pear-shaped nematocyst. Within this structure is an inverted coiled thread-like tube with barbs at the base. When the nematocyst explodes, this tube turns rapidly inside out and is able to penetrate the tissues of other animals (Fig. 67, B; Fig. 68, A). The explosion is probably due to internal pressure produced by osmosis, and may be brought about by various methods such as the application of a little acetic acid or methyl green. Many animals when "shot" by nematocysts are immediately paralyzed and sometimes killed by a poison called hypnotoxin which is injected into them by the tube.

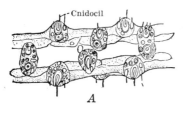
Cnidocil

A

B

FIG. 67. — Nematocysts of *Hydra* and their action. **A**, portion of a tentacle showing the batteries of nematocysts. **B**, insect larva covered with nematocysts as a result of capture by *Hydra*. (From Jennings.)

Two kinds of nematocysts smaller than that just described are also found in the ectoderm of *Hydra*. One of these is cylindrical and contains a thread without barbs at its base; the other is spherical and contains a barbless thread which, when discharged, aids in the capture of prey by coiling around the spines or other structures that may be present (Fig. 68, B).

Certain ectoderm cells of the basal disc of *Hydra* are *glandular* and secrete a sticky substance for the attachment of the animal.

The *entoderm*, the inner layer of cells, is primarily *digestive, absorptive,* and *secretory*. The digestive cells are large, with muscle fibrils at their base, and flagella or pseudopodia at the end which projects into the gastrovascular cavity. The flagella create currents in the gastrovascular fluid, and the pseudopodia capture solid food particles. The glandular cells are small and without muscle fibrils. Interstitial cells are found lying at the base of the other entoderm cells.

The *mesoglea* is an extremely thin

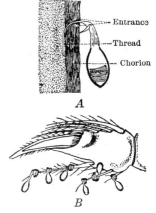
Entrance
Thread
Chorion

A

B

FIG. 68. — The action of nematocysts. **A**, a nematocyst piercing the chitinous covering of an insect. **B**, nematocysts holding a small animal by coiling about its spines. (After Toppe in *Zool. Anz.*)

layer of jelly-like substance situated between the other two layers.

From recent investigations it seems well established that *Hydra* possesses a *nervous system,* though complicated staining methods are necessary to make it visible. In the ectoderm there is a sort of plexus of nerve-cells connected by nerve-fibers with centers in the region of the mouth and foot. Sensory cells in the surface layer of cells serve as external organs of stimulation, and are in direct continuity with fibers from the nerve cells. Some of the nerve-cells send processes to the muscle fibers of the epithelio-muscular cells, and are therefore motor in function. No processes from the nerve-cells to the nematocysts have yet been discovered, though they probably occur. The entoderm of the body also contains nerve-cells, but not so many as are present in the ectoderm.

Physiology. — *Nutrition* — *Hydra* lives on minute aquatic animals which come within reach of its tentacles. The nematocysts, and probably a secretion from the tentacles, paralyze the prey, while the viscid surface of the tentacle prevents it from escaping. Food is carried to the mouth by the bending over of the tentacle which captured it ; other tentacles also assist. The mouth opens and slowly moves around the food, which is then forced down to the basal end of the gastrovascular cavity by the contraction of the body-wall behind it.

Hydras will not capture prey or respond to food stimuli when they have recently been fed. Moderately hungry specimens will exhibit the characteristic food-taking reactions if both chemical and physical stimuli are applied at the same time, *e.g.,* a piece of filter paper soaked in beef juice. A hungry animal will respond by making swallowing movements when a chemical stimulus alone is applied.

Digestion takes place in the gastrovascular cavity and probably also within the entoderm cells. The gland cells of the entoderm secrete a fluid into the gastrovascular cavity ; this fluid dissolves the food. Digestion is aided by the currents set up by the flagella of the entoderm cells and by the churning resulting from the expansion and contraction of the body. Part of the food is evidently engulfed by the pseudopodia of the entoderm cells and undergoes *intracellular* digestion. The dissolved food is *absorbed* by the entoderm cells ; part of it, especially the oil globules, is passed over to the ectoderm, where it is stored until needed.

Behavior. — Hydras are usually found attached to the bottom or sides of the aquarium, or to aquatic plants, or are suspended from the surface film of the water. The position of rest, with the body stretched out and the tentacles widely spread, allows the animal to obtain food from a considerable area. At intervals of several minutes an undisturbed *Hydra*, especially if hungry, will contract rapidly and then slowly expand in a new direction,

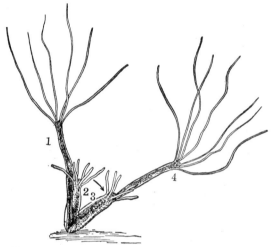

FIG. 69. — Spontaneous changes of positions in an undisturbed *Hydra*. Side view. The extended animal (1), contracts (2), bends to a new position (3), and then extends (4). (From Jennings.)

as shown in Fig. 69. This brings it into a new part of its surroundings, where more food may be present. Finally, these spontaneous movements cease, and the animal moves to another place.

Locomotion is known to be effected in three ways. Usually the animal bends over (Fig. 70, *1*) and attaches itself to the substratum by its tentacles (*2*) ; the basal disc is then released and the animal contracts (*3*) ; the body then expands (*4*), bends over in some other direction and becomes attached (*5*) ; finally the tentacles are released and an upright position is regained (*6*). This method of locomotion has been compared to that of the measuring-worm. At other times the animal uses its tentacles as legs, or glides along on its basal disc.

Hydras react to mechanical *stimulation*, to light, temperature, and electricity. If a watch-glass containing a specimen is jarred, or the surface of the water agitated, a part or all of the body and tentacles contract ; this is the result of a *non-localized mechanical stimulus*.   If the body or a tentacle is touched with a glass rod, the body or tentacles contract, depending on the strength of the stimulus.

Changes in the intensity of the *light* cause *Hydras* to move about until they reach a region where the light is most favorable ; this may be called their *optimum*.   They find this optimum by the method of " *trial and error*," *i.e.* their movements are indefinite, all directions being tried until the proper conditions are encountered.   In a well-lighted area they are most likely to secure the small animals that serve as food, since these are also attracted by light.

When subjected to *heat*, the trial and error method is likewise employed ; the animals escape if they chance to move into a cooler area, but perish if they remain in a heated region too long.

The reactions of a hungry *Hydra* to food indicate that the *physiological condition* of the animal determines to a large extent the kind of reactions produced, not only spontaneously, but also by external stimuli.   " It decides whether *Hydra* shall creep upward to the surface and toward the light, or shall sink to the bottom ;

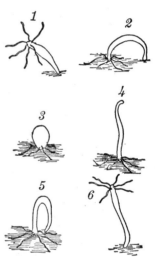

Fig. 70. — *Hydra* moving like a measuring worm.   (From Jennings, after Wagner.)

how it shall react to chemicals and to solid objects ; whether it shall remain quiet in a certain position, or shall reverse this position and undertake a laborious tour of exploration."

Reproduction. — *Hydra* reproduces *asexually* by budding and by *fission*, and *sexually* by the production of eggs and spermatozoa.

Budding (Fig. 65) is quite common, and may easily be observed in the laboratory.   The bud appears first as a slight bulge in the body-wall.   This pushes out rapidly into a stalk, which soon develops a circlet of blunt tentacles about its distal end. The cavities of both stalk and tentacles are at all times directly connected with that of the parent.   When full grown, the bud becomes detached and leads a separate existence. Sometimes the bud may begin to form other buds before it becomes detached from the parent animal. In this way a sort of hydroid colony is produced resembling that of certain marine cœlenterates like *Obelia* (Fig. 73). *Fission* is less common. The distal end of the animal divides first ; then the body slowly splits down the center, the halves finally separating when the basal disc is severed (Fig. 71). *Hydras* have also been found which bore buds reproducing in this manner. This method of multiplication must, however, be rare, since it is so seldom seen. *Transverse fission* has also been reported.

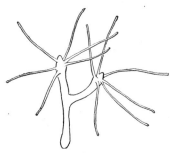

Fig. 71. — *Hydra* reproducing by longitudinal fission. (After Koelitz in *Zool. Anz.*)

The processes concerned in *sexual reproduction* are the production of spermatozoa and eggs, the fertilization of the egg, the development and hatching of the embryo, and the growth of the young larva. The *spermatozoa* arise in the *testis* from ectodermal interstitial cells (Fig. 65) ; they develop in long cysts through the end of which they escape into the surrounding water. The *eggs* arise in the *ovary* from ectodermal interstitial cells. Usually only one egg develops in a single ovary. When a certain period of growth is reached, two *polar bodies* are given off by the egg, which is then said to be mature. *Fertilization* occurs usually within two hours after the polar bodies have been formed.

The *cleavage* of the egg is *total* and almost equal, a *blastula* (Fig. 65) being formed with a distinct cavity, the *blastocœl*. A solid *gastrula-like* structure is produced by the filling up of the blastocœl with cells budded off from the blastula wall. The outer cells may be called ectoderm and the inner cells entoderm. The ectoderm now secretes a thick chitinous *shell* covered with sharp projections. The embryo then separates from the parent and falls to the bottom, where it remains unchanged for several weeks. Then interstitial cells make their appearance. A subsequent resting period is followed by the breaking away of the outer chitinous envelope and the elongation of the escaped embryo. Mesoglea is now secreted by the ectoderm and entoderm cells ;

a circlet of tentacles arises at one end, and a mouth appears in their midst. The young *Hydra* thus formed soon grows into the adult condition.

Regeneration. — An account of the phenomenon of regeneration is appropriate at this place, since the power of animals to restore lost parts was first discovered in *Hydra* by Trembley in 1744. This investigator found that if *Hydras* were cut into two, three, or four pieces, each part would grow into an entire animal. Other experimental results obtained by Trembley are that the hypostome, together with the tentacles, if cut off, may produce a new indi-

vidual ; that each piece of a *Hydra* split longitudinally into two or four parts, becomes a perfect polyp, and that when the head end is split in two and the parts separated slightly, a two-headed animal results (Fig. 72, A).

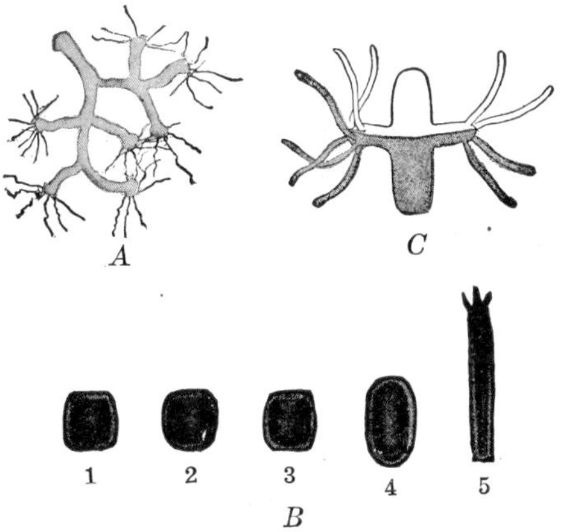

Regeneration may be defined as the replacing of an entire organism by a part of the same. It takes place not only in *Hydra*, but in many other cœlenterates, and in some of the representatives of almost every phylum of the animal kingdom.

FIG. 72. — Regeneration and grafting in *Hydra*. **A**, seven-headed *Hydra* made by splitting distal ends lengthwise. **B**, a piece of *Hydra* regenerating an entire animal. **C**, part of one *Hydra* grafted upon another. (From Morgan, A, after Trembley ; B, after Morgan ; C, after King.)

Hydra, however, is a species that has been quite widely used for experimentation. Pieces of *Hydra* that measure $\frac{1}{6}$ mm. or more in diameter are capable of becoming entire animals (Fig. 72, B). The tissues in some cases restore the lost parts by a multiplication of their cells ; in other cases, they are worked over directly into a new but smaller individual. Parts of one *Hydra* may easily be grafted upon another (Fig. 72, C). In this way many bizarre effects have been produced.

Space will not permit a detailed account of the many interesting questions involved in the phenomenon of regeneration, but enough has been given to indicate the nature of the process. The benefit to the animal of the ability to regenerate lost parts is obvious. Such an animal, in many cases, will succeed in the struggle for existence under adverse conditions, since it is able to regain its normal condition even after severe injuries. *Physiological regeneration* takes place continually in all animals ; for example, new cells are produced in the epidermis of man to take the place of those that are no longer able to perform their proper functions.

Both internal and external factors have an influence upon the rate of regeneration and upon the character of the new part. Temperature, food, light, gravity, and contact are some of the external factors. In man, various tissues are capable of regeneration ; for example, the skin, muscles, nerves, blood-vessels, and bones. Lost parts are not restored in man because the growing tissues do not coordinate properly. Many theories have been advanced to explain regenerative processes, but none has gained sufficient acceptance to warrant its inclusion here.

2. Class I. Hydrozoa

Hydra is the Hydrozoon which is most easily obtained for study, and by means of *Hydra* the principal characteristics of the cœlenterates have been illustrated. There are, however, a vast number of related animals that differ widely in form, structure, and habits. The two chief shapes assumed by the Hydrozoa are the *hydroid*, or *polyp*, like *Hydra* and *Obelia* (Fig. 73), and the *jellyfish*, or *medusa*, like *Gonionemus* (Fig. 74). There are many variations of each of these, and frequently one species may exhibit both conditions at different periods in its life-history.

a. A Colonial Hydrozoon — Obelia [1]

Obelia (Fig. 73) is a colonial cœlenterate which lives in the sea, where it is usually attached to rocks, to wharves, or to *Laminaria*, *Rhodymenia*, and other algæ. It may be found in low water and to a depth of forty fathoms along the coast of northern Europe and from Long Island Sound to Labrador.

Anatomy and Physiology. — An *Obelia* colony consists of a basal stem, the *hydrorhiza*, which is attached to the substratum ; this gives off at intervals upright branches, known as *hydrocauli*. At every bend in the zigzag hydrocaulus a side branch arises.

---

[1] *Campanularia* is similar to *Obelia* in most respects.

The stem of this side branch is ringed and is expanded at the end into a hydra-like structure, the *hydranth* (Fig. 73, A). A single polyp consists of a hydranth and the part of the stalk between the hydranth and the point of origin of the preceding branch. Full-grown colonies usually bear reproductive members (*gonangia*) in the angles where the hydranths arise from the hydrocaulus (Fig. 73, A).

The *Obelia* colony as just described and as shown in Fig. 73, A, resembles the structure that would be built up by a budding *Hydra* if the buds were to remain attached to the parent and in turn produce fixed buds.

All of the soft parts of the *Obelia* colony are protected by a chitinous covering called the *perisarc* (Fig. 73, A) ; this is ringed at various places and is expanded into cup-shaped *hydrothecæ* to accommodate the hydranths, and into *gonothecæ* to enclose the reproductive members.

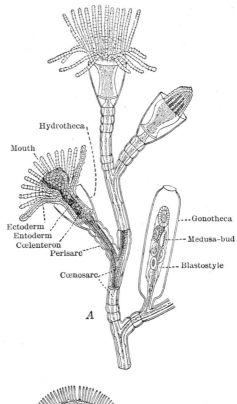

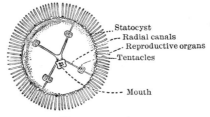

FIG. 73. — *Obelia*. **A**, stalk bearing hydranths. **B**, medusa. (From Parker and Haswell.)

A shelf which extends across the base of the hydrotheca serves to support the hydranth. The soft parts of the hydrocaulus and of the stalks of the hydranths constitute the *cœnosarc*, and are attached to the perisarc by minute projections. The cœnosarcal cavities of the hydrocaulus open into those of the branches and thence into the hydranths, producing in this way a common *gastrovascular cavity.*

A longitudinal section of a hydranth and its stalk (Fig. 73, A) shows the cœnosarc to consist of two layers of cells — an outer layer, the *ectoderm,* and an inner layer, the *entoderm.* These layers are continued into the hydranth. The *mouth* is situated in the center of the large knob-like *hypostome,* and the *tentacles,* about thirty in number, are arranged around the base of the hypostome in a single circle. Each tentacle is solid, consisting of an outer layer of ectoderm cells and a single axial row of entoderm cells ; at the extremity are a large number of nematocysts. The hydranth captures, ingests, and digests food as in *Hydra.*

The *reproductive members* arise, as do the hydranths, as buds from the hydrocaulus, and represent modified hydranths. The central axis of each is called a *blastostyle,* and together with the gonothecal covering is known as the *gonangium.* The blastostyle gives rise to *medusa-buds* which soon become detached (Fig. 73, B) and pass out of the gonotheca through the opening in the distal end.

Some of the *medusæ* of *Obelia* (Fig. 73, B) produce eggs, and others produce spermatozoa. The fertilized eggs develop into colonies like that which gave rise to the medusæ. The medusæ provide for the dispersal of the species, since they swim about in the water and establish colonies in new habitats. The structure of a medusa (*Gonionemus*) will be described in section *c* of this chapter. The medusa of *Obelia* is shown in Figure 73, B ; it is shaped like an umbrella with a fringe of tentacles and a number of organs of equilibrium on the edge. Hanging down from the center is the *manubrium* with the mouth at the end. The gastrovascular cavity extends out from the cavity of the manubrium into four *radial canals* on which are situated the reproductive organs.

The *germ-cells* of the medusæ of *Obelia* arise in the ectoderm of the manubrium, and then migrate along the radial canals to the reproductive organs. When mature, they break out into the water. The eggs are *fertilized* by spermatozoa which have escaped from other medusæ. *Cleavage* is similar to that of *Hydra,* and a hollow *blastula* and solid *gastrula-like* structure are formed. The gastrula-like structure soon becomes ciliated and elongates into a free-swimming larva called a *planula*. This soon acquires a central cavity, becomes fixed to some object, and proceeds to found a new colony.

b. *Metagenesis*

Metagenesis is the alternation of a generation which reproduces only asexually by division or budding with a generation which reproduces only sexually by means of eggs and spermatozoa. This phenomenon occurs in other groups of the animal kingdom, but finds its best examples among the cœlenterates. *Obelia* is an excellent illustration of a metagenetic animal. The asexual generation, the colony of polyps (Fig. 73, A), forms buds of two kinds, the hydranths and the gonangia. The medusæ (Fig. 73, B), or sexual generation, reproduce the colony by means of eggs and spermatozoa.

The polyp and medusa stages are not equally important in all HYDROZOA ; for example, *Hydra* has no medusa stage and *Geryonia* no polyp or hydroid stage. Various conditions may be illustrated by different HYDROZOA. In the following list, O represents the fertilized ovum, H, a polyp, M, a medusa, m, an inconspicuous or degenerate medusa, and h, an inconspicuous or degenerate polyp.

1. O — H — O — H — O (*Hydra*).
2. H — m — O — H — m — O (*Sertularia*).
3. O — H — M — O — H — M — O (*Obelia*).
4. O — h — M — O — h — M — O (*Liriope*).
5. O — M — O — M — O (*Geryonia*).

c. *A Jellyfish or Medusa — Gonionemus*

The structure of a hydrozoan jellyfish or medusa may be illustrated by *Gonionemus* (Fig. 74). This jellyfish is common along the eastern coast of the United States. It measures about half an inch in diameter, without including the fringe of tentacles around the margin. In general form it is similar to the medusa of *Obelia* (Fig. 73, B). The convex or aboral surface is called the *exumbrella;* the concave, or oral surface, the *subumbrella.* The subumbrella is partly closed by a perforated membrane called the *velum.* Water is taken into the subumbrellar cavity and is then forced out through the central opening in the velum

by the contraction of the body ; this propels the animal in the
opposite direction, thus enabling it to swim about.

The *tentacles*, which vary in number from sixteen to more than
eighty, are capable of considerable contraction.   Near their tips

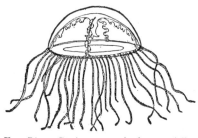

are *adhesive* or *suctorial pads*
at a point where the tentacle
bends at a sharp angle.   Hanging down into the subumbrellar cavity is the *manubrium*
with the *mouth* at the end.
surrounded by four frilled *oral
lobes*.   The mouth opens into
a *gastrovascular cavity* which

Fig. 74. — *Gonionemus*, a hydrozoan jellyfish.   (From Washburn, after Hargitt.)

consists of a central " *stomach* "
and four *radial canals*.   The
radial canals enter a *circumferential canal* which lies near the margin of the umbrella.

The cellular layers in *Gonionemus* are similar to those in *Hydra*,
but the *mesoglea* is extremely thick and gives the animal a jelly-
like consistency.   Scattered about beneath the ectoderm are
many *nerve cells*, and about the velum is
a *nerve ring*.   *Sensory cells* with a tactile
function are abundant on the tentacles.
The margin of the umbrella is supplied
with two kinds of sense organs : (1) at the
base of the tentacles are round bodies
which contain pigmented entoderm cells
and communicate with the circumferential
canal ; (2) between the bases of the tentacles are small outgrowths which are
probably organs of equilibrium and, therefore, *statocysts*.   *Muscle fibers*, both exumbrella and subumbrella, are present,
giving the animal the power of *locomotion*.

Fig.   75. — Hydralike
stage in the development
of *Gonionemus*.   One of the
tentacles is carrying a
worm (w) to the mouth.
Tentacles in contracted
state.   (From the Cam-
bridge Natural History,
after Perkins.)

Suspended beneath the radial canals are
the sinuously folded *reproductive organs* or
gonads.   *Gonionemus* is diœcious, each individual producing either
eggs or spermatozoa.   These reproductive cells break out directly
into the water, where *fertilization* takes place.   A ciliated *planula*
develops from the egg as in *Obelia*.   This soon becomes fixed to

some object, and a mouth appears at the unattached end. Then four tentacles grow out around the mouth and the *Hydralike* larva is able to feed (Fig. 75). Other similar *Hydralike* larvæ bud from its walls. How the medusæ arise from these larvæ is not known, but it seems probable that a direct change from the hydroid form to the medusa occurs.

d. *Hydroid and Medusa Compared*

Although the medusæ upon superficial examination appear to be very different from the polyps or hydroids, they are constructed on the same general plan as the latter. Figure 76 illustrates in a diagrammatic fashion the resemblance between the

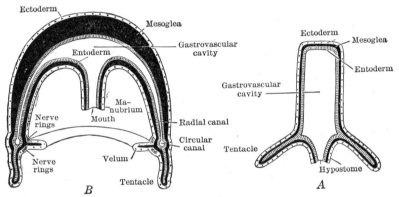

Fig. 76. — Diagrams showing the similarities of a polyp (**A**) and a medusa (**B**).
(From Parker and Haswell.)

polyp (A) and the medusa (B) by means of longitudinal sections. If the medusa were grasped at the center of the aboral surface and elongated, a hydralike form would result. Both have similar parts, the most noticeable difference being the enormous quantity of mesoglea present in the medusa.

e. *Polymorphism*

The division of labor among the cells of a METAZOON has already been noted (p. 72). When division of labor occurs among the members of a colony, the form of the individual is suited to the function it performs. A colony containing two kinds of members is said to be *dimorphic;* one containing more than two kinds, *polymorphic*. Some of the most remarkable cases of polymorphism occur among the HYDROZOA. The " Portuguese man-of-war " (Fig. 77), for example, consists of a float with a sail-like crest from which a number of polyps hang down into the water. Some of these polyps are nutritive, others are tactile ; some contain batteries of nematocysts, others are male reproductive zooids, and still others give rise to egg-producing medusæ.

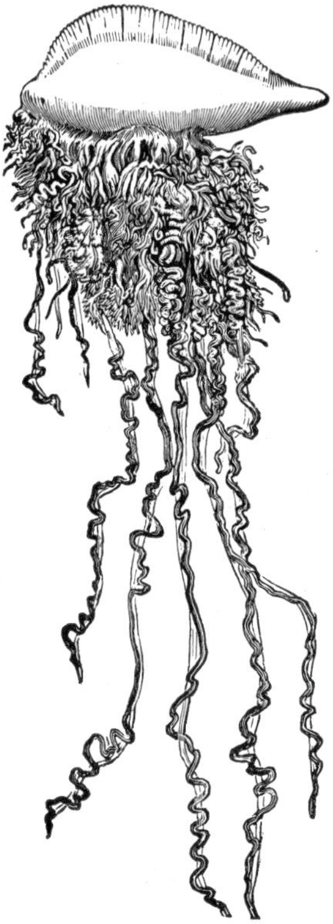

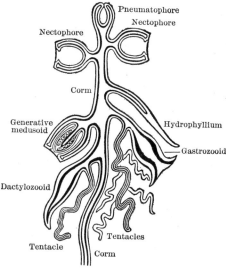

FIG. 78. — Diagram showing possible modifications of medusoids and hydroids of a hydrozoan colony of the order SIPHONOPHORA. The thick black line represents entoderm, the thinner line ectoderm. (From Lankester's Treatise, after Allman.)

FIG. 77. — *Physalia* or Portuguese man-of-war, a colonial HYDROZOON. (After Agassiz.)

Tables V and VI present briefly the various modifications that may occur among the members of colonial HYDROZOA.

f. *Reproduction in the Hydrozoa*

The methods of reproduction differ so widely among the HYDROZOA that only a brief general account can be given here. Reference should be made to the descriptions for *Hydra* (p. 109), *Obelia* (p. 114), and *Gonionemus* (p. 116).

TABLE V

POLYMORPHIC MODIFICATIONS OF THE MEDUSOIDS OF THE HYDROZOA

Name	Structure	Function
Sexual medusoid	Like typical medusa of Anthomedusæ (p. 120) or modified because of arrested development (Fig. 78)	Production of ova or spermatozoa
Nectophore	Without tentacles, manubrium, and mouth (Fig. 78)	Locomotion
Hydrophyllium	Shield shaped (Fig. 78)	Protective
Pneumatophore	Air sac (Fig. 78)	Hydrostatic
Aurophore	Ovoid	Unknown

TABLE VI

POLYMORPHIC MODIFICATIONS OF THE HYDROIDS OF THE HYDROZOA

Name	Structure	Function
Gastrozooid	With large mouth, nematocysts, and tentacle bearing nematocysts (Fig. 78)	Ingestion of food
Dactylozooid	Without mouth; with many nematocysts and tentacle (Fig. 78)	Offense and defense
Blastostyle	Without mouth or tentacles	Produces sexual medusoids by budding

Asexual reproduction is characteristic of some HYDROZOA and rare or absent in others. The most common method is by *budding* (*Hydra*, p. 109, Fig. 65). The wall of the hydroid sends out a hollow protrusion which may become either a new hydroid or a medusa. Certain medusæ also produce medusæ by budding. *Fission* is rare in hydroids (*Hydra*, p. 110, Fig. 71) and very rare in medusæ.

Sexual Reproduction. — Both male and female germ-cells are rarely developed by a single individual as in *Hydra* (Fig. 65). Usually a colony produces either ova or spermatozoa, or these originate in different individuals of a single colony. Sometimes one blastostyle may give rise to both kinds of germ-cells. The *development* of the fertilized egg has already been described in *Hydra* (p. 110), *Obelia* (p. 114), and *Gonionemus* (p. 116).

g. *Classification of the Hydrozoa*

The HYDROZOA may be distinguished from the SCYPHOZOA and ANTHOZOA by the absence of a stomodæum and mesenteries (Fig. 84), and by the fact that their sexual cells are discharged directly to the exterior. In classifying the HYDROZOA, both the hydroids and medusæ are considered. The arrangement adopted in this book is from Fowler in Lankester's *Treatise on Zoology*.

Order 1. Anthomedusæ. HYDROZOA usually with two forms of individuals, (1) non-sexual fixed hydroids, and (2) fixed or free-swimming sexual medusæ. The perisarc (absent in *Hydra*) does not form hydrothecæ around the polyp nor gonothecæ around the reproductive zooids. The reproductive organs are in the wall of the manubrium. The hydroids are usually colonial, with solid tentacles in one or more whorls. Examples: *Hydra, Hydractinia, Eudendrium, Tubularia.*

Order 2. Leptomedusæ. — HYDROZOA with an alternation of non-sexual fixed hydroids and free or fixed sexual medusæ. The hydrothecæ and gonothecæ are specialized portions of the perisarc. The sexual organs are on the radial canals. The medusæ possess eye-spots (ocelli) and statocysts containing statoliths of ectodermal origin. Examples: *Obelia* (Fig. 73), *Campanularia, Plumularia, Sertularia, Clytia.*

Order 3. Trachymedusæ. — HYDROZOA without alternation of generations, the medusa developing more or less directly from the egg. The sexual organs are on the radial canals. The medusæ possess sensory organs called tentaculocysts, containing entodermal statoliths which are usually enclosed in vesicles. Examples: *Trachynema, Persa,* and *Liriope.*

Order 4. Narcomedusæ. — HYDROZOA without alternation of generations. The sexual organs are on the subumbral floor of the gastric cavity or gastric pouches. The tentaculocysts contain entodermal statoliths which are not enclosed in vesicles. Examples: *Cunocantha, Cunina.*

Order 5. Hydrocorallinæ. — Colonial HYDROZOA with alternation of generations and a massive or branching calcareous skeleton into which the nutritive polyps (gastrozooids) and protective polyps (dactylozooids) may be drawn. These HYDRO-CORALLINÆ are often called corals and are found on coral reefs, but they differ in structure from the true corals (Figs. 86–91). Example: *Millepora*. The staghorn coral (*Millepora alcicornis*) occurs in Florida.

Order 6. Siphonophora. — Colonial free-swimming HYDROZOA with alternation of generations and highly modified (polymorphic) hydroid and medusoid members. Example: *Physalia* (Portuguese man-of-war, Fig. 77). The hydroids and medusoids of the SIPHONOPHORA may be modified as shown in Tables V and VI.

3. CLASS II. SCYPHOZOA

Most of the larger jellyfishes belong to the SCYPHOZOA. They can be distinguished easily from the hydrozoan medusæ by the presence of notches, usually eight in number, in the margin of the umbrella. They are called *acraspedote* (without velum or craspedon) medusæ in contrast to the *craspedote* (with velum or craspedon) medusæ of the HYDROZOA. The SCYPHOZOA range from an inch to three or four feet in diameter. They are usually found floating near the surface of the sea, though some of them are attached to rocks and weeds. There is an alternation of generations in their life-history, but the asexual stage (the scyphistoma, Fig. 81, *D*) is subordinate.

a. A Scyphozoan Jellyfish — Aurelia

Aurelia (Fig. 79) is one of the commonest of the scyphozoan jellyfishes. The species *A. flavidula* ranges from the coast of Maine to Florida. Members of the genus may be recognized by the eight shallow lobes of the umbrella margin, and the fringe of many small tentacles.

In structure *Aurelia* differs from *Gonionemus* and other hydrozoan medusæ in the absence of a velum, the characteristics of the canals system, the position of the gonads, and the arrangement and morphology of the sense-organs.

The *oral lobes* or *lips* of *Aurelia* (Fig. 79) which hang down from the square mouth are long and narrow, with folded margins. The *mouth* opens into a short *gullet*, which leads to the somewhat rectangular " *stomach.*" A *gastric pouch* extends laterally from each side of the stomach. Within each gastric pouch is a *gonad* and a row of small *gastric filaments* bearing *nematocysts*. Numerous *radial canals*, some of which branch several times, lead from the stomach to a *circumferential canal* at the margin. The gonads are frill-like organs lying in the floor of the gastric pouches. They have a pinkish hue in the living animal. The eggs or spermatozoa pass through the stomach and out of the mouth.

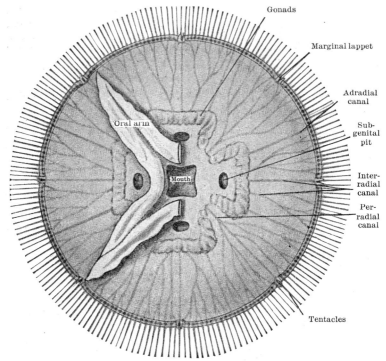

FIG. 79. — *Aurelia*, ventral view with two of the oral arms removed. (From Parker and Haswell.)

The eight *sense-organs* of *Aurelia* lie between the marginal lappets (Fig. 79) and are known as *tentaculocysts*. They are considered to be organs of *equilibrium*. As shown in Figure 80, each tentaculocyst is a hollow projection connected with the entodermal canal. It contains a number of calcareous concretions formed by the entoderm; and bears an ectodermal pigment spot, the *ocellus*, which is sensitive to light. The tentaculocyst is protected by an aboral hood and by lateral lappets. *Olfactory pits* are situated near by.

An *alternation of generations* occurs in *Aurelia*, but the hydroid stage is subordinate. The eggs develop into free-swimming planulæ which become attached to some object and produce hydra-like structures, each of which is called a *hydra-tuba*. This buds like *Hydra* during most of the year, but finally a peculiar process called *strobilization* takes place. The hydra-tuba divides into discs which cause it to resemble a pile of saucers (Fig. 81, E, F); at this stage it is known as a *strobila*. Each disc develops tentacles (G, H), and, separating from those below it, swims away as a minute medusa called an *ephyra*. The ephyra gradually develops into an adult jellyfish.

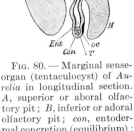

FIG. 80. — Marginal sense-organ (tentaculocyst) of *Aurelia* in longitudinal section. *A*, superior or aboral olfactory pit; *B*, inferior or adoral olfactory pit; *con*, entodermal concretion (equilibrium); *End*, entoderm; *Ent*, entodermal canal continued into the tentaculocyst; *H*, bridge between the two marginal lappets; *oc*, ectodermal pigment (ocellus); *T*, tentaculocyst. (From Lankester's Treatise, after Eimer.)

b. Classification of the Scyphozoa

Four orders of SCYPHOZOA are usually recognized. The most obvious ordinal characteristics are the presence or absence of stomodæum and mesenteries, and the position of the tentacles and tentaculocysts. The *stomodæum* or *gullet* is a passageway between the mouth and the gastrovascular cavity or "stomach"; it is often held in place by membranes called *mesenteries*. The position of the tentacles and tentaculocysts is described with regard to their relation to the four radial canals. Those at the ends of the radial canals are said to be *perradial* (Fig. 79); those halfway between two perradii are called *interradial;* and those halfway between a perradius and an interradius are termed *adradial.*

Order 1. Stauromedusæ. — SCYPHOZOA without tentaculocysts; tentacles perradial and interradial; umbrella goblet-shaped; sometimes attached by the aboral pole; a stomodæum is present, suspended by four mesenteries; no alternation of generations. Examples: *Tessera* (Fig. 82, A), *Lucernaria.*

Order 2. Peromedusæ. — SCYPHOZOA with four interradial tentaculocysts; tentacles perradial and adradial; umbrella coni-

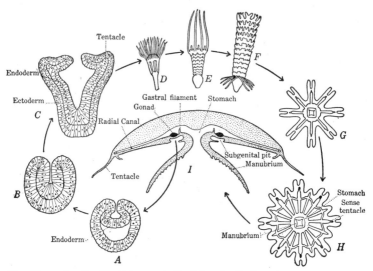

FIG. 81. — *Aurelia*, life-history. A, B, C, longitudinal sections through gastrula stages; D, scyphistoma: E, F, strobila; G, H, ephyra; I, vertical section through adult. (A, B, and C are more highly magnified than the other figures.) (From Kerr.)

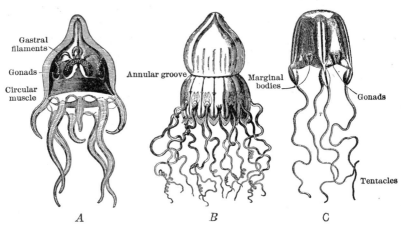

FIG. 82. — SCYPHOZOA. A, *Tessera princeps*, order STAUROMEDUSÆ. B, *Periphylla hyacinthina*, order PEROMEDUSÆ. C, *Charybdea marsupialis*, order CUBOMEDUSÆ. (From Sedgwick, after Haeckel.)

cal, with transverse constriction; a stomodæum is present suspended by four mesenteries; no alternation of generations. Example: *Periphylla* (Fig. 82, B).

Order 3. Cubomedusæ. — SCYPHOZOA with four perradial
tentaculocysts; tentacles interradial; umbrella four-sided, cup-
shaped; no alternation of generations. Example: *Charybdea*
(Fig. 82, C).

Order 4. Discomedusæ. — SCYPHOZOA with four or more
perradial and four or more interradial tentaculocysts; umbrella
disc-shaped; alternation of generations. Examples: *Aurelia*
(Fig. 79), *Pelagia, Cassiopea.*

4. CLASS III. ANTHOZOA (ACTINOZOA)

There are no medusæ among the ANTHOZOA. The polyps
may be distinguished from those of the HYDROZOA by the presence of a well-developed stomodæum or gullet, which is fastened

FIG. 83. — Sea anemones. (From Coleman.)

to the body-wall by a number of radially arranged membranes
called mesenteries. Many of the polyps are solitary, but the
majority produce colonies by budding. Most of the ANTHOZOA
secrete a calcareous skeleton, known as coral. Two types are
described in the following pages: (1) the sea-anemone, and (2) the
coral polyp.

a. A Sea-Anemone — Metridium

Metridium marginatum is a sea-anemone which fastens itself to the piles of wharves and to solid objects in tidepools along the North Atlantic coast. It is a cylindrical animal with a crown of hollow *tentacles* arranged in a number of circlets about the slit-like *mouth*. The tentacles as well as the body can be expanded

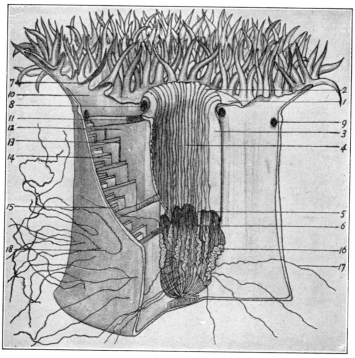

Fig. 84. — *Metridium marginatum*, a sea-anemone, partly cut away so as to show its structure. *1*, intermediate zone; *2*, lip; *3*, siphonoglyphe; *4*, gullet; *5*, inner end of gullet; *6*, edge of mesentery; *7*, cavity of a tentacle; *8*, inner ostium; *9*, outer ostium; *10*, primary mesentery; *11*, muscle-band on primary mesentery; *12*, abnormal tertiary mesentery; *13*, secondary mesentery; *14*, tertiary mesentery; *15*, quaternary mesentery; *16*, reproductive gland; *17*, mesenterial filament. (Redrawn from Linville and Kelly.)

and contracted, and the animal's position may be changed by a sort of creeping movement of its *basal disc*. The *skin* is soft but tough and contains no skeletal structures. The tentacles capture small organisms by means of *nematocysts*, and carry the food thus obtained into the mouth. The beating of the *cilia* which cover the tentacles and part of the mouth and *gullet* is necessary to force the food into the *gastrovascular cavity*. At each end of the gullet, or *stomodæum* (Fig. 84, *4*), is a ciliated groove called the *siphonoglyphe* (Fig. 84, *3*). Usually only one or two siphonoglyphes are present, but sometimes three occur in a single specimen. A continual stream of water is carried into the body cavity through these siphonoglyphes, thus maintaining a constant supply of oxygenated water.

If a sea-anomone is dissected as shown in Figure 84, the central or *gastrovascular* (*cœlenteric*) *cavity* will be found to consist of six radial chambers; these lie between the gullet or stomodæum and the body-wall, and open into a common basal cavity. The six pairs of thin, double partitions between these chambers are called *primary septa* or *mesenteries* (Fig. 84, *10;* Fig. 85). Water passes from one chamber to another through pores (*ostia*, Fig. 84, *9*, *8*) in these mesenteries. Smaller mesenteries project out from the body-wall into the chambers, but do not reach the stomo-

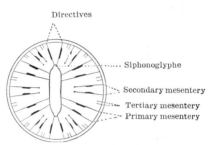

FIG. 85. — Cross section of a sea-anemone showing the arrangement of the mesenteries. (From Weysse.)

dæum; these are *secondary mesenteries* (Fig. 84, *13;* Fig. 85). *Tertiary mesenteries* (Fig. 84, *14;* Fig. 85) and *quaternary mesenteries* (Fig. 84, *15*) lie between the primaries and secondaries. There is considerable variation in the number, position, and size of the mesenteries (Fig. 84, *12*).

Each mesentery possesses a longitudinal retractor *muscle band* (Fig. 84, *11*). The bands of the pairs of mesenteries face each other except those of the primaries opposite the siphonoglyphes. These primaries, which are called *directives* (Fig. 85), have the muscle bands on their outer surfaces. The edges of the mesenteries below the stomodæum are provided with *mesenteric filaments* having a secretory function. Near the base these filaments bear long, delicate threads called *acontia* (Fig. 84, *17*). The acontia are armed with *gland cells* and *nematocysts*, and can be protruded from the mouth or through minute pores (*cinclides*) in the body-wall (Fig. 84, *18*). They probably serve as organs of offense and defense.

Near the edge of the mesenteries lying parallel to the mesenteric filaments are the *gonads* (Fig. 84, *16*). The animals are diœcious, and the eggs or spermatozoa are shed into the gastro-vascular cavity and pass out through the mouth. The fertilized egg probably develops as in other sea-anemones, forming first a free-swimming planula and then, after attaching itself to some object, assuming the shape and structure of the adult.

Asexual reproduction is of common occurrence, new anemones being formed by *budding* or *fragmentation* at the edge of the basal disc. *Longitudinal fission* has also been reported.

b. *A Coral Polyp — Astrangia*

Astrangia danæ (Fig. 86) is a coral polyp inhabiting the waters of our North Atlantic coast. A number of individuals live together in colonies attached to rocks near the shore. Each polyp looks like a small sea-anemone, being cylindrical in shape and

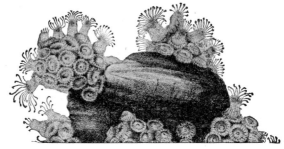

Fig. 86. — *Astrangia danæ*, a cluster of our Northern coral-polyps, resting on limy bases of their own secretion. (From Davenport, after Sorel.)

possessing a crown of tentacles. The most noticeable difference is the presence of a basal cup of calcium carbonate termed the *theca* (Fig. 87). This structure of calcium carbonate is what we commonly call coral. It is produced by the ectoderm of the coral polyp and increases gradually during the life of the animal.

The *calcareous cup* is divided into chambers by a number of radial *septa* (Fig. 87) which are built up between the pairs of mesenteries of the polyp. The center of the cup is occupied by a *columella* formed in part by the fusion of the inner ends of septa, and in part by projections from the base of the polyp. Although *Astrangia* builds a cup less than half an inch in height, it produces enormous masses of coral in the course of centuries.

c. *Coral Reefs and Atolls*

Coral polyps build *fringing reefs, barrier reefs,* and *atolls.* These occur where conditions are favorable, principally in tropical seas, the best known being among the Maldive Islands of the Indian Ocean, the Fiji Islands of the South Pacific Ocean, the Great Barrier Reef of Australia, and in the Bahama Island region.

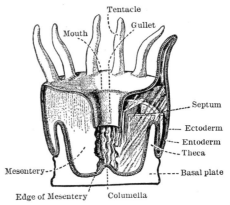

A *fringing* or *shore reef* is a ridge of coral built up from the sea bottom so near the land that no navigable channel exists between it and the shore. Frequently breaks occur in the reef, and irregular channels and pools are created which are often inhabited by many different kinds of animals, some of them brilliantly colored.

Fig. 87. — Semi-diagrammatic view of half a simple coral. (From Shipley and MacBride, partly after Bourne.)

A *barrier reef* is separated from the shore by a wide, deep channel. The Great Barrier Reef of Australia is over 1100 miles long and

Fig. 88. — A small atoll, being a sketch of Whitsunday Island in the South Pacific. (From Sedgwick, after Darwin.)

encloses a channel from 10–25 fathoms deep and is some places 30 miles wide. Often a barrier reef entirely surrounds an island.

An *atoll* (Fig. 88) is a more or less circular reef enclosing a lagoon. Several theories have been advanced to account for the production of atolls. Charles Darwin, who made extensive studies of coral reefs and islands, is responsible for the subsidence theory. According to Darwin, the reef was originally built up around an oceanic island which slowly sank beneath the ocean, leaving the coral reef enclosing a lagoon. John Murray believes that the island enclosed by the reef does not necessarily sink, but may be worn down by erosion.

Besides producing islands and reefs, corals play an important rôle in protecting the shore from being worn down by the waves. They have also built up thick strata of the earth's crust.

d. *Classification of the Anthozoa*

The ANTHOZOA may be divided into two subclasses and ten orders.

SUBCLASS I. ALCYONARIA. — ANTHOZOA with eight hollow, pinnate tentacles, and eight complete mesenteries; with one siphonoglyphe, ventral in position; and with the retractor muscles of the mesenteries all on the side toward the siphonoglyphe.

Order 1. Stolonifera. — ALCYONARIA colonial in habit; with stolon attached to a stone or other foreign object; polyps free except at base or joined together by horizontal bars; skeleton either horny or of calcareous spicules. Example: *Tubipora* (Fig. 89, A).

The organ-pipe coral, *Tubipora* (Fig. 89, A), is common on coral reefs. It has bright green tentacles and a skeleton of a dull red color, and adds considerably to the beauty of the coral reef.

Order 2. Alcyonacea. — Colonial ALCYONARIA; zooids united into a compact mass by fusion of body-walls; skeleton of calcareous spicules which do not form a solid axial support. Example: *Alcyonium* (Fig. 89, B).

Order 3. Gorgonacea. — Colonial ALCYONARIA; skeletal axis branched and not perforated by gastrovascular cavities of the zooids. Example: *Corallium* (Fig. 89, C).

This order includes the sea-fans which are to be found in almost every museum, and the precious red coral (*Corallium*, Fig. 89, C), which occurs in the Mediterranean and is widely used in the manufacture of jewelry.

Order 4. Pennatulacea. — ALCYONARIA forming bilaterally symmetrical colonies; zooids usually borne on branches of an axial stem, which is supported by a calcareous or horny skeleton.

Examples: *Pennatula* (Fig. 89, D), *Renilla*. The sea-pens (Fig. 89, D) live with their stalks embedded in muddy or sandy sea-bottoms. Many of them are phosphorescent.

SUBCLASS II. ZOANTHARIA. — ANTHOZOA with usually many simple hollow tentacles, arranged generally in multiples of five or six; two siphonoglyphes as a rule; mesenteries vary in num-

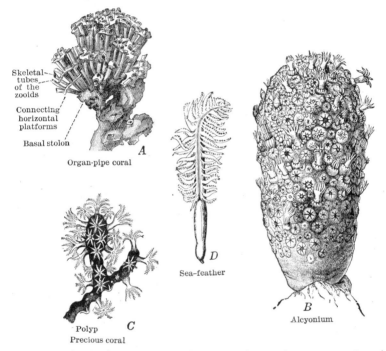

Skeletal tubes of the zooids

Connecting horizontal platforms

Basal stolon

A

Organ-pipe coral

D

Sea-feather

Polyp   *C*
Precious coral

B
Alcyonium

FIG. 89. — Coral. **A**, *Tubipora musica*, organ-pipe coral, a young colony. **B**, *Alcyonium digitatum*, with some zooids expanded. **C**, *Corallium*, a branch of precious coral. **D**, *Pennatula sulcata*, a sea-feather. (A and B, from Cambridge Natural History; C, from Sedgwick, after Lacaze Duthiers; D, from Sedgwick, after Kölliker.)

ber, the retractor muscles never arranged as in the ALCYONARIA; skeleton absent or present; simple or colonial; dimorphism rare.

Order 1. Edwardsiidea. — A few shallow water ZOANTHARIA with eight complete mesenteries and from fourteen to twenty or more tentacles.

Order 2. Actiniaria. — ZOANTHARIA usually solitary; many complete mesenteries; no skeleton. Examples: *Metridium* (Fig. 84), *Halcampa*, *Bunodes*.

These are the sea-anemones. Some of them are parasitic; *Bicidium* is parasitic on the jellyfish *Cyanea.* Many sea-anemones are beautifully colored; in the large Stoichactis of the Great

Barrier Reef of Australia, "the spheroidal bead-like tentacles occur in irregularly mixed patches of gray, white, lilac, and emerald green, the disk being shaded with tints of gray, while the oral orifice is bordered with bright yellow." (Kent.)

Order 3. Madreporaria. — Zoantharia usually colonial; many complete mesenteries; calcareous skeleton formed by ectoderm cells. Examples: *Astrangia* (Fig. 86), *Oculina* (Fig. 90), and *Madrepora.*

Fig. 90.—*Oculina speciosa,* a branch of madreporarian coral. (From Sedgwick, after Ed. H.)

Most of the stony corals belong to this order. *Astrangia* has already been described (p. 128, Fig. 86). *Oculina* (Fig. 90) and *Madrepora* are branching corals. *Meandrina* (Fig. 91) is a more compact "brain" coral. Many of the coral polyps are tinted with pink, lilac, yellow, green, violet, red, etc., and give the coral reefs the wonderful color effects for which they are famous.

Order 4. Zoanthidea. — Zoantharia usually colonial; only one siphonoglyphe; mesenteries differ from those of Actiniaria; no skeleton, but often incrusted by sand.

Certain Zoanthidea are the black corals of the Mediterranean; others live symbiotically with· hermit crabs or sponges.

Order 5. Antipathidea. — Colonial Zoantharia

Fig. 91. — *Meandrina,* a rose-coral of the order Madreporaria. (From Weysse.)

with a horny, usually branching axial skeleton, but no calcareous spicules.

The corals belonging to this order are found in all the large seas, usually at a depth of from fifty to five hundred fathoms.

Order 6. Cerianthidea. — Solitary ZOANTHARIA without a skeleton; one siphonoglyphe; no bands of retractor muscles on mesenteries. Example: *Cerianthus.*

This order contains a single genus, *Cerianthus.* One species *C. americanus*, occurs on the eastern coast of North America; other species occur in widely separated localities.

5. CŒLENTERATES IN GENERAL

Definition. — Phylum CŒLENTERATA. — POLYPS, JELLYFISHES, CORALS. — Diploblastic, radially symmetrical animals, with four or six antimeres ; a single gastrovascular cavity ; no anus ; body-wall contains peculiar structures known as nematocysts or stinging cells.

Morphology. — The foregoing account has shown that cœlenterates all possess a body-wall composed of two layers of cells, an outer ectoderm and an inner entoderm. They are therefore *diploblastic*, although many ANTHOZOA have a fairly well developed mesoderm. Between these layers is a jelly-like non-cellular substance, the mesoglea. The body-wall encloses a single cavity, the *cœlenteron* or *gastrovascular cavity*, in which both digestion and circulation take place. In some of the cœlenterates, like *Hydra* (Fig. 65), this cavity is simple, but in others, like *Aurelia* (Fig. 79), it is modified so as to include numerous pouches and branching canals.

The two principal types of cœlenterates are the *polyp* or *hydroid*, and the *jellyfish* or *medusa*. These are fundamentally similar in structure (Fig. 76), but are variously modified (Tables V and VI). Both polyps and medusæ are *radially symmetrical.*

So far as is known, all cœlenterates possess stinging cells called *nematocysts;* these are organs of offense and defense. *Muscle fibrils* are present in a more or less concentrated condition. *Nerve-fibers* and *sensory organs* are characteristic structures; they may be few in number and scattered as in *Hydra* (p. 107), or numerous and concentrated as in *Aurelia* (p. 122, Fig. 80).

Physiology. — The *food* of cœlenterates consists principally of small, free-swimming animals, which are usually captured by means of nematocysts and carried into the mouth by tentacles and cilia. *Digestion* is mainly *extracellular*, enzymes being discharged into the gastrovascular cavities for this purpose. The digested food is transported to various parts of the body by currents

. in the gastrovascular cavity, and is then taken up by the entoderm cells and passed over the ectoderm cells. Both *respiration* and *excretion* are performed by the general surface of the ectoderm and entoderm. *Motion* is made possible by muscle fibrils, and many species have also the power of *locomotion*. There is no true *skeleton*, although the stony masses built up by coral polyps support the soft tissues to a certain extent. The nervous tissue and sensory organs provide for the perception of various kinds of stimuli and the conduction of impulses from one part of the body to another. Cœlenterates are generally sensitive to light intensities, to changes in the temperature, to mechanical stimuli, to chemical stimuli, and to gravity. *Reproduction* is both asexual, by budding and fission, and sexual, by means of eggs and spermatozoa.

Economic Importance. — Cœlenterates as a whole are of very little economic importance. The coral built up by coral polyps form reefs and islands and thick strata of the earth's crust. Some corals are used as ornaments and for the manufacture of jewelry (Fig. 89, C). Cœlenterates are probably very seldom used as food by man but are eagerly devoured by fishes.

CHAPTER VI

PHYLUM CTENOPHORA [1]

The Phylum Ctenophora (Gr. *ktenos*, of a comb; *phoreo*, I bear) includes a small group of free-swimming marine animals which are even more nearly transparent than the cœlenterate jellyfishes. They have been placed by many authors under the Phylum Cœlenterata, but the present tendency is to separate them from that group and rank them as a distinct phylum (p. 21). They are widely distributed, being especially abundant in warm seas.

Ctenophores are commonly called *sea walnuts* because of their shape (Fig. 92), or *comb jellies* on account of their jelly-like consistency and the comb-like locomotor organs arranged in eight rows on the sides of the body (Fig. 93, A, Fig. 93, B). A few species have a slender ribbon-like shape and may, like Venus' girdle (Fig. 94), reach a length of from six inches to four feet.

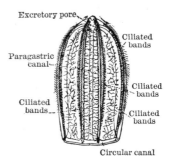

FIG. 92. — A ctenophore, *Idyia roseola*. (From Weysse, after Agassiz.)

The general *structure* of a ctenophore is shown in Figure 93. It is said to possess *biradial symmetry*, since the parts, though in general radially disposed, lie half on one side and half on the other side of a median longitudinal plane. An end view, as in Figure 93, B, illustrates this fact. The *mouth* (Fig. 93, A) is situated at one end (*oral*) and a *sense-organ* (Fig. 93, A) at the opposite or *aboral* end. Extending from near the oral surface to near the aboral

---

[1] This chapter on the Ctenophora is included in this book for the sake of completeness since the ctenophores represent an aberrant group of very little general interest, although of great importance to specialists. It should therefore be assigned for reference only.

end are eight meridional *ciliated bands* (Fig. 93, A, Fig. 93, B); these are the *locomotor organs.* Each band has the cilia arranged upon it in transverse rows and fused at the base; each row thus resembles a comb. These are raised and lowered alternately, starting at the aboral end, and cause an appearance like a series of waves traveling from this point toward the mouth. The animal is propelled through the water with the oral end forward. Light is refracted from these moving rows of cilia, and brilliant, changing colors are thus produced. Some species are phosphorescent.

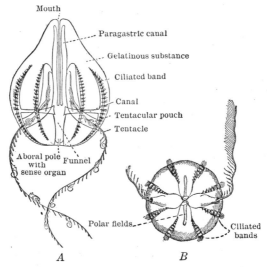

FIG. 93. — Ctenophora. **A,** *Hormiphora plumosa.* Side view. **B,** *Pleurobrachia pileus.* Aboral view. (A, after Chun. B, from Lankester's Treatise.)

Most ctenophores possess two solid, contractile *tentacles* (Fig. 93, A) which emerge from blind pouches, one on either side (Fig. 93, B). With one exception, the tentacles are not provided with nematocysts as are those of the CŒLENTERATA, but are supplied with adhesive or *glue cells* called *colloblasts* (Fig. 95). The colloblasts produce a secretion of use in capturing small animals which serve as food. The spiral filament in each colloblast is contractile, and acts as a spring, often preventing the struggling prey from tearing the cell away.

The Digestive System. — The *mouth* (Fig. 93, A) opens into a flattened *stomodæum,* where most of the food is digested; this leads to the " *infundibulum* " or funnel which is flattened at right angles to the stomodæum. Six canals arise from the infundibulum. Two of these, called *excretory canals*, open to the exterior near an aboral sense-organ; undigested food probably does not pass through them, but is ejected through the mouth. The two *paragastric canals* (Fig. 93, A) lie parallel to the stomodæum,

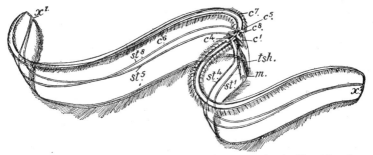

FIG. 94. — *Cestus veneris*, Venus' girdle. *m*, mouth; c^1—c^8, ciliated bands; *st*, st^8, x^1, x^2, canals. (From Lankester's Treatise.)

ending blindly near the mouth. The two *tentacular canals* pass out toward the pouches of the tentacles, then each gives rise to four branches; these lead into *meridional canals* lying just beneath the ciliated bands.

The aboral sense-organ (Fig. 96) is a *statocyst* or organ of equilibrium. It consists of a vesicle of fused cilia enclosing a ball of calcareous granules, the statolith, which is supported by four tufts of fused cilia. It is probable that when the body is at an angle, the calcareous ball presses more heavily on the inclined side, and thus stimulates the ciliated bands on that side to greater activity. Just beneath the statocyst is a ciliated area supposed to be sensory in function, and on either side is a ciliated prolongation called the polar field (Fig. 93, B).

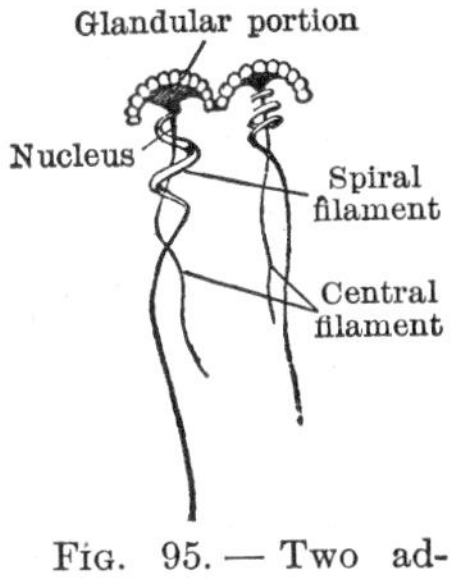

Ctenophores are *hermaphroditic*. The *ova* are formed on one side and the *spermatozoa* on the other side of each meridional

Glandular portion

Nucleus

Spiral filament

Central filament

FIG. 95. — Two adhesive cells from a ctenophore. (From Lankester's Treatise, after Samassa.)

canal just beneath the ciliated bands (Fig. 93, A). The germ-cells pass into the infundibulum and thence to the outside through the mouth. The fertilized eggs develop directly into the adult without the intervention of an asexual generation as in many cœlenterates.

The *cellular layers* of ctenophores constitute a very small part of the body, most of it being composed of the transparent jelly-like *mesoglea*. The thin ciliated *ectoderm* covers the exterior and lines the stomodæum; and the *entoderm*, also ciliated, lines the infundibulum and the canals to which it gives rise. The *muscle fibers* which lie just beneath the ectoderm and entoderm are derived from the *mesoderm* cells of the embryo. Ctenophores are therefore *triploblastic* animals, and represent a higher grade of development than that of the cœlenterates.

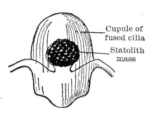

FIG. 96. — Sense organ of *Hormiphora plumosa*, a ctenophore. Side view. (From Lankester's Treatise.)

Definition. — Phylum CTENOPHORA. — SEA WALNUTS or COMB JELLIES. — Triploblastic animals; radial combined with bilateral symmetry; eight radially arranged rows of paddle plates.

The CTENOPHORA differ from the cœlenterates in several important respects besides the presence of a distinct mesoderm. With one probable exception, ctenophores do not possess nematocysts, and the adhesive cells (Fig. 95) which take their place are not homologous to nematocysts. Their ciliated bands, aboral sense-organs, and pronounced biradial symmetry are peculiarities which warrant placing ctenophores in a phylum by themselves. They probably evolved from cœlenterate-like ancestors, but can no longer be combined with that phylum. A discussion of the resemblances between ctenophores and the flatworms (PLATY-HELMINTHES) is reserved for the next chapter.

CHAPTER VII

PHYLUM PLATYHELMINTHES [1]

The Phylum PLATYHELMINTHES (Gr. *platus*, broad; *helmins*, an intestinal worm) includes the planarians, liver-flukes, tapeworms, and many other " flatworms." Some of these are free-living in fresh water, salt water, or less frequently on land, whereas others are parasitic. Many of the parasites pass through a number of complex stages, and live in the bodies of several species of animals during their life-history. The parasitic flatworms frequently are responsible for serious diseases of man and other animals.

The three classes of the PLATYHELMINTHES are as follows: —

CLASS I. TURBELLARIA (Lat. *turbo*, I disturb), with ciliated ectoderm; free-living habit (*Planaria*, Fig. 97);

CLASS II. TREMATODA (Gr. *trema*, a pore; *eidos*, resemblance), with non-ciliated ectoderm; suckers; parasitic habit (*Fasciola*, Fig. 105); and

CLASS III. CESTODA (Gr. *kestos*, a girdle; *eidos*, resemblance), with body of segments; without mouth or alimentary canal; parasitic (*Tænia*, Fig. 107).

1. A FRESH-WATER FLATWORM — PLANARIA

Planaria (Fig. 97, and Fig. 98, *2*) is a flatworm found only in fresh water, usually clinging to the underside of logs or stones.

[1] The flatworms are the lowest of the strictly bilateral animals. They serve to illustrate the various modifications involved in this type of symmetry and also the advances in morphology and physiology, especially in the development of systems of organs, brought about by the presence of the third germ layer, the mesoderm. The TURBELLARIA exhibit remarkable powers of regeneration and the phenomenon of axial gradients. The parasitic flatworms illustrate the wonderfully complex relations between parasites and their hosts and intermediate hosts. Among them are some very important human parasites. They are not usually studied in elementary courses, but it is suggested that sufficient time be spent on them to bring out the various specializations and degenerations made necessary by a parasitic existence, such as the enormously increased powers of reproduction, the various types of life cycles, and the methods of securing transfer from the definitive host to the one or more species of intermediate hosts.

Its body is *bilaterally symmetrical* and *dorso-ventrally flattened.* The anterior end is rather blunt, the posterior end, more pointed. It may reach half an inch in length. *Planaria maculata,* the common American species, is difficult to study because of the

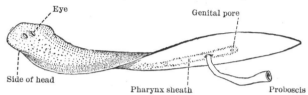

Fig. 97. — *Planaria polychroa,* a fresh-water flatworm. (From Shipley and MacBride.)

great amount of coloring matter in its body (Fig. 98, *2*), but an allied flatworm, *Dendrocœlum lacteum* (Fig. 98, *1*), is cream-colored, and its anatomy is more easily made out.

Anatomy and Physiology. — *External Features.* — Figure 97 shows the principal external features of a planarian. A pair of *eye-spots* are present on the dorsal surface near the anterior end. The *mouth* is in a peculiar position near the middle of the ventral surface. From it the muscular *proboscis* may extend. Posterior

Fig. 98. — Fresh-water flat-worms. *1, Dendrocœlum lacteum. 2, Planaria.* (After Woodworth.)

to the mouth is a smaller opening, the *genital pore.* The surface of the body is covered with *cilia* which propel the animal through the water. This is not the only method of locomotion, since muscular contraction is also effective.

INTERNAL ANATOMY AND PHYSIOLOGY. — A study of the structure of the adult and of the early embryonic stages shows *Planaria* to be a *triploblastic* animal possessing three germ-layers, *ectoderm, mesoderm,* and *entoderm,* from which several systems of organs have been derived. There are well-developed muscular, nervous, digestive, excretory, and reproductive systems; these are constructed in such a way as to function without the coordination of a circulatory system, respiratory system, cœlom, and anus.

Digestive System. — The digestive system (Fig. 99) consists of a *mouth*, a *pharynx* lying in a muscular sheath, and an *intestine* of three main trunks and a large number of small lateral extensions. The muscular pharynx can be extended as a *proboscis* (Fig. 97); this facilitates the capture of food. *Digestion* is both *intercellular* and *intracellular, i.e.* part of the food is digested in the intestinal trunks by secretions from cells in their walls; whereas other food particles are engulfed by pseudopodia thrust out by cells lining the intestine, and are digested inside of the cells in vacuoles. The digested food is absorbed by the walls of the intestinal trunks, and, since branches from these penetrate all parts of the body, no circulatory system is necessary to carry nutriment from one place to another. As in *Hydra,* no anus is present, the fæces being ejected through the mouth.

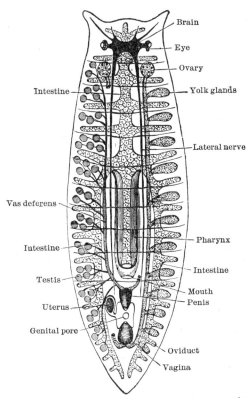

FIG. 99. — Diagram showing the internal organs of a flatworm. (From Lankester after v. Graff.)

Excretory System. — The excretory system comprises a pair of longitudinal, much-coiled tubes, one on each side of the body; these are connected near the anterior end by a transverse tube, and open to the exterior by two small pores on the dorsal surface. The longitudinal and transverse trunks give off numerous finer tubes which ramify through all parts of the body, usually ending in a flame-cell. The *flame-cell* (Fig. 100, A) is large and hollow, with a bunch of flickering cilia extending into the central cavity.

Since it communicates only with the excretory tubules, it is considered excretory in function, though it may also carry on respiratory activities.

MUSCULAR SYSTEM. — The power of changing the shape of its body, which may be observed when *Planaria* moves from place

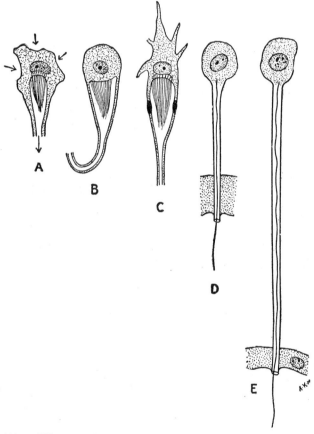

FIG. 100. — "Flame-cells" (highly magnified). **A**, *Planaria*; **B**, miracidium stage of liver fluke, *Fasciola*; **C**, tapeworm, *Tænia*; **D**, a polychæte, *Phyllodoce*; **E**, *Amphioxus*. The highly evolved tubular type of flame-cell shown in **D** and **E** is given the special name solenocyte. (From Kerr.)

to place, lies principally in three sets of muscles: a circular layer just beneath the ectoderm, external and internal layers of longitudinal muscle fibers, and a set of oblique fibers lying in the mesoderm.

Nervous System. — *Planaria* possesses a well-developed nervous system consisting of a bilobed mass of tissue just beneath the eye-spots called the *brain* (Fig. 99), and two lateral longitudinal *nerve-cords* connected by transverse nerves. From the brain, *nerves* pass to various parts of the anterior end of the body, imparting to this region a highly sensitive nature.

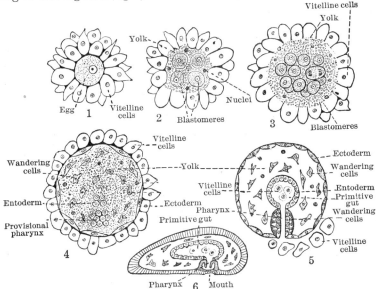

Fig. 101. — Development of *Planaria lactea.* **1**, egg surrounded by yolk. **2**, four blastomeres from segmented egg. **3**, later stage; blastomeres more numerous. **4**, much later stage; blastomeres differentiated into ectoderm, entoderm, a provisional pharynx, and wandering cells. **5**, cellular differentiation more advanced; **6**, embryo changes shape to a flattened ovoid. (From Lankester's Treatise, after Hallez.)

Reproductive System. — Reproduction is by *fission* or by the *sexual* method. Each individual possesses both male and female organs, *i.e.* is *hermaphroditic.* The *male organs* may be located easily in Figure 99; they consist of numerous spherical *testes* connected by small tubes called *vasa deferentia;* the vas deferens from each side of the body joins the *cirrus* or *penis,* a muscular organ which enters the *genital cloaca.* A *seminal vesicle* lies at the base of the penis, also a number of unicellular, *prostate glands.* Spermatozoa originate in the testes, and pass, by way of the vasa deferentia, into the seminal vesicle, where they remain until needed for fertilization.

The *female reproductive organs* comprise two *ovaries,* two long oviducts with many yolk-glands entering them, a vagina which opens into the genital cloaca, and the *uterus* which is also connected with this cavity. The *eggs* originate in the ovary, pass down the oviduct, collecting yolk from the yolk-glands on the way, and finally reach the uterus. Here *fertilization* occurs, and *cocoons* are formed, each containing from four to more than twenty eggs, surrounded by several hundred yolk cells. The development of the egg is illustrated and explained in Figure 101.

Regeneration. — Planarians show remarkable powers of regeneration. If an individual is cut in two (Fig. 102, A), the anterior end will regenerate a new tail (B, B^1), while the posterior part develops a new head (C, C^1). A crosspiece (D) will regenerate both a head at the anterior end and a new tail at the posterior end $(D^1 - D^1)$. The head alone of a planarian will grow into an entire animal $(E - E^3)$. Pieces cut from various parts of the body will also regenerate completely.

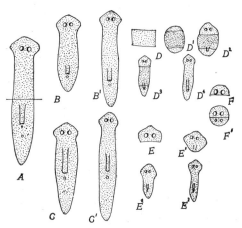

Fig. 102. — Diagrams illustrating regeneration and grafting in planarians. (From Morgan.)

No difficulty is experienced in grafting pieces from one animal upon another, and many curious monsters have been produced in this way.

Axial Gradients. — *Planaria* is an animal that illustrates admirably the theory of axial gradients. The primary axis or axis of polarity is an imaginary line extending from the anterior to the posterior end of the body. In *Planaria* the head has a relatively high rate of metabolism and dominates the rest of the body. Experiments have shown that a gradient of metabolic activity proceeds from the anterior to the posterior end. For example, if planarians are cut into four pieces the anterior piece will be found to use up more oxygen and give off more carbon dioxide than any of the others; the second piece comes next in its rate of metabolism;

the third piece next; and the tail piece gives the lowest rate of all. Thus is demonstrated an axial gradient in the metabolism of the animal from the anterior to the posterior end.   This is particularly well brought out in older planarians especially at the time of transverse division.

When a planarian is young, it is relatively short and its whole body, especially the head, has a relatively high rate of metabolism. As it grows older it becomes longer and its whole metabolic rate slows down.   When young, the high metabolic rate of the head was able to exercise a dominance, through the transmission of stimuli down the gradient, over the entire length of the animal. With a slowing down of the metabolic rate of the apical end and an increase in the length of the path over which the impulse travels, there comes a time when the apical end can no longer maintain a physiological dominance over the entire axis.   At the point where dominance fades out, an independent part of the body arises through what is known as physiological isolation.   The isolated piece, the second zooid, has its own gradient, the metabolic rate of the anterior end being the highest. This region now becomes a new apical end or, morphologically

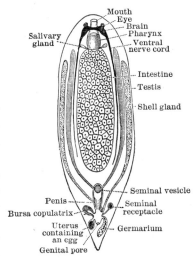

Fig. 103. — Plan of structure of a Rhabdocœlous Turbellarian. (After v. Graff.)

speaking, the head of a new zooid.   No structural indications of a new individual are visible, however, at this time.   The only tests of the presence of a second or third individual are physiological tests. . . .   The isolated posterior zooid now forms a new head, with eyes, brain, and other parts.   The new head then reorganizes the rest of the piece into a complete new individual.

2. Class I. Turbellaria

The Turbellaria (the class to which *Planaria* belongs) are free-living Platyhelminthes with ciliated epidermis.   Special

ectodermal cells secrete mucus or produce rod-like bodies called
" rhabdites."

Order 1. Rhabdocœlida (Fig. 103). Small Turbellaria,
often microscopic, with simple unbranched intestine. Examples:
Microstoma, in fresh water; *Monoscelis* and *Monops*, marine.

Order 2. Tricladida (Fig. 99). Turbellaria with intestine
of three main branches — one median anterior branch and two
lateral posterior branches; many lateral cæca arise from the
main branches. Examples: *Planaria* (Fig. 98), *Polyscelis*, and

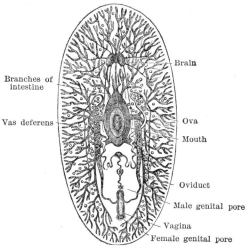

Fig. 104. — Plan of structure of a pollyclad Turbellarian. (From Sedgwick,
after Quatrefages.)

Dendrocœlum (Fig. 98, *1*) in fresh water; *Bipalium* in the tropics
living in moist earth, and accidentally introduced into hothouses
all over the world; *Bdelloura*, *Gunda*, and *Polychœrus* in the sea.

Order 3. Polycladida (Fig. 104). Marine Turbellaria with
a central digestive chamber which gives off many lateral branches.
Examples: *Stylochus* and *Leptoplana*.

3. Class II. Trematoda

a. *The Liver-fluke — Fasciola hepatica*

The liver-fluke is a flatworm which lives as an adult in the
bile ducts of the liver of sheep, cows, pigs, etc., and is occasionally
found in man. Figures 105 and 106, H show the shape and most

of the anatomical features of a mature worm. The *mouth* (Fig. 106, H) is situated at the anterior end and lies in the middle of a muscular disc, the *anterior sucker*. A short distance back of the mouth is the *ventral sucker;* it serves as an organ of attachment.

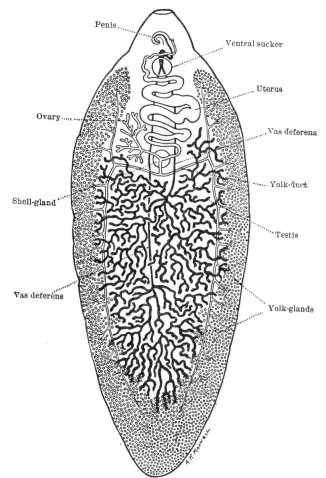

Penis

Ventral sucker

Uterus

Ovary

Vas deferens

Yolk-duct

Shell-gland

Testis

Vas deferens

Yolk-glands

FIG. 105. — *Fasciola hepatica* — genital organs, seen from the ventral side. (From Kerr.)

Between the mouth and the ventral sucker is the *genital opening* through which the eggs pass to the exterior. The *excretory pore* lies at the extreme posterior end of the body (Fig. 106, H), and another pore, the opening of Laurer's canal, is situated in the mid-dorsal line about one-third the length of the body from the anterior end.

The *digestive system* is simple. The *mouth* opens into a short globular *pharynx* which leads into another short tube, the *œsopha-*

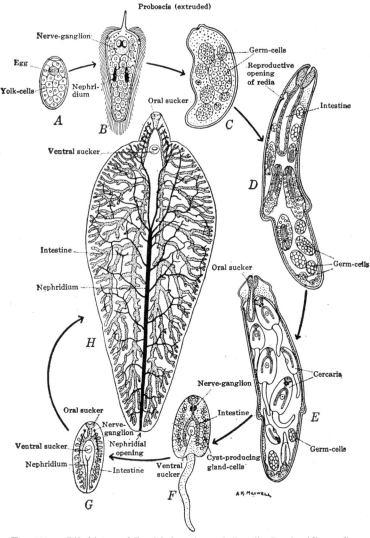

FIG. 106. — Life-history of *Fasciola hepatica*. *A*, "egg"; *B*, miracidium; *C*, sporocyst; *D*, *E*, rediæ; *F*, cercaria; *G*, tail-less encysted stage; *H*, adult (neither reproductive organs nor nervous system are shown). (From Kerr.)

gus. The *intestine* (Fig. 106, H) consists of two branches, one extending from near the anterior to the posterior end on each side of the body. Many small branches are given off from the intestine as in *Planaria* (Fig. 99, *i*) and no circulatory system is therefore necessary for the transportation of food material.

The *excretory system* (Fig. 106, H) is similar to that of *Planaria* (p. 141), but only one main tube and one exterior opening are present. The *nervous system* also resembles that of *Planaria* (Fig. 99).

The *suckers* are provided with special sets of *muscles* enabling them to fasten the animal to its host. Three layers of muscles lie just beneath the ectoderm: (1) an outer circular layer, (2) a middle longitudinal layer, and (3) an inner diagonal layer.

The body of the liver-fluke is *triploblastic*. The *ectoderm* is a thin, hard covering often called the *cuticle;* it protects the underlying tissues from the juices of the host. The ectoderm contains chitinous scales and unicellular glands. The *entoderm* lines the alimentary tract. The *mesoderm* is represented by the muscles, the excretory organs, the reproductive ducts, and the parenchyma. The *parenchyma* is a loose tissue lying between the body-wall and the alimentary canal; within it are embedded the various internal organs described above, as well as the reproductive system.

Both male and female *reproductive organs* are present in every adult; they are extremely well developed, and, as in *Planaria*, quite complex. The *male* organs are as follows: (1) a pair of branched *testes* (Fig. 105) in which the spermatozoa arise; (2) two ducts, the *vasa deferentia*, which carry the spermatozoa from the testes to (3) a pear-shaped sac, the *seminal vesicle;* (4) a convoluted tube, the *ejaculatory duct*, which leads to the end of (5) a muscular copulatory organ, the *penis*.

The *female organs* are (1) a single-branched *ovary* (Fig. 105) in which the eggs are produced; (2) a convoluted *oviduct* which transports the eggs from the ovary to (3) the *shell gland*, at which place (4) the *vitelline* or *yolk duct* brings in and surrounds the eggs with yolk globules derived from (5) the *vitelline* or *yolk glands* (Fig. 105); the shell gland then furnishes a chitinous shell, and the eggs pass on into (6) a tube called the *uterus*, which leads to the *genital pore*.

One liver-fluke may produce as many as five hundred thousand eggs, and, since the liver of a single sheep may contain more than two hundred adult flukes, there may be one hundred million eggs formed in one animal. The *eggs segment* in the uterus of the fluke (Fig. 106, A), then pass through the bile ducts of the sheep into its intestine, and finally are carried out of the sheep's body with the fæces. Those eggs that encounter water and are kept at a temperature of about 75° F. continue to develop, producing a *ciliated larva* (Fig. 106, B) which escapes through one end of the egg-shell and swims about. This larva, called a *miracidium*, possesses a double *eye-spot* on the dorsal surface near the anterior end, a pair of *excretory organs*, the *nephridia*, and a number of centrally placed *germ-cells*. It swims about until it encounters a certain fresh-water snail, *Lymnæa truncatula* of Europe, or probably *Lymnæa humilis* in this country. If no snail is found within eight hours, the larva dies.

When a snail is reached, the larva forces its anterior proboscis (Fig. 106) into its tissue, and by a whirling motion bores its way into the soft parts of the body. Here in about two weeks it changes into a sac-like *sporocyst* (Fig. 106, C). Each *germ-cell* within the sporocyst, after passing through blastula and gastrula stages, develops into a second kind of larva, called a *redia* (Fig. 106, D). The rediæ soon break through the wall of the sporocyst and enter the tissue of the snail. Here, by means of germ-cells (Fig. 106, D) within their bodies, they usually give rise to one or more generations of *daughter rediæ* (Fig. 106, E), after which they produce a third kind of larva known as a *cercaria* (Fig. 106, F). The cercariæ leave the body of the snail, swim about in the water for a time, and then encyst (Fig. 106, G) on a leaf or blade of grass. If the leaf or grass is eaten by a sheep, the cercariæ escape from their cyst wall and make their way from the sheep's alimentary canal to the bile ducts, where they develop into mature flukes in about six weeks.

It will be seen from the above description that the life-history of the liver-fluke is complicated by the interpolation of several generations which develop from unfertilized germ-cells;

(1) The fertilized egg produces a ciliated larva, the miracidium (Fig. 106, B);

(2) The miracidium changes to a sporocyst (C) within which rediæ D are developed from unfertilized germ-cells (Fig. 106, C);

(3) The rediæ produce other rediæ E from unfertilized germ-cells (Fig. 106, D);

(4) The rediæ finally give rise to cercariae F from unfertilized germ-cells (Fig. 106, E); and

(5) The cercariae develop into mature flukes (Fig. 105).

The great number of eggs produced by a single fluke is necessary, because the majority of the larvæ do not find the particular kind of snail, and the cercariæ to which the successful larvæ give rise have little chance of being devoured by a sheep. The generations within the snail of course increase the number of larvæ which may develop from a single egg. This complicated *life-history* should also be looked upon as enabling the fluke to gain access to new hosts. The liver-fluke is not so prevalent in the sheep of this country as in those of Europe.

b. *Trematoda in General*

The TREMATODA are parasitic Platyhelminthes without cilia but with a hardened ectoderm in the adult stage. The body is usually flattened and leaf-shaped. One or more ventral suckers are present at or near the posterior end and in the mouth region.

Trematodes may be *ectoparasitic, i.e.* living on the body of another animal, like *Gyrodactylus*, which clings to the gills of the carp, or *entoparasitic, i.e.* living in the body of another animal, like the liver-fluke. Some of the modifications due to parasitic habits are the absence of eye-spots in most species, the poorly developed brain and sense-organs, and the highly specialized sexual organs.

The two orders of TREMATODA differ principally in their method of development.

Order 1. Monogenea. Trematodes which develop directly from the egg; they possess a large posterior, ventral, terminal sucker, and usually one or two suckers near the mouth.

Most of the MONOGENEA are ectoparasitic on aquatic animals, *e.g. Sphyranura* on the skin of the salamander (*Necturus*), *Polystomum* on the gills of the tadpole and later in the urinary bladder of the adult frog, and *Epibdella* on the body of the halibut.

Order 2. Digenea. Entoparasitic TREMATODA which pass through several different forms in their life-history; they possess an anterior and often a ventral sucker.

The best-known member of this order is the liver-fluke, which has a fairly representative life-history. Usually the DIGENEA occupy two, but sometimes three, hosts during their development;

one host is generally a vertebrate, one a snail, and the third an insect or other animal. *Clonorchis sinensis* and *Paragonimus ringeri* attack human beings in China. A few TREMATODA and their hosts are given in Table VII. (From the *Cambridge Natural History*.)

TABLE VII

THE LIFE-HISTORIES OF A FEW DIGENETIC TREMATODES

SPECIES	FINAL HOST	HOST LARVA ENTERS AND CERCARIÆ FORMED	HOST CERCARIÆ ENTER: EATEN BY FINAL HOST
1. Distomum atriventre	Frogs and toads of North America	*Physa heterostro-phia*, a snail	Not known.
2. D. retusum	The frog, *Rana*	The snail, *Lym-næa stagnalis*	The snail, *Lym-næa stagnalis*, and larvæ of caddice flies.
3. Gasterosto-mum fim-briatum	Perch and pike, *Perca* and *Esox*	Fresh water clams, *Unio* and *Anodonta*	*Leuciscus erythro-phthalmus*, a small fish.
4. Monostomum flavum	*Anas*, a duck	A snail, *Planorbis corneus*	Omitted.
5. Diplodiscus subclavatus	Frogs, toads, and salamanders, *Rana*, *Bufo*, and *Triton*	Snails, *Planorbis* and *Cyclas*	Insect larvæ, frogs (*Rana*) and Toads (*Bufo*). Often omitted.

4. CLASS III. CESTODA

a. *The Tapeworm — Tænia*

The tapeworm, *Tænia solium*, is a common parasite which lives as an adult in the alimentary canal of man. A nearly related species, *T. saginata*, is also a parasite of man. *Tænia*, as shown in Figure 107, is a long flatworm consisting of a knob-like head, the *scolex* (Fig. 107, *B*), and a great number of similar parts, the *proglottides*, arranged in a linear series. The animal clings to the wall of the alimentary canal by means of *hooks* (Fig. 107, *B*) and *suckers* on the scolex. Behind the scolex is a short *neck* followed by a string of proglottides which gradually increase in size from the

anterior to the posterior end.   The worm may reach a length of
ten feet and contain eight or nine hundred proglottides.   Since the
proglottides are budded off from the neck (Fig. 107, *B*), those at
the posterior end are the oldest.   The production of proglottides
may be compared to the formation of
ephyræ by the hydra-tuba of *Aurelia*
(Fig. 81), and is called *strobilization*.

The *anatomy* of the tapeworm is
adapted to its parasitic habits.   There
is *no alimentary canal*, the digested
food of the host being absorbed through
the body-wall.   The *nervous system* is
similar to that of *Planaria* and the
liver-fluke, but not so well developed
(Fig. 108).   Longitudinal *excretory
tubes*, with branches ending in *flame-
cells*, open at the posterior end and
carry waste matter out
of the body (Fig. 108).

A *mature proglottid*
is almost completely
filled with *reproductive
organs;* these are shown
in Figure 108.   *Sperma-
tozoa* originate in the
spherical *testes*, which
are scattered about
through the proglottid;
they are collected by

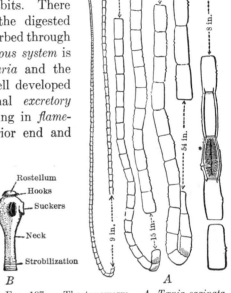

Rostellum
Hooks
Suckers
Neck
Strobilization

B   *A*

Fig. 107. — The tapeworm. *A, Tænia saginata.
B, Tænia solium*, scolex. (*A*, from the Camb. Nat.
Hist., *B*, from Shipley and MacBride.)

fine tubes and carried to the *genital pore* by way of the *vas deferens.*
Eggs arise in the bilobed *ovary* and pass into a tube, the *oviduct.*
Yolk from the *yolk-gland* enters the oviduct and surrounds the
eggs.   A chitinous shell is then provided by the *shell gland* and
the eggs pass into the *uterus.*   The eggs have in the meantime
been *fertilized* by spermatozoa, which probably come from the
same proglottid, and move down the *vagina.*   As the proglottides
grow older the uterus becomes distended with eggs and sends
off branches (Fig. 107*), while the rest of the reproductive organs
are absorbed.   The ripe proglottides break off and pass out of
the host with the fæces.

The eggs of *Tænia solium* develop into *six-hooked embryos* (Fig. 109, a) while still within the proglottid. If they are then

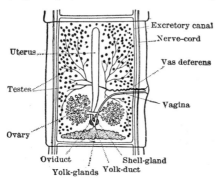

eaten by a pig, they escape from their envelopes (Fig. 109, b) and bore their way through the walls of the alimentary canal into the voluntary muscles, where they form *cysts* (Fig. 109, c). A head is developed from the cyst wall (Fig. 109, d) and then becomes everted (e). The larva is known as a *bladder-worm* or *cysticercus* at this stage. If insufficiently cooked pork

Fig. 108. — Illustrating the arrangement of the genital organs in a sexually mature proglottid of *Tænia*. (From Kerr.)

containing cysticerci is eaten by man, the bladder is thrown off, the head becomes fastened to the wall of the intestine, and a series of proglottides is developed.

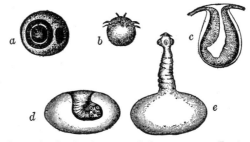

Fig. 109. — Stages in the development of the tapeworm, *Tænia solium*, to the cysticercus stage. a, egg with embryo. b, free embryo. c, rudiment of the head as a hollow papilla on wall of vesicle. d, bladder-worm (cysticercus) with retracted head. e, the same with protruded head. (From Sedgwick.)

b. *Cestoda in General*

The CESTODA are all *entoparasitic* flatworms, called tapeworms; they inhabit the alimentary canal of vertebrates in the adult stage. The body consists of a head or " scolex," followed by a chain of similar joints or " proglottides " which are budded off from the " neck." *Archigetes* (Fig. 110) differs from other tapeworms both in structure and habit; it has only one proglottid, and lives in the cœlom of an annelid, *Tubifex*.

A few Cestodes and their hosts are given in Table VIII (from the *Cambridge Natural History*).

TABLE VIII

THE LIFE-HISTORIES OF A FEW CESTODES

Name	Final Host	Intermediate Host
1. Tænia saginata	Man	Ox, giraffe (in muscles).
2. T. serrata	Dog	Rabbit, hare, mice (liver and peritoneum).
3. Dipylidium caninum	Man, dog, cat	Flea of dog (body-cavity).
4. Hymenolepis diminuta	Man, mouse, rat	Meal-moth, *Asopia farinalis;* also certain Orthoptera and Coleoptera.
5. Drepanidotænia setigera	Goose	Water-flea, *Cyclops brevicaudatus.*
6. Bothriocephalus latus	Man, dog	Pike, perch, trout, etc.

5. FLATWORMS IN GENERAL

Definition. — Phylum PLATYHELMINTHES. — FLATWORMS. — Triploblastic animals; bilaterally symmetrical; single gastrovascular cavity; no anus; presence of cœlom doubtful.

The flatworms are more highly organized than the CŒLENTERATA or CTENOPHORA and are distinctly *triploblastic*. The middle germ-layer, the mesoderm, which is well developed in flatworms, is connected with several important systems of organs, since it is from this layer that the muscles, the excretory system, and the reproductive ducts originate. The development of these systems of organs is correlated with the thickness of the body-wall. The excretory system is necessary, since it is no longer possible for the animal to get rid of the waste products of metabolism through the general surface of the body. Likewise a system

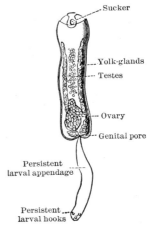

Sucker

Yolk-glands

Testes

Ovary

Genital pore

Persistent larval appendage

Persistent larval hooks

FIG. 110. — A unisegmental cestod, *Archigetes sieboldii*, from the cœlom of a worm, *Tubifex rivulorum*. (From the Cambridge Natural History, after Leuckart.)

of ducts is required to transport the germ-cells to the exterior. No circulatory system appears in the flatworms, but in most cases the food is transported directly to the tissues through the much-branched digestive tract, which serves, as in the CŒLENTERATA and CTENOPHORA, as a gastrovascular cavity.

Definite *bilateral symmetry* is exhibited by flatworms and should be considered an advance in morphological development, since the most successful animals have their bodies constructed on this plan. With bilateral symmetry is probably correlated the concentration of nervous tissue, the brain, in the head; the end of the body directed forward in moving would receive sensations first, and nerve-cells would be developed in the region of greatest stimulation. It is believed by some authorities that the body-cavity in the larval stages (sporocyst and redia) of liver-flukes represents the cœlom (p. 87) and that the reproductive ducts of the adults should be considered true cœlomic cavities.

Our present knowledge of the flatworms seems to indicate that they, as well as the CTENOPHORA, have evolved from cœlenterate stock. Forms like the simplest TURBELLARIA, the RHADOCŒLIDA, have probably given rise to the more complex members of that class. From these also were probably derived the TREMATODA, no doubt in response to the changed conditions of life resulting from a parasitic habit. Many of the adult CESTODA appear so closely related to certain TREMATODA that these two classes may have arisen together, or else the former have become separated from the complex TREMATODA (Digenea) as a distinct group.

Some authorities believe that the two curious animals *Ctenoplana* and *Cœloplana* are connecting links between the CTENOPHORA and PLATYHELMINTHES. *Ctenoplana* has been recorded once from the Indian Ocean and once from New Britain. *Cœloplana* inhabits the Red Sea.

Economic Importance of Flatworms. — The TURBELLARIA are of practically no economic importance. Trematodes are parasitic in a great many vertebrates, but for the most part do not cause serious injuries. The liver-fluke of the sheep, and the trematode *Schistosoma hæmatobium* which infests the blood-vessels of the urinary bladder and alimentary tract of man, in Africa, are the most important species.

The adult tapeworms found in the alimentary canal of man and other animals interfere seriously with the digestion and absorption of food, but the larvæ are more dangerous. For example, the tapeworm, *Tænia echinococcus*, which lives as an adult in the dog, gives rise to a larva called *Echinococcus polymorphus*. These larvæ may form large vesicles in man, known to physicians as *hydatides*, which may break with serious or even fatal results. The organism which causes " gid " or " staggers" in sheep is the larva, called *Cœnurus cerebralis*, of the dog tapeworm, *Tænia cœnurus*. It becomes lodged in the brain or spinal cord. Goats, cattle, and deer are also attacked by the same species.

CHAPTER VIII

PHYLUM NEMATHELMINTHES [1]

THE NEMATHELMINTHES (Gr. *nēma*, thread; *helmins*, an intestinal worm) are called *round* or *thread worms*. They are usually long and slender, and more or less cylindrical. They may be distinguished from the segmented worms (Phylum ANNELIDA, Chap. XI) by the entire absence of internal and external segmentation. The microscopic animal which lives in vinegar and is known as the vinegar-eel is a nemathelminth. Other roundworms live as parasites in the alimentary canal of man and other animals, or, like *Trichinella* (Fig. 113), live for a time embedded in the tissues of the body.

1. A PARASITIC ROUNDWORM — ASCARIS LUMBRICOIDES

External Features. — *Ascaris* (Fig. 111) is a genus of roundworms parasitic in the intestines of pigs, horses, and man. The sexes are separate. The female, being the larger, measures from five to eleven inches in length and about one-fourth of an inch in diameter. The body is light brown in color; it has a dorsal and a ventral white narrow stripe running its entire length, and a broader lateral line is present on either side. The anterior end possesses a *mouth opening*, surrounded by one dorsal and two ventral *lips* (Fig. 112 a, b, c). Near the posterior end is the *anal opening* from which, in the male, extend *penial setæ* (Fig. 112 a, a, Sp.) for use during copulation. The male can be distinguished from the female by the presence of a bend in the posterior part of the body (Fig. 112 a, a).

Internal Anatomy. — If an animal is cut open along the dorsal line (Fig. 111), it will be found to contain a straight alimentary

---

[1] The roundworms are particularly interesting because many of them are important parasites of man and of lower animals. Everyone should know something about these organisms, but a detailed knowledge of their morphology is essential only for advanced students.

canal, and certain other organs, lying in a central cavity, the cœlom. The *alimentary canal* is very simple, since the food is taken from material already digested by the host whose intestine the worm inhabits. It opens at the posterior end through the *anus*, which is not present in the members of the phyla already discussed. A muscular *pharynx* draws the fluids into the long non-muscular *intestine,* through the walls of which the nutriment is absorbed. Just before the anal opening is reached, the intestine gradually becomes smaller; this portion is known as the *rectum.*

The *excretory system* consists of two *longitudinal canals* (Fig. 111), one in each lateral line; these open to the outside by a single pore situated near the anterior end in the ventral body-wall (Fig. 112 a, c, P).

A ring of *nervous tissue* surrounds the pharynx and gives off two large nerve-cords, one dorsal, the other ventral, and a number of other smaller strands and connections.

The *male reproductive organs* are a single, coiled thread-like *testis,* from which a *vas deferens* leads to a wider tube, the *seminal vesicle;* this is followed by the short muscular *ejaculatory duct* which opens into the rectum. In the *female* lies a Y-shaped reproductive system. Each branch of

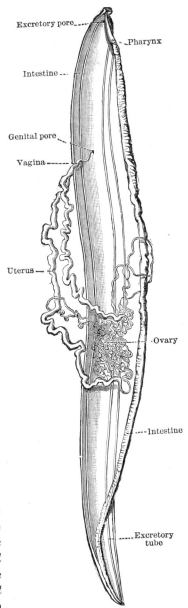

Fig. 111. — A female *Ascaris lumbricoides* cut open to show internal organs. (From Shipley and MacBride.)

the Y consists of a coiled thread-like *ovary* (Fig. 111) which is continuous with a larger canal, the *uterus*. The uteri of the two branches unite into a short muscular tube, the *vagina*, which opens to the outside through the *genital aperture*. *Fertilization* takes place in the uterus. The egg is then surrounded by a *shell of chitin*, and passes out through the genital pore. The chitinous egg-shell prevents the digestion of the egg within the intestine of the host.

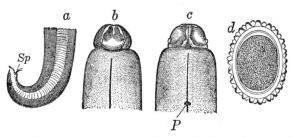

Fig. 112 a. — Parts of *Ascaris lumbricoides*. *a*, hind end of male with the two penial setæ (*Sp*). *b*, anterior end from the dorsal side, showing the dorsal lip with its two papillæ. *c*, the same from the ventral side with the two lateral ventral lips and the excretory pore (*P*). *d*, egg with external membrane of small clear spherules. (From Sedgwick, after Leuckart.)

The relations of the various organs to one another, as well as the structure of the body-wall, and the character of the cœlom, are shown in Figure 112 b, which is a transverse section of a female specimen of *Ascaris lumbricoides*. The body of the worm should be considered as consisting of two tubes, one the intestine, lying within the other, the *body-wall;* while between them is a cavity, the *cœlom*, in which lie the reproductive organs.

The *body-wall* is composed of several layers, an outer chitinous *cuticle*, a thin layer of *ectoderm* just beneath it, and a thick stratum of *longitudinal muscle fibers*, mesodermal in origin, lining the cœlom. Thickenings of the ectoderm form the *dorsal, ventral,* and *lateral lines*. In each of the last-named lies one of the longitudinal excretory tubes. The nerve-cords are also embedded in the body-wall.

The *intestine* consists of a single layer of columnar cells, the *entoderm*, coated both within and without by a thin cuticle.

The *cœlom* (see p. 87) of *Ascaris* differs from that of the higher animals in several respects. Typically the cœlom is a cavity in the mesoderm lined by an epithelium; into it the excretory organs open, and from its walls the reproductive cells originate. In *Ascaris* the so-called cœlom is lined only by the mesoderm of the body-wall, there being no mesoderm surrounding the intestine. Furthermore, the excretory organs open to the exterior through the excretory pore, and the reproductive cells are not derived from the cœlomic epithelium. The body-cavity of *Ascaris*, therefore, differs structurally and functionally from that of a true cœlom, but nevertheless is similar in many respects.

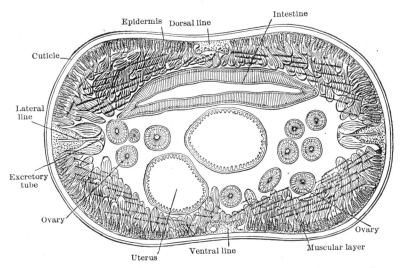

FIG. 112 b. — Transverse section of *Ascaris lumbricoides*. (From Parker and Haswell, after Vogt and Yung.)

2. NEMATHELMINTHES IN GENERAL

Definition. — Phylum NEMATHELMINTHES. — ROUNDWORMS. — Bilaterally symmetrical, triploblastic animals with an elongated cylindrical body; alimentary canal has a mouth opening at the anterior end and an anal opening on the ventral surface near the posterior end, and lies in a body-cavity, which is probably a cœlom; no cilia present in any part of the body; both free-living and parasitic; sexes separate.

It has been customary to place the NEMATOMORPHA (see p. 167) and ACANTHOCEPHALA (see p. 168) in the Phylum NEMA-THELMINTHES, but the relationships of these animals are so obscure that it is considered best to treat them separately. The phylum, therefore, contains only one class, the NEMATODA, whose members have all of the characteristics cited above.

Ascaris lumbricoides is but one of the interesting and important nematodes. It belongs with a number of other similar forms to the family ASCARIDÆ.

The family STRONGYLIDÆ contains several dangerous parasites: *Ancylostoma duodenalis*, the European hookworm, is frequently very injurious and sometimes fatal. Nematodes of this species are taken into the alimentary canal with drinking water, or enter the body through the skin, and thousands are sometimes present. Anæmia is caused by their biting into the intestinal wall and destroying the capillaries. *Syngamus* is the parasite

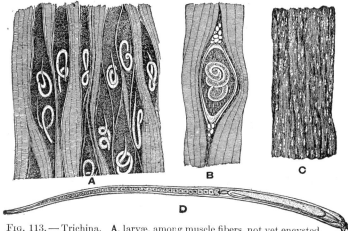

Fig. 113. — Trichina. **A**, larvæ, among muscle fibers, not yet encysted.
  B, a single larva encysted.
  C, piece of pork, natural size, containing many encysted worms.
  D, adult trichina, much enlarged. (After Leuckart.)

that causes the disease known as gapes in poultry and game birds. The birds swallow the young syngamids, which soon become mature in the trachea and bronchi.

To the family TRICHINELLIDÆ belongs *Trichinella spiralis* (Fig. 113), which causes the disease of human beings, pigs, and rats called *trichinosis*. The parasites enter the human body when inadequately cooked meat from an infected pig is eaten. The larvæ soon become mature in the human intestine, and each mature worm deposits probably about 10,000 young. These young are either placed directly into the lymphatics by the female worms or burrow through the intestinal wall; they encyst in muscular tissue in various parts of the body. As many as 15,000 encysted parasites have been counted in a single gram of muscle. Pigs acquire the disease by eating offal or infested rats. In a few countries pork is inspected for this and other parasites by government agents.

The family FILARIIDÆ is also important because of the human diseases caused by certain of its members. The most injurious species is *Filaria bancrofti*, a parasite in the blood of man. The larvæ of this species are about $\frac{1}{100}$ inch long. During the daytime they live in the lungs and larger arteries, but at night they migrate to the blood-vessels in the skin. Mosquitoes, which are active at night, suck up these larvæ with the blood of the infected person. The larvæ develop in the mosquito's body, becoming about one-twentieth of an inch long; make their way into the mouth parts of the insect; and enter the blood of the mosquito's next victim. From the blood they enter the lymphatics and may cause serious disturbances, probably by obstructing the lymph passages. This results in a disease called *elephantiasis*. The limbs or other regions of the body swell up to an enormous size, but there is very little pain. No successful treatment has yet been discovered, and the results are often fatal. It is said that from 30 per cent to 40 per cent of the natives of certain South Sea Islands are more or less seriously afflicted.

One of the most recent discoveries with regard to parasitic roundworms is that the shiftlessness of the " poor whites " of the South is to a certain degree the result of the attack of the *hookworm, Necator americanus*. The larvæ of the hookworm develop in moist earth and usually find their way into the bodies of human beings by boring through the skin of the foot. In the localities where the hookworm is prevalent, many of the people go barefoot. The larval hookworms enter the veins and pass to the heart; from the heart they reach the lungs, where they make their way through the air passages into the windpipe, and thence into the intestine. To the walls of the intestine the adults attach themselves and feed upon the blood of their host. When the intestinal wall is punctured, a small amount of poison is poured into the wound by the worm. This poison prevents the blood from coagulating, and therefore results in a considerable loss of blood, even after the worm has left the wound. The victims of the hookworm are anæmic, and also subject to tuberculosis because of the injury to the lungs. It is estimated that

2,000,000 persons are afflicted by this parasite. The hookworm disease can be cured by thymol (which causes the worm to loosen its hold) followed by Epsom salts or by oil of chenopodium or carbon tetrachloride. The most important preventive measure is the disposing of human fæces in rural districts, mines, brick-yards, etc., in such a manner as to avoid pollution of the soil, thus giving the eggs of the parasites contained in the fæces of infested human beings no opportunity to hatch and develop to the infectious larval stage.

CHAPTER IX

INVERTEBRATES OF MORE OR LESS UNCERTAIN SYSTEMATIC POSITION [1]

THERE are a number of groups of animals whose relationships are so difficult to determine that authorities do not agree as regards their position in the animal series. Most of these groups contain only a few marine species which are of very little economic importance. A few groups like the ROTIFERA and BRYOZOA include fresh-water species which are quite common.

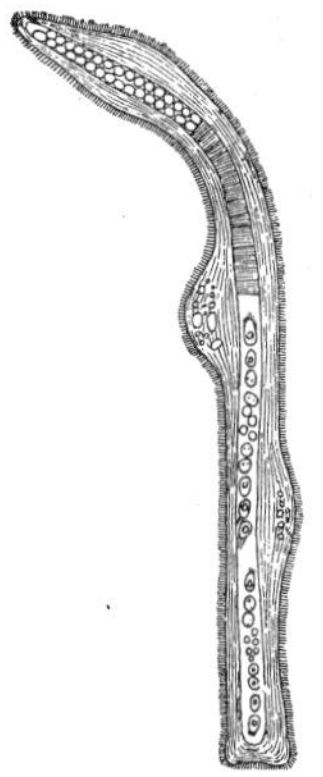

1. MESOZOA

The term MESOZOA (Gr. *mesos*, middle; *zoon*, animal) has been employed by a number of zoologists to include three families of para-

sites of obscure systematic position, (1) the DICYEMIDÆ, (2) the ORTHONECTIDÆ, and (3) the HETEROCYEMIDÆ. They have been regarded as intermediate between the PROTOZOA and MET-

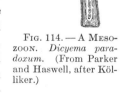

FIG. 114. — A MESO-ZOON. *Dicyema para-doxum.* (From Parker and Haswell, after Köl-liker.)

AZOA, hence the name MESOZOA. It is probable, however, that they are degenerate METAZOA, closely allied to the flatworms.

FIG. 115. — A MESO-ZOON, *Rhopalura giardii*, male. (From Sedgwick, after v. Beneden.)

The DICYEMIDÆ (Fig. 114) and HETERO-CYEMIDÆ are parasites in the kidneys of CEPHALOPODA (cuttlefishes and octopods).

[1] This chapter is introduced here in order to make our survey of the animal king-dom complete, and is intended for reference purposes only. The groups BRYOZOA and ROTIFERA contain species that are frequently encountered in fresh water, but the others are seldom seen.

165

The ORTHONECTIDÆ (Fig. 115) are parasites in TURBELLARIA (Chap. VII), NEMERTINEA, ANNELIDA (Chap. XI), and brittle-stars (OPHIUROIDEA, p. 185).

2. NEMERTINEA

The NEMERTINEA (Gr. *nemertes,* true) (Figs. 116, 117) have a superficial resemblance to flatworms and are by some authorities placed in the Phylum PLATYHELMINTHES either as a distinct class or as a supplementary group. Some of them are very long,

FIG. 116. — *Micrura verrilli,* one of the NEMERTINEA found on the Pacific Coast. (From Weysse, after Coe.)

reaching a length of ninety feet. A few species live in moist earth and fresh water, but most of them are marine. *Cerebratulus* (Fig. 117) and *Micrura* (Fig. 116) are marine; *Geonemertes* and some species of *Tetrastemma* are terrestrial; and *Malacobdella* is a parasite in certain mollusks.

The most important anatomical features of the NEMERTINEA are the presence of: (1) a long *proboscis* (Fig. 117, *2, 10*), which lies in a proboscis sheath just above the digestive tract, and may be everted and used as a tactile, protective, and defensive organ; (2) a *blood vascular system* consisting usually of a median dorsal and two lateral trunks (Fig. 117, *9*); and (3) an *alimentary canal* with both *mouth* (Fig. 117, *7*) and *anal openings.* The blood vascular system is here encountered for the first time. NEMERTINEA possess a *mesoderm* and *nervous* and *excretory systems* which

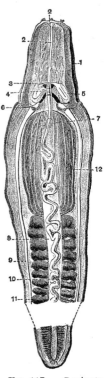

FIG. 117. — *Cerebratulus fuscus,* a NEMERTINE. *1,* cephalic slits; *2,* opening leading into retracted proboscis; *3,* dorsal commissure of nervous system; *4,* ventral commissure; *5,* brain; *6,* posterior lobe of brain; *7,* mouth; *8,* proboscis; *9,* lateral vessel; *10,* proboscis; *11,* pouches of alimentary canal; *12,* stomach. (From Shipley and MacBride, after Bürger.)

do not differ markedly from those of the flatworms. The proboscis sheath may represent the *cœlom*, but this is not certain.

Nemertines feed on other animals, both dead and alive. They live, as a rule, coiled up in burrows in the mud or sand, or under stones, but some of them frequent patches of seaweed. *Locomotion* is effected by the *cilia* which cover the surface of the body, by contractions of the body muscles, or by the attachment of the proboscis and subsequent drawing forward of the body. *Cerebratulus* (Fig. 117) swims actively like a leech (Chap. XI). The power of regenerating lost parts is well developed.

During development a peculiar *larval stage* called the *Pilidium* (Fig. 118), is usually passed through.

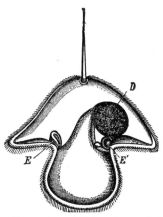

FIG. 118. — *Pilidium* larva of a NEMERTINE. *D*, alimentary canal; *E, E'*, the two pairs of ectodermal invaginations. (From Sedgwick, after Metschnikoff.)

This resembles a helmet with cilia on the surface and a long tuft of cilia at the apex. The *adult* develops from this larva by the formation of ectodermal invaginations (Fig. 118, *E, E'*) which surround the alimentary canal (*D*). This invaginated portion escapes from the *Pilidium* and grows into the adult nemertine.

3. NEMATOMORPHA

This group (Gr. *nema*, thread; *morphē*, form) contains a single family, the GORDIIDÆ, and two genera, *Gordius*, which lives in fresh water, and *Nectonema* in the sea. They are long, slender, thread-like animals (Fig. 119) often found in ditches and commonly called horsehair snakes. Some authors consider them an order of NEMATODA; whereas

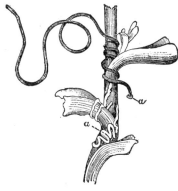

FIG. 119. — *Gordius* (of the group NEMATOMORPHA) twining around a water plant and laying eggs. *a, a,* clump and string of eggs. (From the Cambridge Natural History, after von Linstow.)

others rank them as a class under the Phylum NEMATHELMINTHES. It seems best to include them with the other invertebrates of more or less uncertain systematic position.

Their resemblance to the NEMATODA, indicated by the term NEMATOMORPHA, does not hold for the internal anatomy. A distinct *epithelium* lines the body-cavity; *no lateral lines* are present; there is a pharyngeal nerve-ring and a single ventral nerve-cord; and the ovaries, which are segmentally arranged, discharge the eggs into the body-cavity.

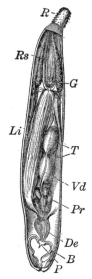

FIG. 120. — *Echinorhynchus augustatus* (of the group ACANTHOCEPHALA), male. *B,* retracted bursa; *De,* ejaculatory duct; *G,* ganglion; *Li,* ligament; *P,* penis; *Pr,* prostatic sacs; *R,* proboscis; *Rs,* sheath of proboscis; *T,* testes; *Vd,* vasa deferentia. (From Sedgwick, after Leuckart.)

The larvæ of *Gordius* usually migrate into the immature stages of aquatic insects; these are then devoured by other animals in whose intestines the young live and develop until they finally escape into the water.

4. ACANTHOCEPHALA

The ACANTHOCEPHALA (Gr. *akantha,* a spine; *kephale,* the head) are parasitic worms which are also considered by many a class in the Phylum NEMATHELMINTHES. They are *spineheaded worms* which fasten themselves to the intestinal wall of vertebrates by means of a protrusible proboscis covered with hooks (Fig. 120, *R*). The presence of this *proboscis,* and of a complex *reproductive system,* and the *absence of an alimentary canal,* distinguish the ACANTHOCEPHALA from the NEMATODA and NEMATOMORPHA.

The adults are most common in fishes, but all vertebrates, including man, are parasitized by them. There is an alternation of hosts during development. For example, the larva of *Echinorhynchus gigas* lives in the June bug, the adult in the pig.

5. CHÆTOGNATHA

The CHÆTOGNATHA (Gr. *chaite,* horsehair; *gnathos,* the cheek) are marine animals which swim about near the surface of the sea.

The best-known genus is *Sagitta*, the arrow-worm.   Figure 121 shows most of the anatomical features of *Sagitta hexaptera*.   There is a distinct *cœlom*, an *alimentary canal* with mouth, intestine and anus, a well-developed *nervous system*, two eyes, and other *sensory organs*.   The mouth has a lobe on either side provided with bristles which are used in capturing the minute animals and plants that serve as food.   The members of the group are *hermaphroditic*, possessing both male and female reproductive organs.

The CHÆTOGNATHA are included under the NEMATHELMINTHES by some authorities and are placed in a separate phylum by others.

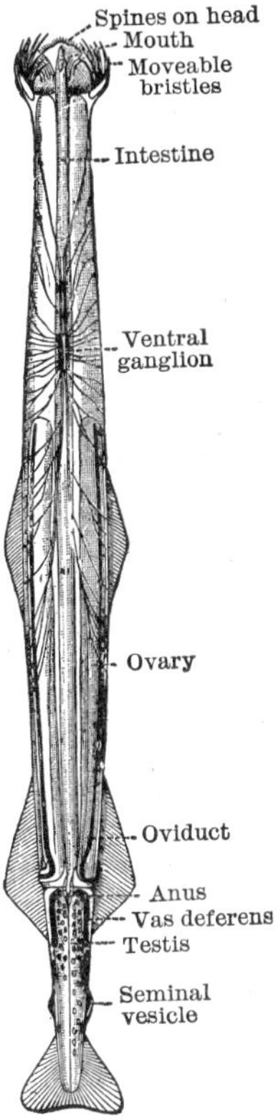

6. ROTIFERA (ROTATORIA)

The ROTIFERA (Lat. *rota*, a wheel; *fero*, I carry) (Fig. 122), commonly known as wheel animalcules, are extremely small METAZOA.   They were at one time considered INFUSORIA.   Most of them are inhabitants of fresh water, but some are marine and a few parasitic.   The anatomy of a ROTIFER is shown in Figure 123.   The *head* is provided with *cilia* which aid in locomotion and draw food into the mouth.   The *tail* or *foot* is bifurcated and adheres to objects by means of a secretion from a *cement gland*.   The body is usually cylindrical and is covered by a shell-like *cuticle*.

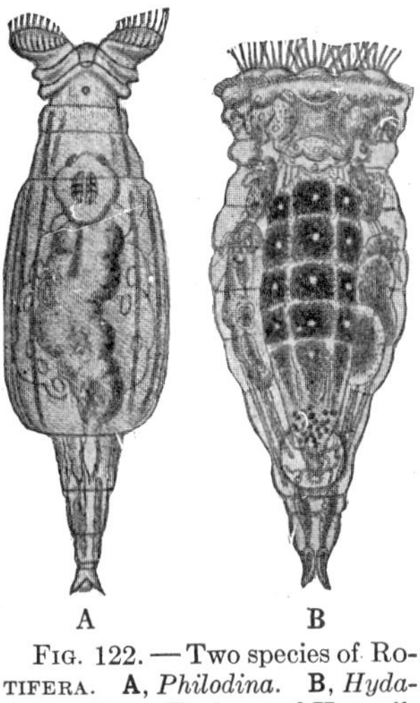

The PROTOZOA and other minute organisms used as *food* are swept by

FIG. 121. — The arrow-worm, *Sagitta hexaptera* (of the group CHÆTOG-NATHA), ventral view. (After Hertwig.)

A   B

FIG. 122. — Two species of Rotifera. **A**, *Philodina*. **B**, *Hydatina*. (From Parker and Haswell, after Hudson and Gosse.)

the cilia through the *mouth* into the *pharynx,* also called the *mastax* or chewing stomach. Here chitinous *jaws,* which are constantly at work, break up the food. The movements of these jaws easily distinguish a living rotifer from other organisms. The food is *digested* in the glandular *stomach.* Undigested particles pass through the *intestine* into the *cloaca* and out of the *anus.*

Two coiled tubes, which give off a number of ciliated lobules, and enter a bladder, constitute the *excretory system.* The bladder contracts at intervals, forcing the contents out of the anus. Since the amount of fluid expelled by the bladder is very large, it is probable that *respiration* is also a function of this organ, the oxygen

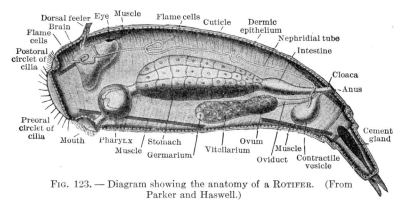

Fig. 123. — Diagram showing the anatomy of a ROTIFER. (From Parker and Haswell.)

being taken into the animal with the water which diffuses through the body-wall, and the carbonic acid being cast out with the excretory fluid. The body-cavity is not a true cœlom.

The *sexes* of rotifers are separate. The *female* possesses an *ovary* (Fig. 123) in which the eggs arise, a *yolk-gland* which supplies the eggs with yolk, and an *oviduct* which carries the eggs into the cloaca. From here the eggs reach the exterior through the anus. The *males* are usually smaller than the females, and often degenerate. They possess a *testis* in which the spermatozoa arise, and a *penis* for transferring the spermatozoa to the female.

Two kinds of eggs are produced by rotifers: (1) summer eggs, and (2) winter eggs. The *summer eggs,* which develop parthenogenetically, are thin-shelled, and of two sizes; the larger produce females and the smaller males. The *winter eggs,* which are fertilized, have thick shells, and develop females.

One peculiarity of the rotifers worth mentioning is their *power to resist desiccation.* Certain species, if dried slowly, secrete gelatinous envelopes which prevent further drying; in this condition they live through seasons of drought, and may be subjected to extremes of temperature without perishing.

The resemblances between rotifers and the trochophore larvæ of certain mollusks, annelids, and other animals to be described later, is quite striking. The larva of the NEMERTINEA (*Pilidium,* Fig. 118) is likewise similar in some respects to an adult rotifer. This has led to the theory that the rotifers are animals somewhat closely connected with the ancestors of the mollusks, annelids, and certain other groups.

7. BRYOZOA (POLYZOA)

The BRYOZOA (Gr. *bruon,* moss; *zoön,* an animal), PHORONIDEA, and BRACHIOPODA are sometimes placed together under one phylum, the MOLLUSCOIDEA, because they are mollusk-like in form. It seems probable, however, that they not only represent distinct, but widely divergent groups, and should therefore be discussed separately.

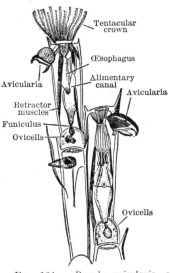

The BRYOZOA, or *moss-animals,* are mostly *colonial.* They resemble hydroids, like *Obelia* (Fig. 73),

FIG. 124. — *Bugula avicularia,* a BRYOZOON. (From Sedgwick, after v. Nordmann.)

in form, but differ from them markedly in structure. The majority of them live in the sea, but a few inhabit fresh water. *Bugula* (Fig. 124) is a common marine genus which shows the principal characteristics of the group.

The soft parts constituting the *polypide* lie within the true *cœlomic cavity* bounded by the body-wall or *zoœcium.* The *mouth* lies in the midst of a crown of *ciliated tentacles* (Fig. 124) called the *lophophore,* which serve to draw food particles into the body. The U-shaped *alimentary canal* consists of a ciliated *œsophagus,* a *stomach,* and an *intestine* which opens by means of an anus lying just outside the lophophore. One *retractor muscle* serves to draw the polypide into the zoœcium.   The *funiculus* is a strand of meso-dermal tissue attached to the base of the stomach.   There are no circulatory nor excretory organs.

Both an *ovary* and a *testis* are present in each individual; they may be found attached to the funiculus or the body-wall.   The *eggs* are probably fertilized in the cœlom and then develop in a modified portion of the zoœcium called the *oœcium*.   The larvæ of some BRYOZOA resemble a trochophore (see p. 171).

Certain members of *Bugula* colonies are modified into structures called *aviculariæ* (Fig. 124).   These have jaws which probably protect the colony from the attacks of small organisms and prevent the larvæ of other animals from settling upon it.

The BRYOZOA may be separated into two distinct groups, the ECTOPROCTA and ENTOPROCTA.   In the former the anus opens outside of the lophophore, as in *Bugula*, and a cœlom is present.   *Plumatella* and *Pectinatella* are fresh-water ECTOPROCTA.   The ENTOPROCTA have the anal opening within the lophophore, and the space between the intestine and body-wall is filled with mesoderm cells.   *Pedi-cellina* and *Urnatella* belong to this group.

FIG. 125. — *Phoronis buskii* (of the group PHORONIDEA) re-moved from its tube and seen from behind. (From Sedgwick, after M'Intosh.)

8. PHORONIDEA

This group consists of a single genus, *Phoronis* (Gr. *Phoronis*, name of a king, Fig. 125), contain-ing wormlike animals which live in the sand, enclosed in membranous tubes.   Their systematic position is still more or less uncertain, but their structure indicates a probable relationship to the ECTOPROCTA.

9. BRACHIOPODA

The BRACHIOPODA (Gr. *brachion*, the arm; *pous*, a foot) are marine animals living within a calcareous bivalve *shell* (Fig. 126). They are usually attached to some object by a *peduncle* (Fig. 127). Because of their shell they were for a long time regarded as mol-lusks.   The valves of the shell, however, are dorsal (Fig. 126) and ventral instead of lateral as in the bivalve mollusks (Fig. 173).

Within the shell (Fig. 127) is a conspicuous structure called the *lophophore*, which consists of two coiled ridges, called arms; these bear ciliated tentacles. *Food* is drawn into the *mouth* by the

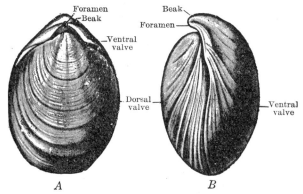

FIG. 126. — *Magellania flavescens* (of the group BRACHIOPODA). **A**, dorsal aspect of shell. **B**, shell as seen from the left side. (From Weysse, after Davidson.)

lophophore. A true *cœlom* is present, within which lie the *stomach*, *digestive gland*, and the *heart*.

The group BRACHIOPODA is extremely old, and, although found in all seas to-day, brachiopods were formerly more numerous in

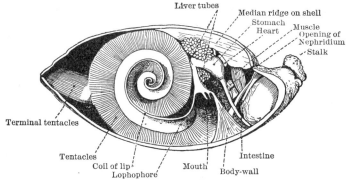

FIG. 127. — Anatomy of a brachiopod, *Waldheimia australis*. (From Shipley and MacBride.)

species and of much greater variety in form than at present. Some of them, for example *Lingula*, are apparently the same to-day as they were in the Silurian period estimated at about twenty-five million years ago.

10. Gephyrea

The Gephyrea (Gr. *gephura*, a mound) are worm-like animals that have been classed by many zoologists with the Phylum Annelida (Chap. XI). Their relations to this phylum are, however, uncertain, and the affinities of the Gephyrea to one another are even doubtful. Consequently they have been separated provisionally from the Annelida and divided into three groups as follows: —

(1) **The Echiuroidea** (Fig. 128) have traces of *segmentation* in the adult, a *proboscis* (*a*), a pair of *ventral hooked setæ* (*b*), and

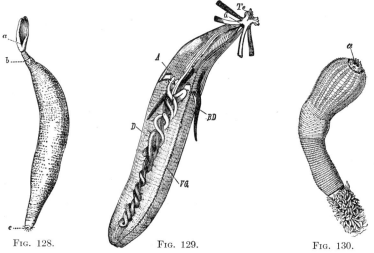

Fig. 128.   Fig. 129.   Fig. 130.

Fig. 128. — *Echiurus pallasii* (of the group **Gephyrea**). *a*, mouth at the end of the grooved proboscis; *b*, ventral hooks; *c*, anus. (From the Cambridge Natural History.)

Fig. 129. — *Sipunculus nudus* (of the group **Gephyrea**) laid open from the side. *A*, anus; *BD*, brown tubes (nephridia); *D*, intestine; *G*, brain; *Te* tentacles; *G*, ventral nerve-cord. (From Sedgwick, after Keferstein.)

Fig. 130. — *Priapulus caudatus* (of the group **Gephyrea**). *a*, mouth surrounded by spines. (From the Cambridge Natural History.)

a terminal *anus* (*c*). They usually live in crevices in rocks, using their proboscis for locomotion, for capturing prey, and as an organ of sense. There is a trochophore stage (p. 171) in development.

(2) **The Sipunculoidea** (Fig. 129) are *unsegmented*, with only one pair of *nephridia* (*BD*), a large *cœlom*, and an *anus* (*A*) on the

dorsal surface near the anterior end. They live in the sand or bore into coral rock, and are capable of slow, creeping locomotion. The anterior part of the body can be drawn into the larger posterior portion, and is therefore called the *introvert*. *Tentacles* (*Te*) are usually present at the anterior end.

(3) **The Priapuloidea** (Fig. 130) are *unsegmented*, with an anterior *mouth* (*a*) surrounded by chitinous *teeth*, and a posterior *anus*. They live in the mud or sand with the anterior end projecting from the surface.

CHAPTER X

PHYLUM ECHINODERMATA [1]

THE ECHINODERMATA (Gr. *echinos*, a sea-hedgehog; *derma*, skin) are " spiny-skinned " animals that live in the sea. They represent the most complex of all radially symmetrical animals. For a long time they were placed with the CŒLENTERATA in a group called RADIATA, but when their structure and life-history had been thoroughly made out, they were found to have closer affinities with the higher METAZOA.

Five classes of echinoderms are recognized by most zoologists. Besides these there are several groups of fossil forms.

Phylum ECHINODERMATA. — STARFISHES, BRITTLE-STARS, SEA-URCHINS, SEA-CUCUMBERS, SEA-LILIES. Triploblastic, radially symmetrical animals; usually five antimeres, cœlom well developed; anus usually present; locomotion in many species accomplished by characteristic organs known as tube-feet; a spiny skeleton of calcareous plates generally covers the body.

Class I. ASTEROIDEA (Gr. *aster*, a star; *eidos*, resemblance) (Fig. 131). Typically pentamerous; arms usually not sharply marked off from the disc; ambulacral groove present. Examples: *Asterias, Astropecten, Culcita.* — **Starfishes.**

Class II. OPHIUROIDEA (Gr. *ophis*, a snake; *oura*, a tail; *eidos*, form) (Fig. 138). Typically pentamerous; arms sharply marked off from the disc; no ambulacral groove. Examples: *Ophiura, Amphiura, Astrophyton.* — **Brittle-stars.**

Class III. ECHINOIDEA (Gr. *echinos*, hedgehog; *eidos*, form) (Fig. 141). Pentamerous, without arms or free rays; test of

---

[1] The echinoderms form a very complex, aberrant cœlomate group, and their study may be deferred until later if desirable. The starfish is the best type of the group. Comparative studies of the sea urchin and sea cucumber may be made if time allows. Of particular interest are the phenomena of regeneration and autotomy exhibited by certain members of the phylum; the development of the larval stages and their relation to the origin of vertebrates; and the experiments on artificial parthenogenesis.

calcareous plates bearing movable spines. Examples: *Cidaris,
Arbacia, Toxopneustes, Strongylocentrotus.* — **Sea-urchins**; *Echinarachnius.* — **Sand-dollar**; *Spatangus.* — **Heart-urchin.**

Class IV. HOLOTHURIOIDEA (Gr. *holos*, whole; *thourios*,
rushing)(Fig. 146). Long ovoid; muscular body-wall; tentacles
around mouth. Examples: *Holothuria, Thyone, Caudina.* —
Sea-cucumbers.

Class V. CRINOIDEA (Gr. *krinon*, a lily; *eidos*, form) (Fig.
148). Arms generally branched and with pinnules; aboral
pole sometimes with cirri but usually with stalk, for temporary
or permanent attachment. Examples: *Antedon.* — **Feather-star**;
Pentacrinus. — **Sea-lily.**

1. ANATOMY AND PHYSIOLOGY OF THE STARFISH — ASTERIAS

External Features. — The starfishes are common along many
sea-coasts, where they may be found usually upon the rocks with
the mouth down. The upper surface is therefore *aboral* or *abacti-
nal.* On the *aboral
surface* (Fig. 131) are
(1) many *spines* (Fig.
133) of various sizes,
(2) *pedicellariæ* (Fig.
133) at the base of
the spines, (3) a *mad-
reporite* (Fig. 131,
mad), which is the
entrance to the water-
vascular system, and
(4) the anal opening
(*anus*). A glance at
the *oral surface* (Fig.
132) reveals a *mouth*
centrally situated in
the membranous *peri-
stome*, and five *grooves*
(*ambulacral*), one in

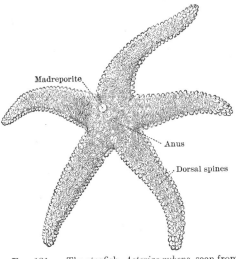

FIG. 131. — The starfish, *Asterias rubens*, seen from
the aboral surface. (From the Cambridge Natural
History.)

each arm, from which two or four rows of *tube-feet* extend (Fig. 133).

The Skeleton. — The skeleton is made up of *calcareous plates*
or *ossicles* bound together by fibers of connective tissue (Fig.

133). The ossicles are regularly arranged about the mouth and in the ambulacral grooves and often along the sides of the arms, but are more or less scattered elsewhere. The *ambulacral* and *adambulacral ossicles* (Fig. 133) have muscular attachments and are so situated that when the animal is disturbed they are able to close the groove and thus protect the tube-feet. The *spines* of the starfish (Fig. 131; Fig. 133) are short and blunt and covered with *ectoderm* (Fig. 133). Around their bases are many whitish modified

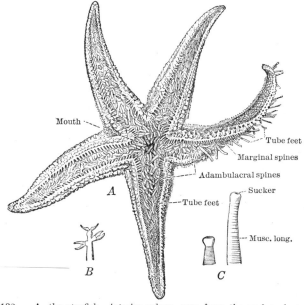

Fig. 132. — **A**, the starfish, *Asterias rubens*, seen from the oral surface. **B**, an adambulacral spine, showing three straight pedicellariæ. **C**, a tubefoot expanded and contracted. (From the Cambridge Natural History.)

spines called *pedicellariæ*. These are little jaws which when irritated may be opened and closed by several sets of muscles. Their function is to protect the *dermal branchiæ* to prevent débris and small organisms from collecting on the surface, and to capture food. The skeleton serves to give the animal definite shape, to strengthen the body-wall, and as a protection from the action of waves and from other organisms.

The Muscular System. — The *arms* of the starfish are not rigid, but may be flexed slowly by a few muscle fibers in the body-wall. The *tube-feet* are also supplied with muscle fibers.

Cœlom. — The true body-cavity of the starfish is very large and may be separated into several distinct divisions. The *perivisceral part of the cœlom* (Fig. 133) surrounds the alimentary canal and extends into the arms. It is lined with *peritoneum* and filled with sea-water containing some albuminous matter. Oxygen is taken into the cœlomic fluid and carbon dioxide given off through outpushings of the body-wall known as *papulæ* or *dermal branchiæ*. The cœlom also has an *excretory function*, since cells from the peritoneum are budded off into the cœlomic fluid, where they

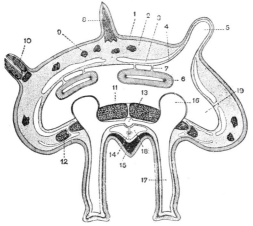

Fig. 133.— Diagram of a transverse section of the arm of a starfish. *1*, ectoderm ; *2*, jelly ; *3*, peribranchial space in the skin ; *4*, peritoneal lining of the body-cavity ; *5*, a branchia ; *6*, pyloric cæcum ; *7*, mesentery supporting a cæcum ; *8*, spine ; *9*, ossicle in skin ; *10*, pedicellaria ; *11*, ambulacral ossicle ; *12*, adambulacral ossicle ; *13*, radial trunk of water-vascular system ; *14*, radial septum separating the two perihæmal spaces ; *15*, radial nerve-cord ; *16*, ampulla of tube-foot ; *17*, tube-foot ; *18*, perihæmal space ; *19*, cœlom. (From Shipley and MacBride.)

move about as amœbocytes gathering waste matters. These cells make their way into the dermal branchiæ, through the walls of which they pass to the outside, where they disintegrate.

The Water-vascular System. — The water-vascular system (Fig. 134) is a division of the cœlom peculiar to echinoderms. Beginning with the *madreporite* the following structures are encountered: the *stone-canal* running downwards enters the *ring-canal*, which encircles the mouth; from this canal five *radial canals* (Fig. 134, Fig. 133), one in each arm, pass outward just above the ambulacral grooves. The radial canals give off side branches from which arise the *tube-feet* (Fig. 134, Fig. 133) and *ampullæ*

(Fig. 134, Fig. 133). The ampullæ are bulb-like sacs extending into the cœlom; they are connected directly with the tube-feet, which pass through tiny pores between the ambulacral ossicles (Fig. 133). Sea-water is forced into this system of canals by cilia which occur in grooves on the outer surface of the madreporite and in the canals which penetrate it. Arising from the ring-canal near the ampullæ of the first tube-feet are nine vesicles called, after the name of their discoverer, " Tiedemann's bodies." These structures produce amœbocytes which pass into the fluid of the water-vascular system. *Polian vesicles* (Fig. 134) are present in some starfishes, but not in *Asterias*.

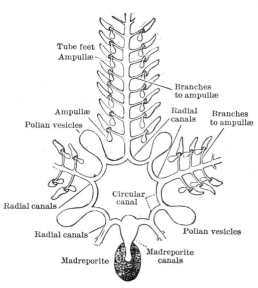

FIG. 134. — Water-vascular system of a starfish. (From Parker and Haswell, after Gegenbaur.)

The most interesting structures of the water-vascular system are the *tube-feet*. They are primarily locomotory and function as follows: " When the tube-foot is to be stretched out, the ampulla contracts and drives the fluid downwards. The contraction of the ampulla is brought about by muscles running circularly around it. The tube-foot is thus distended and its broad flattened end is brought in contact with the surface of the stone over which it is moving and is pressed close against it. The muscles of the tube-foot itself, which are arranged longitudinally, now commence to act, and the pressure of the water preventing the tearing away of the sucker from the object to which it adheres, the starfish is slowly drawn forward, whilst the fluid in the tube-foot flows back into the ampulla." Tube-feet are also sensory (p. 183).

A number of other spaces and canals have been considered as

parts of the cœlom and at one time were supposed to be a " blood "-vascular system.   These are the *axial sinuses* lying along the stone-canal and opening to the outside through the madreporite, the *inner circumoral perihæmal canal*, the *outer perihæmal canal* beneath the ring-canal, the *aboral sinus*, and the *peribranchial spaces*.   The functions of these various cavities are not clear.

Digestion. — The *alimentary canal* of the starfish (Fig. 135) is short and greatly modified.   The *mouth* opens into an *œsophagus* which leads into a thin-walled sac, the *stomach*.   Following this is the *pyloric sac*.   From the pyloric sac a tube passes into each arm, then divides into two branches, each of which

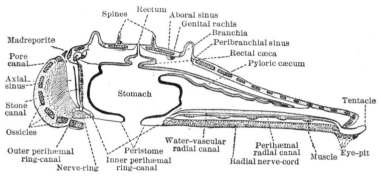

Fig. 135. — Diagrammatic longitudinal section of a starfish.   (From the Cambridge Natural History.)

possesses a large number of lateral pouches; these branches are called *pyloric* or *hepatic cæca* (Fig. 135).   They are green in color. Above the pyloric sac is the slender *rectum*, which may open to the outside through the *anus*.   Two branched pouches, brown in color, arise from the rectum and are known as *rectal cæca*.

The *food* of the starfish consists of fish, oysters, mussels, barnacles, clams, snails, worms, Crustacea, etc.   When a mussel is to be eaten, the animal seizes it with the tube-feet " and places it directly under its mouth, folding its arms down over it in umbrella fashion (Fig. 136).   The muscles which run around the arms and disc in the body-wall contract, and the pressure thus brought to bear on the incompressible fluid contained in the cœlom, forces out the thin membranous peristome and partially turns the stomach inside out.   The everted edge of the stomach is wrapped round the prey.   Soon the bivalve is forced to relax

its muscles and allow the valves to gape. The edge of the stomach
is then inserted between the valves and applied directly to the
soft parts of the prey, which is thus completely digested. When
the starfish moves away, nothing but the cleaned shell is left
behind. If the bivalve is small, it may be completely taken into
the stomach, and the empty shell later rejected through the
mouth." (MacBride.) Schiemenz has shown " (1) that whilst
a bivalve may be able to resist a sudden pull of 4000 grammes it
will yield to a pull of 900
grammes long continued;
(2) that a starfish can exert a
pull of 1350 grammes; (3) that
a starfish is unable to open a
bivalve unless it be allowed to
raise itself into a hump (Fig. 136)
so that the pull of the central
tube-feet is at right angles to
the prey. A starfish confined
between two glass plates walked
about all day carrying with it a
bivalve which it was unable to
open." (MacBride.)

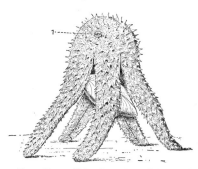

FIG. 136. — Side view of starfish (*Echi-
naster*) devouring a mussel. *1*, madreporite. (From the Cambridge Natural
History.)

The lining of the stomach secretes mucus; that of the pyloric
sac and cæca secretes ferments; these change proteids into diffu-
sible peptones, starch into maltose, and fats into fatty acids and
glycerine. Thus is digestion accomplished. Undigested matter
is ejected through the mouth, and very little, if any, matter passes
out of the anus. The rectal cæca secrete a brownish material
of unknown function, probably excretory.

Circulation. — The fluid in the cœlom is kept in motion by
cilia and carries the absorbed food to all parts of the body.

Excretion. — This is accomplished by the *amœbocytes* (*neph-
rocytes*) in the cœlomic fluid (p. 179), probably aided by the
rectal cæca.

Respiration. — The dermal branchiæ (Fig. 133, *5*) function
as respiratory organs (p. 179).

The Nervous System. — Besides many *nerve-cells* which lie
among the ectoderm cells, there are ridges of nervous tissue,
the *radial nerve-cords* (Fig. 135; Fig. 133), running along
the ambulacral grooves, and uniting with a *nerve-ring* (Fig. 135)

encircling the mouth. The *apical nervous system* consists of a trunk in each arm which meets the other trunks at the center of the disc; these trunks innervate the dorsal muscles of the arms.

Sense-organs. — The *tube-feet* are the principal sense-organs. They receive nerve-fibers from the radial nerve-cords. At the end of each radial canal (Fig. 135) the radial nerve-cord ends in a *pigmental mass*; this is called the *eye*, since it is a light-perceiving organ. The dermal branchiæ are probably sensory, also.

Reproduction. — The *sexes* of starfishes are distinct. The *reproductive organs* are dendritic structures, two in the base of each arm; they discharge the eggs or sperms out into the water through pores in the aboral surface at the interspace between two adjacent arms. The *eggs* of many starfishes are fertilized in the water; they are *holoblastic* (p. 84), undergo *equal cleavage*, and form a *blastula* and *gastrula* similar to those shown in Figure 50, *K, M*. The opening (*blastopore*) of the gastrula becomes the anus, and a new opening, the mouth, breaks through. Ciliated projections develop on either side of the body, and a larva, called a *Bipinnaria* (Fig. 150, B), results. This changes (metamorphosis) into the starfish.

Behavior. — The starfish moves from place to place by means of its tube-feet (p. 180). During the day it usually remains quiet in a crevice, but at night it is most active.

The *responses* of the starfish *to stimuli* are too complex to be stated definitely. When a starfish is placed on its aboral surface it performs the " righting reaction," *i.e.* it turns a sort of hand-spring by means of its arms. Professor Jennings taught individuals to use a certain arm in turning over. One animal was trained in eighteen days (180 lessons), and after an interval of seven days apparently " remembered " which arm to use. Old individuals could not be trained as readily as young specimens.

Regeneration. — The starfish has remarkable powers of regeneration. A single arm with part of the disc will regenerate an entire body. If an arm is injured, it is usually cast off near the base at the fourth or fifth ambulacral ossicle. This is *autotomy* (see also pp. 111 and 144).

Economic Importance. — Oyster beds are seriously affected by starfishes. One starfish which was placed in a dish containing clams devoured over fifty of them in six days. Formerly starfishes were taken, cut in two, and thrown back; this of course only increased the number, since each piece regenerated an entire animal. They are now often captured in a mop-like tangle, to the threads of which the pedicellariæ cling. They are then thrown out on the shore above high-water mark and left to die in the sun, or killed in hot water.

Fig. 137. — *Pentaceros reticularis*, oral aspect. A large starfish common on the coast of Florida. (From Weysse.)

2. Class I. Asteroidea — Starfishes

Little need be said of the Asteroidea beyond what has been stated above concerning one of the common species of the widespread genus *Asterias*. The number of arms ranges from five to more than forty, but aside from this diversity the chief differences in shape among the starfishes are brought about by the variations in the length and breadth of the arms and by their lateral fusion. In some cases this adhesion has gone so far as to result in a pentagonal form (Fig. 137). The skeleton differs in structure in different species and is of importance in classification.

The distinctive characteristics of the Asteroidea are as follows: Typically pentamerous; body commonly more or less flattened; arms long or short, usually not sharply marked off from disc; viscera extend into arms; ambulacral groove on ventral surface of arms; anus and madreporite dorsal.

3. Class II. Ophiuroidea — Brittle-stars

Distinctive Characteristics. — Body flattened; arms distinct from disc; no cæca nor gonads in arms; no ambulacral grooves nor anus; madreporite on oral surface.

Structural Peculiarities. — The *arms* of the brittle-stars (Fig. 138) and basket-fish (Fig. 139) are noticeably different from

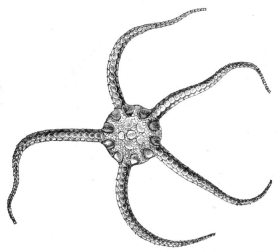

Fig. 138. — Aboral view of *Ophioglypha bullata*, a brittle-star. (From Shipley and MacBride, after Thompson.)

those of the starfish. They are slender and exceedingly flexible. The ambulacral groove is absent, being covered over by skeletal plates and converted into the *epineural canal.* Each arm is covered by four rows of *plates*, one aboral, one oral, and two lateral. *Spines* are restricted to the lateral plates. Within the arm are plates which have fused together and are known as *vertebræ.* The *muscular system* of the arm is well developed.

The *water-vascular system* differs in several respects from that of the starfish. The *madreporite* is on the oral surface. The *tube-feet* have lost their locomotor function and serve as tactile organs; the *ampullæ* have consequently disappeared.

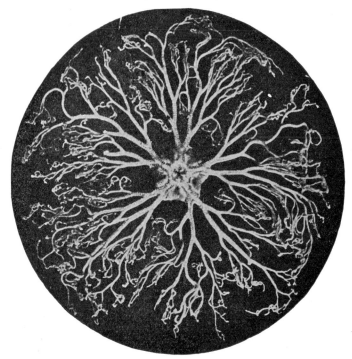

FIG. 139. — A basket star. (From Clark.)

Nutrition. — The *food* of the brittle-stars consists of minute organisms and decaying organic matter lying on the mud of the

sea bottom. It is scooped into the mouth by special tube-feet, two pairs to each arm, called the *oral tube-feet*. The rows of spines which extend out over the mouth opening serve as strainers (Fig. 140). The *stomach* is a simple sac without cæca; it cannot be pushed out of the mouth. There is no anus.

FIG. 140. — Oral view of *Ophioglypha bullata*, a brittle-star. (From the Cambridge Natural History, after Thompson.)

Behavior. — The locomotion of brittle-stars is comparatively rapid. The arms are bent laterally, and enable animals belonging to certain species to " run," or climb, and probably to swim. Apparently they cannot be taught like starfishes.

Regeneration. — The term *brittle-star* is derived from the fact that these animals break off their arms if they become injured. This *autotomy* often allows the individual to escape from its enemies, and is of no serious consequence, since new arms are speedily regenerated. In a number of species the aboral covering of the disc is normally cast off, probably for reproductive purposes.

4. CLASS III. ECHINOIDEA. — SEA-URCHINS

Distinctive Characteristics. — Pentamerous, without arms or free rays; skeleton usually of twenty columns of firmly united plates, five pairs of ambulacral rows, and five pairs of interambulacral rows.

Structural Peculiarities. — The starfish type may be changed to that of the sea-urchin quite easily. The latter (Figs. 141–142)

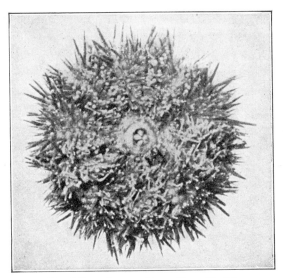

FIG. 141. — A sea urchin. (From Clark.)

resembles a starfish whose aboral surface has become exceedingly reduced, being represented by a small area, the *periproct* (Fig. 142), and the tips of whose arms have at the same time been bent upward and united near the center of the aboral surface.

The *skeleton* of the sea-urchin is known as a *shell* or *test*, and is shown in detail in Figure 142   The *apical system* of plates contains the *madreporite*, four other *genital plates*, with *genital pores*, and five *ocular plates*, each with a mass of *pigmental cells*. There are five pairs of columns of *ambulacral plates*, so called because they are penetrated by tube-feet and five pairs of columns of *interambulacral plates*. On the inside of the test around the peristome in many sea-urchins are five arches, often incomplete, called *auricles*. Most of the plates bear *spines* which are attached by muscles and move freely on little knob-like elevations called

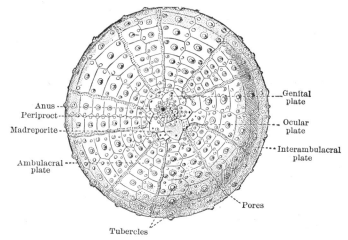

FIG. 142. — Dried test of a sea-urchin, *Echinus esculentus*. (From the Cambridge Natural History.)

tubercles. The *pedicellariæ* are more specialized than those of the starfish; they commonly have three jaws. The *mouth* is provided with five white *teeth;* these are part of a complicated structure known as " Aristotle's Lantern " (Fig. 143).

Nutrition. — The *food* of the sea-urchin consists of marine vegetable and animal matter which is ingested by means of " Aristotle's Lantern." The *intestine* (Fig. 143) is very long; it takes one turn around the inside of the body and then bends upon itself and takes a turn in the opposite direction. A small tube, the *siphon*, accompanies the intestine part way, opening into it at either end. The *anus* (Fig. 142) of the sea-urchin is near the center of the aboral surface.

Respiration. — A large part of the respiration takes place in most echinoids through *ten branched pouches* situated on the area

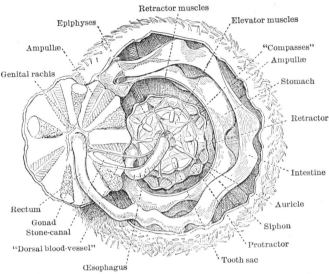

Retractor muscles
Epiphyses
Elevator muscles
Ampullæ
"Compasses"
Ampullæ
Genital rachis
Stomach
Retractor
Intestine
Rectum
Auricle
Gonad
Stone-canal
Siphon
"Dorsal blood-vessel"
Protractor
Œsophagus
Tooth sac

Fig. 143. — Internal anatomy of a sea-urchin, *Echinus esculentus*. (From the Cambridge Natural History.)

surrounding the mouth, one pair in each angle between the ambulacral plates. The tube-feet also are respiratory in function.

Locomotion. — Both *tube-feet* and *spines* are used in locomotion. " The spines are pressed against the substratum and keep the animal from rolling over under the pull of the tube-feet and also help to push it on."

Echinoidea in General. — The common sea-urchins just described live principally on rocky shores. The *cake-urchins* (Fig. 144) live at or near the surface of the sand; a common form on the eastern coast of North America is the sand-

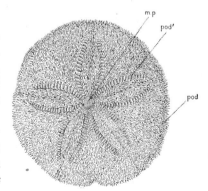

m.p
pod'
pod

Fig. 144. — Aboral view of a "sand-dollar," *Echinarachnius parma*. *m.p*, madreporite; *pod*, small tube-foot; *pod'*, flattened respiratory tube-foot. (From the Cambridge Natural History.)

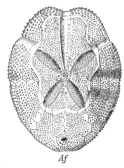

Fig. 145. — Aboral view of the test of a heart-urchin, *Brissopsis lyrifera*. *Af*, anus. (From Sedgwick, after Claus.)

dollar, *Echinarachnius*. The *heart-urchins* (Fig. 145) bury themselves in the mud to a depth of from a few inches to a foot.

5. Class IV. Holothurioidea. — Sea-cucumbers

Distinctive Characteristics. — Elongated on principal axis; body-wall muscular with small calcareous plates; contractile tentacles around mouth; no external madreporite.

Structural Peculiarities. — The most striking external features of the sea-cucumber (Fig. 146) are its *muscular body-wall* almost devoid of large skeletal plates, its *branching tentacles* surrounding the mouth, and its *lateral position* when at rest or moving about on the sea bottom.

The *water-vascular system* (Fig. 147) is homologous to those of the other classes of echinoderms. There is a *circular canal* around the œsophagus, five *radial canals* which end blindly near

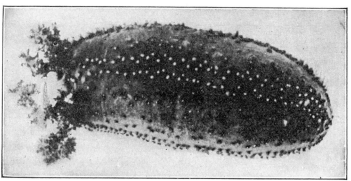

Fig. 146. — A sea cucumber. (From Clark.)

the anus, and *tube-feet* (Fig. 146). The circular canal gives off a *polian vesicle* and one or more *stone-canals* ending in internal *madreporites*. From ten to thirty of the tube-feet surrounding the mouth are modified as *tentacles* for procuring food.

The *alimentary canal* includes a long looped *intestine* (Fig. 147) the posterior end of which is a muscular enlargement called the *cloaca.* Water flows into the cloaca through the *anus* and passes into two long branching tubes, the *respiratory trees;* here part of it probably finds its way through the walls into the body-cavity. *Respiration* is carried on by the cloaca, respiratory trees, tentacles, tube-feet, and body-wall. The cloaca and respiratory trees also function as excretory organs.

Nutrition. — The *food* of most sea-cucumbers consists of organic particles extracted from the sand or mud which is taken into the

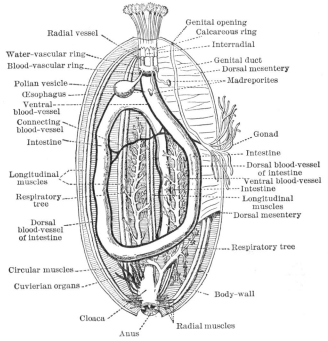

Fig. 147. — Internal anatomy of a sea-cucumber, one of the *Aspidochirotæ.* (From Sedgwick, after Leuckart.)

alimentary canal. Some species are said to stretch out their sea-weed-like tentacles on which many small organisms come to rest. " When one tentacle has got a sufficient freight it is bent round and pushed into the mouth, which is closed on it. It is then forcibly drawn out through the closed lips so that all the living cargo is swept off." (Shipley and MacBride.)

Behavior. — The tube-feet, when present, are organs of *locomotion.* They pull the animal along on its ventral, flattened surface. Waves of muscular contraction which travel from one end of the body to the other are important in locomotion, and the tentacles may also assist.

The common sea-cucumbers, *Thyone briareus*, are sensitive to contact with solid objects, and many of them burrow in the sand or mud. They are extremely sensitive to a decrease in the light intensity and will contract the body if an object passes between them and the source of light. They are also negatively phototropic, since they move away from the light. The following has been written concerning this species: " Passing most of its life buried in the mud, *Thyone* probably does not often fall a prey to large enemies, but it is protected from them by the withdrawing reaction, by its locomotion away from the light, and by its habit of pulling eel grass and other débris over the body." (Pearse.)

Regeneration. — Sea-cucumbers possess remarkable powers of regeneration. When one is irritated it contracts the muscles of the body-wall, and " since the fluid in the body-cavity is practically incompressible, the effect is to set up a tremendous pressure. As a result of this, the wall of the intestine near the anus tears, and a portion or the whole of the intestine is pushed out. The gill trees are the first to go, and in some species the lower branches of these are covered with a substance which swells up in sea-water into a mass of tough white threads in which the enemies of the animal are entangled. A lobster has been rendered perfectly helpless as a consequence of rashly interfering with a sea-cucumber. These special branches are termed Cuvierian organs.

" A Holothurioid is only temporarily inconvenienced by the loss of its internal organs. After a period of quiescence it is again furnished with the intestine and its appendages. Some species, which are able to pull in the mouth end of the body with their tentacles, when strongly irritated snap off even this, and yet are able to repair the loss." (Shipley and MacBride.)

Economic Importance. — Among the South Pacific islands and on the coasts of Queensland and in southern China, dried holothurians are known as " bêche-de-mer " or " trepang " and are used for food. The trade mounts into hundreds of thousands of dollars annually.

6. Class V.   Crinoidea — Sea-lilies or Feather-stars

Distinctive Characteristics. — Attached by aboral apex of body during early stages of development; arms usually branched and bearing pinnules; tube-feet like tentacles, without ampullæ.

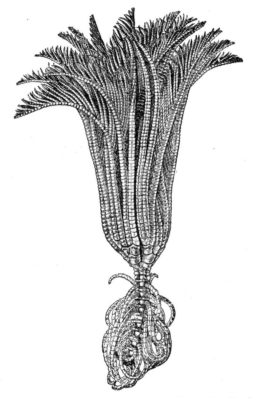

Fig. 148. — A crinoid, *Pentacrinus maclearanus*.   (From the Cambridge Natural History.)

There are five or six hundred living representatives of this class; fossil remains are very abundant in limestone formations.   Most of the living crinoids are found at moderate depths, a few are deep-sea forms, and some inhabit shallow water.   They are often attached by a jointed stalk. . Some species break off from the stalk when they become mature, and probably swim about by means of muscular contractions of the arms.

The *arms* of crinoids are usually five in number. The apparently greater number is due to branching near the base (Fig. 148). The branches may be equal, or one large and the other small; in the latter case the smaller branch is called a *pinnule*.

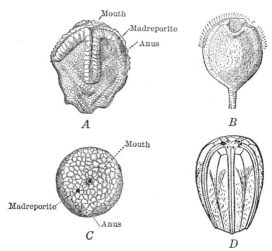

FIG. 149. — Fossil Echinoderms. **A**, *Thecocystis sœculus* (THECOIDEA). **B**, *Trochocystis bohemicus* (CARPOIDEA). **C**, *Echinosphœrites aurantium* (CYSTOIDEA). **D**, *Granatocrinus* (BLASTOIDEA). (A, B, C, from the Cambridge Natural History. A and B, after Jackel; C, after Zittel; D, from Weysse.)

Some authors place the class CRINOIDEA in the subphylum PELMATOZOA along with four classes of fossil echinoderms, the THECOIDEA (Fig. 149, *A*), CARPOIDEA (Fig. 149, B), CYSTOIDEA (Fig. 149, C), and BLASTOIDEA (Fig. 149, D).

7. DEVELOPMENT OF ECHINODERMS

In most of the echinoderms, the eggs pass through a ciliated blastula stage, a gastrula stage, and a larval stage, which, in the course of from two weeks to two months, metamorphoses into an adult. The larvæ (Fig. 150, A) of the four principal classes of echinoderms resemble one another, but are nevertheless quite distinct. They are bilaterally symmetrical, and swim about by means of a ciliated band which may be complicated by a number of arm-like processes. The alimentary canal consists of a mouth (Fig. 150, A), œsophagus, stomach, intestine, and anus. From

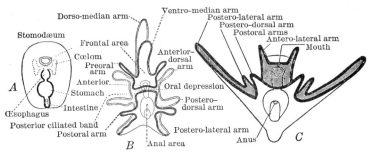

FIG. 150. — Larval Echinoderms. **A**, a young larval echinoderm. **B**, a larval Asteroid, *Bipinnaria elegans*. **C**, a larval Ophiuroid (*Ophiopluteus*). (A, from the Cambridge Natural History; B and C, from Sedgwick, — B, after Mortensen; C, after Müller.)

the digestive tract two cœlomic sacs are budded off; these develop into the body-cavity, water-vasular system, and other cœlomic cavities of the adult.

The larvæ of the different classes have been given names as follows: those of the ASTEROIDEA are called *Bipinnaria* (Fig. 150, B); OPHIUROIDEA, *Ophiopluteus* (Fig. 150, C); ECHINOIDEA, *Echinopluteus* (Fig. 151, A); and HOLOTHURIOIDEA, *Auricularia* (Fig. 151, B). The adults which develop from these larvæ are, as we have seen, radially symmetrical, although many of them, notably the HOLOTHURIOIDEA, are more or less bilateral in structure. The bilateral condition of the larvæ indicates that the ancestors of the echinoderms were either bilaterally symmetrical or

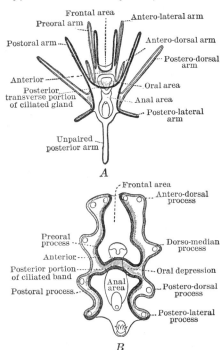

FIG. 151. — Larval Echinoderms. **A**, a larval Echinoid (*Echinopluteus*). **B**, a larval Holothurioid (*Auricularia stelligera*). (From Sedgwick, after J. Müller.)

that the larvæ have become adapted to an active life in the water.

8. Artificial Parthenogenesis

The eggs of echinoderms pass through a total and equal cleavage, and are easily fertilized and reared to the larval stage in the laboratory. For these reasons they have become classical material for embryological studies and for experimental purposes.

One of the most interesting phenomena discovered by means of experiments with echinoderm eggs is the development of a larva from an unfertilized egg when subjected to certain environmental conditions. This phenomenon is known as *artificial parthenogenesis*. The eggs of other animals, for example, annelids, are also capable of developing under certain conditions without fertilization, and those of some species, like plant lice (Chap. XIII) and rotifers (p. 170), are normally parthenogenetic, but echinoderm eggs have been used for experimental purposes more frequently than any others.

Loeb reared normal larvæ from unfertilized eggs of echinoderms by immersing them in solutions such as chloride of sodium, potassium bromide, cane-sugar, etc. He considered the increased osmotic pressure the cause of development, and thought it probable that in ordinary fertilization the spermatozoon brings a solution with a high osmotic pressure into the egg, thereby causing the withdrawal of water. Sea-water concentrated to 70 per cent of its volume has a similar result. A lowering of the temperature of sea-water to the freezing-point causes eggs of *Asterias* and *Arbacia* to develop; when combined with a chemical reagent, a higher per cent of blastulæ results. Eggs exposed to a higher temperature (35° to 38° C.) during the early maturation period develop parthenogenetically, and even mechanical agitation may have a similar effect. Normal mitotic figures appear during the cleavage of these eggs. None of the larvæ thus produced was reared to the adult stage.

The ease with which echinoderm eggs can be handled has led to some experiments that have an important bearing upon heredity. Of these may be mentioned the fertilization of the eggs of one species with the spermatozoa of another species, and the fertilization of enucleated fragments of sea-urchins' eggs with spermatozoa of another species.

9. The Position of Echinoderms in the Animal Kingdom

Echinoderms and cœlenterates, because of their radial symmetry, were at one time placed together in a group called Radiata. The anatomy of the adult and the structure of the larvæ, however, show that these phyla really occupy widely separated positions in the animal kingdom. The adult echinoderms cannot be compared with any other group of animals, and we must look to the

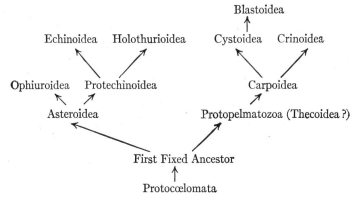

Fig. 152. — Diagram showing the probable relations of the classes of Echinoderms. (After MacBride.)

larvæ for signs of relationship. The bilateral larva is either a modification for a free-swimming life or an indication of the condition of its ancestors. The latter view is accepted by most zoologists. The ancestors of echinoderms were doubtless bilateral, wormlike animals which became fixed and were then modified into radially symmetrical adults. The probable relations of the classes of echinoderms are shown in Figure 152 (MacBride).

It is interesting to compare the echinoderm larva with that of a supposed primitive chordate, the *Tornaria* of *Balanoglossus* (Chap. XIV, Fig. 334). The remarkable similarity of these larvæ suggests that chordates (Chap. XIV) and echinoderms may have had the same or similar ancestors (see also Chap. XXII).

CHAPTER XI

PHYLUM ANNELIDA [1]

THE annelids (Lat. *annellus*, a little ring) can, in most cases, be distinguished from other worms, like *Planaria* (Fig. 97) and *Ascaris* (Fig. 111), by the fact that the body is divided into a number of similar parts called *segments, metameres,* or *somites;* these are arranged in a linear series and are visible externally because of the grooves which encircle the body. The earthworms and leeches are well-known examples. Annelids live in fresh water, salt water, and on land; some are parasitic upon other animals.

The ANNELIDA form three classes: —

(1) CLASS ARCHIANNELIDA (Gr. *arche*, beginning; Lat. *annellus*, a little ring) (Fig. 162), without setæ (Fig. 153) or *parapodia* (Fig. 164);

(2) CLASS CHÆTOPODA (Gr. *chaite*, bristle; *pous*, foot) (Fig. 163), with setae; and

(3) CLASS HIRUDINEA (Lat. *hirudo*, a leech), without setæ or parapodia, but with suckers (Fig. 169).

1. THE EARTHWORM — LUMBRICUS

The earthworm has been for many years and is still a favorite type for illustrating the anatomy and physiology of annelids, and for teaching general zoological principles. The common earthworm, *Lumbricus terrestris*, lives in the ground where the soil is not too dry or sandy; it comes to the surface only at night or after a

---

[1] The earthworm is a valuable type for the elucidation of certain zoological principles. Metamerism, the importance of the cœlom, and the complex circulatory system are particularly noteworthy. The morphology and functions of the nervous system, involving the neuron theory and the reflex arc, are here studied to excellent advantage. The reactions of the earthworm to stimuli, the phenomena of regeneration and grafting and the development of the trochophore larva deserve special mention. The sections on the ARCHIANNELIDA, CHÆTOPODA and HIRUDINEA are included principally for reference.

rain. In many parts of this country the species *Allolobophora* (*Helodrilus*) *longa* or one of the species of *Diplocardia* are more abundant in cultivated soil than *L. terrestris*.

External Features. — The body of *Lumbricus* is cylindroid, and varies in length from about six inches to a foot. The *segments*, of which there are over one hundred, are easily determined externally because of the grooves extending around the body.

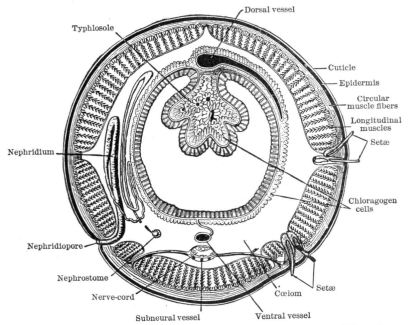

Fig. 153. — Transverse section of an earthworm. (From Parker and Haswell, after Marshall and Hurst.)

At the anterior end a fleshy lobe, the *prostomium* (Fig. 156), projects over the *mouth;* this is not considered a true segment. It is customary to number the segments with Roman numerals, beginning at the anterior end, since both external and internal structures bear a constant relation to them. Segments XXXI or XXXII to XXXVII are swollen in mature worms, forming a saddleshaped enlargement, the *clitellum*, of use during reproduction. Every segment except the first and last bears four pairs of *f*-shaped chitinous bristles, the *setæ*, situated as indicated in Figure 153; these may be moved by retractor and protractor muscles, and are renewed if lost. The setæ on somite XXVI are in mature worms modified for reproductive purposes.

The body is covered by a thin, transparent *cuticle* (Fig. 153) secreted by the cells lying just beneath it. The cuticle protects the body from physical and chemical injury; it contains numerous *pores* to allow the secretions from unicellular glands to pass through, and is marked with fine *striæ*, causing the surface to appear iridescent.

A number of *external openings* of various sizes allow the entrance of food into the body, and the exit of fæces, excretory products, reproductive cells, etc. (1) The *mouth* is a crescentic opening situated in the ventral half of the first somite (Fig. 156); it is overhung by the prostomium. (2) The oval *anal aperture* lies in the last somite. (3) The openings of the sperm ducts or *vasa deferentia* are situated one on either side of somite XV. They have swollen lips; a slight ridge extends posteriorly from them to the clitellum. (4) The openings of the *oviducts* are small, round pores one on either side of somite XIV; eggs pass out of the body through them. (5) The openings of the *seminal receptacles* appear as two pairs of minute pores concealed within the grooves which separate somites IX and X, and X and XI. (6) A pair of *nephridiopores* (Fig. 153), the external apertures of the excretory organs, open on every somite except the first three and the last. They are usually situated immediately anterior to the outer seta of the inner pair. (7) The body-cavity or *cœlom* communicates with the exterior by means of *dorsal pores*. One of these is located in the mid-dorsal line at the anterior edge of each somite from VIII or IX to the posterior end of the body.

General Internal Anatomy. — If a specimen is cut open from the anterior to the posterior end by an incision passing through the body-wall a trifle to one side of the mid-dorsal line, a general view of the internal structures may be obtained (Fig. 154). As in *Ascaris* (p. 161, Fig. 112 b), the body is essentially a double tube (Fig. 153), the body-wall constituting the outer, the straight alimentary canal, the inner; between the two is a cavity, the cœlom. The external segmentation corresponds to an internal division of the cœlomic cavity into compartments by means of partitions, called *septa* (Fig. 154), which lie beneath the grooves. These septa are absent in *Ascaris*. The alimentary canal passes through the center of the body, and is suspended in the cœlom by the partitions. Septa are absent between somites I and II, and incomplete between somites III and IV, and XVII and XVIII.

The walls of the cœlom are lined with an epithelium, termed the *peritoneum*. The cœlomic cavity is filled with a colorless fluid which flows from one compartment to another when the body of the worm contracts. In somites IX to XVI are the reproductive organs (Fig. 158); running along the upper surface of the alimentary canal is the dorsal blood-vessel (Fig. 153); and just beneath it lie the ventral blood-vessels and nervecord.

Detailed Anatomy and Physiology. — *Digestion.* — The *alimentary canal* (Fig. 154) consists of (1) a *mouth cavity* or *buccal pouch* in somites I to III, (2) a thick muscular *pharynx* lying in somites IV and V, (3) a narrow, straight tube, the *œsophagus* which extends through somites VI to XIV, (4) a thin-walled enlargement, the *crop* or *proventriculus*, in somites XV and XVI, (5) a thick

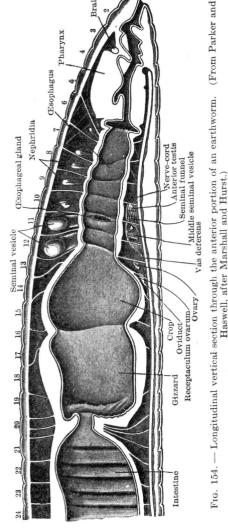

Fig. 154. — Longitudinal vertical section through the anterior portion of an earthworm. (From Parker and Haswell, after Marshall and Hurst.)

muscular-walled *gizzard* in somites XVII and XVIII, and (6) a thin-walled *intestine* extending from somite XIX to the *anal aperture*. The intestine is not a simple cylindrical tube; but its dorsal wall is infolded, forming an internal longitudinal ridge, the *typhlosole* (Fig. 153). This increases the digestive surface. Surrounding the alimentary canal and dorsal blood-vessel is a layer of *chloragogen cells*. The functions of these cells are not known with certainty, but they probably aid in the elaboration of food and are excretory. Three pairs of *calciferous glands* lie at the sides of the œsophagus (Fig. 154) in segments X to XII; they produce carbonate of lime, which probably neutralizes acid foods.

The *food* of the earthworm consists principally of pieces of leaves and other vegetation, particles of animal matter, and soil. This material is gathered at night. At this time the worms are active; they crawl out into the air, and, holding fast to the tops of their burrows with their tails, explore the neighborhood. Food particles are drawn into the buccal cavity by suction produced when the pharyngeal cavity is enlarged by the contraction of the muscles which extend from the pharynx to the body-wall.

In the pharynx, the food receives a secretion from the pharyngeal glands; it then passes through the œsophagus to the crop, where it is stored temporarily. In the meantime the secretion from the calciferous glands in the œsophageal walls is added, neutralizing the acids. The gizzard is a grinding organ; in it the food is broken up into minute fragments by being squeezed and rolled about. Solid particles, such as grains of sand, which are frequently swallowed, probably aid in this grinding process. The food then passes on to the intestine, where most of the digestion and absorption takes place.

Digestion in the earthworm is very similar to that of higher animals. The digestive fluids act upon proteids, carbohydrates, and fats; in them are special chemical compounds, called *ferments* or *enzymes*, which break up complex molecules without themselves becoming changed chemically. The three most important enzymes are: (1) trypsin, which dissolves proteid; (2) diastase, which breaks up molecules of carbohydrates; and (3) steapsin, which acts upon fats. These three enzymes are probably present in the digestive fluids of the earthworm. The proteids are changed into peptones, the carbohydrates into a sugar compound, and the fats are divided into glycerine and fatty acids.

The food is now ready for *absorption*. This is accomplished through the wall of the intestine by a process known as *osmosis*, assisted by an ameboid activity of some of the epithelial cells. Osmosis is the passage of a liquid through a membrane. Upon reaching the blood, the absorbed food is carried to various parts of the body. Absorbed food also makes its way into the cœlomic cavity and is carried directly to those tissues bathed by the cœlomic fluid. In one-celled animals, and in such METAZOA as *Hydra*, *Planaria*, and *Ascaris*, no circulatory system is necessary, since the food either is digested within the cells or comes into direct contact with them; but in large, complex animals a special system of organs must be provided to enable the proper distribution of nutriment.

Circulation. — The *blood* of the earthworm is contained in a complicated system of tubes which ramify to all parts of the body. A number of these tubes are large and centrally located; these give off branches which likewise branch, finally ending in exceedingly thin tubules, the *capillaries*. The functions of this system of tubes are to carry nourishment from the alimentary canal to all parts of the body, to transport waste products, and to convey the blood to a point near the surface of the body where oxygen may be obtained and supplied to the tissues.

The *blood* of the earthworm consists of a plasma in which are suspended a great number of colorless cells, called corpuscles. Its red color is due to a pigment termed *hæmoglobin* which is dissolved in the plasma. In vertebrates the hæmoglobin is located in the blood corpuscles.

There are *five longitudinal blood-vessels* connected with one another and with various organs by branches, more or less regularly arranged. These are shown in Figure 155, and are as follows: (1) the dorsal or supra-intestinal vessel, (2) the ventral or subintestinal trunk, (3) the subneural trunk, (4) two lateral neural trunks, (5) five pairs of hearts in segments VII to XI, (6) two intestino-tegumentary vessels (in A and B) arising in segment X and extending to the œsophagus, integument, and nephridia in segments X to VI, (7) branches from the ventral trunk to the nephridia and body-wall (D), (8) parietal vessels connecting the dorsal and subneural trunks in the intestinal region, (9) branches from the dorsal trunk to the intestine, (in C), (10) a typhlosolar vessel connected by branches with the intestine and dorsal trunk, and (11) branches from the ventral vessel to the nephridia and body-wall (in D).

The dorsal trunk and hearts determine the direction of the blood flow, since they furnish the power by means of their muscular walls. Blood is forced forward by wavelike contractions of the dorsal trunk, beginning at the posterior end and traveling quickly anteriorly. These contractions are said to be *peristaltic*,

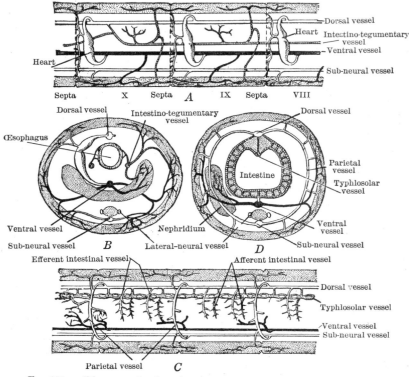

Fig. 155. — Diagrams showing the arrangement of the blood-vessels in the earthworm. **A**, longitudinal view of the vessels in somites VIII, IX, and X. **B**, transverse section of same region. **C**, longitudinal view of the vessels in the intestinal region. **D**, transverse section through the intestinal region. (From Bourne, after Benham.)

and have been likened to the action of the fingers in the operation of milking. *Valves* in the walls of the dorsal trunk prevent the return of blood from the anterior end. In somites VII to XI the blood passes from the dorsal trunk into the hearts, and is forced by them both forward and backward in the ventral trunk. Valves in the heart also prevent the backward flow. From the ventral trunk the blood passes to the body-wall and nephridia.

Blood is returned from the body-wall to the lateral-neural trunks. The flow in the subneural trunk is toward the posterior end, then upward through the parietal vessels into the dorsal trunk. The anterior region receives blood from the dorsal and ventral trunks. The blood which is carried to the body-wall and integument receives oxygen through the cuticle, and is then returned to the dorsal trunk by way of the subneural trunk and the intestinal connectives. Because of its proximity to the subneural trunk, the nervous system receives a continuous supply of the freshest blood.

Respiration. — The earthworm possesses no respiratory system, but obtains oxygen and gets rid of carbon dioxide through the moist outer membrane. Many capillaries lie just beneath the cuticle, making the exchange of gases easy. The oxygen is combined with the hæmoglobin.

Excretion. — Most of the excretory matter is carried outside of the body by a number of coiled tubes, termed *nephridia* (Fig. 153), a pair of which are present in every somite except the first three and the last. A nephridium occupies part of two successive somites; in one is a ciliated funnel, the *nephrostome*, which is connected by a thin ciliated tube with the major portion of the structure in the somite posterior to it. Three loops make up the coiled portion of the nephridium. The cilia on the nephrostome and in the nephridium create a current which draws solid waste particles from the cœlomic fluid. Glands in the coiled tube take waste matter from the blood, and the current in the tube carries it out through the *nephridiopore*.

Nervous System. — The nervous system

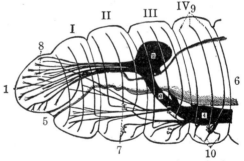

Fig. 156. — Diagram of the anterior end of an earthworm to show the arrangement of the nervous system. *1*, prostomium; *2*, brain; *3*, circumpharyngeal connective; *4*, subpharyngeal ganglion; *5*, mouth; *6*, pharynx; *7*, setæ; *8*, tactile nerves to prostomium; *9*, dorsal nerves; *10*, ventral nerves. (From Shipley and MacBride.)

differs from that of the types studied heretofore in being more concentrated. There is a bilobed mass of nervous tissue, the *brain* or *suprapharyngeal ganglion,* on the dorsal surface of the pharynx in segment III (Fig. 156). This is connected by two *circum-pharyngeal connectives* with a pair of *subpharyngeal ganglia* which lie just beneath the pharynx. From the latter the *ventral nerve-cord* (Fig. 154) extends posteriorly near the ventral body-wall (Fig. 153). The ventral nerve-cord enlarges into a ganglion in each segment and gives off three pairs of nerves in every segment posterior to IV. Each ganglion really consists of two ganglia fused together. Near the dorsal surface of every ganglionic mass are three longitudinal cords, the *neurochords* or " giant fibers "

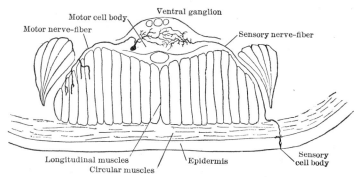

Fig. 157. — Transverse section of the ventral nerve chain and surrounding structures of an earthworm. (From Parker in *Pop. Sci. Monthly*, modified after Retzius.)

(Fig. 157). The brain and nerve-cord constitute the *central nervous system;* the nerves which pass from and to them represent the *peripheral nervous system.*

The nerves of the peripheral nervous system are either efferent or afferent. *Efferent* nerve-fibers (Fig. 157) are extensions from cells in the ganglia of the central nervous system. They pass out to the muscles or other organs, and, since impulses sent along them give rise to movements, the cells of which they are a part are said to be *motor nerve-cells.* The *afferent* fibers originate from nerve-cells in the epidermis which are sensory in function, and extend into the ventral nerve-cord.

The functions of nervous tissue are perception, conduction, and stimulation. These are usually performed by nerve-cells, called *neurons.* The neuron theory " supposes that there is no nerve-fiber independent of nerve-cell and that the cell with all its prolongations is a unit or a neuron; that these units are not united to one another anatomically, but act together physiologically by contact; that the entire nervous system consists of superimposed neurons; . . ." (Parker.)

The *reflex* carried out either consciously or unconsciously is considered the physiological unit of nervous activity. The apparatus required for a simple reflex in the body of an earthworm is represented in Figure 157. A primary sensory neuron, lying at the surface of the body, sends a fiber into the ventral nerve-cord, where it branches out; these branches are in physiological continuity with branches from a primary motor neuron lying in the ganglion of the ventral nerve-cord. The second neuron sends · fibers into a reacting organ, which in this case is a muscle. These fibers extending to the reacting organ are called motor fibers; those leading to the ventral nerve-cord are termed sensory fibers. The first neuron, or *receptor*, receives the stimulus and produces the nerve impulse; the second neuron, the *adjustor*, receives, directs, and modifies the impulse; and the muscle or other organ stimulated to activity is the *effector*. Within the ventral nerve-cord are *association neurons* whose fibers serve to connect structures within one ganglion or two succeeding ganglia. These short neurons overlap one another, and are doubtless responsible for the muscular waves which pass from the anterior to the posterior end of the worm during locomotion. The three giant fibers, which lie in the dorsal part of the ventral nerve-cord throughout almost its entire length, are connected by means of fibrils with nerve-cells in the ganglia, and probably distribute the impulse that causes a worm to contract its entire body when strongly stimulated.

Sense Organs. — The sensitiveness of *Lumbricus* to light and other stimuli is due to the presence of a great number of *epidermal sense-organs*. These are groups of sense-cells connected with the central nervous system by means of nerve-fibers and communicating with the outside world through *sense-hairs* which penetrate the cuticle. More of these sense-organs occur at the anterior and posterior ends than in any other region of the body.

Reproduction. — Both male and female sexual organs occur in a single earthworm. Figure 158 shows diagrammatically the position and shape of the various structures. The *female system* consists of: (1) a pair of *ovaries* in segment XIII; (2) a pair of *oviducts* which open by a ciliated funnel in segment XIII, enlarge into an *egg sac* in segment XIV, and then open to the exterior; and (3) two pairs of *seminal receptacles* or *spermathecæ*, in somites IX and X. The *male organs* are (1) two pairs of glove-shaped *testes* in segments X and XI, (2) two *vasa deferentia* which lead from ciliated funnels to the exterior in segment XV, and

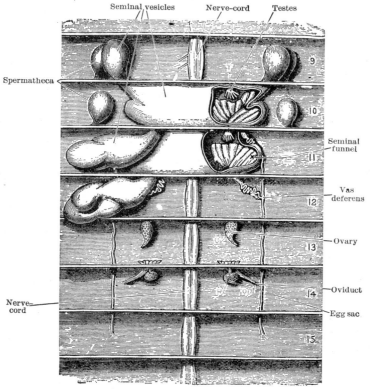

FIG. 158. — Diagram of the reproductive organs of the earthworm, dorsal view.
(From Marshall and Hurst.)

(3) three pairs of *seminal vesicles* in segments IX, XI, and XII, and two central reservoirs.

Self-fertilization does not take place, but spermatozoa are transferred from one worm to another during a process called *copulation*. Two worms come together, as shown in Figure 159, A; slime tubes are formed, and then a band-like *cocoon* is secreted about the clitellar region. Eggs and spermatozoa are deposited in the cocoon, but fertilization does not occur until the cocoon is slipped over the head (Fig. 159, B).

The *eggs* of the earthworm are *holoblastic*, but cleavage is unequal. A hollow blastula is formed and a gastrula is produced by invagination. The mesoderm develops from two of the blastula cells, called *mesomeres*. These cells divide, forming two *mesoblastic bands* which later become the epithelial lining of the cœlom. The embryo escapes from the cocoon as a small worm in about two or three weeks.

Behavior. — *External Stimuli.* — The external stimuli that have been most frequently employed in studying the behavior of earthworms are those dealing with thigmotropism, chemotropism, and phototropism.

Thigmotropism. — Mechanical stimulation, if continuous and not too strong, calls forth a positive reaction; the worms live where

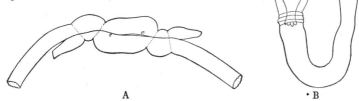

their bodies come in contact with solid objects; they apparently like to feel the walls of their burrows against their bodies, or, when outside of their burrows, to lie or crawl upon the ground. Reaction to sounds are not due to the presence of a sense of hearing, but to the contact stimuli produced by vibrations. Darwin showed that musical tones produced no response, but that the worms contained in a flower-pot drew back into their burrows immediately when a note was struck, if the pot were placed upon a piano, this result being due to vibrations.

A   • B

FIG. 159. — **A,** the anterior segments of two copulating earthworms. Slime tubes encircle the pair from the 8th to the 33d segment. **B,** cocoon, freshly deposited, of an earthworm, surrounded by one-half of a slime tube. (After Foot, in *Journ. Morph.*)

Chemotropism. — In certain cases chemotropic reactions result in bringing the animal into regions of favorable food conditions, or turning it away from unpleasant substances. Moisture, which is necessary for respiration, and consequently for the life of the earthworm, causes a positive reaction, provided it comes in contact with the body, no positive reactions being produced by chemical stimulation from a distance. Negative reactions, on the other hand, such as moving to one side or back into the burrow, are produced even when certain unpleasant chemical agents are still some distance from the body. These reactions are quite similar to those caused by contact stimuli. Darwin explained the preference of the earthworm for certain kinds of food by supposing that the discrimination between edible and inedible substance was possible when in contact with the body. This would resemble the sense of taste as present in the higher animals.

Phototropism. — No definite visual organs have been discovered in earthworms, but nevertheless these animals are very sensitive to light, as is proved by the fact that a sudden illumination at night will often cause them to " dash like a rabbit " into their burrows. One investigator claims to have found cells in the ectoderm, especially in the prostomium and posterior end, which act as visual organs. The entire surface of the body, however, is sensitive to light, although the anterior region is more sensitive than the tail, and the middle less than either of the others. Very slight differences in the intensity of the light are distinguished, since, if a choice of two illuminated regions is given, that more faintly lighted is, in the majority of cases, selected. A positive reaction to faint light has been demonstrated for the manure worm, *Allolobophora fœtida.* This positive phototropism to faint light may account for the emergence of the worms from their burrows at night.

Physiological State. — From the foregoing account it might be inferred that only external stimuli are factors in the behavior of the earthworm. This, however, is not the case, since the physiological condition, which depends largely upon previous stimulation, determines the character of the response. Different physiological states may be recognized, ranging from a state of rest in which slight stimuli are not effective, to a state of great excitement caused by long-continued and intense stimulation, in which condition slight stimuli cause violent responses.

Regeneration and Grafting. — Earthworms have considerable powers of regeneration and grafting (p. 111). Some of the results of experiments along this line are shown in Figure 160. A posterior piece may regenerate a head of five segments (A) or in certain cases a tail (B). Such a double-tailed worm slowly starves to death. An anterior piece regenerates a tail (C). Three pieces from several worms may be united so as to make a long worm (D);

two pieces may fuse, forming a worm with two tails (E); and an anterior piece may be united with a posterior piece to make a short worm (F). In all these experiments the parts were held together by threads until they became united.

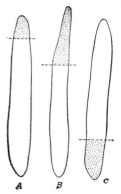

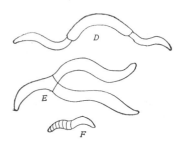

FIG. 160. — Regeneration and grafting in the earthworm. **A**, head end of five segments regenerated from the posterior piece of a worm. **B**, tail regenerated from the posterior piece of a worm. **C**, tail regenerated from an anterior piece of a worm. **D**, union of three pieces to make a long worm. **E**, union of two pieces to make a double-tailed worm. **F**, anterior and posterior pieces united to make a short worm. The dotted portion represents regenerated material. (From Morgan.)

Economic Importance. — Charles Darwin in his book on the *Formation of Vegetable Mold through the Action of Worms* has shown by careful observations extending over a period of forty years how great is the economic importance of earthworms. One acre of ground may contain over fifty thousand earthworms. The fæces of these worms are the little heaps of black earth, called " castings " which strew the ground, being especially noticeable early in the morning. Darwin estimated that more than eighteen tons of earthy castings may be carried to the surface in a single year on one acre of ground, and in twenty years a layer three inches thick would be transferred from the subsoil to the surface. By this means objects are covered up in the course of a few years. Darwin speaks of a stony field which was so changed that " after

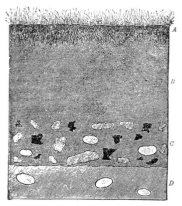

FIG. 161. — Section of top soil showing stones (c) covered over by fine soil (A, B) brought up by earthworms. (From Darwin.)

thirty years (1871) a horse could gallop over the compact turf from one end of the field to the other, and not strike a single stone with its shoes " (Fig. 161).

The continuous honeycombing of the soil by earthworms makes the land more porous and insures the better penetration of air and moisture. The thorough working over of the surface layers of earth also helps to make the soil more fertile.

2. Classification of Annelids

Definition. — Annelids are segmented worms, the body consisting of a linear series of more or less similar parts. Many of the internal organs are segmentally arranged, notably the blood-vessels, excretory organs, and nervous system. A large perivisceral cœlom is usually present, and in some cases a trochophore stage (Fig. 162) appears in development. Setæ are characteristic of the majority.

The classes of annelids are as follows: —

(1) **Class Archiannelida.** — Marine worms without setæ or parapodia. There is only one family, including two genera. Example: *Polygordius* (Fig. 162).

(2) **Class Chætopoda.** — Marine, fresh-water, or terrestrial worms with setæ and a perivisceral cœlom; often divided by septa. Examples: *Lumbricus* (Fig. 154), *Nereis* (Fig. 163).

(3) **Class Hirudinea.** — Marine, fresh-water, or terrestrial worms without setæ or parapodia. Anterior and posterior suckers are present. Examples: *Hirudo* (Fig. 169), *Clepsine* (Fig. 171).

3. Class I. Archiannelida

A single family, Polygordiidæ, belongs to this class; it includes two genera, *Polygordius* (Fig. 162, A) and *Protodrilus*. *Polygordius* is a marine worm living in the sand. It is about an inch and one half long, and only indistinctly segmented externally. The *prostomium* (Fig. 162) bears a pair of *tentacles*. The *mouth opening* is in the ventral part of the first segment, and the *anal opening* in the last segment. A pair of *ciliated pits*, one on either side of the prostomium, probably serve as sense-organs.

Internally *Polygordius* resembles the earthworm, but in some respects is more primitive. The cœlom is divided into compartments by septa. The internal organs are repeated so that

almost every segment possesses cœlomic cavities, longitudinal
muscles, a pair of nephridia, a pair of gonads, a section of the alimentary canal, and part of the ventral nerve-cord. The *development* of *Polygordius* includes a *trochophore stage.* As shown in
Figure 162, B, the trochophore larva at first resembles a top with
cilia around the edge, an eye-spot, and a digestive tract with both

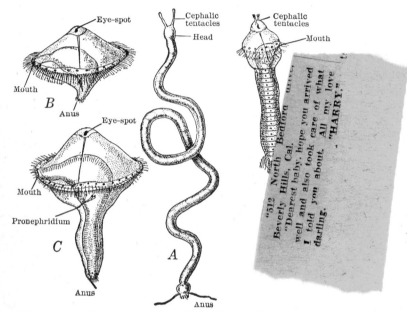

Fig. 162. — *Polygordius appendiculatus.* **A,** dorsal view. **B,** trochosphere larva.
C and **D,** stages in development of trochosphere into the worm. (From Bourne,
after Fraipont.)

mouth and anal openings. This larva resembles the *Pilidium*
larva of the NEMERTINEA (Fig. 118) and certain adult rotifers
(Figs. 122–123). The adult develops from the larva by the growth
and elongation of the anal end as shown in Figure 162, B, C. This ·
elongation becomes segmented (D) and by continued growth
transforms into the adult (A).

4. CLASS II. CHÆTOPODA

The CHÆTOPODA are annelids which possess conspicuous setæ.
Two subclasses are recognized: (1) the POLYCHÆTA, like *Nereis*
(Fig. 163), with many setæ situated on paired fleshy outgrowths,

the *parapodia* (Fig. 164), and the sexes usually separate; and (2) the OLIGOCHÆTA, like the earthworm, with a lesser number of sessile setæ projecting out from the body-wall; hermaphroditic.

Subclass 1. *Polychæta*

Nereis. — *Nereis* (Fig. 163), the sand or clam worm, is a common annelid living in burrows in the sand or mud of the seashore at tide level. The burrows are sometimes two feet deep and are kept

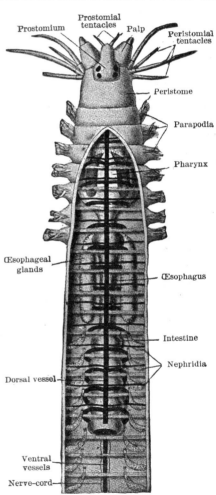

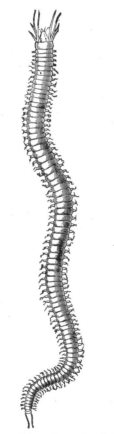

FIG. 163. — A marine Polychæta, *Nereis*. (From Shipley and MacBride, after Oersted.)

FIG. 164. — Anatomy of *Nereis*. (From Parker and Haswell.)

from collapsing by a lining of mucus which holds together the grains of sand. By day the sandworm rests in its burrow, but at night it extends its body in search of food, or may leave the burrow entirely.

A comparison of the figures of *Nereis* (Figs. 163–165) with those of the earthworm (Figs. 153–154) shows that these two animals have much in common, but nevertheless many differences. Both are segmented externally and internally, but *Nereis* possesses parapodia (Fig. 164), a pair of

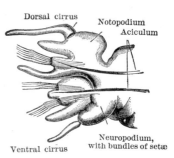

Fig. 165. — Parapodium of *Nereis.* (From Sedgwick, after Quatrefages.)

chitinous jaws, a pair of tentacles, and two pairs of eyes on the prostomium, a pair of palpi, and four pairs of tentacles on the peristome.

The *parapodia* (Fig. 165) are primarily used as locomotor organs, but the lobes are supplied with numerous blood-vessels and serve also as *respiratory organs* or *gills.* Each parapodium bears jointed *locomotor setæ,* and is moved by muscles attached to a sort of internal skeleton consisting of two buried bristles called *acicula.*

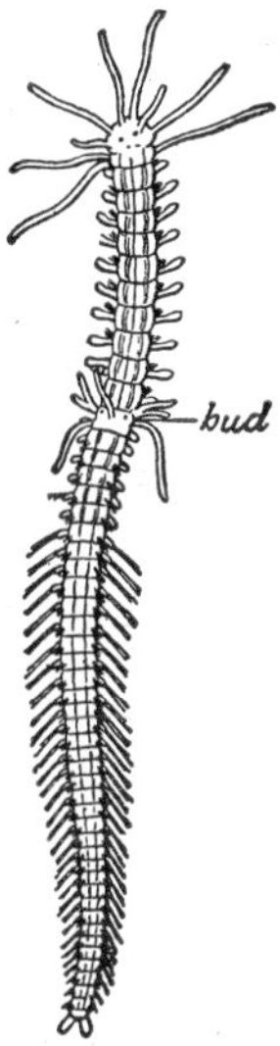

The *sense organs* of Nereis are more highly developed than those of the earthworm. The *tentacles* (Fig. 164) are organs of *touch,* the *palpi* are probably organs of *taste,* and the *eyes,* organs of *sight.*

The two principal groups of the POLYCHÆTA are the PHANEROCEPHALA and CRYPTOCEPHALA.

Fig. 166. — A Polychæta, *Autolytus,* which reproduces by buds. *bud,* head of the budded individual. (From Davenport, after Agassiz.)

Order 1. Phanerocephala. — POLYCHÆTA with most of the segments similar, a distinct head (prostomium) and a protrusible pharynx usually provided with chitinous jaws. Examples: *Nereis* (Fig. 163), *Aphrodite, Autolytus* (Fig. 166).

Fig. 167. — *Amphitrite johnstoni.* *g,* gills; *t,* prostomial tentacles. (From Sedgwick, after Cunningham and Ramage.)

Order 2. Cryptocephala. — Polychæta with head (prostomium) usually small and indistinct; segments differentiated, forming two or more regions, the thorax and abdomen, and palpi often divided into a crown of gills. Examples: *Amphitrite* (Fig. 167), *Spirorbis*, *Terebella*, *Sabella*.

Subclass 2. Oligochæta

The earthworm illustrates the chief characteristics of this subclass. There are usually only a few setæ, and no parapodia nor tentacles. The sexes are united, *i.e.* hermaphroditic. Most of

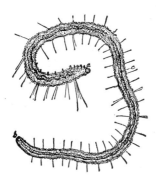

FIG. 168. — *Nais. a,* mouth ; *b,* anus ; *c,* intestine. (From Davenport, after Leunis.)

the OLIGOCHÆTA are either terrestrial or live in fresh water. Two orders are recognized: (1) the MICRODRILI, and (2) the MACRODRILI.

Order 1. Microdrili (Limicola). — These are mostly small fresh-water animals. Examples: *Tubifex*, *Dero*, *Nais* (Fig. 168). Many of them reproduce by transverse fission as well as sexually.

Order 2. Macrodrili. (Terricola). — This order contains the terrestrial OLIGOCHÆTA. Examples: *Lumbricus* (Fig. 154), *Allolobophora*, *Diplocardia*.

5. CLASS III. HIRUDINEA

The animals included in this class are commonly called *leeches* (Fig. 169). They are usually flattened dorso-ventrally, but differ externally from the flatworms (PLATYHELMINTHES, Chap. VII) in being distinctly segmented. The external segmentation, however, does not correspond exactly to the internal segmentation, since there are a variable number of external grooves (from two to fourteen) to every real segment, *e.g.* usually five in the medicinal leech, *Hirudo* (Fig. 169), and its allies, and three in *Clepsine*. Anatomical features which distinguish the HIRUDINEA from the ARCHIANNELIDA and CHÆTOPODA are (1) the presence of a definite number of segments (thirty-three), (2) two suckers, one formed around the mouth and the other at the posterior end, and (3) the absence of setæ (except in one genus). They are hermaphrodites.

Hirudo medicinalis, the medicinal leech (Fig. 169), is usually selected as an example of the class. It is about four inches long, but is capable of great contractions and elongation. The *suckers* are used as organs of attachment, and during locomotion are alternately fastened to and released from the substratum, the animal looping along like a measuring-worm. Leeches are also able to swim through the water by undulating movements.

The *alimentary tract* (Fig. 170) is fitted for the digestion of the blood of vertebrates, which forms the principal food of some leeches. The *mouth* lies in the anterior sucker (Fig. 169) and is provided with three *jaws* armed with chitinous teeth for biting. The blood flow caused by the bite of a leech is difficult to stop, since a secretion from glands opening near the jaws tends to prevent coagulation. Blood is sucked up by the dilation of the muscular *pharynx* (Fig. 170). The short *œsophagus* leads from the pharynx into the *crop*, which has eleven pairs of lateral branches. Here the blood is stored until digested in the small globular *stomach*. A leech is able to ingest three times its own weight in blood, and, since it may take as long as nine months to digest this amount, meals are few and far between. The *intestine* leads directly to the *anus*.

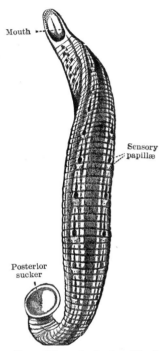

FIG. 169. — A leech, *Hirudo medicinalis*. (From Shipley and MacBride.)

The absorbed food passes into the *blood-vessels* (Fig. 170) and the *cœlomic cavities*, and is carried to all parts of the body. The cœlom is usually small because of the development of a peculiar kind of connective tissue known as *botryoidal tissue*. The spaces in the body which are not filled up by this tissue are called sinuses, and in many species contain a fluid very much like true blood.

Respiration is carried on at the surface of the body, oxygen being taken into and carbon dioxide given off by many blood capillaries

in the skin. Waste products are extracted from the blood and
cœlomic fluid by seventeen pairs of *nephridia* (Fig. 170) which

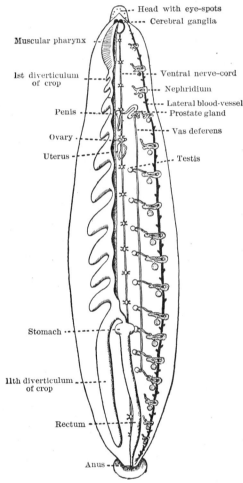

Head with eye-spots

Cerebral ganglia

Muscular pharynx

1st diverticulum of crop

Ventral nerve-cord

Nephridium

Lateral blood-vessel

Penis

Prostate gland

Vas deferens

Ovary

Uterus

Testis

Stomach

11th diverticulum of crop

Rectum

Anus

Fig. 170. — Internal organs of a leech, *Hirudo medicinalis*. (From Shipley and MacBride.)

resemble those of the
earthworm (Fig. 153),
but frequently lack
the internal opening.

Leeches are *hermaphroditic*, but the eggs
of one animal are fertilized by spermatozoa
from another leech.
The *spermatozoa* arise
in the nine pairs of
segmentally arranged
testes (Fig. 170): they
pass into the *vas deferens*, then into a convoluted tube called
the *epididymus*, where
they are fastened into
bundles called *spermatophores*, and are finally deposited within
the body of another
leech by means of the
muscular *penis*. The
eggs arise in the *ovaries*
of which there is a
single pair; they pass
into the *oviducts*, then
into the *uterus*, and
finally out through the
genital pore ventrally
situated in segment
XI. *Copulation* and
the formation of a *cocoon* are similar to these processes in the
earthworm (p. 208).

Many leeches have jaws resembling those of *Hirudo*, for example
Hæmopis and *Macrobdella*, but others have a slender protrusible
proboscis in place of jaws. *Clepsine* (Fig. 171) belongs to the

latter type; it feeds chiefly on fish and snails. *Ichthyobdella* and *Pontobdella* (Fig. 171) are marine jawless leeches which are parasitic on fish.

6. ANNELIDS IN GENERAL

Three morphological characteristics of the ANNELIDA are especially worthy of notice: (1) metamerism, (2) the cœlom, and (3) the trochophore stage in development.

Metamerism. — The segmentation of the body as exhibited in annelids is called *metamerism*, and is here encountered for the first time. This type of structure is of considerable interest, since the most successful groups in the animal kingdom, the ARTHROPODA and VERTEBRATA, have their parts metamerically arranged. How this condition has been brought about is still doubtful, but many theories have been proposed to account for it. According to one view the body of a metameric animal has evolved from that of a nonsegmented animal by transverse fission. The individuals thus produced remained united end to end and gradually became integrated both morphologically and physiologically so that their individualities were united into one complex individuality. Some zoologists maintain that the segmental arrangement of organs such as nephridia, blood-vessels, and reproductive organs has been caused by the division of a single ancestral organ, and not by the formation of new organs as the fission theory demands.

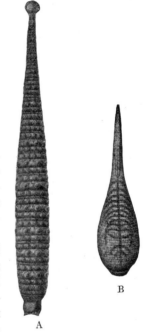

FIG. 171. — Two leeches. A, *Pontobdella*. B, *Clepsine*. (From Parker and Haswell. A, after Bourne; B, after Cuvier.)

True metamerism, as exhibited by annelids, should not be confused with the *pseudometamerism* of the tapeworms (p. 153, Fig. 107). The proglottides of the tapeworms are individuals budded off from the posterior end and differing from one another only in the degree of development. The tapeworm may be considered a row of incomplete individuals.

The Cœlom. — The cœlom has already been defined (p. 87) as a cavity in the mesoderm lined by an epithelium; into it the excretory organs open, and from its walls the reproductive cells originate. The development of the cœlom is described on page 87.

The importance of the cœlom should be clearly understood, since it has played a prominent rôle. in the progressive development of complexity of structure. The appearance of this cavity between the digestive tract and body-wall brought about great physiological changes and is correlated with the origin of nephridia for transporting waste products out of the body, and of genital ducts for the exit of eggs and spermatozoa. The cœlom also affected the distribution of nutritive substances within the body, since it contains a fluid which takes up material absorbed by the alimentary canal and carries it to the tissues. Excretory matter finds its way into the cœlomic fluid and thence out of the body through the nephridia.

So important is the cœlom considered by most zoologists that the METAZOA are frequently separated into two groups: (1) the ACŒLOMATA without a cœlom, and (2) the CŒLOMATA with a cœlom. The PORIFERA, CŒLENTERATA, and CTENOPHORA are undoubtedly ACŒLOMATA. Likewise the ANNELIDA, ECHINODERMATA, ARTHROPODA, MOLLUSCA, and CHORDATA are certainly CŒLOMATA. But whether the PLATYHELMINTHES, NEMATHELMINTHES, and a number of other groups possess a cœlom is still uncertain (see p. 22).

The Trochophore. — The term *trochophore* has been applied to the larval stages of a number of marine animals. The description and figures of the development of *Polygordius* (p. 212, Fig. 162) are sufficient to indicate the peculiarities of this larva.

Many other marine annelids pass through a trochophore stage during their life-history; those that do not are supposed to have lost this step during the course of evolution.

Since a trochophore also appears in the development of animals belonging to other phyla, for example, MOLLUSCA and BRYOZOA, and resembles very closely certain ROTIFERA, the conclusion has been reached by some embryologists that these groups of animals are all descended from a common hypothetical ancestor, the trochozoon. Strong arguments have been advanced both for and against this theory.

CHAPTER XII

PHYLUM MOLLUSCA [1]

THE Phylum MOLLUSCA (Lat. *mollis*, soft) includes the snails, slugs, clams, oysters, octopods, and nautili. They are primitively bilaterally symmetrical, but unsegmented, and many of them possess a shell of calcium carbonate. Mussels (Fig. 173), clams, snails (Fig. 180), and squids (Fig. 191) do not appear at first sight to have much in common, but a closer examination reveals several structures possessed by all. One of these is an organ called the *foot*, which in the snail (Fig. 172, I) is usually used for creeping over surfaces, in the clam (II) generally for plowing through the mud, and in the squid (III) for seizing prey. In each there is a space called the *mantle cavity* (Fig. 172) between the

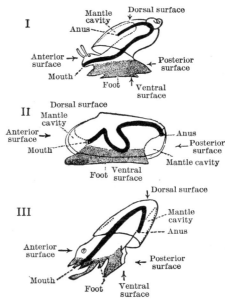

FIG. 172. — Diagrams of three types of mollusks, — I, a Prosobranch Gastropod, II, a Lamellibranch, and III, a Cephalopod, to show the form of the foot and its regions and the relations of the visceral hump to the antero-posterior and dorso-ventral axes. (From Shipley and MacBride, after Lankester.)

---

[1] The phylum MOLLUSCA includes a vast number of species, some of which are of great economic importance. The structure of the mollusks is more complex than that of any of the types considered heretofore, nevertheless the various forms within this phylum can be reduced to a single plan. The fresh-water mussel has been selected as the principal type since it is a widespread inhabitant of ponds and streams. Equally common are the snails, but these mollusks are more difficult to study. Many species of mollusks occur only in salt water. The larvæ of certain mollusks are interesting because of the trochophore stage through which they pass ; this stage links them to the annelids and other types. Most of Chapter XII is intended for reference purposes only.

main body and an enclosing envelope, the *mantle*. The *anus* opens into the mantle cavity.

The mollusks are divided into five classes according to their symmetry and the characters of the foot, shell, mantle, gills, and nervous system.

Definition. — Phylum MOLLUSCA. CLAMS, SNAILS, SQUIDS, OCTOPI. Triploblastic, bilaterally symmetrical animals; anus and cœlom present; no segmentation; shell usually present; the characteristic organ is a ventral muscular foot.

CLASS I. AMPHINEURA (Gr. *amphi*, on both sides; *neuron*, a nerve), the chitons (Fig. 179), with bilateral symmetry, often a shell of eight transverse calcareous plates, and many pairs of gill filaments;

CLASS II. GASTROPODA (Gr. *gaster*, the belly; *pous*, a foot), the snails (Fig. 180), slugs (Fig. 184), whelks, etc., with asymmetry and usually a spirally coiled shell;

CLASS III. SCAPHOPODA (Gr. *skaphe*, a boot; *pous*, a foot), the elephants'-tusk shells (Fig. 188), with tubular shell and mantle;

CLASS IV. PELECYPODA (Gr. *pelekos*, hatchet; *pous*, a foot), the clams, mussels (Fig. 174), oysters, and scallops, usually with bilateral symmetry, a shell of two valves, and a mantle of two lobes;

CLASS V. CEPHALOPODA (Gr. *kephale*, head; *pous*, a foot), the squids (Fig. 191), cuttlefishes, octopods (Fig. 196), and nautili (Fig. 194), with bilateral symmetry, a foot divided into arms provided with suckers, and a well-developed nervous system concentrated in the head.

1. THE PEARLY FRESH-WATER MUSSEL — ANODONTA AND THE UNIONES

The fresh-water mussel is a mollusk belonging, together with the oyster, the long-neck clam, the scallop, and other similar animals, to the class PELECYPODA. Mussels inhabit the lakes and streams of this country wherever the water contains carbonate of lime and does not entirely evaporate during any part of the year. *Anodonta* and the *Uniones* are similar except for minor details.

External Features. — Mussels usually lie almost entirely buried in the muddy or sandy bottom of lakes or streams. They burrow and move from place to place by means of the *foot* (Fig. 173, *9*), which can be extended from the anterior end of the shell. Water loaded with oxygen and food material is drawn in through a slit-like opening at the posterior end, called the *ventral siphon* (*8*), and excretory substances and fæces along with deoxygenated water are carried out through a smaller *dorsal siphon* (*7*).

THE SHELL. — The shell consists of two parts, called *valves* (Fig. 173), which are fastened together at the dorsal surface by an elastic ligamentous hinge. In *Unio* the valves articulate with each other by means of projections called teeth, but these are almost entirely atrophied in *Anodonta*. A number of concentric ridges appear on the outside of each valve; these are called *lines of growth* (Fig. 173, *10*), and, as the name implies, represent the intervals of rest between successive periods of growth. The small area situated dorsally toward the anterior end is called the *umbo* (*6*); this is the part of the

FIG. 173. — External features of a clam, *Anodonta mutabilis. 1, 2*, attachment of anterior muscles; *3, 4*, attachment of posterior muscles; *5*, line of growth; *6*, umbo; *7*, dorsal siphon; *8*, ventral siphon; *9*, foot; *10*, lines of growth. (From Shipley and MacBride.)

shell with which the animal was provided at the beginning of its adult stage. The umbo is usually eroded by the carbonic acid in the water.

The *structure of the shell* is easily determined. There are three layers: (1) an outer thin, horny layer, the *periostracum*, which is secreted by the edge of the mantle, — it serves to protect the underlying layers from the carbonic acid in the water, and gives the exterior of the shell most of its color; (2) a middle portion of crystals of carbonate of lime, called the *prismatic layer*, which is also secreted by the edge of the mantle; and (3) an inner *nacreous layer* (mother-of-pearl), which is made up of many thin lamellæ secreted by the entire surface of the mantle, and produces in the light an iridescent sheen.

Anatomy and Physiology. — *General Account.* — The valves of
the shell are held together by two large *transverse muscles* which
must be cut in order to gain access to the internal organs. These
muscles are situated one close to either end near the dorsal surface;
they are called *anterior adductors* (Fig. 174; Fig. 175), and *posterior
adductors* (Fig. 175). As the shell grows, they migrate outward
from a position near the umbo, as indicated by the faint lines in
Figure 173. When these muscles are cut, or when the animal
dies, the shell gapes open, the valves being forced apart by the
elasticity of the *ligamentous dorsal hinge*, which is compressed when
the shell is closed.

The two folds of the dorsal wall of the mussel which line the
valves are called the *mantle* or *pallium* (Fig. 175). The mantle

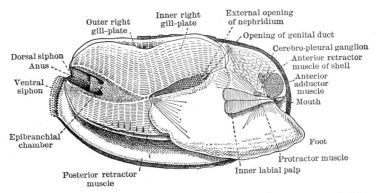

FIG. 174. — Right side of *Anodonta mutabilis* with mantle cut away and right
gills folded back. (From Shipley and MacBride, after Hatschek and Cori.)

flaps are attached to the inner surface of the shell along a line
shown at *5* in Figure 173. The space between the mantle-flaps
containing the two pairs of *gill plates* (Fig. 174), the *foot*, and the
visceral mass, is called the *mantle cavity*.

Digestion. — The *food* of the mussel consists of organic material
carried into the mantle cavity with the water which flows through
the ventral siphon (Fig. 173, *8;* Fig. 174). The *mouth* (Fig. 174;
Fig. 175) lies between two pairs of triangular flaps, called *labial
palps* (Fig. 174; Fig. 175). The *cilia* on these palps drive the
food particles into the mouth. A short *œsophagus* leads from the
mouth to the *stomach* (Fig. 175). On either side of the stomach
is a lobe of a glandular mass called the *digestive gland* or *liver;*

a digestive fluid is secreted by the liver and is carried into the stomach by ducts, one for each lobe.

The food is mostly digested and partly absorbed in the stomach; it then passes into the *intestine* (Fig. 175), by whose walls it is chiefly absorbed. The intestine coils about in the basal portion of the foot, then passes through the *pericardium*, runs over the posterior adductor muscle, and ends in an *anal papilla*. The fæces pass out of the anus and are carried away by the current of water flowing through the dorsal siphon (Fig. 173, 7).

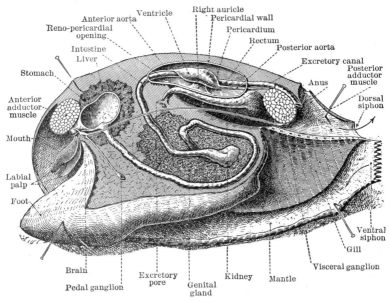

FIG. 175. — Internal organs of a mussel. (From Jammes.)

Circulation. — The circulatory system comprises a heart, blood-vessels, and spaces called sinuses. The *heart* (Fig. 175) lies in the *pericardium*. It consists of a *ventricle*, which surrounds part of the intestine, and a pair of *auricles*. The ventricle by its contractions drives the blood forward through the *anterior aorta* and backward through the *posterior aorta*. Part of the blood passes into the mantle, where it is oxygenated, and then returns directly to the heart. The rest of the blood circulates through numerous spaces in the body and is finally collected by a vessel called the *vena cava*, which lies just beneath the pericardium.

From here the blood passes into the kidneys, then into the *gills*, and finally through the auricles and into the ventricle. Nutriment and oxygen are carried by the blood to all parts of the body, and carbon dioxide and other waste products of metabolism are transported to the gills and kidneys.

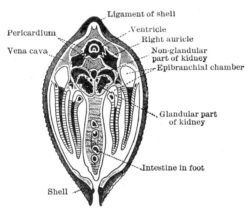

Fig. 176. — Diagrammatic section through *Anodonta* near posterior edge of foot. (From Shipley and MacBride, after Howes.)

Respiration. — The respiratory organs of the mussel are the *gills* or *branchiæ* or *ctenidia*. A pair of these hang down into the mantle cavity on either side of the foot (Fig. 176).

Each *gill* is made up of two plates or lamellæ (Fig. 177) which lie side by side and are united at the edges except dorsally (Fig. 176). The cavity between the lamellæ is divided into vertical *water tubes* by partitions called *interlamellar junctions* (Fig. 177). Each lamella consists of a large number of *gill filaments*, each supported by two *chitinous rods* (black spots in Fig. 177), and covered with *cilia*. Openings, called *ostia*, lie between the gill filaments, and blood-vessels are present in the interlamellar junctions and filaments.

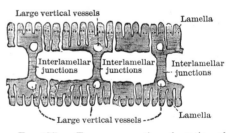

Fig. 177. — Transverse section of portion of an outer gill-plate of *Anodonta*. (From the Cambridge Natural History, after Peck.)

Water is drawn through the ostia into the water-tubes by the cilia which cover the gill filaments; it flows dorsally into the *epibranchial chamber* (Fig. 176); from here it enters the dorsal mantle cavity and passes out through the dorsal siphon (Fig. 175). The blood which circulates through the gills discharges carbon dioxide into the water and takes oxygen from it. Respiration also takes place through the surface of the mantle.

Excretion. — The organs of excretion are two U-shaped *kidneys* or *nephridia* lying just beneath the pericardium, one on either side of the vena cava (Fig. 175). Each kidney consists of a ventral glandular portion into which the pericardium opens by a ciliated slit and a dorsal thin-walled bladder which opens to the exterior through the *renal aperture*. Some excretory matter is probably driven into the kidney from the pericardium by cilia, and other excretory matter is taken from the blood by the glandular portion. These waste products of metabolism are carried out of the body through the dorsal siphon.

Nervous System. — There are only a few ganglia in the body of the mussel. On each side of the œsophagus is a so-called *cerebropleural ganglion* (Fig. 175), connected with its fellow by a nerve called the *cerebral commissure* which passes above the œsophagus. From each cerebropleural ganglion a nerve-cord passes ventrally, ending in a *pedal ganglion* in the foot. The two pedal ganglia are closely joined together. Each cerebropleural ganglion also gives off a *cerebrovisceral connective* which may be enclosed by the kidneys and leads to a *visceral ganglion*.

Sensory Organs. — Fresh-water mussels are not well provided with sensory organs. A small vesicle, the *statocyst*, containing a calcareous concretion, the *statolith*, lies a short way behind the pedal ganglia. It is an organ of equilibrium. A thick patch of yellow epithelial cells covers each visceral ganglion and is known as an *osphradium*. The functions of the osphradia are not certain. They probably test the water which enters the mantle cavity. The edges of the mantle are provided with *sensory cells;* these are especially abundant on the ventral siphon (Fig. 175), and are probably sensitive to contact and light.

Reproduction. — Mussels are usually either male or female; a few are hermaphroditic. The *reproductive organs* are situated in the foot (Fig. 175). They are paired bunches of tubes and open just in front of the renal aperture on each side. The *spermatozoa* are carried out through the dorsal siphon of the male and in through the ventral siphon of the female. The eggs pass out of the genital aperture and come to lie in various parts of the gills according to the species. The spermatozoa enter the gill of the female with the water and fertilize the eggs. That portion of the gill in which the eggs develop is termed the *marsupium*.

The *eggs* undergo complete but unequal segmentation. Blastula and gastrula stages are passed through, and then a peculiar larva known as a *glochidium* is produced (Fig. 178). The glochidium has a shell consisting of two valves which are hooked in some species; these may be closed by a muscle when a proper stimulus is applied. A long, sticky thread called the *byssus* extends out from the center of the larva, and bunches of *setæ* are also present.

In *Anodonta* the eggs are fertilized usually in August, and the glochidia which develop from them remain in the gills of the mother all winter. In the following spring they are discharged,

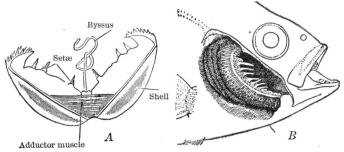

FIG. 178. — *A*, a young mussel or glochidium. (After Balfour.) *B*, the gills of a fish in which are embedded many young mussels forming " blackheads." (After Lefevre and Curtis.)

and, if they chance to come in contact with the external parts of a fish, this *contact stimulus* causes them to seize hold of it by closing the valves of their shell. The glochidium probably chemically stimulates the skin of the fish to grow around it, forming the well-known " worms " or " blackheads." While thus embedded the glochidium receives nourishment from the fish and undergoes a stage of development (metamorphosis), during which the foot, muscles, and other parts of the adult are formed. After a *parasitic life* within the tissues of the fish of from three to twelve weeks the young mussel is liberated and takes up a free existence.

In *Unio* the eggs are fertilized during the late spring and summer, and the glochidia are discharged before the middle of September. The glochidium of *Unio* is smaller than that of *Anodonta* and is usually hookless. It does not as a rule become permanently attached to the fins, operculum, or mouth as in *Anodonta*, but usually lodges on the gill filaments of the fish.

One result of the parasitic habit of larval mussels is the *dispersal of the species* through the migrations of the fish. Only in this way can we account for the rapid colonization of certain streams by mussels, since the adult plows its way through the muddy bottom very slowly.

Economic Importance. — Fresh-water mussels are of considerable importance in certain parts of this country, especially in Iowa and Illinois, because their shells are used extensively in the manufacture of pearl buttons. Often, also, pearls of considerable value are found in fresh-water bivalves. The decrease in the number of mussels in the Mississippi River and its tributaries has led the United States Bureau of Fisheries to investigate the possibility of artificially propagating them so as to restock the depleted waters. It seems probable that this can be done successfully. Mussels are instrumental in purifying the water in which they live by using as food the organic particles contained in it.

2. CLASS I. AMPHINEURA

The Amphineura are marine mollusks of wide distribution. Two rather distinct groups of animals belong to this class.

Order 1. Polyplacophora. — These are the *chitons* (Fig. 179, A, B). They are characterized by a broad, flat foot (B, *f*), a shell of eight transverse calcareous pieces (A), and a row of gills (B, *g*) between the mantle (*pa*) and the foot (*f*). The mouth (*m*)

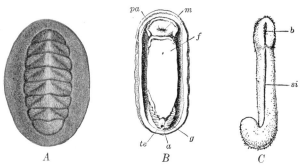

FIG. 179. — CHITONES. **A**, upper surface of *Onithochiton*. **B**, under surface of *Lepidopleurus*. *a*, anus; *f*, foot; *g*, gills; *m*, mouth; *pa*, mantle; *te*, pallial tentacles. **C**, ventral view of *Paramenia*. *b*, mouth; *si*, foot groove. (A from Tryon; B and C, from Lankester's Treatise.)

is at one end and the anus (*a*) at the other. Examples: *Amicula, Trachydermon, Chiton.*

The chitons are slow-moving mollusks which live near the seashore in shallow water. They are usually herbivorous.

Order 2. Aplacophora. — These are wormlike mollusks (Fig. 179, C) without a shell, but with many calcified spicules over the surface. The mantle surrounds the entire body, and the foot lies in a groove (*si*). Example: *Chætoderma.*

The Aplacophora live on coral polyps and hydroids. They are most abundant at a depth of about fifty fathoms.

3. Class II. Gastropoda

The snails, slugs, limpets, and other similar mollusks belonging to this class possess a foot, a mantle, and a mantle cavity comparable with those of the mussel (Fig. 172, I–II), but they differ considerably in the form and structure of their bodies as well as in their life-histories. Three peculiarities are characteristic of most Gastropoda: (1) asymmetry, (2) a well-developed head, and (3) frequently a spirally coiled shell formed of one piece.

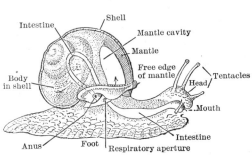

Fig. 180. — Diagram showing the structure of a snail. (After Schmeil.)

a. *A Land-snail*

External Features. — The body of a snail consists of a *head* (Fig. 180), *neck, foot,* and *visceral hump.* The *head* bears two pairs of *tentacles:* (1) a short anterior pair containing the olfactory nerves, and (2) a longer pair containing the *eyes.* The *mouth* is in front and below the tentacles, and just beneath the mouth is the opening of the pedal *mucous gland.* The *foot* is broad and flat; it is a muscular organ of locomotion with a mucous-secreting integument. Both the foot and head may be withdrawn into the *shell.*

The *spiral shell* encloses the visceral hump, consisting of parts of the digestive, circulatory, respiratory, excretory, and reproductive systems. The *mantle* lines the shell, and is thin except where it joins the foot; here it forms a thick collar which secretes most of the shell. An opening beneath this collar is the *respiratory aperture* leading into the mantle cavity. The *anus* opens just back of this aperture. The *genital pore* is on the side of the head.

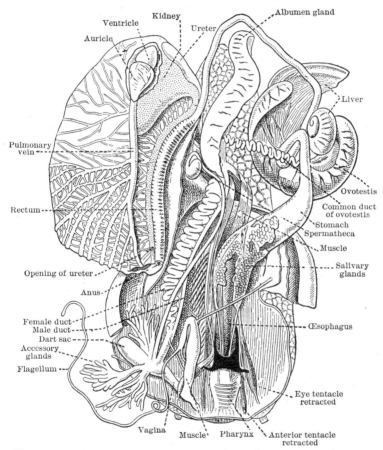

Fig. 181. — Diagram showing the anatomy of a snail, *Helix pomatia*. (From Shipley and MacBride, after Hatschek and Cori.)

Anatomy and Physiology. — *Digestion.* — The general anatomy of a snail is shown in Figure 181. The *digestive organs* include *a buccal mass, œsophagus, salivary glands, crop, stomach, digestive glands, intestine, rectum,* and *anus.*

The *food* is chiefly, if not entirely, vegetation, such as lettuce. This is scraped up by a horny jaw or *mandible* and devoured after being rasped into five particles by a band of teeth termed the *radula* (Fig. 182). The radula and the cartilages and muscles that move it backward and forward constitute the buccal mass. The *salivary glands* (Fig. 181) which lie one on either side of the crop pour their secretion by means of the *salivary ducts* into the buccal cavity, where it is mixed with the food.

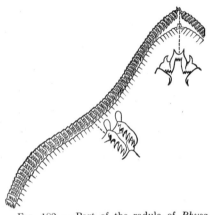

The *œsophagus* leads to the *crop*, and from here the food enters the *stomach*. The two *digestive glands* occupy a large part of the visceral hump. They secrete a diastatic ferment which converts starchy matters into glucose, and are comparable to the pancreas in vertebrate animals. This secretion enters the stomach

FIG. 182. — Part of the radula of *Physa fontinalis*, with central tooth and two marginal teeth highly magnified. (From the Cambridge Natural History.)

and aids in digestion. Absorption takes place chiefly in the *intestine*, and the fæces pass out through the *anus* (Fig. 180, *A*; Fig. 181).

Circulation and Respiration. — The *blood* of the snail consists of a colorless plasma containing corpuscles, and serves to transport nutriment, oxygen, and waste products from one part of the body to another. The heart lies in the *pericardial cavity* (Fig. 181). The muscular *ventricle* forces the blood through the blood-vessels by rhythmical pulsations. One large *aorta* arises at the apex of the ventricle; this gives rise at once to a *posterior branch*, which supplies chiefly the digestive gland, stomach, and ovotestis, and an *anterior branch* which carries blood to the head and foot. The blood passes from the arterial capillaries into *venous capillaries* and flows through these into *sinuses*. *Veins* lead from these sinuses to the walls of the mantle cavity, where the blood, after taking in oxygen and giving off carbon dioxide, enters the *pulmonary vein* and is carried to the single *auricle* and finally into the ventricle again.

Excretion. — The glandular *kidney* (Fig. 181) lies near the heart. Its duct, the *ureter* or *renal duct*, runs along beside the rectum and opens near the anus.

Nervous System. — Most of the nervous tissue of the snail is concentrated just back of the buccal mass and forms a ring about the œsophagus (Fig. 181, in black; Fig. 183). There are five sets of ganglia and four ganglionic swellings. The *supra-œsophageal* or *cerebral ganglia* are paired and lie above the œsophagus. Nerves extend anteriorly from them, ending in the two *buccal ganglia*, the two *eyes*, the two *ocular ganglionic swellings*, the two *olfactory ganglionic swellings,* and the mouth. Nerves called commissures connect the supra-œsophageal ganglia with the ganglia which lie beneath the œsophagus. Here are four pairs of ganglia lying close together — the *pedal, pleural, parietal*, and *visceral.* Nerves pass from them to the visceral hump and the basal parts of the body.

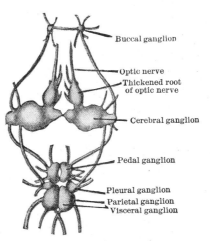

Buccal ganglion

Optic nerve
Thickened root of optic nerve

Cerebral ganglion

Pedal ganglion

Pleural ganglion
Parietal ganglion
Visceral ganglion

FIG. 183. — Central portion of the nervous system of *Helix pomatia*. (From Lang.)

Sense-organs. — Both the foot and the tentacles are sensitive to contact, and are liberally supplied with nerves. Each long tentacle (Fig. 180) bears an *eye.* These eyes are probably not organs of sight, but only sensitive to light of certain intensities. Many snails feed mostly at night, and their eyes may be adapted to dim light.

Snails possess a sense of *smell*, since some of them are able to locate food, which is hidden from sight, at a distance of eighteen inches. We are not certain where the sense of smell is located, but investigators are inclined to believe that the small tentacles (Fig. 180) are the *olfactory organs.* A sense of *taste* is doubtful.

There are two organs of equilibrium (*statocysts*), one on either side of the supra-œsophageal ganglia. They are minute vesicles containing a fluid in which are suspended small calcareous bodies (*statoliths*). Nerves connect them with the supra-œsophageal ganglia.

Locomotion. — The snail moves from place to place with a gliding motion. The slime gland which opens just beneath the mouth deposits a film of slime, and on this the animal moves by means of wave-like contractions of the longitudinal muscular fibers of the foot. *Snails* have been observed to travel two inches per minute (Baker).

Reproduction. — Some gastropods are diœcious; others are monœcious. *Helix* is *hermaphroditic*, but the union of two animals is necessary for the fertilization of the eggs, since the spermatozoa of an individual do not unite with the eggs of the same animal. The *spermatozoa* arise in the *ovotestis* (Fig. 181); they pass through the coiled *hermaphroditic duct* and into the *sperm duct;* they then enter the *vas deferens* and are transferred to the *vagina* of another animal by means of a cylindrical *penis* which is protruded from the *genital pore.*

The *eggs* also arise in the *ovotestis* and are carried through the *hermaphroditic duct;* they receive material from the *albumen gland* and then pass into the *uterine canal;* they move from here down the *oviduct* into the *vagina*, where they are *fertilized* by spermatozoa which were transferred to the *seminal receptacle* by another snail. In almost all other land pulmonates impregnation is mutual, each animal acting during copulation as both male and female.

b. *Gastropoda in General*

Classification. — There is considerable diversity among gastropods both in form and structure. The chief characteristics used in dividing them into groups are the structure of the nervous system, the method of respiration and structure of the respiratory organs, and the condition of the sexual organs. There are two subclasses, each containing two orders.

SUBCLASS I. STREPTONEURA. — Diœcious GASTROPODA with visceral connectives usually twisted into a figure 8; the heart is usually posterior to the gills.

Order 1. Aspidobranchia. STREPTONEURA with usually two gills, two auricles, and two nephridia. Examples: *Acmæa* (limpet), *Haliotis* (ear-shell), *Margarita*.

Order 2. Pectinibranchia. STREPTONEURA with one kidney, one auricle, and one gill. Examples: *Littorina*, *Sycotypus* (Fig. 186, A), *Crepidula* (Fig. 186, B), *Urosalpinx*.

SUBCLASS II. EUTHYNEURA. Monœcious GASTROPODA with visceral connectives not twisted (Fig. 183); the gill when present is posterior to the heart.

Order 1. Opisthobranchia. Marine EUTHYNEURA usually with a gill and mantle. Examples: *Bulla, Clione, Doris.*

Order 2. Pulmonata. Land and fresh-water EUTHYNEURA which breathe air; gill usually aborted and mantle cavity converted into a lung. Examples: *Helix, Polygyra* (Fig. 185, C), *Lymnæa* (Fig. 185, G), *Limax* (Fig. 184), *Physa* (Fig. 185, D), *Planorbis* (Fig. 185, B).

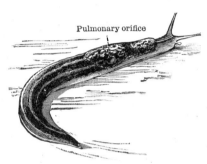

FIG. 184. — *Limax maximus.* (From the Cambridge Natural History.)

Air-breathing Gastropods. — The air-breathing gastropods belong chiefly to the order PULMONATA, and inhabit fresh water or live on land. The slugs also live on land, but are without a well-developed shell. *Limax maximus* (Fig. 184) is a large slug. It was introduced from Europe and is now more or less of a pest in greenhouses because of its fondness for green leaves. The shell of *Limax* is a thin plate embedded in the mantle.

Three common fresh-water snails with shells are *Physa, Lymnæa,*

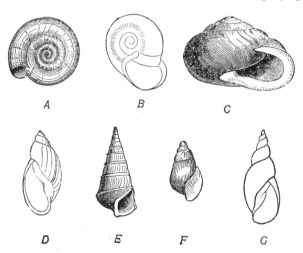

FIG. 185. — The shells of certain GASTROPODA. **A,** *Helicodiscus parallelus.* **B,** *Planorbis trivolvis.* **C,** *Polygyra albolabris.* **D,** *Physa gyrina.* **E,** *Pleurocera elevatum.* **F,** *Goniobasis liviscens.* **G,** *Lymnæa palustris.* (From various authors.)

and *Planorbis*. *Physa* (Fig. 185, D) lives in ponds and brooks and feeds on vegetable matter. It is a *sinistral* snail, since if the shell is held so that the opening faces the observer and the

spire points upward, the aperture will be on the left. *Lymmæa* (Fig. 185, G) is the common pond-snail. Its shell is coiled in an opposite direction from that of *Physa* and is called *dextral*. Both *Physa* and *Lymnæa* usually come to the surface to breathe. In dry weather many snails have the power of secreting a *mucous epiphragm* over the mouth of the shell so as to prevent the evaporation of moisture from their bodies.

A   B

FIG. 186. — Two marine GASTROPODS. **A,** *Sycotypus caniculatus*. **B,** *Crepidula*. (A, from Davenport; B, from Weysse.)

Planorbis (Fig. 185, B) differs from *Physa* and *Lymnæa* in having a shell coiled in one plane like a watchspring.

Marine Gastropods. — The majority of the marine gastropods have shells, but many of them do not; some of the latter are called *nudibranchs*. *Littorina littorea*, the periwinkle, is a very common shelled snail on the North Atlantic seashore. It was introduced from Europe, where in many localities it is used as an article of food by the natives. In *Crepidula* (Fig. 186, B) the spiral has almost disappeared, and the shell is boatlike. *Acmæa*, the limpet, is a sea-snail modified so as to cling closely to rocks. Its shell is conical. In Europe limpets are used as food. *Sycotypus* (Fig. 186, A) is a very large marine gastropod that lives in shallow water and feeds on other mollusks. *Urosalpinx*, the oyster drill, and several other marine snails, make a practice of boring through the thick

FIG. 187. — A NUDIBRANCH, *Eolis*. (From Davenport.)

shells of oysters and other bivalves with their radulas and taking out the soft body of the victims through the hole.

The term *nudibranch* is applied to certain shell-less marine gastropods. The nudibranchs resemble the terrestrial slugs; they do not breathe air, however, but take oxygen from the water by means of naked gills, or through the mantle. *Eolis* (Fig. 187) and *Dendronotus* are common genera.

The shelled marine GASTROPODA usually breathe by means of gills. In *Sycotypus*, for example, there is a trough-like extension of the collar, the *siphon*, which leads a current of water into the mantle cavity where the gill is situated. The direction of this current of water prevents contamination by the fæces and excretory products.

4. CLASS III. SCAPHOPODA

This class contains only a few aberrant marine mollusks called *tooth shells*. The mantle forms a tube around the body and secretes a crescent-shaped tubular calcareous shell larger at one end than at the other. Both ends of the shell are open. The *foot* (Fig. 188), which is used for boring in the sand, can be protruded from the larger anterior aperture. The *head* is rudimentary, but a radula is present. Eyes and a heart are absent. The sexes are separate. Example: *Dentalium* (Fig. 188).

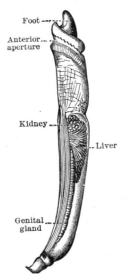

FIG. 188. — A SCAPHO-POD, *Dentalium*. (After Lacaze-Duthiers.)

5. CLASS IV. PELECYPODA

The PELECYPODA or LAMELLIBRANCHIATA, as they are often called, are the mussels, clams, oysters, and other bivalves. They are simple in structure and therefore favorite mollusks for laboratory dissection (pp. 222 to 229), but are probably less primitive than the GASTROPODA. They do not possess a head or radula. The mantle is bilobed and secretes a bivalve shell. The gills are usually lamellate.

The PELECYPODA are all aquatic and mostly marine. They feed on minute organisms. Most of them burrow into the sand or mud; a few bore cavities for themselves in calcareous rocks; and still others are sessile, like the oyster. Some PELECYPODA live commensally or parasitically on or in the bodies of ascidians, sponges, and echinoderms.

Classification. — The PELECYPODA are divided into four orders according to the structure of the gills.

Order 1. Protobranchia (Fig. 189, A). PELECYPODA with plate-like gill filaments (*e, i*) which are not reflected; mantle cavity not divided into two parts. Examples: *Nucula, Leda, Yoldia*.

Order 2. Filibranchia (Fig. 189, B). PELECYPODA with gill filaments reflected and united by ciliary junctions. Examples: *Arca, Mytilus, Modiola, Pecten*.

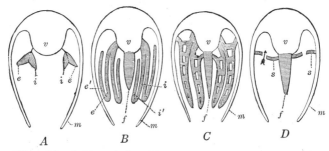

FIG. 189. — Morphology of the gills of PELECYPODA, seen diagrammatically in section. **A**, PROTOBRANCHIA. **B**, FILIBRANCHIA. **C**, EULAMELLIBRANCHIA. **D**, SEPTIBRANCHIA. *e, e*, external row of filaments; *i, i*, internal row of filaments; *e'*, external row or plate folded back; *i'*, internal row folded back; *f*, foot; *m*, mantle; *s*, septum; *v*, visceral mass. (From the Cambridge Natural History, after Lang.)

Order 3. Eulamellibranchia (Fig. 189, C). PELECYPODA with gill filaments forming plates or lamellæ. Examples: *Ostrea, Cyclas, Unio, Anodonta, Mactra, Venus, Mya, Teredo* (Fig. 190), *Solen*.

Order 4. Septibranchia (Fig. 189, D). PELECYPODA with gills transformed into a muscular septum (*s*) and not functioning as respiratory organs. Examples: *Silenia, Cuspidaria*.

Economic Importance. — Several of the PELECYPODA are of considerable importance as food for man. The most valuable are the oyster and the long-neck or soft-shell clam. Razor-shells, hen-clams, mussels, scallops, and a number of other bivalves are also eaten.

The oyster, *Ostrea virginiana*, inhabits the shallow water along the Atlantic coast from Massachusetts to Florida. It is attached to rocks and other objects by its left valve, and does not move about in the adult stage. The Chesapeake Bay oyster beds are large and important. The value of the oyster industry along the Atlantic seaboard is from twenty to thirty million dollars annually. Oysters lay an enormous number of eggs. Professor Brooks placed the number for a single female in one season at nine million or more. Those eggs which are fertilized and not eaten by fishes and other animals develop into free-swimming larvæ which soon become fixed to some object and grow into the adults. The larvæ are preyed upon by many animals, especially crabs (Chap. XIII). Those that reach the adult stage may be attacked by starfishes (p. 182), boring snails (p. 236), sponges (p. 101), and parasites.

The value of the pearl-button industry has already been mentioned (p. 229). Pearl-fishing should also be noted. Pearls are produced by secretions of the mantle around a foreign substance, such as a grain of sand or a parasitic worm. The PELECYPODA of the Persian Gulf yield the finest pearls.

One bivalve, the shipworm, *Teredo navalis* (Fig. 190), is injurious to ships and piles. It burrows into the wood with its shell, sometimes to a depth of two feet.

6. CLASS V. CEPHALOPODA

The Cephalopoda are the squids, octopods, and nautili. They are constructed on the same fundamental plan as other mollusks (Fig. 172, III), but are very different in form and habits.

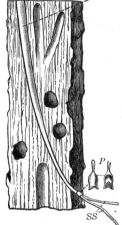

a. *The Common Squid — Loligo*

Loligo pealii (Fig. 191) is one of the common squids found along the eastern coast of North America from Maine to

FIG. 190. — A ship "worm," *Teredo navalis*, in a piece of timber. *P*, pallets; *SS*, siphons; *T*, tube; *V*, valves of shell. (From the Cambridge Natural History, after Möbius.)

South Carolina. It probably lives in deep water during the
winter, but about May 1 it enters shallow water in large
schools to lay its eggs.   Squids are of some economic importance,
since they are used as food by Chinese and Italians, and as bait
for line and trawl fishing.   They feed on small fish, Crustacea,
and other squids, and in turn furnish food for cod and other
large fish.

Anatomy and Physiology. — The body of *Loligo* is spindle-
shaped.   When swimming through the water the morphological
ventral surface is usually anterior (Fig. 191); the dorsal surface
is posterior; the anterior surface is
dorsal; and the posterior surface is
ventral.   The *skin* may change
color rapidly; sometimes it is bluish
white, at others, mottled red or
brown.

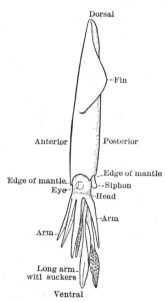

FIG. 191. —The squid, *Loligo pealii,*
side view.   (From Williams.)

The *foot* consists of *ten lobes* and
a *funnel.*   Eight of the lobes are
arms and two are long *tentacles.*
The inner surfaces of both arms
and tentacles are provided with
suckers.   The arms are pressed together and used for steering when
the squid swims, but when capturing
prey the tentacles are extended,
seize the victim with their suckers,
and draw it back to the arms, which
hold it firmly to the mouth.   The
funnel is a muscular tube extending
out beyond the edge of the *mantle
collar* beneath the *head.*   Water is
expelled from the *mantle cavity* (Fig. 192) through it.   The funnel
is the principle steering organ; if it is directed forward, the jet
of water passed through it propels the animal backward; if
directed backward, the animal is propelled forward.

A thick muscular *mantle* encloses the visceral mass and mantle
cavity.   It terminates ventrally in a *collar* (Fig. 191) which articulates with the visceral mass and funnel by three pairs of inter-
locking surfaces.   Water is drawn into the mantle cavity at the
edge of the collar by the expansion of the mantle and forced out

through the funnel by the contraction of the mantle. On each side of the animal is a triangular finlike projection of the mantle (Fig. 191); these *fins* may propel the squid slowly forward or backward by their undulatory movements, or may change the direction of the squid's progress by strong upward or downward strokes.

The *shell* or *pen* of *Loligo* (Fig. 192) is a feather-shaped plate concealed beneath the skin of the back (anterior surface).

The *true head* is the short region between the arms and the mantle collar; it contains two large *eyes*.

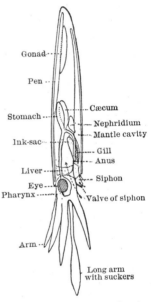

The *digestive system* includes a *pharynx* or buccal mass (Fig. 192), *œsophagus, salivary glands, stomach, cæcum, intestine, rectum, inksac, liver,* and *pancreas.* There are two powerful chitinous *jaws* in the pharynx; they resemble a parrot's beak inverted, and are moved by strong muscles. A *radula* is also present. Two *salivary glands* lie on the dorsal surface of the pharynx, and one is embedded in the ventral end of the *liver;* they all pour their secretions into the mouth. The œsophagus leads from the pharynx through the liver and into the stomach. Closely connected with the muscular stomach is the large, thin-walled cæcum. Food is probably partially digested in the stomach by fluids brought in from

Fig. 192. — Diagram showing the structure of a squid, *Loligo pealii.* (From Williams.)

the pancreas and liver; it then passes into the cæcum, where digestion is completed and absorption takes place. Bones and other indigestible material are forced from the stomach into the intestine and out through the *anus.*

The *blood* of the squid is contained in a double, closed vascular system. Arterial blood is forced by a muscular *systemic heart* to all parts of the body by three *aortæ:* (1) anterior, (2) posterior, and (3) genital. It passes from *arterial capillaries* into *venous capillaries,* and thence into the large *veins.* From these it enters the right and left *branchial hearts,* and is then forced into the *gills* through the *branchial arteries*. In the gills the blood is aërated, and is finally carried by the *branchial veins* back to the systemic heart.

There are two *gills* in the squid (Fig. 192). The water which enters the mantle cavity flows over them, supplying oxygen to the blood and carrying away carbon dioxide.

The two *nephridia* or *kidneys* (Fig. 192) are white triangular bodies extending forward from the region of the branchial hearts and opening on either side of the intestine at the ends of small papillæ.

The *nervous system* consists of a number of ganglia mostly in the head. The principal ones are the supra-œsophageal, infra-œsophageal, suprabuccal, infrabuccal, stellate, and optic ganglia.

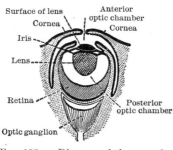

Fig. 193. — Diagram of the eye of a squid, *Loligo*. (After Grenacher.)

The *sensory organs* are two very highly developed *eyes*, two *statocysts*, and probably an *olfactory organ*. The *statocysts* are two vesicles lying side by side in the head; each contains a concretion, the *statolith*, and is probably an organ of equilibrium. The *eyes* (Fig. 192; Fig. 193) are large and somewhat similar superficially to those of vertebrates (compare Fig. 193 with Fig. 351). Just behind the eye is a fold which projects backward under the collar, and is probably olfactory.

Squids are either male or female. The *reproductive organs* (Fig. 192) of the *male* are the *testis*, a *vas deferens*, a *spermatophoric sac*, which contains sperms bound together into bundles called *spermatophores*, and a copulatory organ, the *penis*. The *female organs* are an *ovary*, *oviduct*, *oviducal gland*, and *nidamental gland*.

b. *Cephalopoda in General*

Classification. — The CEPHALOPODA may be divided into two orders according to the number of gills, kidneys, and auricles, and the character of the shell.

Order 1. Tetrabranchia. CEPHALOPODA with four gills, four kidneys, and four auricles; with a large, external shell; no suckers; and very short arms. Example: *Nautilus* (Fig. 194).

Order 2. Dibranchia. CEPHALOPODA with two gills, two kidneys, and two auricles; with shell enveloped by the mantle; and long arms provided with suckers.

Suborder 1. Decapoda. DIBRANCHIA with ten arms — two long and eight short. Examples: *Loligo* (Fig. 191), *Ommastrephes, Russia.*

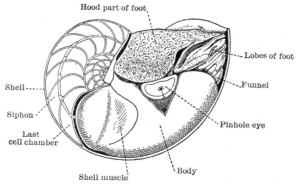

FIG. 194. — The chambered nautilus, *Nautilus.* (From Shipley and MacBride, after Kerr.)

Suborder 2. Octopoda. DIBRANCHIA with eight arms of equal length. Examples: *Octopus* (Fig. 196), *Alloposus.*

Nautili. — There are only a few living species belonging to the genus *Nautilus* in the order TETRABRANCHIA. The chambered or pearly nautilus, *Nautilus pompilius* (Fig. 194), lives on the bottom of the sea near certain islands of the South Pacific. The shell is spirally coiled in one plane and is composed of compartments of different sizes, which were occupied by the animal in successive stages in its growth. The compartments are filled with gas and are connected by a calcareous tube in which is a cylindrical growth of the animal called the *siphuncle* (Fig. 194). The gas in the compartments counterbalances the weight of the shell.

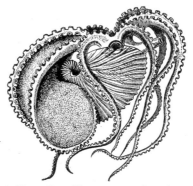

FIG. 195. — The paper nautilus, *Argonauta argo* (female), swimming. (From Sedgwick.)

Octopods. — The OCTOPODA differ from the decapods, like *Loligo*, in the absence of the two long tentacular arms (Fig. 191). The paper nautilus, *Argonauta argo* (Fig. 195), is an octopod, the female of which secretes a delicate, slightly coiled shell. The octopus or devil-fish, *Octopus vulgaris* (Fig. 196), lives in the Mediterranean Sea and West Indies. It may reach a length of over ten feet and a weight of seventy-five pounds. Devil-fishes have been accused of serious attacks on man, but are probably not so bad as generally supposed.

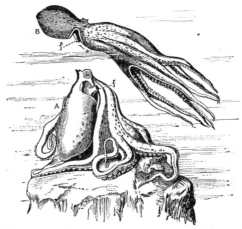

Fig. 196. — The octopus, *Octopus vulgaris.* **A**, at rest ; **B**, in motion. *f*, funnel ; the arrow shows direction of propelling current of water. (From the Cambridge Natural History, after Merculiano.)

7. Mollusca in General

Morphology. — The Mollusca are unsegmented, triploblastic animals with bilateral symmetry (except in most of the Gastropoda and certain Pelecypoda). There is usually a ventral muscular foot, a mantle fold, a radula, and a cœlom. The shell, if present, is usually univalve, bivalve, eight-parted, or pen-shaped.

The *bodies* of mollusks are soft (Lat. *mollis* = soft) and generally covered by a slimy integument. They are therefore fitted for life in the water or in moist places. In most cases the body is supported and protected by a *shell*. As shown in Figure 172, the *foot* is present in all mollusks, but is variously modified; it enables the mussel to plow its way through the sand, the snail to glide along, and the squid to swim through the water and capture its prey. The *mantle* is a fold of the body-wall which secretes the shell. If there are two lobes, a bivalve shell is produced, as in the mussel. If only one lobe is present, a univalve shell is formed, as in snails. The *shape* of the animal does not depend upon the shell so much as upon the mantle which secretes it.

The MOLLUSCA possess a distinct *cœlom* which is usually recognizable in the adult as (1) the pericardial cavity, and (2) the cavities of the reproductive organs.

Metabolism. — Mollusks eat both vegetable and animal *food*. *Jaws* are present in many of them, especially the gastropods and cephalopods. A rasping organ, the *radula* (Fig. 182), exists in the buccal cavity of many mollusks; it consists of rows of chitinous teeth which tear up the food by being drawn across it. In the stomach the food is acted upon by secretions from the liver, which is physiologically a hepato-pancreas, and may also excrete waste products into the alimentary canal.

The cavities which contain the blood represent the *hæmocœl*. The blood is forced through these cavities by the muscular contractions of the *heart*. Oxygen, absorbed food, and excretory substances are transported by it. *Respiration* takes place either in the gills or in the mantle. Most of the fresh-water and land-snails (pulmonate gastropods) take air into the mantle cavity, which thus serves the purpose of a *lung*. The PELECYPODA, CEPHALOPODA, and marine gastropods breathe mainly by means of gills.

Reproduction. — No cases of asexual reproduction have been reported in mollusks. The sexes are usually separate, though the members of one entire subclass of GASTROPODA (EUTHYNEURA) are hermaphroditic. The number of eggs laid by some mollusks is very great; for example, 9,000,000 in the oyster. In all such cases the eggs are subjected to the dangers of the ocean waves and to numerous enemies, and also pass through a metamorphosis after hatching. Other mollusks lay very few eggs, for example, *Lymnæa*, twenty to one hundred; *Helix*, forty to one hundred; and *Paludina*, about fifteen. These are terrestrial or fresh-water species whose eggs produce young in the adult form, or, as in *Paludina;* the eggs hatch within the body of the parent.

The *development* of the eggs of most mollusks includes a *trochophore stage* (Fig. 197, A) which becomes a *veliger larva* (Fig. 197, B), so called because of the presence of a band of cilia, the *velum*, in front of the mouth. The *velum* is an organ of locomotion and is largely responsible for the dispersion of the species, since with its help the larvæ may travel long distances. The primary *germ-layers* (*ectoderm* and *entoderm*) arise either by the *invagination* of a blastula (Fig. 198, B) or by the growing over

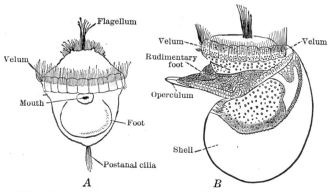

FIG. 197. — Stages in the development of a mollusk, *Patella*. **A**, trochophore stage. **B**, veliger stage, 130 hours old. (After Patten.)

of certain cells (*epibole*, Fig. 198, C). The *mesoderm* originates in two primitive mesoderm cells derived from one of the larger cells (*marcromeres*) of the cleavage stage (Fig. 198, A). Two *mesoderm bands* (Fig. 198, B) are produced by the multiplication of the primitive mesoderm cells.

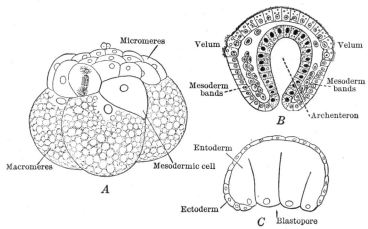

FIG. 198. — Stages in the development of mollusks' eggs. **A**, cleavage of the egg of *Crepidula*, showing the origin of the first mesodermic cell. **B**, frontal section of an embryo of *Paludina*, showing gastrulation by the invagination of a blastula (embolic). **C**, an embryo of *Crepidula*, showing epibolic gastrulation. (A and C, after Conklin; B, after Tönniges.)

The Position of the Mollusks in the Animal Kingdom. — We are not at all certain as to the relations of the Phylum MOLLUSCA to other phyla. Some investigators have sought to derive the mollusks from turbellarian-like ancestors. Considerable importance is attached to the presence of a trochophore in the developmental history of certain mollusks, and many embryologists are inclined to consider this stage an indication of the ancestral condition. According to this view, the mollusks, annelids, and other animals which pass through a trochophore stage in their ontogeny were all derived from a similar ancestral form.

CHAPTER XIII

PHYLUM ARTHROPODA [1]

1. Introduction

THE ARTHROPODA (Gr. *arthron*, a joint; *pous*, a foot) are the crayfishes, water-fleas, barnacles, centipedes, millipedes, scorpions, spiders, mites, and insects. All of these animals have a common plan of construction, as shown in Figure 199. The body

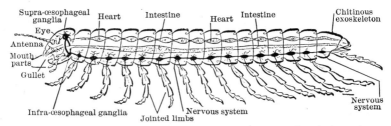

FIG. 199. — Diagrammatic representation of the structure of an Arthropod. From (Schmeil.)

consists of a series of segments some or all of which bear jointed appendages. The body is covered by a chitinous exoskeleton secreted by the cells just beneath it. Within the body is a central

[1] The arthropods are in number of species and in number of individuals the dominant animals on the earth's surface at the present time. Their economic importance is very great, and they offer excellent material for the study of biological principles. The crayfish is a common type ; it presents opportunities for the study of homologies and analogies between appendages, of vision by means of compound eyes, regeneration, autotomy and animal behavior. The section on classification of the CRUSTACEA is for reference purposes only, but this class should not be passed over without a detailed study of the biogenetic law.

The ONYCHOPHORA and MYRIAPODA are comparatively unimportant and do not require detailed study. The insects, especially the honey-bee, are especially favorable for the study of adaptation and behavior. The more generalized features of insects are exhibited by the grasshopper. The general survey of the orders of insects presents a few facts about some of the more interesting species, especially in their relation to man. The section on the ARACHNIDA includes descriptions of certain interesting species but can hardly be studied to advantage by beginning students.

tube, the alimentary canal, with an anterior mouth opening and a posterior anal opening. Dorsal to the alimentary canal is a blood-vessel called the heart, and ventral to the alimentary canal is the nerve-cord. There is a ganglionic mass, the brain, dorsally situated in the head.

The Phylum ARTHROPODA includes a greater number of species than all of the other phyla of the animal kingdom combined. This number is estimated at from one million up, although only about four hundred thousand species have been described.

Economically certain members of this phylum are of great importance. We need only mention the lobster as an article of food, the honey-bee as a producer of honey and beeswax, the silkworm as the source of silk, the gypsy-moth caterpillar as a destroyer of trees, and the mosquito and housefly as carriers of disease germs.

The ARTHROPODA may be grouped for convenience in the following manner: —

Phylum Arthropoda. CRAYFISH, CRABS, CENTIPEDES, INSECTS, SPIDERS, SCORPIONS, TICKS. Triploblastic, bilaterally symmetrical animals; anus present; cœlom poorly developed; segmented, somites usually more or less dissimilar; paired, jointed appendages present on all or a part of the somites; chitinous exoskeleton.

SECTION A. BRANCHIATA. Mostly aquatic ARTHROPODA usually breathing by means of gills.

Class I. Crustacea. Examples: crayfish (Fig. 202), water-flea (Fig. 211), barnacle (Fig. 214), sow-bug (Fig. 220).

SECTION B. TRACHEATA. Air-breathing ARTHROPODA with tracheæ (Fig. 243).

Division 1. *Protracheata.* Primitive tracheates which possess nephridia and other annelid characteristics, and tracheæ and other insect characteristics.

Class II. Onychophora. Example: *Peripatus* (Fig. 228).

Division 2. *Antennata.* Tracheates with one pair of antennæ (Fig. 250).

Class III. Myriapoda. Antennata with many similar legs. Examples: centipedes (Fig. 233), millipedes (Fig. 232).

Class IV. Insecta. Antennata with three pairs of legs, and usually wings. Examples: grasshopper (Fig. 249), honey-bee (Fig. 236).

Division 3. Arachnida. Tracheates without antennæ, and with tracheæ, book lungs, or book gills.

Class V. Arachnida. Examples: scorpion (Fig. 318), spider (Fig. 313), mite (Fig. 322), king-crab (Fig. 327).

2. Class I. Crustacea

a. *The Crayfish — Cambarus*

The crayfish is abundant both in this country and in Europe. In the eastern United States *Cambarus affinis* is common. *Cambarus virilis* is plentiful in the Middle states. The European crayfish is *Astacus (Potomobius) fluviatilis.* The anatomy and physiology of these three species as well as of the lobster agree except in minor details, and the following account may be used as a description of any of them.

Crayfishes usually hide by day under rocks or logs at the bottom of ponds and streams. They may be captured by hand, with a net, or with a string baited with a piece of meat. They thrive in an aquarium, and their entire life-history may be observed in the laboratory.

Anatomy and Physiology. — *External Features.* — The crayfish is a *segmented* animal, but the joints have been obliterated

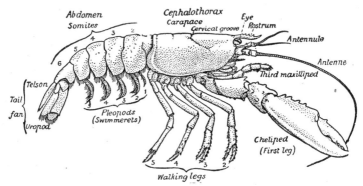

Fig. 200. — External anatomy of a lobster. (After Calman.)

on the dorsal surface of the anterior end. The body (Fig. 200) shows two distinct regions, an anterior rigid portion, the *cephalothorax,* and a posterior flexible *abdomen.* A *chitinous exoskeleton,* impregnated with lime salts, supports and protects the soft parts of the body.

A typical *segment* consists of a *tergum*, a *sternum*, two *pleura*, and two *epimera*. The cephalothorax includes segments I–XIII; a cervical groove separates the cephalic or head region from the thoracic region. The dorsal shield of the cephalothorax is called the *carapace;* its anterior pointed extension is known as the *rostrum*, and the heavy flap on either side protecting the gills, as a *branchiotegite*. There are six segments and a terminal extension, the *telson*, in the abdomen.

Appendages. — Each segment bears a pair of jointed appendages which in most cases differ from the other pairs in structure and function, but all are probably variations of a *biramous type* consisting of a basal *protopodite*, an inner branch, the *endopodite*, and an outer branch, the *exopodite*. Three types of appendages can be distinguished in an adult crayfish: (1) *foliaceous* (second maxilla, Fig. 201, *Mx. 2*), (2) *biramous* (swimmerets), and (3) *uniramous* (walking legs, Fig. 201, *L. 4*). Figure 202 shows the position and shape of most of the appendages, and Table IX gives a brief description of each and the modifications due to differences in function.

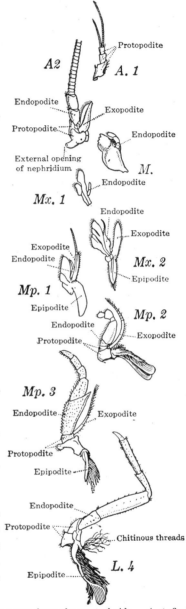

FIG. 201. — Appendages of Crayfish as seen from the ventral side. *A. 1*, first antenna; *A2*, second antenna; *L. 4*, fourth walking leg; *M*, mandible; *Mp. 1*, first maxilliped; *Mp. 2*, second maxilliped; *Mp. 3*, third maxilliped; *Mx. 1*, first maxilla; *Mx. 2*, second maxilla. (From Kerr.)

Internal Organs. — Definite systems of organs are present in the crayfish for the performance of the various functions. The *cœlom* is small, and is restricted to the cavities of the reproductive organs

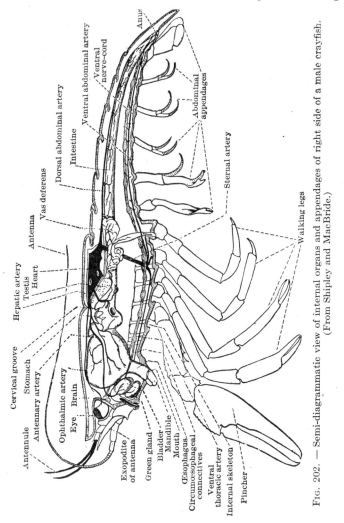

FIG. 202. — Semi-diagrammatic view of internal organs and appendages of right side of a male crayfish. (From Shipley and MacBride.)

and green glands. The cavities around the alimentary canal are blood spaces, and therefore represent a *hæmocœl*. Some of the organs, like the muscles and nervous ganglia, are *segmentally arranged;* others like the excretory organs are concentrated in a small space.

TABLE IX

DESCRIPTIVE TABLE OF THE APPENDAGES OF THE CRAYFISH

Appendage	Protopodite	Exopodite	Endopodite	Function
I. Antennule	3 segments; statocyst in basal segment	Many-jointed filament	Many-jointed filament	Tactile; chemical; equilibration
II. Antenna	2 segments; excretory pore in basal segment	Broad, thin, dagger-like lateral projection	A long, many-jointed "feeler"	Tactile; chemical
III. Mandible	2 segments; a heavy jaw and basal segment of palp	Absent	Small; 2 distal segments of palp	Crushing food
IV. 1st Maxilla	2 thin lamellae extending inward	Absent	A small outer lamella	
V. 2d Maxilla	2 bilobed lamellae	Dorsal half of plate, the scaphognathite	1 segment; small, pointed	Creates current of water in gill chamber
VI. 1st Maxilliped	2 thin segments extending inward; a broad plate, the epipodite extending outward	A long basal segment bearing a many-jointed filament	Small; 2 segments	Chemical; tactile; holds food

TABLE IX. — DESCRIPTIVE TABLE OF THE APPENDAGES OF THE CRAYFISH — *Continued.*

APPENDAGE	PROTOPODITE	EXOPODITE	ENDOPODITE	FUNCTION
VII. 2d Maxilliped	2 segments; a basal coxopodite bearing a gill, and a basipodite bearing the exopodite and endopodite	Similar to VI	5 segments; the basal one long and fused with the basipodite	Similar to VI
VIII. 3d Maxilliped	Similar to VII	Similar to VI	Similar to VII, but larger	Similar to VI
IX. 1st Walking Leg (Cheliped or Pincher)	2 segments; coxopodite, and basipodite	Absent	5 segments, the terminal two forming a powerful pincher	Offense and defense; aids in walking; tactile
X. 2d Walking Leg (Pereiopod)	Similar to IX	Absent	As in IX, but not so heavy	Walking; prehension; toilet implements
XI. 3d Walking Leg	Similar to IX; coxopodite of female contains genital pore	Absent	Similar to X	Similar to X
XII. 4th Walking Leg	Similar to IX	Absent	Similar to X, but no pincher at end	Walking
XIII. 5th Walking Leg	Similar to IX; coxopodite of male bears genital pore	Absent	Similar to XII	Walking; cleaning abdomen and eggs

XIV. 1st Abdominal (1st Pleopod or Swimmeret)				Reduced in female; in male, protopodite and endopodite fused together, forming an organ for transferring sperm
XV. 2d Abdominal (2d Pleopod or Swimmeret)	In female 2 segments	In female many-jointed filament	In female like exopodite, but longer	In female as in XVI; in male modified for transferring sperm to female
XVI. 3d Abdominal (3d Pleopod or Swimmeret)	2 segments	Many-jointed filament	Like exopodite, but longer	Creates current of water; in female used for attachment of eggs and young
XVII. 4th Abdominal (4th Pleopod or Swimmeret)	2 segments	As in XVI	As in XVI	As in XVI
XVIII. 5th Abdominal (5th Pleopod or Swimmeret)	As in XVII	As in XVI	As in XVI	As in XVI
XIX. 6th Abdominal (Uropod)	1 short, broad segment	Flat oval plate divided by transverse groove into two parts	Flat oval plate	Swimming

Digestion. — Crayfishes live chiefly on living snails, tadpoles, young insects, and the like, but sometimes eat one another, and may also devour decaying organic matter. They feed at night, being most active at dusk and daybreak. The maxillipedes and maxillæ hold the food while it is being crushed into small pieces by the mandibles. The food particles pass down the *œsophagus* (Fig. 202) into the anterior, *cardiac* chamber of the *stomach*, where they are ground up by a number of chitinous ossicles, called the *gastric mill.* When fine enough, the food passes through a sieve-like *strainer* of hair-like setæ into the *pyloric* chamber of the stomach; here it is mixed with a secretion from the digestive glands brought in by the hepatic ducts. The dissolved food is absorbed by the walls of the *intestine.* Undigested particles pass on into the posterior end of the intestine, where they are gathered together into fæces, and egested through the anus.

Circulation. —*The Blood.* — The *blood* into which the absorbed food passes is an almost colorless liquid in which are suspended a number of ameboid cells, the blood corpuscles or *amebocytes.* The principal *functions* of the blood are the transportation of food materials from one part of the body to another, of oxygen from the gills to the various tissues, of carbon dioxide to the gills, and of urea to the excretory organs.

Blood-vessels. — The principal blood-vessels are a *heart,* seven *arteries,* and a number of spaces called *sinuses.* Blood enters the heart from the surrounding sinus through three pairs of valvular *ostia.* Rhythmical contractions then force it forward, backward, and downward.

(1) The *ophthalmic artery* (Fig. 202) supplies part of the stomach, the œsophagus, and head.

(2, 3) The two *antennary arteries* carry blood to the stomach, antennæ, excretory organs, and other cephalic tissues.

(4, 5) The two *hepatic arteries* lead to the digestive glands.

(6) The *dorsal abdominal artery* supplies the intestine and surrounding tissues.

(7) The *sternal artery* divides into a *ventral thoracic* and a *ventral abdominal* artery which carry blood to the appendages and other ventral organs.

Sinuses. — The blood passes from the arteries into spaces lying in the midst of the tissues, called sinuses. The heart lies in the *pericardial sinus.* The thorax contains a large ventral blood space, the *sternal sinus*, and a number of *branchio-cardiac canals* extending from the bases of the gills to the pericardial sinus. A *perivisceral sinus* surrounds the alimentary canal in the cephalothorax.

The Blood Flow. — The heart, by means of the rhythmical contractions, forces the blood through the arteries to all parts of the body. *Valves* are present in every artery where it leaves the heart; they prevent the blood from flowing back. The finest branches of these arteries, the *capillaries*, open into spaces between the tissues, and the blood eventually reaches the sternal sinus. From here it passes into the afferent channels of the gills and into the gill filaments, where the carbonic acid in solution is exchanged for oxygen from the water in the branchial chambers. It then returns by way of the efferent gill channels, passes into the branchio-cardiac sinuses, thence to the pericardial sinus, and finally through the ostia into the heart. The valves of the ostia allow the blood to enter the heart, but prevent it from flowing back into the pericardial sinus.

Respiration. — Between the branchiostegites and the body-wall are the *branchial chambers* containing the respiratory organs, the *gills*. At the anterior end of the branchial chamber is a channel in which the scaphognathite of the second maxilla (Fig. 201, *Mx. 2*) moves back and forth, forcing the water out through the anterior opening. Fresh water flows in through the posterior opening of the branchial chamber.

TABLE X

THE NUMBER AND POSITION OF THE GILLS OF THE CRAYFISH
(*Cambarus*)

SEGMENT	PODO-BRANCHIÆ	ARTHROBRANCHIÆ		TOTAL NUMBERS
		Anterior	Posterior	
VI	0 (ep.)	0	0	0 (ep.)
VII	1	1	0	2
VIII	1	1	1	3
IX	1	1	1	3
X	1	1	1	3
XI	1	1	1	3
XII	1	1	1	3
	6 (ep.)	6	5	17 (ep.)

Gills. — There are two rows of gills; the outer, *podobranchiæ*, are fastened to the coxopodites of certain appendages (see Table X) and the inner double row, the *arthrobranchiæ*, arise from the mem-branes at the bases of these appendages. In *A stacus* there is a third row, the *pleuro-branchiæ*, attached to the walls of the thorax. The number and arrangement of these gills are shown in Table X. Each gill possesses a number of gill filaments.

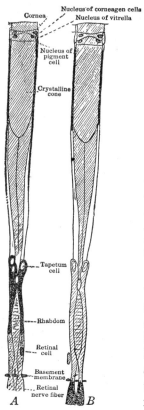

Excretion. — The waste products of metabolism are taken from the blood by a pair of rather large bodies, the "*green glands*" (Fig. 202) situated in the ven-tral part of the head anterior to the œsophagus. Each green gland consists of a glandular portion, green in color, a thin-walled dilatation, the bladder, and a duct opening to the exterior through a pore at the top of the papilla on the basal segment of the antenna.

Nervous System. — The morphology of the nervous system of the crayfish is in many respects similar to that of the earthworm. The central nervous system includes a dorsal ganglionic mass, the *brain* (Fig. 202), in the head, and two *circumæsophageal connectives* passing to the *ventral nerve-cord*, which lies near the median ventral surface of the body. The brain sends nerves to the eyes, antennules, and antennæ. Each segment posterior to VII possesses a ganglionic mass, which sends nerves to the surround-ing tissues. The large subœsophageal ganglion in segment VII consists of the

Fig. 203. — Longitudinal sections of two ommatidia of the crayfish. *A*, pigment ar-ranged as influenced by light. *B*, pigment arranged as in-fluenced by darkness. (From Sedgwick's Zoology, after Parker.)

ganglia of segments III–VII fused together. It sends nerves to the mandibles, maxillæ, and first and second maxillipeds. *Visceral nerves* arise from the brain and extend posteriorly to the viscera.

Sense-organs. — *Eyes.* — The eyes of the crayfish (Fig. 202) are situated at the end of movable stalks, one on either side of the head. Each eye is covered by a modified portion of the chitinous cuticle called the *cornea*. The cornea is divided into rectangular areas known as *facets*, which are the ends of long visual rods, the *ommatidia*. The average number of ommatidia in a single eye is 2500. The parts of an ommatidium are shown in Figure 203.

Vision. — The eyes of the crayfish are supposed to produce an erect mosaic or " apposition image "; this is illustrated in Figure 204, where the ommatidia are represented by *a–e*, and the fibers from the optic nerve by *a′–e′*. The rays of light from any point *a*, *b*, or *c* will all encounter the dark pigment cells surrounding the ommatidia and be absorbed, except the ray which passes directly through the center of the cornea, as *d* or *e*; this ray will penetrate to the fibers from the optic nerve. One ommatidium thus receives a single impression, and since the ommatidia are directed to different, though adjoining, regions, the sum of the resulting images may be compared to a mosaic. This method

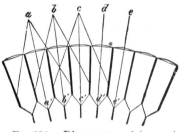

Fig. 204. — Diagram to explain mosaic vision (see text). (From Packard, after Lubbock.)

of image formation is especially well adapted for recording motion, since any change in the position of a large object affects the entire 2500 ommatidia.

When the pigment surrounds the ommatidia (Fig. 203, A), vision is as described above; but it has been found that in dim light the pigment migrates partly toward the outer and partly toward the basal end of the ommatidia (Fig. 203, B). When this occurs, the ommatidia no longer act separately, but a combined image is thrown on the retinular layer.

Statocysts. — The statocysts of *Cambarus* are chitinous-lined sacs situated one in the basal segment of each antennule. In the statocyst are a number of *sensory hairs*, among which are a few grains of sand, called *statoliths*, placed there by the crayfish. The contact of the statoliths with the hairs determines the orientation of the body while swimming. Statocysts are, therefore, *organs of equilibration*. When the crayfish changes its exoskeleton in the process of molting, the statocyst is also shed. Individuals that have just molted, or have had their statocysts removed, lose much of their powers of orientation. Perhaps the most convincing proof of the function of equilibration is that furnished by the experiments of Kreidl. This investigator placed shrimps, which had just molted and were therefore without statoliths, in filtered water. When supplied with iron filings, the animals filled their statocysts with them. A strong electromagnet was then held near the statocyst, and the shrimp took up a position corresponding to the resultant of the two pulls, that of gravity and of the magnet.

Muscular System. — The principal muscles in the body of the crayfish are situated in the abdomen, and are used to bend that part of the animal forward upon the ventral surface of the thorax, thus producing backward locomotion in swimming. Other muscles extend the abdomen in the preparation for another stroke. The appendages are all supplied with muscles which give them the power of motion. It is of interest to note that the muscles are internal, and attached to the inner surface of the skeleton. In man, on the contrary, the skeleton is internal and the muscles external.

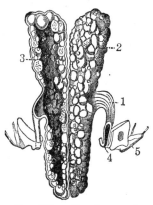

FIG. 205. — Female reproductive organs of the crayfish. *1*, right oviduct; *2*, right lobe of ovary; *3*, left lobe opened to show central cavity; *4*, external opening of oviduct; *5*, base of third walking leg. (From Shipley and MacBride.)

Reproduction. — The sexes of crayfishes are normally separate (diœcious). In the *male* the spermatozoa arise in the bilobed testis (Fig. 202), pass through the paired vasa deferentia and out of the genital apertures, one in the base of each fifth walking leg.

In the *female* the eggs arise in the bilobed ovary (Fig. 205), pass through the paired oviducts, and out of the genital apertures, one in the base of each third walking leg.

The spermatozoa are transferred from the male to the seminal receptacle of the female during copulation, which usually takes place in the autumn. The *seminal receptacle* is a cavity in a fold of cuticle between the fourth and fifth pairs of walking legs. The eggs are laid in April and are probably fertilized by the spermatozoa at this time. They are fastened with a sort of glue to the swimmerets, and are aërated by being moved back and forth through the water (Fig. 206).

The *cleavage* of the egg is superficial (Fig. 207, A), and the embryo appears first as a thickening on one side (Fig. 207, B). The eggs hatch in from five to eight weeks, and the larvæ cling to the eggshell. In about two days they shed their cuticular covering, a process known as *molting* or *ecdysis*. This casting off of the

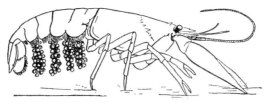

Fig. 206. — Female crayfish aërating eggs by raising and straightening abdomen and waving swimmerets back and forth. (From Andrews in *Am. Nat.*)

covering of the body is not peculiar to the young, but occurs in adult crayfishes as well as in young, and adults of many other animals. In the larval crayfish the cuticle of the first stage becomes loosened and drops off. In the meantime, the hypodermal cells have secreted a new covering. Ecdysis is necessary before growth can proceed, since the chitin of which the exoskeleton is composed does not allow expansion. In adults it is also

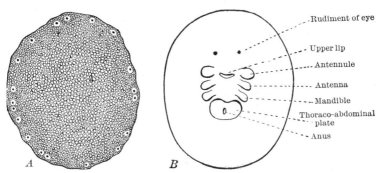

Fig. 207. — Stages in the development of the egg of the crayfish. **A**, superficial cleavage of the egg. **B**, embryo in the *Nauplius* stage. (From Korschelt and Heider, after Reichenbach.)

a means of getting rid of an old worn-out coat and acquiring a new one. The young stay with the mother for about one month, and then shift for themselves. They molt at least seven times during the first summer. The life of a crayfish usually extends over a period of three or four years.

Regeneration. — The crayfish and many other crustaceans have the power of regenerating lost parts, but to a much more limited extent than such animals as *Hydra* and the earthworm. Experiments have been performed upon almost every one of the appendages as well as the eye. The growth of regenerated tissue is more frequent and rapid in young specimens than in adults. The new structure is not always like that of the one removed. For example, Figure 208 shows an antenna which regenerated in place of an eye in a marine crustacean, *Palæmon.*

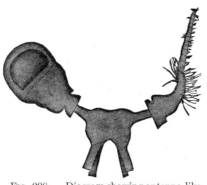

Fig. 208. — Diagram showing antenna-like organ regenerated in place of an eye of *Palæmon.* (From Morgan, after Herbst.)

Autotomy. — Perhaps the most interesting morphological structure connected with the regenerative process in *Cambarus* is the definite breaking point near the bases of the walking legs. If the chelæ are injured, they are broken off by the crayfish at the breaking point. The other walking legs, if injured, may be thrown off at the free joint between the second and third segments. A new leg, as large as the one lost, develops from the end of the stump remaining. This breaking off of the legs at a definite point is known as *autotomy*, a phenomenon that also occurs in a number of other animals. The leg is separated along the breaking point by several successive muscular contractions. It has been shown " that autotomy is not due to a weakness at the breaking point, but to a reflex action, and that it may be brought about by a stimulation of the thoracic ganglion as well as by a stimulation of the nerve of the leg itself." (Reed.)

The power of autotomy is of advantage to the crayfish, since the wound closes more quickly if the leg is lost at the breaking point. No one has yet offered an adequate theory to account for autotomy. It is probably " a process that the animal has acquired in connection with the condition under which it lives, or, in other words, an adaptive response of the organism to its condition of life." (Morgan.)

Behavior. — When at rest, the crayfish usually faces the entrance to its place of concealment, and extends its antennæ. It is thus in a position to learn the nature of an approaching object without being detected. Activity at this time is reduced to the movements of a few of the appendages and the gills; the scaphognathites of the second maxillæ move back and forth, baling water out of the forward end of the gill chambers; the swimmerets are in constant motion creating a current of water; the maxillipeds are likewise kept moving; and the antennæ and eye-stalks bend from place to place.

Locomotion. — Locomotion is effected in two ways, walking and swimming. Crayfishes are able to *walk* in any direction, forward usually, but also sidewise, obliquely, or backward. *Swimming* is not resorted to under ordinary conditions, but only when the animal is frightened or shocked. In such a case the crayfish extends the abdomen, spreads out the uropod and telson, and, by sudden contractions of the bundles of flexor abdominal muscles, bends the abdomen and darts backward. The swimming reaction apparently is not voluntary, but is almost entirely reflex. If turned over on its back, the crayfish either raises itself on one side and topples over, or else gives a quick backward flop.

Reactions to Stimuli. — THIGMOTROPISM. — The crayfish " is sensitive to touch over the whole surface of the body, but especially on the chelæ and chelipedes, the mouth parts, the ventral surface of the abdomen, and the edge of the telson." (Bell.)

Positive thigmotropism is exhibited by crayfishes to a marked degree, the animals seeking to place their bodies in contact with a solid object, if possible. The normal position of the crayfish when at rest under a stone is such as to bring its sides or dorsal surface in contact with the walls of its hiding place. Thigmotropism, no doubt, is of distinct advantage, since it forces the animal into a place of safety.

Chemotropism. — The reactions of the crayfish to food are due in part to a chemical sense, and, since " the animals react to chemical stimulation on any part of the body . . . we must assume that there are chemical sense-organs all over the body." (Bell.) The anterior appendages, however, are the most sensitive, especially the outer ramus of the antennule. Positive reactions result from the application of food substances. For example, if meat juice is placed in the water near an animal, the antennæ move slightly, and the mouth parts perform vigorous chewing movements. Acids, salts, sugar, and other chemicals produce a sort of negative reaction indicated by scratching the carapace, rubbing the chelæ, or pulling at the part stimulated.

Habit Formation. — It has been shown by certain simple experiments that crayfishes are able to learn habits and to modify them. They learn by experience and modify their behavior slowly or quickly, depending upon their familiarity with the situation. One investigator has trained them to come to him for food. (Holmes.)

b. *Crustacea in General*

(1) **Distinguishing Features.** — The CRUSTACEA (Lat. *crusta*, skin) are arthropods most of which live in the water and breathe by means of gills. The body is divided into head, thorax, and abdomen, or the head and thorax may be fused, forming a cephalo-thorax. The head usually consists of five segments fused together; it bears two pairs of antennæ (feelers), one pair of mandibles (jaws), and two pairs of maxillæ. The thorax bears a variable number of appendages, some of which are usually loco-motory. The abdominal segments are generally narrow and more mobile than those of the head and thorax; they bear appendages which are often reduced in size.

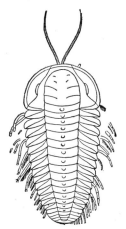

FIG. 209. — Dorsal surface of a Trilobite, *Triarthrus becki*. (From Sedgwick's Zoology, after Beecher.)

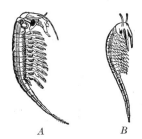

FIG. 210. — Order PHYLLOPODA. **A,** *Branchipus stagnalis;* **B,** *Artemia salina.* (From Verworn, after Semper.)

(2) **Classification of the Crustacea.**[1] — The CRUSTACEA belonging to Subclasses I–IV are often placed in one group and called ENTOMOSTRACA. They are of small size, with a variable number of body segments, and usually no gastric mill in the stomach.

[1] Somewhat simplified from Calman in Lankester's *Treatise on Zoology.*

They are apparently more primitively organized than the members of Subclass V, the MALACOSTRACA. Certain fossil animals, called TRILOBITES (Fig. 209), are by many authorities included with the CRUSTACEA. They have one pair of antennæ, and numerous body segments, all of which bear biramous appendages.

SUBCLASS I. BRANCHIOPODA. — CRUSTACEA with an elongated body, usually a carapace or shell, and many pairs of lobed, foliaceous swimming feet.

    Order 1. Phyllopoda. — BRANCHIOPODA with from ten to thirty pairs of leaflike, swimming feet. Examples: *Branchipus* (Fig. 210, A), *Artemia* (Fig. 210, B).

    Order 2. Cladocera. — Small BRANCHIOPODA with bodies usually enclosed in a bivalve shell, large second antennæ used in swimming, and four to six pairs of swimming feet. Examples: *Daphnia* (Fig. 211), *Leptodora*.

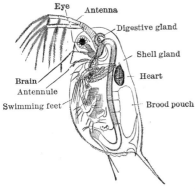

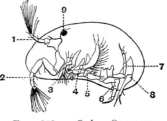

FIG. 211. — Suborder CLADOCERA. *Daphnia*, a water-flea. (From Parker and Haswell, after Claus.)

FIG. 212. — Order OSTRACODA. *Cypris candida*. *1*, antennules; *2*, antennæ; *3*, mandibles; *4*, 1st maxillæ; *5*, 2d maxillæ; *6*, 1st pair of legs; *7*, 2d pair of legs; *8*, tail; *9*, eye. (From Shipley and MacBride, after Zenker.)

SUBCLASS II. OSTRACODA. — Small, laterally compressed CRUSTACEA entirely enclosed in a bivalve shell. Usually seven pairs of appendages. Examples: *Cypris* (Fig. 212), *Candona*.

SUBCLASS III. COPEPODA. — Elongated CRUSTACEA with biramous swimming feet, without shell, and without abdominal appendages. Examples: *Cyclops* (Fig. 213), *Canthocamptus, Diaptomus, Argulus, Sapphirina, Achtheres*.

Subclass IV. Cirripedia. — Crustacea usually fixed or parasitic, with indistinctly segmented body enclosed in a carapace. Often greatly modified because of fixed or parasitic habit. Examples: *Lepas, Balanus* (Fig. 214), *Sacculina, Peltogaster*.

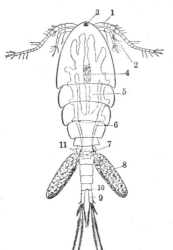

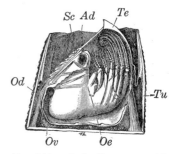

Fig. 213. — Order Copepoda. *Cyclops*, dorsal view of female. *1*, 1st antenna; *2*, 2d antenna; *3*, eye; *4*, ovary; *5*, uterus; *6*, oviduct; *7*, spermatheca; *8*. egg-sacs; *9*, caudal fork; *10*, position of anus; *11*, segment consisting of last thoracic and first abdominal. (From Shipley and MacBride, partly after Hartog.)

Fig. 214. — Order Cirripedia. *Balanus tintinnabulum*, one-half of shell has been removed. *Ad*, adductor muscle; *Od*, oviduct; *Oe*, opening of oviduct; *Ov*, ovary; *Sc*, scutum; *Te*, tergum; *Tu*, section of outer shell. (From Sedgwick's Zoology, after Claus.)

Subclass V. Malacostraca. — Crustacea usually of large size, with five segments in the head, eight in the thorax, and six in the abdomen, and with a gastric mill in the stomach.

Order 1. Nebaliacea. — Small, shrimp-like Malacostraca with head and middle portion of body enclosed in a bivalve

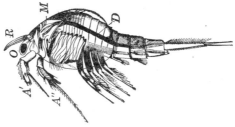

Fig. 215. — Order Nebaliacea. *Nebalia geoffroyi*, female. *A'*, antennule; *A''*, antenna; *D*, intestine; *M*, crop; *O*, stalked eye; *R*, movable head plate. (From Sedgwick's Zoology, after Claus.)

shell, with eight thoracic segments, eight abdominal segments, and a terminal caudal fork. Example: *Nebalia*
(Fig. 215).

Order 2. Anaspidacea. — MALACOSTRACA with distinct thoracic
segments, pedunculate eyes, and no carapace. Example:
Anaspides.

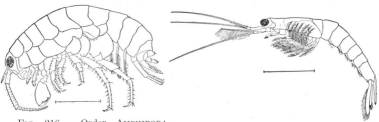

FIG. 216. — Order AMPHIPODA.
Talorchestia megalopthalmia. (From   FIG. 217. — Order MYSIDACEA. *Mysis*
Paulmier.)   *stenolepis.* (From Paulmier, after Verrill.)

Order 3. Mysidacea. — MALACOSTRACA of small size, with
biramous antennules, thoracic limbs with natatory exopo-
dites, and a large carapace. Example: *Mysis* (Fig. 217).

Order 4. Cumacea. — MALACOSTRACA with a slender abdomen, four or five free thoracic segments, and a small
carapace. Example: *Diastylis* (Fig. 218).

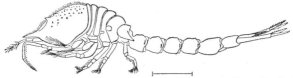

FIG. 218. — Order CUMACEA. *Diastylis quadrispinosa.* (From Paulmier, after
Verrill.)

Order 5. Tanaidacea. — MALACOSTRACA with free thoracic
segments except the first two, which are fused with the
head and extend on the sides, forming a respiratory chamber. Example: *Apseudes* (Fig. 219).

FIG. 219. — Order TANAIDACEA. *Apseudes spinosus.* (From Sedgwick's
Zoology, after Sars.)

Order 6. Isopoda. — MALACOSTRACA with a body generally broad and flat, seven free thoracic segments, leaflike legs, and no carapace. Examples: *Asellus* (Fig. 220, **A**), *Armadillium, Oniscus* (Fig. 220, **B**), *Porcellio.*

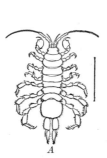
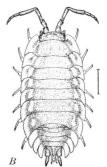

FIG. 220. — Order ISOPODA.   **A**, *Asellus communis*, a fresh-water species. **B**, *Oniscus asellus*, a terrestrial species.   (From Paulmier; A, after Smith.)

Order 7. Amphipoda. — MALACOSTRACA laterally compressed, with elongated abdomen bearing three pairs of posteriorly directed springing feet and three pairs of anterior swimming feet, and without a carapace. Examples: *Gammarus* (Fig. 221, **A**), *Talorchestia* (Fig. 216), *Caprella* (Fig. 221, **B**).

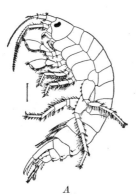
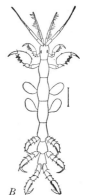

FIG. 221. — Order AMPHIPODA.   **A**, *Gammarus fasciatus*, a fresh-water species. **B**, *Caprella geometrica*, a marine species.   (From Paulmier.)

Order 8. Euphausiacea. — MALACOSTRACA with all thoracic segments covered by carapace, pedunculate eyes, none of thoracic limbs specialized as maxillipeds, and only podobranchiæ present. Example: *Meganyctiphanes.*

Order 9. Decapoda. — MALACOSTRACA with first three pairs of thoracic limbs specialized as maxillipeds, with five pairs of thoracic walking legs, with generally all of the thoracic segments covered by a carapace, and with stalked, compound eyes.

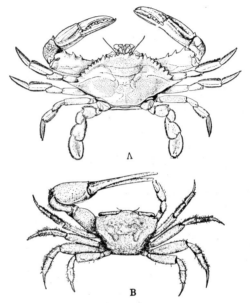

FIG. 222. — Order STO-MATOPODA. (From Daven-port, after Rathbun.)

FIG. 223. — Order DECAPODA. **A,** *Callinectes hastatus*, edible or blue crab. (From Paulmier, after Rathbun.) **B,** *Gelasimus minax*, fiddler or soldier crab. (From Paulmier.)

Suborder 1. Natantia. — DECAPODA with body usually laterally compressed, legs generally slender, and pleopods always present in full number, well developed, and used for swimming. Examples: *Penæus, Alpheus, Palæmonetes* (Fig. 224), *Stenopus.*

Suborder 2. Reptantia. — DECAPODA with body not compressed, legs strong, pleopods often reduced or absent, not used for swimming. Examples: *Hyas, Cancer, Callinectes* (Fig. 223), *Pinnotheres, Cambarus* (Fig. 202), *Homarus, Palinurus, Eupagurus, Gelasimus* (Fig. 223, B).

Order 10. Stomatopoda. — MALACOSTRACA with five pairs of anterior maxillipeds on the thorax, and three pairs of

thoracic, biramous legs, with caudal fin, and short carapace covering only part of the thorax. Examples: *Squilla*
(Fig. 222), *Gonodactylus.*

FIG. 224. — Order DECAPODA. *Palæmonetes vulgaris*, a shrimp. (From
Davenport.)

(3) **Entomostraca.** — The CRUSTACEA belonging to the EN-
TOMOSTRACA are the BRANCHIOPODA, OSTRACODA, COPEPODA,
and CIRRIPEDIA. They live in fresh water, in salt water, on
land, or as parasites on other animals. The enormous numbers
of these little creatures may be ascertained by counting the specimens that are captured if a fine gauze net is drawn through the
waters of lakes or streams. It has been estimated that, on the
average, each cubic meter of water in the small Wisconsin lakes
contains about 40,000 individuals, and that 160 billion, weighing
altogether about twenty tons, may exist at one time in a lake of
eighty square kilometers. Usually a lesser number are present
in the waters of streams. The ocean is likewise populated with
billions of these minute CRUSTACEA.

These small CRUSTACEA are of little if any direct economic
importance to man, but indirectly they are of considerable value,
since they form the chief food of many edible fishes.

The TRILOBITA are extinct CRUSTACEA which are known only
from their fossil remains. They are associated in the strata of
the earth's crust with the remains of CRINOIDEA (Fig. 148), BRA-
CHIOPODA (Fig. 126), and CEPHALOPODA (Fig. 191). The best-
known species, *Triarthrus becki* (Fig. 209), is from the Utica shales
(Lower Silurian) of New York State. It has two antennæ and
many biramous appendages.

The BRANCHIOPODA include the leaf-legged CRUSTACEA (PHYL-
LOPODA), and the water-fleas (CLADOCERA). The fairy-shrimp,
Branchipus (Fig. 210, A), is a common fresh-water phyllopod;
Artemia (Fig. 210, B) is a genus found in salt-water lakes, such
as the Great Salt Lake of Utah. *Daphnia* (Fig. 211) is a water-
flea (CLADOCERA) abundant in fresh-water ponds and lakes.

Its body is enclosed in a shell, and the second antennæ (*ant. 2*) are modified to form swimming appendages. During the spring and summer only females are present, and at this time " summer " eggs are produced which develop parthenogenetically in the brood-pouch (*br.p*) of the mother. In the autumn males are developed; they fertilize the " winter " eggs, which are larger and fewer in number than the summer eggs.

The OSTRACODA (Fig. 212) are bivalved CRUSTACEA which protrude their antennæ (*2*) from the two valves of their shell and use them as oars in swimming. They are common in ponds and streams.

A well-known fresh-water COPEPOD is *Cyclops* (Fig. 213), an animal that has a single compound eye (*e*) in the middle of the head. The antennæ (*1*) are used for locomotion. The female may be recognized easily during the summer because of the two brood sacs (*8*) full of eggs that she carries about with her.

The subclass CIRRIPEDIA contains the barnacles (Fig. 214). These are sessile CRUSTACEA, many of which possess shells causing them to resemble mollusks. The larvæ are free swimming and resemble those of other CRUSTACEA, but they pass through a metamorphosis, during which some or all of the appendages and other parts of the body are lost, and usually a calcareous shell is formed. The rock-barnacle, *Balanus balanoides* (Fig. 214), is abundant along the North Atlantic coast, where it lives attached to rocks and other objects. The movements of the appendages create a current of water which brings food into the shell. The goose barnacle, *Lepas*, has a bivalve shell and is attached by a peduncle. *Sacculina* is a barnacle parasitic on the crab, *Carcinus*, and in the adult stage resembles a tumor, consisting almost entirely of reproductive organs. Most barnacles are hermaphroditic.

(4) **Malacostraca.** — The MALACOSTRACA are, as a rule, larger than the ENTOMOSTRACA, and include the more familiar CRUSTACEA, such as crayfishes, lobsters, crabs, shrimps, and sow-bugs. Some of them are aquatic, others are terrestrial, and a few are parasitic.

The order ISOPODA contains a number of common MALACOSTRACA (Fig. 220). Most of them are marine, but some live in fresh water and on land. They are the largest group of terrestrial CRUSTACEA. The sow-bug, *Oniscus*, and the pill-bug, *Armadillium*, live under stones, boards, and similar places that are dark and moist. Although land animals, they breathe by means of gills situated on the under surface of the abdomen.

The AMPHIPODA are aquatic, except a few species which leap about on the beach, and are called beach-fleas. *Gammaruc* (Fig. 221) is called the fresh-water shrimp. *Talorchestia* (Fig. 216) is a sand-hopper common on sandy beaches between the tide-marks. *Caprella* is a peculiar brown amphipod which so closely resembles the seaweeds or hydroids among which it lives that it can be detected only by an experienced eye.

The mantis shrimps belong to the order STOMATOPODA. This common name was derived from their resemblance to the insect called the praying-mantis (Fig. 270). They are exclusively marine. *Squilla empusa* (Fig. 222) lives along the eastern coast of the United States.

The order DECAPODA contains the lobsters, crayfishes, crabs, and shrimps, and is the most important group of the CRUSTACEA. The name DECAPODA refers to the fact that only the last five pairs of thoracic appendages are used for locomotion.

The lobster is of considerable economic importance. It is most abundant along the Atlantic coast from Labrador to Delaware Bay, and lives on the bottom from near shore to a depth of one hundred fathoms. About fifteen million lobsters are sent to market annually, and unless their capture is regulated, they will soon be exterminated. Shrimps and prawns are also used as food for man. *Palæmonetes* (Fig. 224) is a common shrimp living among seaweeds; it is almost transparent. The hermit-crab, *Eupagurus*, lives in an empty snail-shell which protects it from many enemies. Some hermit-crabs place sea-anemones or hydroid colonies upon their shells; these furnish additional protection.

The edible or blue crab, *Callinectes*, lives along the Atlantic and Gulf coasts and is captured in large numbers for market. It is called the soft-shelled crab just after molting. The fidler-crabs, *Uca pugilator*, are common along our eastern coast, where they dig holes in the mud and sand. The spider-crab, *Libinia*, has long slender legs, which enable it to run over uneven surfaces with ease. The Japanese spider-crab is very large, sometimes measuring twenty feet across from tip to tip of the first pair of legs.

(5) **The Biogenetic Law.** — Early in the past century it was noticed that animals could be arranged in a series beginning with

the PROTOZOA and passing through the simpler diploblastic forms, and that the stages in this series correspond to the early stages in the embryology of the METAZOA. This led to the formulation of the biogenetic law, *i.e.* that the development of the individual recapitulates the stages in the evolution of the race, or *ontogeny recapitulates phylogeny.* These stages contrasted appear as follows: —

PHYLOGENETIC STAGE	ONTOGENETIC STAGE
(1) Single-celled animal	Egg cell
(2) Ball of cells	Blastula
(3) Two-layered sac	Gastrula
(4) Triploblastic animal	Three-layered embryo

Zoologists soon became interested in the recapitulation theory, and enlarged upon it. Of these, Fritz Müller and Ernst Haeckel are especially worthy of mention. The latter expressed the facts as he saw them in his " fundamental law of biogenesis." The ancestor of the many-celled animals was conceived by him as a two-layered sac something like a gastrula, which he called a *Gastræa.* The cœlenterates were considered to be gastræa slightly modified.

Fritz Müller derived strong arguments in favor of biogenesis from a study of certain CRUSTACEA belonging to the MALACOSTRACA. Many members of this group do not

FIG. 225. — Larva of lobster in *Mysis* stage. (From Sedgwick, after Sars.)

emerge from the egg so nearly like the adult as does the crayfish. The lobster, for example, upon hatching (Fig. 225) resembles a less specialized prawnlike crustacean called *Mysis* (Fig. 217), and is said to be in the *Mysis* stage.

The shrimp, *Penæus,* passes through a number of interesting stages before the adult condition is attained. It hatches as as larva, termed a *Nauplius* (Fig. 226, A), possessing a frontal eye and three pairs of appendages; this *Nauplius* molts and grows into a *Protozoæa* stage (Fig. 226, B), which bears three more pairs of appendages and the rudiments of segments. The *Protozoæa* stage grows into the *Zoæa* stage (Fig. 227, A). The

cephalothorax and abdomen are distinct at this time; eigh,
pairs of appendages are present and six more are developing,
The *Zoæa* grows and molts and becomes a *Mysis* (Fig. 227, B)
with thirteen pairs of appendages (I–VIII) on the cephalothorax.
Finally, the *Mysis* passes into the adult shrimp, which possesses
the characteristic number of appendages (I–XIX), each modified
to perform its particular
function. The *Nauplius* of
Penæus resembles the larvæ
of many simple crustaceans;
the *Zoæa* is somewhat similar to the condition of an

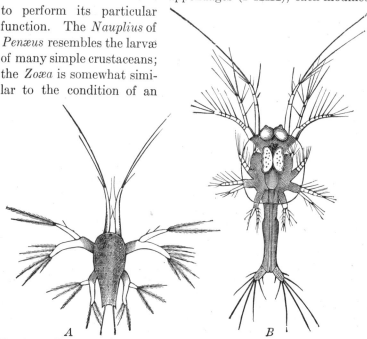

FIG. 226. — Two stages in the development of the shrimp, *Penæus*. **A**, *Nauplius*
stage. **B**, *Protozoæa* stage. (From Sedgwick's Zoology, after Fritz Müller.)

adult *Cyclops* (Fig. 213); the *Mysis* is like the adult *Mysis* (Fig.
217); and finally the adult *Penæus* is more specialized than any
of its larval stages, and belongs among the higher CRUSTACEA.
The above facts have convinced some zoologists that *Penæus*
recapitulates in its larval development the progress of the race;
that the lobster has lost many of these stages, retaining only
the *Mysis;* and that the crayfish hatches in practically the adult
condition. The *Nauplius* stage of the latter is supposed to be
represented by a certain embryonic phase (Fig. 207, B).

The law of biogenesis has been criticized severely by many
prominent zoologists, but it has furnished an hypothesis, which

has concentrated the attention of scientists upon fundamental embryological processes, and has, therefore, had a great influence upon zoological progress.

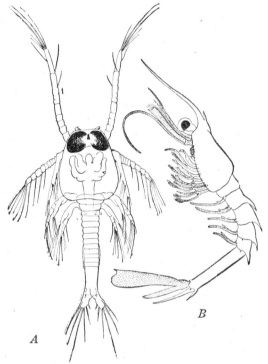

FIG. 227. — Two later stages in the development of *Penœus*. **A**, *Zoœa* stage. **B**, *Mysis* stage. (From Korschelt and Heider, after Claus.)

3. CLASS II. ONYCHOPHORA

This class (Gr. *onux*, a claw; *phoreo*, I bear) contains about fifty species of a peculiar arthropod, usually placed in a single genus, *Peripatus* (Fig. 228), but probably belonging to a number of genera. *Peripatus* has been reported from isolated regions in Africa, Australia, New Zealand, Tasmania, New Britain, Mexico, South America, West Indies, and Malaya, and is, there-fore, an excellent example of an animal with a discontinuous distribution. It lives in crevices of rock, under bark and stones, and in other dark places. As the animal moves slowly from place to place by means of its legs, the two extremely sensitive antennæ test the ground over which it is to travel, while the eyes, one at the base of each antenna, enable it to avoid the light. When irritated, *Peripatus* often ejects slime, sometimes to the distance of almost a foot, from a pair of glands which open on the

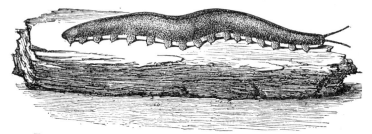

FIG. 228. — *Peripatus capensis*, drawn from life.   (From Sedgwick.)

oral papillæ.   This slime sticks to everything but the body of the animal itself; it is used principally to capture flies, wood-lice, termites, and other small animals, and in addition is probably a weapon of defense.   A pair of modified appendages serve as jaws and tear the food to pieces.

Most species of *Peripatus* are viviparous, and a single large female may produce thirty or forty young in a year.   These young resemble the adults when born, differing chiefly in size and color.

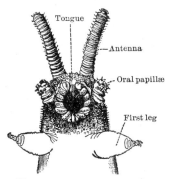

FIG. 229. — *Peripatus capensis*, ventral view of head.   (From Sedgwick.)

The external appearance of *Peripatus capensis* is shown in Figures 228 and 229.   Figure 230 shows the principal internal organs of a male specimen.   The head bears three pairs of appendages: the *antennæ* (Fig. 229), the *oral papillæ*, and the *jaws*, a pair of simple *eyes*, and a ventrally placed *mouth*. The fleshy *legs* number from seventeen pairs to over forty pairs in different species; each (Fig. 229) bears two *claws*.   The *anus* is at the posterior end; the *genital pore* is situated between the last pair of legs; and a *nephridiopore* lies at the base of each leg.   The *skin* is covered with *papillæ*, each bearing a *spine;* these papillæ are especially numerous on the antennæ, lips, and oral papillæ, and are probably *tactile* (Fig. 229).

The *digestive system* (Fig. 230) is very simple, consisting of a muscular *pharynx*, a short *œsophagus*, a long, saccular *stomach*, and a short *intestine*. The pair of *salivary glands*, which open into the mouth cavity, are modified nephridia. The *heart* is the only blood-vessel; it is a dorsal tube with paired ostia connecting it with the pericardial cavity in which it lies. The *body-cavity* is a blood space, *i.e.* a hæmocœl. The breathing organs are air-tubes, called *tracheæ*, which open by means of pores on various parts of the body. The excretory organs are *nephridia*, one at the base of each leg. The vesicular end of the nephridium is part of the cœlom. The nervous system consists of a *brain*, dorsally situated in the head, and a pair of *ventral nerve-cords*, which are connected by many transverse nerves. The sexes are separate, and the cavities of the reproductive organs are cœlomic.

Peripatus is of special interest since its

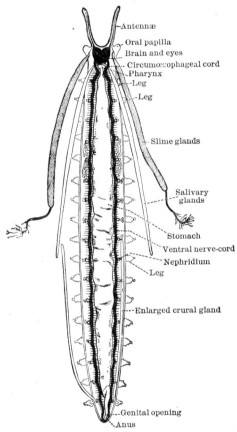

FIG. 230. — *Peripatus capensis*, male, dissected to show the internal organs. (From Shipley and MacBride, after Balfour.)

body exhibits certain structures characteristic of annelids and other structures found only in arthropods. It is, however, undoubtedly an arthropod. The following table (XI) presents briefly these characteristics and shows in what respects it differs from other arthropods: —

TABLE XI

THE CHARACTERISTICS OF PERIPATUS ARRANGED SO AS TO SHOW THE
SIMILARITY TO AND DIFFERENCES FROM ARTHROPODS AND ANNELIDS

Arthropod Characteristics	Annelid Characteristics	Structures Peculiar to Peripatus
Appendages modified as jaws. A hæmocœlic body-cavity. No cœlom around alimentary canal. Tracheæ present.	Paired segmentally arranged nephridia. Cilia in reproductive organs. Chief systems of organs arranged as in annelids.	Number and diffusion of tracheal apertures. Single pair of jaws. Distribution of reproductive organs. Texture of skin. Simplicity and similarity of segments behind the head.

4. Class III. Myriapoda

The Myriapoda (Gr. *murios*, ten thousand; *podes*, feet) are terrestrial arthropods commonly known as centipedes, or wireworms. They do not constitute a compact group of animals, and authorities differ with regard to their classification. The four orders adopted in this book are ranked as phyla by some zoologists. The chief distinguishing characteristics of the group are: (1) a distinct head with one pair of antennæ and one pair of mandibles, (2) numerous body segments bearing similar leglike appendages, (3) tracheæ with segmentally arranged apertures, and (4) excretory organs (malpighian tubules) opening into the intestine.

Order 1. Pauropoda (Fig. 231). — These are small myriapods less than 2 mm. in length which prey on microscopic animals or eat decaying animal and vegetable matter. They are without eyes, heart, and special respiratory organs, and evidently breathe through the general surface of the body, as in the earthworm. The head is distinct, and the body contains twelve segments and bears nine

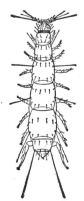

Fig. 231. — Order Pauropoda. *Pauropus huxleyi*. (From Sedgwick's Zoology, after Latzel.)

pairs of legs. The PAUROPODA are apparently primitive myriapods related to the millipedes (DIPLOPODA).

Pauropus and *Eurypauropus* are North American genera.

Order 2. Diplopoda. — The DIPLOPODA are called millipedes (Fig. 232). The body is subcylindrical, and consists of from

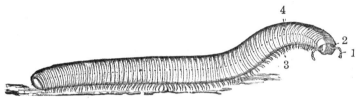

FIG. 232. — A millipede. (From Shipley and MacBride, after Koch.)

about twenty-five to more than one hundred segments, according to the species. Almost every segment bears two pairs of *appendages*, and has probably arisen by the fusion of two segments. The mouth parts are a pair of *mandibles* and a pair of *maxillæ*. One pair of *antennæ* and either simple or aggregated *eyes* are usually present. There are *olfactory hairs* on the antennæ and a pair of *scent glands* in each segment, opening laterally. The breathing tubes (tracheæ) are usually unbranched; they arise in tufts from pouches which open just in front of the legs. The *heart* is a dorsal vessel with lateral ostia; it gives rise to arteries in the head. The two or four *excretory organs* are thread-like tubes (malpighian tubules) which pour their excretions into the intestine.

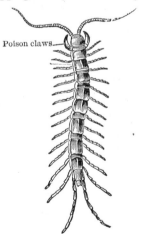

FIG. 233. — A centipede, *Lithobius forficatus*. (From Sedgwick's Zoology, after Koch.)

The millipedes move very slowly in spite of their numerous legs. Some of them are able to roll themselves into a spiral or ball. They live in dark, moist places and feed principally on vegetable substances. The sexes are separate, and the eggs are laid in damp earth. The young have few segments and only three pairs of legs when they hatch, and resemble apterous insects (Fig. 259). Other segments are added just in front of

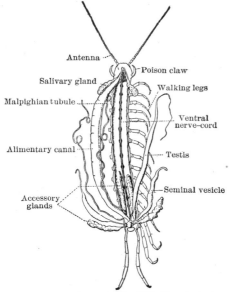

Antenna
Poison claw
Salivary gland
Walking legs
Malpighian tubule
Ventral nerve-cord
Alimentary canal
Testis
Seminal vesicle
Accessory glands

FIG. 234. — A centipede, *Lithobius forficatus*, dissected to show internal organs. (From Shipley and MacBride, after Vogt and Yung.)

the anal segment. Examples: *Julus* (Fig. 232), *Polydesmus, Spirobolus.*

Order 3. Chilopoda.
— The CHILOPODA are called centipedes (Fig. 233). The body is flattened dorso-ventrally, and consists of from fifteen to over one hundred and fifty segments, each of which bears one pair of legs except the last two and the one just back of the head. The latter bears a pair of *poison claws* called maxillipeds, with which insects, worms, mollusks, and other small animals are killed for food.

The internal anatomy of a common centipede is shown in Figure 234. The *alimentary canal* is simple; into it opens the excretory organs — two *malpighian tubules.* The *tracheæ* are branched, and open by a pair of stigmata in almost every segment. The *reproductive organs* are connected with several accessory glands. Eggs are usually laid. Those of *Lithobius* are laid singly and covered with earth.

The centipedes are swift-moving creatures. Many of them live under the bark of logs, or under stones. The genera *Lithobius, Geophilus,* and *Scutigera* are common. The poisonous centipedes of tropical countries belong to the genus *Scolopendra.* They may reach a foot in length, and their bite is painful and even dangerous to man.

Order 4. Symphyla. — The SYMPHYLA are small myriapods with twelve pairs of legs. The head bears antennæ, mandibles, maxillulæ,

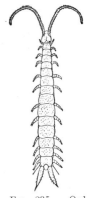

FIG. 235. — Order SYMPHYLA. *Scutigerella immaculata.* (From Sedgwick's Zoology, after Latzel.)

maxillæ, and a labium. Only two genera, *Scolopendrella* and *Scutigerella* (Fig. 235), and twenty-four species belong to the order. They resemble certain wingless insects (APTERA, Fig. 259) in habits and appearance, but have a greater number of legs. They live in moist places and avoid the light. Their food probably consists of small insects.

5. CLASS IV. INSECTA

a. *The Honey-bee*

The honey-bee, *Apis mellifica*, is one of the most interesting of all insects (Lat. *insectus*, cut into) because of its wonderful adaptations to its environment, its complex social life, and its economic value to man. Honey-bees live in colonies of about sixty thou-

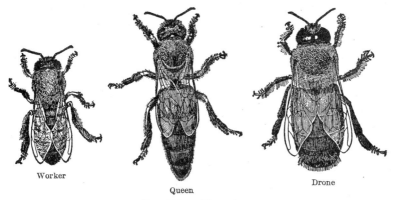

Worker

Queen

Drone

FIG. 236. — Honey-bees.

sand, in which there are three kinds of individuals — workers, drones, and a queen. The *queen* (Fig. 236) normally lays all the eggs. She lives for three years or more and can be distinguished from the other bees by the greater length of her abdomen and the absence of a pollen basket (Fig. 238, *A*). The *drone* (Fig. 236) is the male bee; he does not work, but lives only to mate with the queen. His abdomen is broad; his eyes are very large; and he has no pollen basket. The *worker* (Fig. 236) is a sexually undeveloped female; it does not lay eggs normally, but spends its time caring for the colony. Unless otherwise stated, the following description refers to the worker bee.

Anatomy and Physiology. — *External Features.* — The body of the honey-bee is supported and protected by a firm *exoskeleton* of chitin.   Three regions are recognizable — the head, thorax, and abdomen.

The *head* (Fig. 237) consists of probably six segments fused together, forming a *skull.*   On either side is a large *compound eye;* on top are three *simple eyes;* in front are two *antennæ;* and projecting downward are a number of mouth parts.

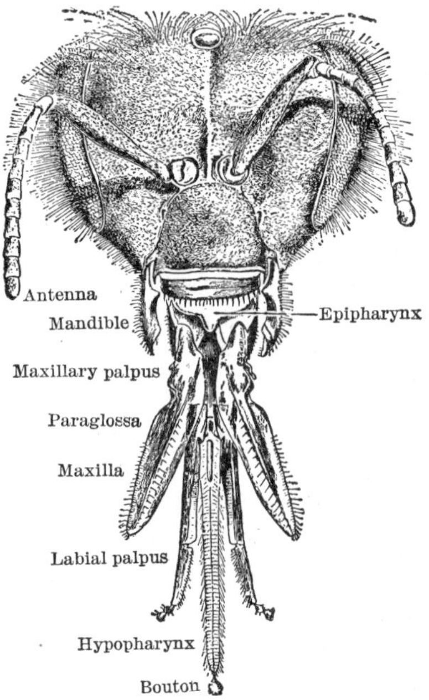

The mouth parts consist of a labrum, or upper lip, the epipharynx, a pair of mandibles, two maxillæ, and a labium, or under lip.   The *labrum* is joined to the *clypeus,* which lies just above it. From beneath the labrum projects the fleshy *epipharynx;* this is probably an organ of taste.   The *mandibles,* or jaws, are situated one on either side of the labrum; they are notched in the queen and drone, but smooth in the worker.   The latter makes use of them in building honeycomb.   The *labium* is a complicated median structure extending downward from beneath the labrum.   It is joined to the back of the head by a triangular piece, the *submentum.*   Next to this is a chitinous, muscle-filled piece, the *mentum,* beyond which is the *ligula,* or tongue, with one *labial palpus* on each side.   The ligula may be drawn in or extended.   It is long and flexible, with a spoon or *bouton* at the end.   Hairs of various kinds are arranged upon it in regular rows; these are used for gathering nectar, and as organs of touch and taste.   The *maxillæ,* or lower jaws, fit over the mentum on either side.   Along their front edges are rows of stiff hairs.   *Maxillary palpi* are also present.

FIG. 237. — Head of worker honey-bee. (From Packard, after Cheshire.)

Antenna
Mandible
Maxillary palpus
Paraglossa
Maxilla
Labial palpus
Hypopharynx
Bouton
Epipharynx

Nectar is collected in the following manner. The maxillæ
and the labial palpi form a tube, in the center of which the tongue
moves backward and forward. When the epipharynx is lowered, a
passage is completed into the œsophagus. The nectar is first
collected by the hairs on the ligula; it is then forced upward
by the pressing together of the maxillæ and labial palpi.

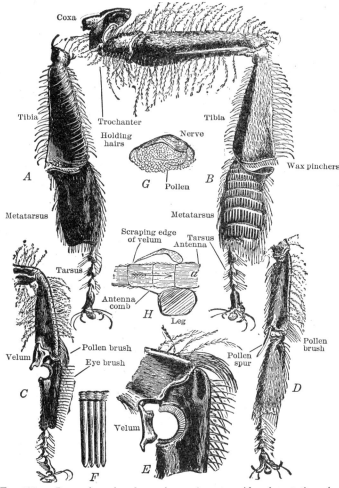

Fig. 238. — Legs of worker honey-bee. *A*, outer side of metathoracic leg.
B, inner side of metathoracic leg. *C*, prothoracic leg. *D*, mesothoracic leg.
E, joint of prothoracic leg. *F*, teeth of antenna comb. *G*, transverse section of
tibia through pollen basket. *H*, antenna in process of cleaning. (From Root, after
Cheshire.)

The *thorax* consists of three segments, each of which bears a pair of legs. The anterior segment is known as the *prothorax,* the middle segment as the *mesothorax,* and the posterior segment, as the *metathorax.* The mesothorax and metathorax each support a pair of *wings.* The segments of the thorax are comparatively large, since they contain the largest and most important muscles of the body. Externally the thorax is covered with flexible branched hairs, which are of use in gathering pollen.

Perhaps the most interesting structures of the honey-bee are the *legs* of the worker (Fig. 238). The parts of a typical insect leg, naming them in order beginning at the proximal end, are the *coxa, trochanter, femur, tibia,* and five-jointed *tarsus.*

The *prothoracic legs* (Fig. 238, *C*) possess the following useful structures. The femur and the tibia are clothed with *branched*

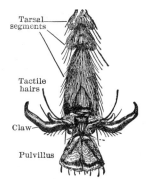

FIG. 239. — Foot of the honey-bee. (From Packard, after Cheshire.)

hairs for gathering pollen. Extending on one side from the distal end of the tibia are a number of curved bristles, the *pollen brush* (*C* and *E*), which are used to brush up the pollen loosened by the coarser spines; on the other side is a flattened movable spine, the *velum* (in *C* and *E*), which fits over a curved indentation in the first tarsal joint or metatarsus (in *C*). This entire structure is called the *antenna cleaner* and the row of teeth (*F*) which lines the indentation is known as the *antenna comb.* Figure 238, *H,* shows in section how the antenna is cleaned by being pulled between the teeth on the metatarsus and the edge of the velum. On the front of the metatarsus is a row of spines (in *C*) called the *eye brush,* which is used to brush out any pollen or foreign particles lodged among the hairs on the compound eyes. The last tarsal joint of every leg (Fig. 239) bears a pair of notched claws which enable the bee to obtain a foothold on rough surfaces. Between the claws is a fleshy glandular lobule, the *pulvillus,* whose sticky secretion makes it possible for the bee to cling to smooth objects. Tactile hairs are also present.

The middle, or *mesothoracic legs* (Fig. 238, *D*), are provided with a *pollen-brush,* but, instead of an antenna cleaner, a *spur* is

present at the distal end of the tibia. This spur is used to pry
the pollen out of the pollen baskets on the third pair of legs, and to
clean the wings.

The *metathoracic legs* (Fig. 238, *A* and *B*) possess three very
remarkable structures, the pollen basket, the wax pinchers (in *B*),
and the pollen combs (in *B*). The *pollen basket* consists of a concavity in the outer surface of the tibia with rows of curved bristles
along the edges (in *A*). By storing pollen in this basket-like structure, it is possible for the bee to spend more time in the field, and
to carry a larger load at each trip. The pollen basket in cross-
section is shown in Figure 238, *G*. The pollen combs (in *B*) serve
to fill the basket by combing out the pollen, which has become
entangled in the hairs on the thorax, and transferring it to the concavity in the tibia of the opposite leg. At the distal end of the
tibia is a row of wide spines; these are opposed by a smooth plate
on the proximal end of the metatarsus. The term *wax pinchers*
(in *B*) has been applied to these structures, since they are used
to remove the wax plates from the abdomen of the worker.

The *wings* are membranes supported by hollow ribs called
nerves or *veins*. The pair of wings on one side of the body may
be joined together by a row of *hooklets* on the anterior margin of
the hind wing, which are inserted into a trough-like fold in the
posterior margin of the fore wing. When flying, the wings act
as inclined planes, and locomotion forward is attained by both
up and down strokes, the tips of the wings moving in a curve
shaped like a figure 8. Motion backward, or a sudden stop, may
be accomplished by changing the inclination of the plane of oscil-
lation.

The *abdomen* is made up of a series of six visible segments;
thin, chitinous membranes connect the segments and make the
movement and expansion of the abdomen possible. Each of the
last four visible segments of the worker bears a pair of *wax glands*.
At the end of the abdomen of the worker and queen is the *sting*,
and the slit-like openings of the sexual organs and *anus*. There
is no sting in the drone, but a *copulatory organ* is present.

The *sting* is a very complicated structure (Fig. 240). Before
the bee stings, a suitable place is selected with the help of the *sting
feelers;* then the two *barbed darts* are thrust forward. The *sheath*
serves to guide the darts, to open up the wound, and to aid in con-
ducting the poison. The *poison* is secreted in a pair of *glands*,

one acid, the other alkaline, and is stored in a *reservoir*.   Generally
the sting, poison glands, and part of the intestine are pulled out
when a bee stings, so that death ensues after several hours, but
if only the sting is lost, the bee is not fatally injured.   The queen
seldom uses her sting except in combat with other queens.

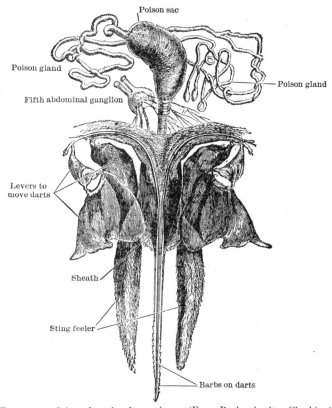

Fig. 240. — Sting of worker honey-bee.   (From Packard, after Cheshire.)

The Anatomy and Physiology of the Internal Organs. — *D*
gestion (Fig. 241). — The *mouth* opens into a narrow *œsophagus*
which leads to the *honey sac*, situated near the anterior end of the
abdomen.   The *stomach mouth*, with its four triangular lips, regulates the passage of the pollen or honey taken in as food into the
true stomach.   The digestive juices secreted by the walls of the true
stomach change the food into *chyme*.   Part of the chyme is absorbed; the rest of the food material is forced by muscular con-

tractions into the *small intestine*, where digestion and absorption
are completed. Undigested particles pass into the *rectum* and
out of the *anus*. One pair of *salivary glands* lie in the head, a
second pair in the thorax; they pour alkaline secretions upon the
food as it is taken into the œsophagus.

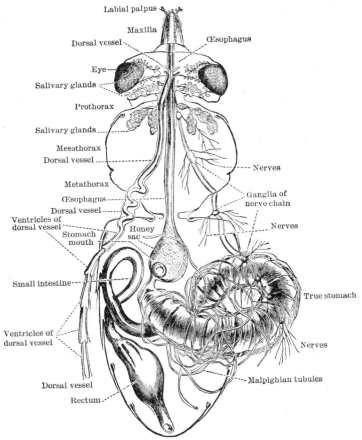

FIG. 241. — Internal organs of honey-bee. (From Packard, after Cheshire.)

Circulation. — The *blood* is a plasma containing ameboid corpuscles, but differs from that of most animals since it carries very
little, if any, oxygen. The *dorsal vessel* or *heart* (Fig. 241) is the
principal organ of circulation. Blood enters it through five pairs
of lateral *ostia*, and is forced forward by rhythmical contractions.

From the head region the blood finds its way through spaces (hæmocœl) to the ventral part of the body, and thence to the *pericardial sinus* just beneath the heart. The muscular *diaphragm* of the pericardial sinus forces the blood through the ostia into the heart.

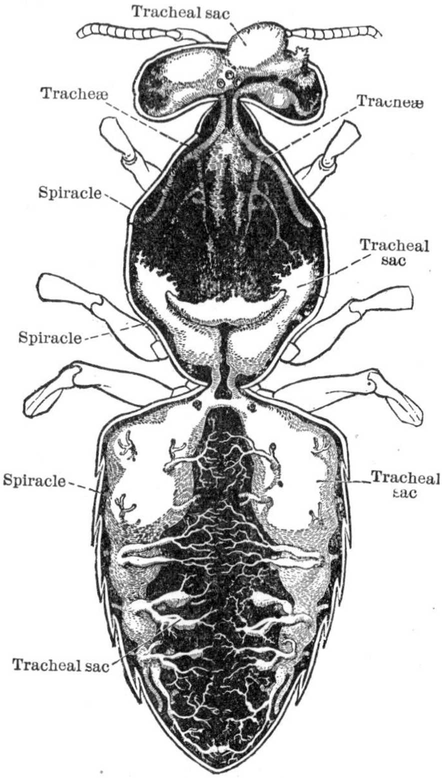

Fig. 242. — Respiratory system of worker honey-bee as seen from above, one anterior pair of abdominal sacs removed and transverse ventral commissures of abdomen not shown. (From Snodgrass, Tech. Series 18, Bur. Ent., U. S. Dep't. of Agric.)

Respiration (Fig. 242). — The honey-bee breathes through seven pairs of lateral openings called *spiracles,* one pair in the prothorax, one in the metathorax, and five in the abdomen. The spiracles open into tubes called *tracheæ* which branch and carry air to all parts of the body. Certain tracheæ are dilated to form *air sacs,* which are supposed to be of value during flight, since they can be enlarged at will and the specific gravity of the insect correspondingly decreased. Figure 243 shows the trachea to consist of a tube of a single layer of cells lined with chitin which is thickened so as to form a *spiral thread.* This chitinous lining keeps the trachea open. Each spiracle is provided with a valve which helps prevent the entrance of dust. Oxygen is carried directly to the tissues by the tracheæ and does not need to be transported by the blood.

Excretion. — The excretory organs are long, thread-like tubes called *malpighian tubules* (Fig. 241). They pour their excretions into the intestine at the point where it joins the stomach.

Nervous System. — There is a complicated bilobed ganglionic mass, the *brain*, in the dorsal part of the head. Nerves connect the brain with the compound eyes, ocelli, antennæ, and labrum. The brain is connected by nerve-cords with the *subœsophageal ganglion* which lies beneath the œsophagus in the head. This ganglion innervates the mandibles, labium, and other mouth parts. From the subœsophageal ganglion a *ventral chain of ganglia* (Fig. 241) extends posteriorly through the thorax and into the abdomen. Small *stomato-gastric ganglia* are connected with the organs of digestion, circulation, and respiration, and a delicate, sympathetic nervous system is also present.

Sense Organs. — The *compound eyes* are constructed on a plan similar to those of the crayfish (p. 258, Fig. 203) and are especially adapted for seeing moving objects. The *ocelli* are less complex than the compound eyes, and are probably of use only to distinguish light from darkness, although they may perceive form at very short distances.

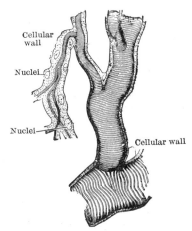

FIG. 243. — Portion of a trachea. (From Packard, after Leydig.)

The principal organs of *smell* are situated on the antennæ. They are hollows in the cuticle (Fig. 244), connected with a cell supplied with nerve-fibers. The queen possesses about 1600 smell hollows on each antenna, the worker 2400, and the drone 37,800. The sense of smell is considered of great importance in the life activities of bees.

Pits near the mouth of the bee have been identified as *taste organs.* Taste setæ are present near the end of the ligula (Fig. 237).

Certain pits on the antennæ are supposed to be end organs of *hearing* (Fig. 244). Sounds are produced by the vibrations of the wings and by the vibrations of a membrane which lies within each spiracular opening of the respiratory system.

Sense-organs of *touch* are hair-like structures on various parts of the body, but especially numerous on the antennæ. Two kinds are shown in Fig. 244, (1) small hairs, and (2) large " conoid " hairs.

Reproduction. — The sexes are separate except in abnormal cases. The spermatozoa arise in the two *testes* (Fig. 245), and pass through the *vasa deferentia* into the *seminal vesicles*, where they

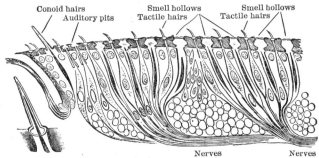

FIG. 244. — Longitudinal section through part of an antenna of a worker honey-bee. (From Cheshire.)

are stored. The seminal vesicles open into large *mucous glands* which unite at a point where the *ejaculatory duct* begins. During mating the spermatozoa pass through the ejaculatory duct and are transferred to the seminal receptacle of the female (Fig. 246) by the *penis* (Fig. 245).

The reproductive organs of the workers are undeveloped ovaries. The abdomen of the queen is almost completely filled by the two

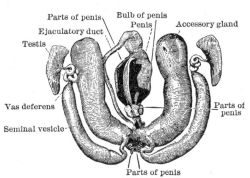

FIG. 245. — Reproductive organs of drone bee, dorsal view, natural position. (From Snodgrass, Tech. S., 18, Bur. Ent., U. S. Dep't. of Agric.)

ovaries (Fig. 246). Each ovary consists of a number of *ovarian tubules* in which are eggs in various stages of development. When ready for deposition, the eggs pass through the *oviducts* into the *vagina*. They are *fertilized* by spermatozoa from the *seminal receptacle* or *spermatheca*. The queen seems to be able to lay fertilized or unfertilized eggs according to the size of the cell in which they are to develop. *Fertilized eggs* are laid either in small worker cells (Fig. 248) or in large irregular queen cells, and develop into queens or workers. *Unfertilized eggs* are usually laid in drone cells, and those that develop become drones. How fertilization is controlled is still unknown.

The egg undergoes superficial *cleavage* (p. 84, Fig. 50, *D*) as in the crayfish (p. 261). A *blastoderm* of a single layer of cells is

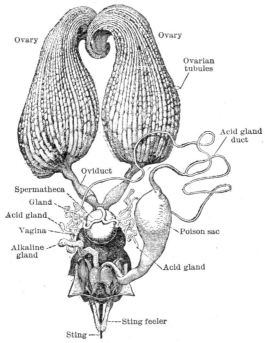

FIG. 246. — Reproductive organs, sting, and poison gland of queen honey-bee. (From Snodgrass, Tech. Series 18, Bur. Ent., U. S. Dep't. Agric.)

formed at the surface; this soon thickens on the ventral side, forming a *germ band*. The germ band segments, sends out protrusions which become appendages, and grows until it completely surrounds the egg. In three days the larva emerges from the eggshell.

The changes that take place in an insect during its growth constitute its *metamorphosis*. The life-history of an individual bee may be divided into four periods (Fig. 247): (1) egg, (2) larva, (3) pupa, (4) adult or imago (Fig. 236). When the larva hatches, it lies at the base of the cell (Fig. 247) floating in the food prepared by the workers and known as *chyle* or " bee milk." Chyle is composed of digested honey and pollen, probably mixed with a glandular secretion, and is given to all of the larvæ by the nurse bees during the first three days. Then the larvæ that will become workers are given honey and digested pollen in gradually increasing amounts; the drone larvæ, after the fourth day, also receive honey and undigested pollen; but the queen larvæ are fed lavishly on the rich albuminous bee milk, the " royal jelly," until they change to pupæ.

Growth during the larval period is accompanied by several *molts* of the chitinous larval envelope. At the end of the larval period the cells containing the young brood are covered over

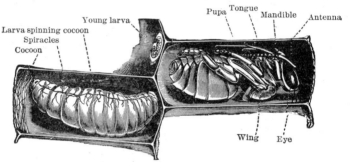

Fig. 247. — Larvæ and pupa of honey-bee in their cells. (From Packard, after Cheshire.)

with wax, feeding ceases, and the larvæ proceed to spin a *cocoon* of silk from their spinning glands (Fig. 247). These spinning glands become the salivary glands of the adult.

It takes the worker thirty-six hours to spin its cocoon, then it slowly changes into a *pupa*, or *chrysalis* (Fig. 247). Practically the entire body is made over at this time; the three regions, head, thorax, and abdomen, become distinct; externally the wings, legs, mouth parts, sting, antennæ, and eyes are visible; and the internal changes are even more striking, the larval organs developing into those of the adult, and new organs appearing. After a period of rest the pupa casts off its exoskeleton, and emerges as an adult.

The Activities of the Workers. — All of the duties necessary for maintaining a successful colony are performed by the workers, except mating with the queen, which is accomplished by the drones, and laying the eggs, which is done by the queen.

Building Honeycomb. — The wax which is used to build honeycomb is secreted in thin scales by the wax glands. The wax is removed by the wax pinchers (Fig. 238, B) and transferred to the mouth, where it is mixed with saliva and kneaded by the mandibles. If new comb is to be built, the wax is plastered to the roof, and in some mysterious way each bee puts its contribution almost exactly where it is to remain. The cells which are built up are hexagonal in shape and of various sizes. Six kinds may be recognized (Fig. 248), (1) *worker cells* in which workers are reared, (2) *drone cells* in which drones develop, (3) *queen cells* which are large and irregular, (4) *transition cells* between worker and drone cells, (5) *attachment cells* which fasten the comb to the top or sides of the hive, and (6) *honey cells* in which honey is stored. Honey may be stored also in drone, worker, and transition cells. Careful measurements

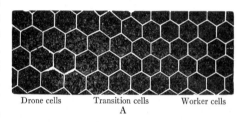

Drone cells   Transition cells   Worker cells
A

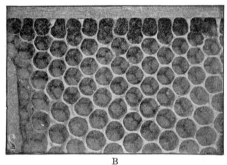

B

Fig. 248. — Honeycomb showing various kinds of cells. **A**, diagram showing comparative size of drone cells and worker cells. **B**, photograph of a piece of honeycomb showing circular cells and attachment cells. (From Root.)

have shown that the cells are seldom perfectly symmetrical, although in many cases they appear so to our eyes. The honey cells are built with entrances slightly above their bases, so that the honey stored in them will not flow out before it becomes " ripe."

The Collection of Propolis. — " Bee glue," as propolis is sometimes called, is a resinous material collected from buds and crevices of trees. It is transported in the pollen baskets, and is used, as soon as collected, to paint the inside of the hive, to fill up cracks, and to strengthen any loose parts.

Gathering Pollen. — Pollen grains are very small, of various shapes and colors, and are formed within a part of the flower known as the anther. To the bee, pollen is invaluable as a food, and is also used in preparing the cells containing pupæ. The peculiar structures on the legs and other parts of the bee's body used in collecting pollen have already been described (p. 284). Upon reaching the hive the pellets of pollen are pried out of the pollen basket by the spur at the termination of the tibia of the middle leg (Fig. 238, D), and deposited usually in worker cells. Pollen is the principal food of the larvæ. It is very rich in nitrogenous material, a food element not found in honey, and without which the young would starve. The gathering of pollen by bees has a great influence upon the flowers visited, since many species depend upon bees for transporting pollen from one to another.

Carrying Water. — During warm weather water is sucked up into the honey sac from dew, or brooks and pools, and carried to the larvæ in the hive.

The Manufacture of Honey. — Bees do not collect honey from flowers, but gather nectar, which is later transformed into honey. The nectar is lapped up by the tongue (Fig. 237), and transferred to the honey sac (Fig. 241), where it is stored while the bee is in the field. Nectar is placed in open cells in the well-ventilated hive until all but 18 to 20 per cent of the water contained in it has evaporated. When a cell is finally filled with " ripe " honey it is sealed with a cap of wax. The flavor of honey depends upon the kind of flowers from which the nectar is collected. The amount of honey produced in one hive in a fair season ranges from an average of about thirty pounds of comb honey to possibly fifty pounds of extracted honey.

Cleaning the Hive. — The health of the swarm depends upon the cleanliness of their domicile, since perfect sanitary conditions are necessary where so many individuals live in such close quarters. Dead bees, pieces of old comb, the excreta of the queen, drones, and others that remain in the hive, and any other waste materials, are immediately removed.

Ventilating the Hive. — Fresh air for the hive is obtained by the exertions of certain of the workers. Many bees near the entrance, and at other places in the hive, are busily engaged in vibrating their wings, and creating a current of air, which keeps the hive fresh, and aids in ripening the nectar. The loud buzzing which accompanies this activity is often heard at night after a large amount of nectar has been collected.

Guarding the Hive. — The hive is guarded against the intrusions of yellow-jackets, bee-moths, and other bees by workers, who wander back and forth near the entrance, and examine every creature that visits the colony. If the swarm is strong, the guards succeed, with the aid of the bee-keeper, in warding off all honey-loving enemies.

Swarming. — The number of bees in a hive increases very rapidly, since the queen usually lays from 950 to 1200 eggs per day. When the colony is in a prosperous condition, and there is danger of overcrowding, queen cells are built by the workers, usually around the fertilized eggs, and new queens are reared. Two queens do not live amicably in one hive, and, if such a condition arises, either there is a battle between the two, resulting in the death of one of them, or the workers kill one, or else the old queen collects from two to twenty thousand workers about her and flies away with them to found a new colony. This is known as swarming. The old hive is not broken up, but continues its existence as before.

Swarming occurs in May, June, or July, according to latitude, and a second swarming period may be inaugurated if weather conditions result in a midsummer flow of honey. Before issuing from the hive, the honey sacs are filled with honey to serve until a new home is found. The swarm, after flying a short distance, comes to rest upon the limb of a tree or other object, where it remains sometimes for several hours. A site for the new colony is sometimes chosen by scouting bees several days before the swarm leaves the parent hive. These scouts may also partially prepare the place by cleaning out loose dirt, bark, etc. The usual choice is a hollow tree, such as the wild ancestors of the honey-bee inhabited, and henceforth is called a " bee tree." One of the duties of the bee-keeper is to hive the swarms before they succeed in escaping to the woods. Swarms may also be formed artificially.

The Enemies and Diseases of Bees. — The bee-moth, *Galleria mellionella*, bee-louse, *Braula cæca*, kingbird, toad, lizard, spider, rat, skunk, bear, and other bees are all enemies of the honey-bee. Weak or neglected hives are especially liable to attack, and the bee-keeper is often obliged to help his bees combat the foe. The principal diseases of bees are foul brood, which is an infectious disease due to bacteria, and dysentery, which is usually caused by improper food or long confinement in the hive.

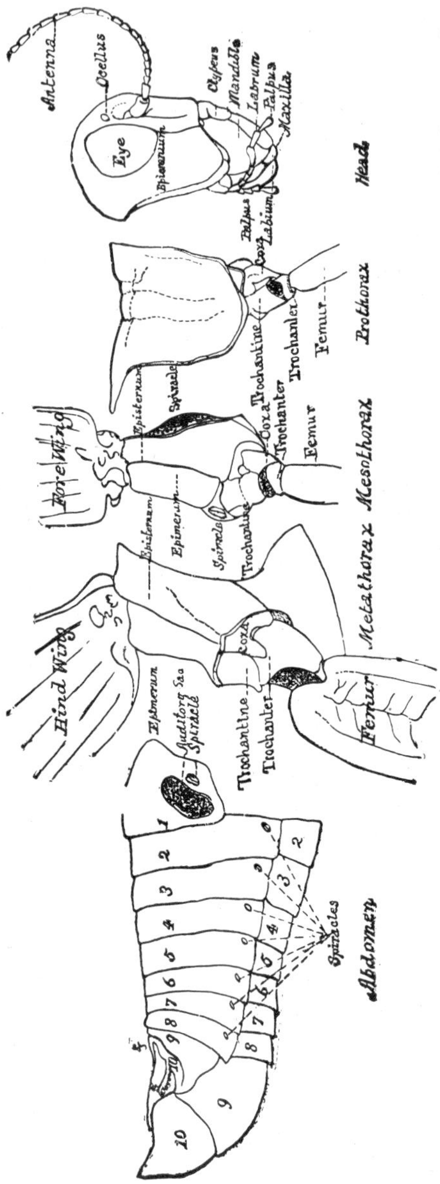

b. *The Anatomy and Physiology of Insects in General*

There are a larger number of species of insects known than of all other animals combined. Over three hundred thousand have been described and the number still unknown can only be imagined. The number of individuals of many species is also enormous. Insects range in size from $\frac{25}{100}$ mm. long (certain parasites) to over 155 mm. in length (*Dynastes hercules*, the Venezuelan beetle).

Anatomy and Physiology. — The honeybee is a highly specialized insect and exhibits adaptive structures to a remarkable extent. It does not, however, illustrate general anatomical features as well as some other species, *e.g.* the grass-

Fig. 249. — External anatomy of a grasshopper, *Melanoplus*, with the thorax separated from head and abdomen, and divided into its three parts. (From Packard.)

hopper (Fig. 249). An insect's body consists of three principal parts, (1) head, (2) thorax, (3) abdomen. The *head* bears a compound eye on either side, three simple eyes (*ocelli*) and a pair of antennæ in front, a frontal piece called the clypeus, and four pairs of appendages constituting the mouth-parts.

The *thorax* contains three segments, — prothorax, mesothorax, and metathorax. The mesothorax and metathorax bear each a pair of wings in most insects. Certain simple species (Aptera, p. 303, Fig. 259) do not possess wings; others (lice and fleas, pp. 310 and 322, Figs. 276 and 296) have no wings, but this is because they are degenerate. The flies (Diptera, p. 320, Fig. 292) have a pair of clubbed threads, called balancers or *halters*, in place of the metathoracic wings. Attached to each thoracic segment is a pair of legs.

The parts of a *thoracic segment* are well shown in the grasshopper. The dorsal part, the *tergum*, is composed of four pieces, termed *sclerites*, which are especially marked on the prothoracic segment. They are named the *præscutum*, *scutum*, *scutellum*, and *postscutellum*. The side of a thoracic segment is called the *pleurum;* it consists of three sclerites, the *episternum*, *epimeron*, and *parapteron*. The underside of each thoracic segment is called the *sternum*.

The *abdomen* is made up of eleven segments. The posterior end in the

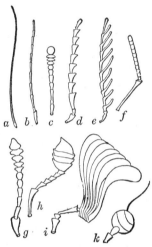

Fig. 250. — Different forms of antennæ of insects. *a*, bristle-like antenna of a grasshopper, *Locusta; b*, filiform, of a beetle, *Carabus; c*, moniliform, of a beetle, *Tenebrio; d*, dentate, of a beetle, *Elater; e*, pectinate, of *Ctenicera; f*, crooked, of honey-bee, *Apis; g*, club-shaped, of beetle, *Silpha; h*, knobbed, of beetle, *Necrophorus; i*, lamellated, of beetle, *Melolontha; k*, with bristle, from fly, *Sargus.* (From Sedgwick's Zoology, after Burmeister.)

female is usually modified by egg-laying structures (*ovipositors*), and in the male by a copulatory apparatus (*genitalia*). The abdomen is usually punctured by seven pairs of breathing pores (spiracles) and the thorax generally by two pairs.

The antennæ, mouth-parts, legs, and wings are among the most interesting external features of insects. The *antennæ* are usually tactile, olfactory, or auditory in function. They differ widely in form and structure, as shown in Figure 250. Often the antennæ of the male differ from those of the female.

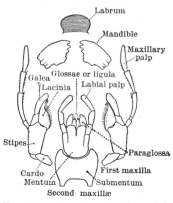

FIG. 251.— Mouth-parts of a cockroach. (From Kerr.)

The *mouth-parts* of insects are in most cases fitted either for biting (*mandibulate*) or sucking (*suctorial*). The cockroach possesses typical mandibulate mouth-parts (Fig. 251) consisting of an upper lip, the labrum, a lower lip, the labium, a pair of jaws, the mandibles, and a pair of auxiliary jaws, the maxillæ. The labium and maxillæ bear jointed feelers or palps which function as sense-organs. The labrum and labium hold the food while it is being masticated by the mandibles and maxillæ. The mandibles of insects that live on vegetation are adapted for crushing; those of carnivorous species are usually sharp and pointed, being fitted for biting and piercing. Suctorial mouth-parts are adapted for piercing the tissues of plants or animals and sucking juices. The mouth-parts of the honey-bee (Fig. 237) are suctorial, but highly modified. In the female mosquito (Fig. 252) the labrum and epipharynx combined form a sucking tube; the mandibles and maxillæ are piercing organs; the hypopharynx carries saliva; and the labium constitutes a sheath in which the other mouth-parts lie when not in use (Dimmock). The proboscis of the butterflies and moths (Fig. 253) is a sucking tube formed by the maxillæ.

The mouth-parts of insects are of considerable importance from an economic standpoint, since insects that eat solid food can be destroyed by spraying the food with poisonous mixtures, whereas those

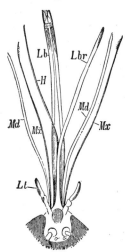

FIG. 252.—Mouth-parts of a mosquito, *Culex memorosus*. *H*, hypopharynx for piercing; *Lb*, lower lip or proboscis; *Lbr*, upper lip; *Lt*, labial palp; *Md*, mandibles; *Mx*, maxillæ. (From Sedgwick's Zoology, after Becher.)

that suck juices must be smothered with gases or have their spiracles closed with emulsion.

The *legs* of insects are used for various purposes and are highly modified for special functions. Those of the honey-bee have already been described (pp. 283 and 284, Fig. 238). A typical leg consists of five parts, — coxa (Fig. 238, B), trochanter, femur, tibia, and tarsus. The tarsus (Fig. 239) is usually composed of five segments and bears at the end a pair of claws, between which is a fleshy lobule, the pulvillus. Figure 254 shows a number of legs adapted for different uses. Running insects possess long, slender legs (*b*); the mantis (*a*) has its fore legs fitted for grasping; the hind legs of the grass-

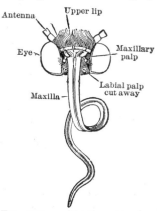

Fig. 253. — Mouth-parts of a moth, *Noctua*. (After Savigny.)

hopper (*c*) are used in leaping; the fore legs of the mole cricket (*d*) are modified for digging; and the hind legs of the water beetle (*e*) are fitted for swimming. Many other types could be mentioned.

The *wings* of insects enable their owners to fly rapidly from place to place and thus to escape from enemies and to find a bountiful food supply. The success of insects in the struggle for existence is in part attributed to the presence of wings. Wings are outgrowths of the skin strengthened by a framework of chitinous tubes, called *veins* or *nervures*, which divide the wing into *cells*. The veins vary in distribution in different

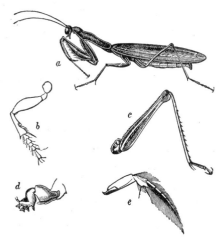

Fig. 254. — Different forms of legs of insects. *a*, predatory leg of praying mantis, *Mantis*; *b*, running leg of a beetle, *Carabus*; *c*, leaping leg of a grasshopper, *Acridium*; *d*, digging leg of mole-cricket, *Gryllotalpa*; *e*, swimming leg of *Dytiscus*. (From Sedgwick's Zoology, after règne animal.)

species, but are quite constant in individuals of any given species; they are consequently used to a considerable extent for purposes of classification. The principal longitudinal veins,

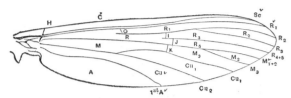

FIG. 255. — The right wing of a male mosquito, *Anopheles maculipennis*. *A*, anal area; *1st A*, anal nervure; *C*, costa; *Cu*, cubitus; *H*, humeral cross-nervure; *I*, cross-nervure between R_2 and R_{4+5}; *J*, cross-nervure between radial and medial systems; *K*, cross-nervure between medial and cubital systems; *M*, media; *O*, cross-nervure between R_1 and R_2; *R*, radius; *Sc*, subcosta. (From Sedgwick's Zoology, after Nuttall and Shipley.)

as shown in Figure 255, are the *costa* (*C*), *subcosta* (*Sc*), *radius* (*R*), *media* (*M*), *cubitus* (*Cu*), and *anal* (*A*). Cross veins (*I*, *J*, *K*) frequently occur. Modifications come about by reduction or by addition. In the beetles (COLEOPTERA) the fore-wings are sheath-like, and are called *elytra*. The fore-wings of ORTHOPTERA (grasshoppers, etc.) are leathery and are known as *tegmina*.

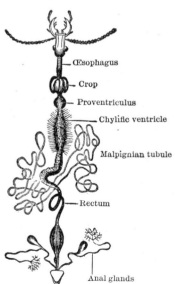

FIG. 256. — Alimentary canal and glandular appendages of a beetle, *Carabus*. (From Sedgwick's Zoology, after Dufour.)

Œsophagus

Crop

Proventriculus

Chylific ventricle

Malpignian tubule

Rectum

Anal glands

Of the *internal organs* of insects the alimentary canal and respiratory systems are of particular interest. The *alimentary canal* is modified according to the character of the food. An insect with mandibulate mouth-parts (Fig. 256) usually possesses (1) an *œsophagus* which is dilated to form a *crop* in which food is stored, (2) a muscular *gizzard* or *proventriculus* which strains the food and may aid in crushing it, (3) a *stomach* or *ventriculus* into which a number of glandular tubes (*gastric cæca*) pour digestive fluids, and (4) an *intestine* with urinary or *malpighian tubules* at the anterior end. Suctorial insects, like the butterflies and moths (Fig. 257), are provided with a *muscular pharynx* which acts as a pumping organ and a *sac* for the storage of juices.

The *respiratory system* of insects is in general like that of the honey-bee (p. 288, Figs. 242 and 243), but modifications occur in many species, especially in the larvæ of those that live in water. Aquatic larvæ, in many cases, do not have spiracles, but get oxygen by means of thread-like or leaf-like cuticular outgrowths at the sides or posterior end of the body, termed *tracheal gills* (Fig. 261, A). Damsel-fly larvæ possess caudal tracheal gills, and the larvæ of the dragon-flies take water into the rectum which is lined with papillæ abundantly supplied with tracheæ. The economic importance of a tracheal respiratory system has already been pointed out.

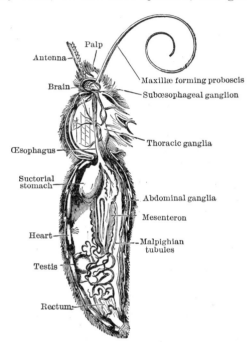

Fig. 257. — Longitudinal section through the body of a moth, *Sphinx ligustri*, showing the alimentary canal of a sucking insect. (From Sedgwick's Zoology, after Newport.)

Growth and Metamorphosis. — Three types of insects may be distinguished with respect to the method of their development, (1) ametabola, (2) heterometabola, and (3) holometabola. The *ametabolous* insects are essentially like the adult, except in size, when they hatch from the egg; they develop to maturity without a metamorphosis. The APTERA (p. 303, Fig. 259) are ametabolous.

The *heterometabolous* insects hatch from the egg and develop into adults without passing through a true pupal period. In the grasshopper, for example (Fig. 258), the young resembles the adult except for the absence of wings and mature reproductive organs. Such a stage is usually spoken of as a *nymph*. Orders II to XI of Table XII contain heterometabolous insects. Many of the species belonging to these orders change considerably during their growth period, but they are all more or less active throughout their development and are said to undergo *direct* or *incomplete metamorphosis*.

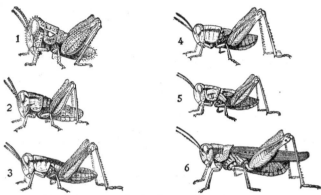

Fig. 258. — Partial metamorphosis of a grasshopper, *Melanoplus femurrubrum*, showing the five nymph stages, and the gradual growth of the wings. (From Packard, after Emerton.)

Holometabolous insects, such as the honey-bee (Fig. 247), pass through both a larval and a pupal stage in their development. The majority of insects belong to this type (Table XII, orders XII to XIX).

c. General Survey of the Orders of Insects

Classification. — Insect classification is based principally on the following characteristics: (1) the presence or absence of wings, and their structure when present, (2) the structure of the mouth-parts, and (3) the character of the metamorphosis. Authorities differ with regard to the number of orders that should be recognized, and two rather definite classifications have resulted; these are known as (1) the condensed classification, and (2) the extended classification, and are correlated in Table XII. Because of the large number of orders space will permit only a few words about each. Illustrations have been provided to show the principal characteristics.

TABLE XII

CONDENSED CLASSIFICATION ORDER	EXTENDED CLASSIFICATION ORDER		COMMON NAMES
I. Aptera	I	Aptera	Springtails, fishmoths.
	II	Ephemerida	May-flies.
	III	Odonata	Dragon-flies.
	IV	Plecoptera	Stone-flies.
II. Pseudoneuroptera	V	Isoptera	Termites or white ants.
	VI	Corrodentia	Book-lice, bark-lice.
	VII	Mallophaga	Biting bird-lice.
	VIII	Thysanoptera	Thrips.
III. Orthoptera	IX	Euplexoptera	Earwigs.
	X	Orthoptera	Grasshoppers, crickets, cockroaches.
IV. Hemiptera	XI	Hemiptera	Lice, bugs, plant-lice.
V. Neuroptera	XII	Neuroptera	Ant-lions, hellgramite.
	XIII	Mecoptera	Scorpion flies.
	XIV	Trichoptera	Caddice-flies.
VI. Lepidoptera	XV	Lepidoptera	Moths, skippers, butterflies.
VII. Diptera	XVI	Diptera	Flies, sheep-ticks.
	XVII	Siphonaptera	Fleas.
VIII. Coleoptera	XVIII	Coleoptera	Beetles.
IX. Hymenoptera	XIX	Hymenoptera	Ants, wasps, bees, saw-flies, ichneumon-flies.

Order 1. Aptera. — SPRINGTAILS AND FISHMOTHS (Figs. 259, 260). — Insects without wings, probably descended from wingless ancestors; biting mouth-parts retracted within the cavity of the head; no metamorphosis.

The very primitive living insect, *Campodea staphylinus* (Fig. 259), belongs to this order. The most common species is the fishmoth, *Lepisma saccharina* (Fig. 260), which lives on dry starchy food such as book bindings and starched clothing. Another interesting species is the snow-flea, *Achorutes nivicola*, which is sometimes a pest in maple sugar camps, since large numbers collect in the sap.

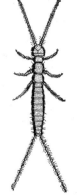

FIG. 259. — Order APTERA. *Campodea staphylinus*. (From Sedgwick's Zoology, after Lubbock.)

FIG. 260. — Order APTERA. *Lepisma saccharina*, the fishmoth. (From Sedgwick's Zoology.)

Order 2. Ephemerida. — MAY-FLIES (Fig. 261). — Insects possessing delicate membranous wings, with many cross veins; the fore-wings large, the hind wings small or wanting; mouth-parts poorly developed; metamorphosis incomplete.

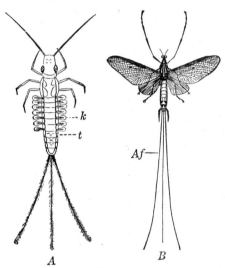

The young (nymph) may-fly (Fig. 261, A) lives in the water and breathes by means of tracheal gills. After from one to three years, depending upon the species, the nymph emerges from the water and becomes a winged adult (Fig. 261, B). This adult is said to be in the subimago stage, since it moults after acquiring wings. No other insect is known to do this. The paired condition of the egg ducts of the female

FIG. 261. — Order EPHEMERIDA. **A**, nymph of the May-fly. *k*, tracheal gills; *t*, principal trunk of tracheal system. **B**, adult may-fly. *Af*, anal filaments. (From Sedgwick's Zoology.)

is also unique. Adult may-flies probably take no food; they mate, lay their eggs, and, after a few hours, die.

Order 3. Odonata. — DRAGON-FLIES AND DAMSEL-FLIES (Fig. 262). — Insects possessing four membranous wings, with many cross veins; hind wings as large as or larger than fore-wings; each wing with joint, the nodus, on front margin; biting mouth-parts; metamorphosis incomplete.

The dragon-flies are also called darning-needles and snake doctors.

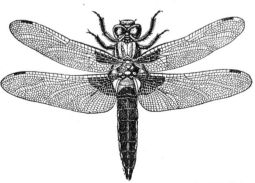

FIG. 262. — Order ODONATA. A dragon-fly, *Libellula depressa*. (From Miall, after Charpentier.)

When at rest they hold their wings horizontally, differing in this respect from the damsel-flies, which hold their wings vertically over their backs. The adult dragon-flies devour large numbers of mosquitoes, but unfortunately feed only by day, whereas some of the mosquitoes are most active after dark. The young live in the water; they breathe by drawing in and expelling water from the rectum, which is lined with tracheal gills. The damsel-flies are more delicate than the dragon-flies. Their young possess leaf-like tracheal gills at the posterior end of the body. The compound eyes of the ODONATA are made up of an enormous number of elements (ommatidia); more than 30,000 facets have been counted in the eye of one species.

FIG. 263. — Order PLECOPTERA. Stone-fly, *Perla maxima*. (From Sedgwick's Zoology, after Pictet.)

Order 4. Plecoptera. — STONE-FLIES (Fig. 263). — Insects with four membranous wings; hind wings large and folded like a fan; biting mouth-parts; metamorphosis incomplete.

The stone-fly nymphs live in brooks on the underside of stones, and breathe by means of filamentous tracheal gills which extend out from just behind the legs. They serve as food for fishes.

Order 5. Isoptera. — TERMITES or WHITE ANTS (Fig. 264). — Insects with four similar wings, leathery in structure and lying

C   D

FIG. 264. — Order ISOPTERA. Termites. **A**, male or king of *Termes*. **B**, female or queen of *Termes*. **C**, worker of *Termes*. **D**, soldier of *Termes*. (From the Cambridge Natural History; C and D, after Grassi.)

A   B

flat on the back, or wingless (workers); biting mouth-parts; metamorphosis incomplete.

The termites are social insects and live in colonies. Each colony contains a queen (Fig. 264, B) that lays all of the eggs, a winged male (A) that fertilizes the queen, a number of wingless workers (C) that build the nest, procure food, and raise the young, and wingless soldiers (D) whose duty it is to protect the colony. The food of termites consists principally of dead wood, and in the tropics of Africa and South America, where white ants abound, a good deal of damage is done to houses, furniture, etc. Even in

FIG. 265. — Order CORRODENTIA. A bark-louse. (From Brehm.)

North America injuries to the timbers in buildings and to books in libraries have been reported. The termites work only in the dark, and build tunnels for this purpose. Their nests are often inhabited by other species of insects; these are called termitophiles. Over one hundred species of termitophiles have been recorded.

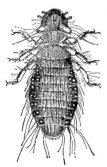

FIG. 266. — Order MALLOPHAGA. Biting bird-louse, *Menopon pallidum*, inhabiting the common fowl. (From Sedgwick's Zoology, after Piaget.)

Order 6. Corrodentia. BOOKLICE AND BARK-LICE (Fig. 265). — Insects without wings or with four membranous wings, with few cross veins; fore-wings larger than hind wings; wings held roof-like over body; biting mouth-parts; metamorphosis incomplete.

Book-lice are wingless insects often found in old books, the paper and bindings of which they devour. Bark-lice (Fig. 265) have wings. They live out of doors on tree trunks and feed on lichens.

Order 7. Mallophaga. — BITING BIRD-LICE (Fig. 266). — Parasitic insects without wings; biting mouth-parts; metamorphosis incomplete.

Bird-lice live among the feathers of birds or hair of mammals. They eat hair, feathers, and epidermal scales, but are not injurious on this account. The irritation caused by their sharp claws makes their hosts restless and consequently weak and thin. Chickens take dust baths to rid themselves of *Menopon pallidum* (Fig. 266), the most common species.

Order 8. Thysanoptera. — THRIPS (Fig. 267). — Insects with four narrow, membranous wings fringed with long hairs; mouth-parts intermediate; the metamorphosis transitional, not complete, but a quiescent stage occurs.

FIG. 267. — Order THYSANOPTERA. Pea-thrips, *Euthrips pyri*. (From Moulton-Bul. 80, Bur. Ent., U. S. Dep't Agric.)

The feet of these insects are without claws, their place being taken by bladders adapted for clinging to leaves or flowers. The males are not common, since parthenogenesis is the usual method of reproduction. Several species are distinct pests; these are the onion-thrips (*Thrips tabaci*), the wheat-thrips (*Euthrips tritici*), the grass-thrips (*Anaphothrips striatus*), and the fruit thrips (*Euthrips pyri*) (Fig. 267).

FIG. 268. — Order EUPLEXOPTERA. Earwig, *Anisolabris maritima*. (From Davenport.)

Order 9. Euplexoptera. — EARWIGS (Fig. 268). — Insects usually with four wings; fore-wings leathery, small, and veinless; biting mouth-parts; posterior end of abdomen bears pair of forceps; metamorphosis incomplete.

This order contains the family FORFICULIDÆ. The earwigs are not common in North America. They feed at night on fruit and flowers, but are not of any economic importance in this country.

Order 10. Orthoptera. — COCKROACHES, WALKING-STICKS, MANTIDS, GRASSHOPPERS, LOCUSTS, KATYDIDS, AND CRICKETS (Figs. 269–274). — Insects with four wings; the fore-wings leathery; the hind wings folded like a fan; biting mouth-parts; metamorphosis incomplete.

The principal families of ORTHOPTERA are as follows:

(1) *Blattidæ* (COCKROACHES, Fig. 269). These insects have legs fitted for running. The common American species are the " croton-bug " (*Ectobia germanica*) which was introduced from Germany, and the " black-beetle " (*Periplaneta orientalis*, Fig. 269) from Asia.

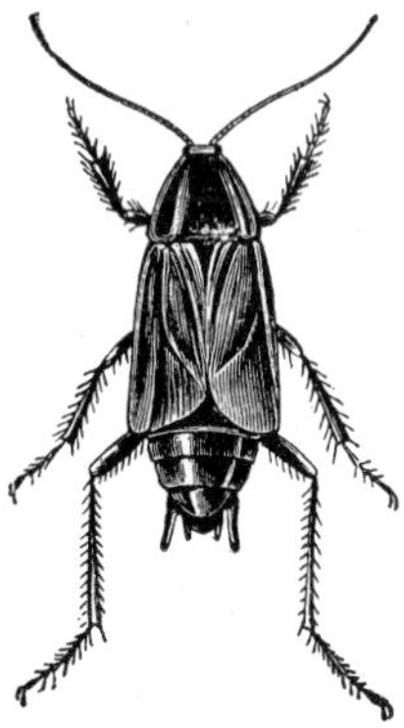

(2) *Mantidæ* (PRAYING-MANTIS, Fig. 270). The fore legs of these insects are fitted for grasping. Their food consists largely of other insects.

(3) *Phasmidæ* (WALKING-STICKS, Fig. 271). The legs of the phasmides are adapted for walking. Walking-sticks feed on foliage and are difficult to distinguish from twigs, hence their name.

(4) *Acridiidæ* (LOCUSTS OR SHORT-HORNED GRASSHOPPERS, Fig. 272). The locusts have leaping legs and short antennæ. They feed on vegetation and often do considerable damage. The most famous species is *Melanoplus spretus*, the Rocky Mountain locust (Fig. 272), which is occasionally migratory and devours everything in its path. The red-legged locust, *Melanoplus femurrubrum*, and the Carolina locust, *Dissosteira carolina*, are common species.

FIG. 269. — Order ORTHOPTERA. Cockroach, *Periplaneta orientalis*. (From Sedgwick's Zoology.)

(5) *Locustidæ* (LONG-HORNED GRASSHOPPERS, Fig. 273). The members of this family have slender antennæ longer than the body. The meadow grasshoppers and katydids belong here.

FIG. 270. — Order ORTHOPTERA. Praying-mantis, *Phasmomantis carolina*. (From Davenport, after Packard.)

(6) *Gryllidæ* (CRICKETS, Fig. 274). The mole crickets burrow in the ground; the true crickets are those that make themselves known by their chirping about houses; the tree crickets inhabit trees.

Order 11. Hemiptera. — Bugs, Lice, Aphids, Scale Insects (Figs. 275–279). — Insects without wings or with four wings; one suborder with fore-wings thickened at base; sucking mouth-parts; metamorphosis incomplete.

Hemiptera may be separated conveniently into three suborders.

(1) *Parasitica* (Lice, Fig. 275). This suborder is represented in North America by

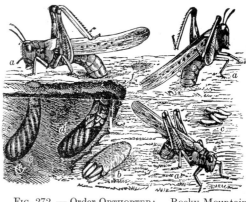

FIG. 272. — Order Orthoptera. Rocky Mountain grasshopper or locust, *Melanoplus spretus*. *a, a, a*, females in different positions, laying eggs; *b*, egg-pod taken from ground, with end broken open; *c*, eggs lying loose on ground; *d, e*, earth partly removed to show egg mass in place (*e*) and one being placed (*d*); *f*, where egg mass has been covered up. (After Riley, from Yearbook Dep't Agric., 1908.)

FIG. 271. — Order Orthoptera. The northern "walking-stick," *Diapheromera femorata*. (From Davenport.)

a single family, the Pediculidæ. These are wingless and parasitic on the bodies of man and other mammals. They have claws fitted for clinging to hairs, and an unjointed beak for penetrating the skin and sucking juices. The species infesting man are

FIG. 273. — Order Orthoptera. Katydid, *Microcentrum retinerve*. (From Sedgwick, after Riley.)

Pediculus capitis, the head-louse (Fig. 275), *P. vestimenti*, the body-louse, and *Phthirius inguinalis*, the crab-louse. Domestic animals are infested by members of the genus *Hæmatopinus*. *H. piliferus* is the dog-louse, *H. urius*, the hog-louse, and *H. spinulosus*, the rat-louse.

Fig. 274.— Order ORTHOPTERA. House-cricket, *Gryllus domesticus*. (From the Cambridge Natural History.)

(2) *Homoptera* (PLANT-LICE, SCALE INSECTS, CICADAS, TREE HOPPERS, SPITTLE INSECTS, Figs. 276–278). The HOMOPTERA have wings, when present, similar in thickness, and a jointed beak which arises from the posterior, ventral part of the head.

The plant-lice or aphids (Family APHIDIDÆ, Fig. 276) are of considerable biological and economic importance. They are very small (less than $\frac{1}{4}$ inch), but extremely prolific. In summer certain females, called the stem mothers, bring forth living young which have developed within their bodies from unfertilized eggs. In the autumn fertilized eggs are laid, which serve to carry the race through the winter. Many aphids are very destructive to vegetation. The grape-phylloxera, *Phylloxera vastatrix* (Fig.

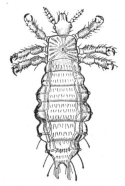

Fig. 275.— Order HEMIPTERA. Head-louse, *Pediculus capitis*. (From the Cambridge Natural History, after Piaget.)

276), is the most notorious; it punctures the roots of grape-vines, causing decay or "cancer" and the formation of tubercles. The woolly apple-aphis attacks the roots and twigs of apple trees; the "green fly" injures wheat, oats, and other grains. A host of other plants are also infested.

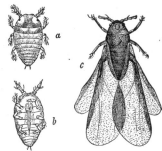

Fig. 276. — Order HEMIPTERA. Grape-louse, *Phylloxera vastatrix*. a, wingless form. b, same, ventral surface. c, winged form. (From Sedgwick's Zoology.)

The scale insects (Family COCCIDÆ) are of the greatest importance to fruit growers. They are small but numerous. The San José scale,

Aspidiotus perniciosus (Fig. 277), was imported from its native home in Japan or China to California. It has increased and spread over a large part of this country and has been the cause of considerable legislation in an effort to control its depredations. The cottony cushion scale, *Icerya purchasi*, which came near ruining the orange groves of California, was successfully controlled by a

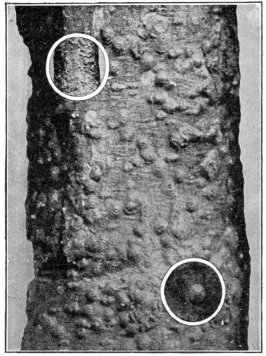

FIG. 277.— San José scales on bark of tree. Small circle above, natural size; small circle below, highly magnified. (Photo by O'Kane.)

lady beetle, *Novius cardinalis* (Fig. 302), introduced from Australia. This beetle is the natural enemy of the cottony cushion scale, which is also a native of Australia. In two or three years these beetles checked the inroads of this species of scale insect.

The cicadas (Family CICADIDÆ, Fig. 278) are especially interesting, since one of them, the seventeen-year cicada or " locust " (*Cicada septendecim*, Fig. 278), lives underground as a nymph for over sixteen years. The eggs (F) are laid in slits made by the female in living twigs (E). The young (A) hatch in about

six weeks, drop to the ground, and burrow beneath the surface
(B). Here they feed on juices from roots and on humus until
the summer of the seventeenth year, when they emerge from

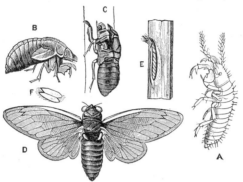

the ground (C) and
transform into adults
(D). Twenty differ-
ent broods are known
in this country, and
it is possible to foretell
approximately   when
and where each swarm
will appear. The com-
mon cicada is the
green dog-day har-
vest-fly, *Cicada tibi-
cen.* The males are
provided with sound-
making organs, and,
since these are lacking

FIG. 278. — Order HEMIPTERA. Seventeen-year
locust, *Cicada septendecim.* **A**, larva, **B**, nymph.
C, nymph skin after emergence of adult. **D**, adult.
E, section of tree showing how eggs are laid. **F**, two
eggs enlarged. (From Sedgwick's Zoology, after
Riley.)

in the female, the philosopher Xenarchos remarked, " Happy is
the cicada, since its wife has no voice."

(3) *Heteroptera* (THE TRUE BUGS, Fig. 279). The first pair
of wings of the HETEROPTERA, when present, are thickened at
the base. The jointed beak arises from
the front part of the head. About twenty-
six families are recognized in this suborder. They include aquatic forms such
as   water-boatmen   (CORISIDÆ),   back
swimmers (NOTONECTIDÆ), giant water-
·bugs (BELOSTOMATIDÆ), water-striders
(HYDROBATIDÆ),   and   marsh-treaders
(LIMNOBATIDÆ), and land-bugs such as
the assassin bugs (REDUVIIDÆ), bedbugs
(ACANTHIIDÆ), chinch-bugs (LYGÆIDÆ,
Fig. 279), squash-bugs (COREIDÆ), and
stink-bugs (PENTATOMIDÆ). The aquatic
members of this suborder show remark-

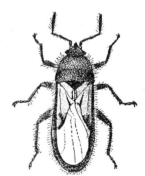

FIG. 279. — Order HEMIP-
TERA.   Chinch-bug, *Blissus
leucopterus.* (After Webster).

able adaptations for life in the water.   In many the legs are modified for swimming, the colors of the body are such as to conceal
them, and the methods of obtaining oxygen while under water are

extremely interesting. Certain of the terrestrial species are of great economic importance. The assassin bugs usually prey upon obnoxious insects, including the bedbug, and are therefore beneficial to man; the chinch-bug (Fig. 279) is noted for the enormous damage it has done to the grain fields in the Mississippi Valley; and the squash bugs infest squash and pumpkin vines.

Order 12. Neuroptera. — Aphis-lions, Dobson-flies, and Ant-lions (Fig. 280). — Insects possessing four membranous wings with many veins; biting mouth-parts; complete metamorphosis.

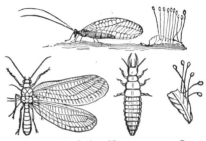

FIG. 280. — Order NEUROPTERA. Lace-wing fly, *Chrysopa*, with eggs and larva. (From Packard.)

Only a few families have been left in the old Linnean order NEUROPTERA; the rest have been taken out and grouped together as distinct orders.

The dobson-fly, *Corydalis cornuta*, is a well-known representative. Its larva has many local names and is used extensively as fish bait. The larvæ of *Hemerobius* and of the lace-wing fly,

FIG. 281. — Order MECOPTERA. Scorpion fly, *Panorpa communis*, male. (From Sedgwick's Zoology, after Sharp.)

Chrysopa (Fig. 280), are called aphis-lions since they destroy countless numbers of aphids by piercing them with their sharp jaws and drinking their blood. The eggs of *Chrysopa* are fastened to the top of upright threads which are attached to a twig or leaf; they are thus protected from predaceous insects, including the young aphis-lions themselves. The larvæ of many ant-lions live at the bottom of pits in the sand, where they capture and drink the blood of any ants that chance to slip down into the trap.

Order 13. Mecoptera. — SCORPION FLIES AND OTHERS (Fig. 281). — Insects possessing four membranous wings with numerous veins; head prolonged into a beak; biting mouth-parts; metamorphosis complete.

The common name of these insects is due to the fact that in some species the abdomen of the male terminates in a structure resembling the sting of a scorpion. Little is known about the habits of the MECOPTERA.

Order 14. Trichoptera. — CADDICE-FLIES (Fig. 282). — Insects possessing four membranous wings with many longitudinal veins and covered with hairs; rudimentary mouth-parts; metamorphosis complete.

The term caddice-fly is derived from the case (Fig. 282, A) which its aquatic larva builds of leaves, grass stems, or grains of sand as a means of protection. The larva (B) can extend the fore part of the body and drag its case from place to place or can retreat into its house for safety. Thread-like tracheal gills are present on the abdomen. Each species builds a certain kind of case which can be distinguished from those built by other species.

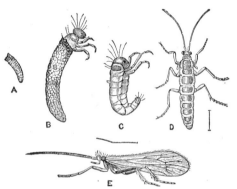

FIG. 282. — Order TRICHOPTERA. Stages in the development of a caddice-fly, *Enoicyla*. **A**, case of full-grown larva. **B**, larva in case, enlarged. **C**, larva removed from case. **D**, wingless adult female. **E**, male. (From the Cambridge Natural History, after Ritseona.)

Order 15. Lepidoptera. — BUTTERFLIES, SKIPPERS, AND MOTHS (Figs. 283-290). — Insects with four membranous wings covered with scales; usually sucking mouth-parts; metamorphosis complete.

The members of this order are famous for their varied and brilliant colors; these are produced by the scales. The mouth-parts form a sucking tube (Fig. 253) which may be five or six inches long and is coiled under the head when not in use. This sucking proboscis is used to obtain nectar from flowers. The larvæ of the LEPIDOPTERA are called caterpillars, and are in many cases extremely injurious to vegetation.

Over seven thousand species of LEPIDOPTERA have been described as inhabitants of this country. These may be separated for convenience into two suborders, (1) the RHOPALOCERA or butterflies and skippers, and (2) the HETEROCERA or moths.

Suborder 1. Rhopalocera (BUTTERFLIES AND SKIPPERS). —
The butterflies and skippers may be distinguished from the moths
by the knoblike swelling near the end of the antennæ. The
skippers usually possess in addition to this knob a terminal recurved point. Moths do not possess knobbed antennæ. The
members of the two suborders differ also in habits. since the butterflies are active during the day, whereas
the moths usually fly at night or twilight.

Most of the skippers belong to the
family HESPERIDÆ. They are generally
small and comparatively dull-colored
RHOPALOCERA that " skip " about close
to the ground from one plant to another,
like a wounded butterfly.

The beautiful swallowtail butterflies
belong to the family PAPILIONIDÆ.
They are characterized by one to three
" tails " projecting backward from their
hind wings. The tiger swallowtail, *Pa-
pilio turnus*, is a well-known species. Its
larvæ feed principally on the wild cherry.
A " negro " variety of the tiger swallowtail called *glaucus* occurs in some localities.

FIG. 283. — The dead-leaf
butterfly, *Kallima paralecta*.
(From Woodruff, after Weis-
mann.)

The family NYMPHALIDÆ, or brush-
footed butterflies, contains many common and interesting species. The
mourning-cloak, *Euvanessa antiopa*, is one of the first to appear
in the spring. Its larvæ are injurious to willows and poplars, the
leaves of which they devour.

Certain butterflies exhibit a condition known as protective
mimicry. An example is the dead-leaf butterfly, *Kallima paralecta* (Fig. 283), which resembles a dead leaf so closely that it is
supposed thereby to escape the notice of its enemies. It is said
to mimic the leaf. Other butterflies are said to mimic one another.
Thus the viceroy, *Basilarchia archippus*, which is supposed to be
relished by butterfly-eating animals, is said to mimic the milkweed
or monarch butterfly, *Anosia plexippus*, which is distasteful and
hence immune to attack. Protective mimicry has also been

described among other animals, for example, the harmless bee-fly, *Eristalis tenax*, is supposed to mimic the honey bee, and the harmless snake, *Cemophora coccinea*, resembles very closely the venomous coral snake in the southern United States. Whether these very close resemblances have any real significance is still an unsettled problem.

The cabbage-butterfly, *Pieris rapæ* (Fig. 284), is a member of the family PIERIDÆ. It is a serious pest because of the destruction to cabbages caused by its green caterpillars. This species was accidentally introduced from Europe. It was first discovered at Quebec in 1860. From there it rapidly spread over a large part of North America.

FIG. 284. — Order LEPIDOPTERA. Cabbage butterfly, *Pieris rapæ.* **a**, caterpillar. **b**, chrysalis. (From Osborn, after Riley.)

Suborder 2. ***Heterocera*** (MOTHS). — The moths are of great importance to man because of the damage done by some of them and the benefits derived from others. The hawk-moths, or humming-bird moths (SPHINGIDÆ), have a thick body and narrow, pointed wings, and, when hovering before a petunia or primrose, resemble a humming-bird. The larvæ live on the leaves of tomato and tobacco plants, Virginia creeper, and many others; they are usually very large. The family ARCTIIDÆ contains the fall-webworm, *Hyphantria cunea*, the larvæ of which live together in a web and eat the leaves of many kinds of trees and shrubs. The white-spotted tussock-moth, whose larvæ feed on the leaves of trees and are often very troublesome, belongs to the family LYMANTRIDÆ. Another important member of this family is the gypsy-moth, *Porthetria dispar* (Fig. 285). The gypsy-moth was imported from Europe. Its caterpillars devour leaves and have killed many of the finest shade trees in certain parts of Massachusetts.

A number of large common moths are placed in the family
BOMBYCIDÆ; for example, the cecropia, *Platysamia cecropia*,
the giant silkworm moth, *Telea polyphemus*, the luna moth, *Tropæa
luna*, the "tent-caterpillar," *Clisiocampa americana* and the silkworm moth, *Bombyx mori*. The silkworm moth (Fig. 286, C)
is thoroughly domesticated
and, so far as is known,
does not occur in a wild
state. The silk industry

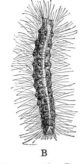

FIG. 285. — Order LEPIDOPTERA.   Gypsy-moth, *Porthetria dispar*.   **A**, female.
B, larva. **C**, pupa.   (From Osborn, after Howard.)

originated in China many centuries B.C. It did not become very
important in this country until the nineteenth century. There are
now about a hundred million dollars invested in the silk industries
of the United States. The moths lay their eggs on cloth or paper
provided for them. The larvæ (Fig. 286, A) are fed principally
on mulberry leaves, and when about forty days old spin a cocoon
(B) of a single continuous thread averaging over a thousand feet

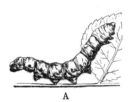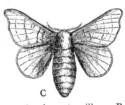

FIG. 286. — Order LEPIDOPTERA.   Silkworm, *Bombyx mori*.   **A**, caterpillar.   **B**,
cocoon.   **C**, adult female moth.   (From Shipley and MacBride.)

long. In the cocoon the larva pupates. Silk is obtained by killing the pupa with heat or boiling water, then clearing away the
loose outside floss, and unwinding the thread.

Among the important moths of the family NOCTUIDÆ are the
army-worm. *Heliophila unipuncta*, the cotton-worm, *Aletia
argillacea*, and the boll-worm, *Heliothis armiger*. The army-worms

(Fig. 287) are striped caterpillars that feed on growing wheat, oats, corn, timothy, blue grass, and other plants. They migrate from one field to another in large numbers, hence their name. The

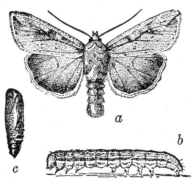

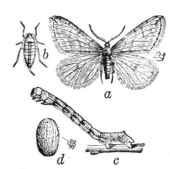

FIG. 287.— Order LEPIDOPTERA. Army-worm, *Heliophila unipuncta*. **a**, adult; **b**, larva, with eggs of a parasitic fly (tachinid) on back; **c**, pupa or chrysalis. (From Webster, Yearbook Dep't. Agric., 1908.)

FIG. 288. — Order LEPIDOPTERA. Spring canker-worm. **a**, male. **b**, female. **c**, larva. **d**, eggs, natural size and enlarged. (From Circ. 9, Bur. Ent., U. S. Dep't. Agric.)

tachina flies parasitize many of them and fungus diseases attack others, so that they are partially held in check by their natural enemies. The cotton worm eats the leaves of the cotton plant. The boll-worm is widely distributed and feeds not only upon the cotton boll but also upon corn, tomatoes, tobacco, and other plants.

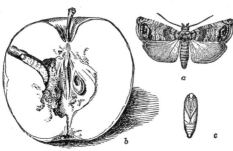

FIG. 289. — Order LEPIDOPTERA. Codlin-moth, *Carpocapsa pomonella*. **a**, adult. **b**, larva in an apple. **c**, pupa or chrysalis. (From Farmer's Bul. 283, U. S. Dept. Agric.)

The larvæ of the GEOMETRIDÆ are called measuring worms because of their looping method of locomotion. One of the most important species is the spring canker-worm, *Paleacrita vernata* (Fig. 288), the larvæ of which eat the foliage of fruit trees in various parts of the country.

The codlin-moth, or apple-worm (Fig. 289), *Carpocapsa pomonella* (Family TORTRICIDÆ), is the foremost apple pest in this country. The annual loss due to this moth is estimated at $11,400,000

(Simpson). The eggs are laid upon the young fruit, and the larvæ eat their way into the core.

The family TINEIDÆ contains a large number of very small moths. The clothes-moth, *Tinea pellionella* (Fig. 290), injures animal textiles of all kinds. Its larvæ feed on fur, feathers, woolen fabrics, etc. The larvæ of the grain moth, *Gelechia cerealella*, bore into kernels of wheat, rye, and corn.

Order 16. Diptera. — FLIES (Figs. 291–295). — Insects with two wings attached to the meso-thorax; the metathorax bears knobbed threads, the halteres; sucking mouth-parts; meta-morphosis complete.

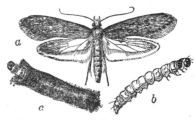

FIG. 290. — Order LEPIDOPTERA. Clothes moth, *Tinea pellionella*. **a**, adult. **b**, larva. **c**, larva in case. (From Riley, in Circ. 36, Bur. Ent., U. S. Dep't. Agric.)

This is one of the largest orders of insects, there being about seven thousand known species in North America. These may be grouped as follows:

SUBORDER 1. DIPTERA GENUINA (true flies).

 Section 1. *Nematocera* (long-horned flies).

 Section 2. *Brachycera* (short-horned flies).

SUBORDER 2. PUPIPARA (ticks and lice).

The NEMATOCERA include the mosquitoes, crane flies, gall-gnats, midges, and black flies.

The *mosquitoes* (CULICIDÆ) have an interesting life-history. The eggs are laid on the surface of the water in a raft-like mass (Fig. 291, **b**) or singly. The larvæ live in the water and are known as wrigglers (Fig. 291, **c**); they have an air tube on the abdomen which is thrust through the surface film of water. The pupa is likewise aquatic. The adult male differs from the female (Fig. 291, **a**) in the structure of the antennæ and in feeding habits. Only the females suck blood; the males, if they eat at all, probably feed on nectar. It has been proved by experiments that mosquitoes of the genus *Anopheles* transmit human malaria (see Chap. II), and that individuals of the genus (*Stegomyia Aedes*) transmit yellow fever germs. The larvæ and pupæ of mosquitoes may be destroyed by draining pools and swamps or by covering the water with a thin layer of oil, which prevents them from obtaining air.

The *crane flies* (TIPULIDÆ) look like large mosquitoes. The *gall-gnats* (CECIDOMYIIDÆ) are terrestrial during their entire lives. Their common name has been given to them because many lay eggs in plant tissue whose larvæ when hatched cause an ab-

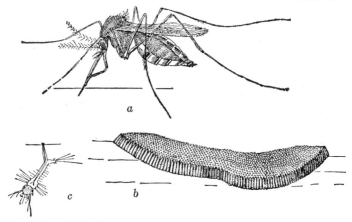

FIG. 291. — Order DIPTERA. Mosquito, *Culex pungens.* **a**, adult female. **b**, egg mass on surface of water. **c**, young hanging from surface of water. (From Howard.)

normal growth called a gall, *e.g.* the pine-cone willowgall. One gall-gnat, the Hessian fly, *Cecidomyia destructor* (Fig. 292), causes a loss of about $10,000,000 annually to the wheat crop in this country. Several species of this family are pædogenetic (see p. 78).

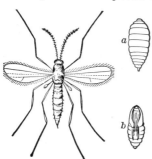

FIG. 292. — Order DIPTERA. Hessian fly, *Cecidomyia destructor.* **a**, larva. **b**, pupa. (From Davenport, after Standard Natural History.)

The *midges* (CHIRONOMIDÆ) are harmless little insects resembling mosquitoes. The larvæ of some of them are the blood-red little worms found in water. The black flies (SIMULIIDÆ) are notorious blood-sucking pests and the special torment of hunters, fishermen, and campers. Their larvæ live in swift streams clinging to the surfaces of rocks, and the adults are therefore found in the vicinity of water.

The BRACHYCERA include the horse-flies, bee-flies, house-flies, bot-flies, and flower-flies. The *horse-flies* (TABANIDÆ) are well-known pests of cattle and horses and often man. The female sucks blood, but the male lives on nectar. The larvæ live in the water or in the earth, where they feed on small animals. The *bee-flies* (BOM-BYLIIDÆ) look somewhat like true bees. They feed on nectar as adults, but the larvæ are carnivorous, living on the young of bees, wasps, and grasshoppers.

The *house-flies* belong to a family (MUSCIDÆ) which contains about a third of all the known DIPTERA. The house-fly, *Musca domestica* (Fig. 293), is dangerous, since it carries disease germs, such as typhoid and tuberculosis, from place to place. Its eggs are laid principally in horse manure and the larvæ are called maggots. The adults can be controlled by keeping the horse manure and other filth under cover. The *flesh-flies* deposit

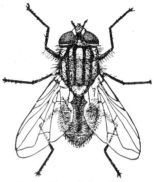

FIG. 293. — Order DIPTERA. House-fly, *Musca domestica.* (From Howard, Circ. 71, Bur. Ent., U. S. Dep't. Agric.)

living young in meat or in open wounds. The *blow-fly* lays its eggs on meat, which is then said to be " blown." The *tachina-flies* are beneficial, since their larvæ are parasitic upon caterpillars (Fig. 287), often exterminating vast hordes of army-worms and other pests. The *fruit-flies* are abundant flies and easily reared.

The *bot-flies* (ŒSTRIDÆ) are responsible for large losses every year because of their attacks on domestic animals. The horse bot-fly, *Gastrophilus equi* (Fig. 294), fastens her eggs to the hair on the legs or shoulders of horses. The larvæ, which are licked off and swallowed, attach themselves to the lining of the stomach, where they live until ready to pupate. They then pass out of the alimentary canal. Other common members of this family are *ox-warble*, the larvæ of which ruin the hides of cattle by boring through the skin, the *sheep bot-fly*, which lives in the nostrils of sheep, and the *rabbit bot-fly*.

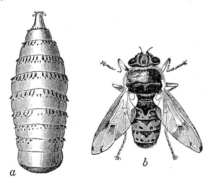

FIG. 294. — Order DIPTERA. Horse bot-fly, *Gastrophilus equi*. **a**, larva. **b**, adult. (From Sedgwick's Zoology, after Brauer.)

The *flower-flies* (SYRPHIDÆ) live on nectar and pollen and are therefore found near flowers. The larvæ feed on other insects or on vegetable matter. The drone-fly, *Eristalis tenax*, resembles a drone honey-bee.

The suborder PUPIPARA contains parasitic insects, including bird, sheep, and horse ticks, and bee-lice. The sheep-tick, *Melophagus ovinus* (Fig. 295), and the horse-tick, *Hippobosca equina*, are common species.

Order 17. Siphonaptera. — FLEAS (Fig. 296). — Degenerate insects without wings; sucking mouth-parts; metamorphosis complete.

FIG. 295. — Order DIPTERA. Sheep-tick, *Melophagus ovinus.* (From Sedgwick's Zoology.)

The fleas live among the hairs or feathers of domestic and wild mammals and birds. Their bodies are laterally compressed, their heads are very small, and their legs are fitted for leaping. The larvæ feed on decaying animal and vegetable matter. The cat and dog flea, *Ctenocephalus canis* (Fig. 296), is the most common species. It does not restrict its attacks to the dog, however, but also visits man. The human flea, *Pulex irritans*, is found all over the world. The rat flea, *Læmopsylla cheopus*, is of considerable importance, since it seems to be able to transmit the bubonic plague from rats to man. The jigger or chigoe flea, *Sarcopsylla penetrans*, burrows into the skin of man and often causes considerable trouble.

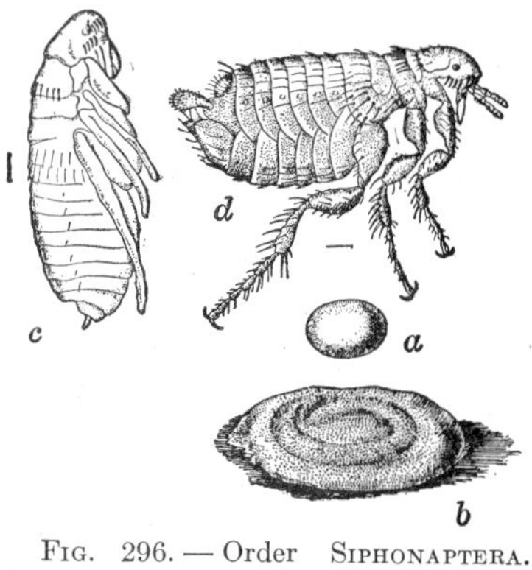

Order 18. Coleoptera. — BEETLES (Figs. 297–304). — Insects with four wings, the forewings sheath-like (elytra) and

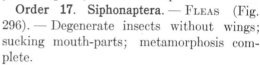

FIG. 296. — Order SIPHONAPTERA. Cat and dog flea, *Ctenocephalus canis.* a, egg. b, larva in cocoon. c, pupa. d, adult. (From Howard, Circ. 108, Bur. Ent., U. S. Dep't. Agric.)

covering the membranous hind wings; biting mouth-parts; metamorphosis complete.

This order contains a great number of species; there are nearly twelve thousand known in North America, north of Mexico. For convenience they have been grouped into eight suborders.

Suborder 1. Adephaga. (CARNIVOROUS BEETLES, Fig. 297.) — The four principal families of carnivorous beetles are the tiger-beetles (CICINDELIDÆ, Fig. 297), predaceous ground beetles (CAR-ABIDÆ), predaceous diving-beetles (DYTISCIDÆ), and whirligig-beetles (GYRINIDÆ). The first two families are terrestrial; they remain on the ground most of the time, where they are busily engaged in capturing other insects for food. The whirligig- and

FIG. 297. — Order COLEOPTERA. Tiger-beetles, CICINDELIDÆ. (From Davenport, after Packert.)

diving-beetles are aquatic and are modified for life in the water. In general it may be said that the carnivorous beetles and carniv-orous insects are beneficial, since they usually destroy other insects harmful to man.

FIG. 298. — Order COLEOPTERA. Car-rion-beetle, *Silpha americana.* (From Davenport, after Standard Natural History.)

Suborder 2. Clavicornia. (CLUB-HORNED BEE-TLES, Fig. 298). — The club-horned beetles have clubbed antennæ. They have little in common; some are aquatic, others terrestrial; some are predaceous, and therefore beneficial; others herbivorous, and consequently harmful; and a few feed on decaying organic matter. Some of the commoner species are known as water-scavenger beetles (HYDROPHILIDÆ), rove-bee-tles (STAPHYLINIDÆ), grain beetles (CUCUJIDÆ), burying-beetles (SILPHIDÆ, Fig. 298), and larder-beetles (DERMESTIDÆ).

Suborder 3. Serricornia. (SAW-HORNED BEETLES, Fig. 299.) — The saw-horned beetles have saw-like antennæ. They comprise the metallic wood borers (BUPRES-TIDÆ) which injure fruit, shade, and forest trees; the click-beetles (ELATERIDÆ, Fig. 299), so called because when laid on their backs they are able to spring up with a click; the death-watch beetles

FIG. 299. — Order COLEOPTERA. Click-beetle. (From Davenport.)

(PTINIDÆ), some of which make a ticking sound against the wood in which they burrow; the fireflies and soldier-beetles (LAMPY-RIDÆ), the former nocturnal and occasionally luminous, the latter diurnal and predaceous; and the checkered beetles (CLERIDÆ), some of which devour the larvæ of wood-boring insects.

Suborder 4. Lamellicornia. (BLADE-HORNED BEETLES, Fig. 300.) The blade-horned beetles have antennæ whose terminal segments form flat teeth or lamellæ. The stag-beetles (LUCANIDÆ) have received their name because of the peculiar antler-like processes of the males of certain species. The leaf chafers and scavenger-beetles (SCARABÆIDÆ) have very different habits, although they belong to one family. The scavenger-beetles eat or bury decaying matter and are therefore beneficial. The tumble bugs make balls of dung in which an egg is laid; the larva feeds on the ball. To this group belongs the Sacred Scarabeus of the Egyptians (Fig. 300). The leaf chafers are injurious. The adults feed on leaves, pollen, and flower-petals.

FIG. 300. — Order COLEOPTERA. Sacred beetle of the Egyptians, *Scarabeus sacer.* (From Sedgwick's Zoology, after Sharp.)

The common June-bug, *Lachnosterna fusca,* the obnoxious rose-chafer, *Macrodactylus subspinosus,* and the rhinoceros-beetles, *Dynastes,* belong to this group. One of the latter, *D. hercules,* found in the West Indies, is six inches long.

Suborder 5. Phytophaga. (PLANT-EATING BEETLES, Fig. 301.) — The plant-eating beetles include the leaf-beetles (CHRYSOMELIDÆ), the pea- and bean-weevils (BRUCHIDÆ), and the long-horn beetles (CERAMBYCIDÆ). The potato-beetle, *Leptinotarsa decimlineata* (Fig. 301), belongs to the first family. It migrated up from Mexico into Colorado and thence east and west until it became an important pest. The elm-leaf beetle, *Galerucella luteola,* is another injurious chrysomelid beetle. It has destroyed a great number of valuable elm trees in Massachusetts and neighboring states.

FIG. 301. — Order COLEOPTERA. Potato-beetle, *Leptinotarsa decimlineata.* (From the Cambridge Natural History.)

The larvæ of the pea- and bean-weevils burrow into peas and beans, making them unfit either for food or seed.

The larvæ of the long-horn beetles burrow in wood and are among the most destructive enemies of trees. Some of the worst pests are the locust borer, *Cyllene robiniæ*, the apple tree borer, *Saperda candida*, and the sugar maple borer, *Plagionotus speciosus*. A common species, *Tetraopes tetraophthalmus*, is found on milkweed.

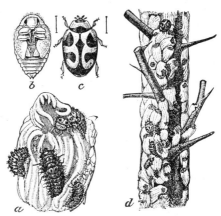

Suborder 6. Trimera. (Ladybird Beetles, Fig. 302.) — The Coccinellidæ, or ladybird beetles, are predaceous, both as larvæ and adults, feeding largely on plant-lice and scale-insects. They are consequently beneficial since they help control these pests (see p. 311).

Fig. 302. — Order Coleoptera. *Novius cardinalis*, Australian ladybird beetle, feeding on the fluted scale, *Icerya purchasi*. *a*, ladybird larvæ feeding on adult female and egg sac; *b*, pupa; *c*, adult ladybird; *d*, orange twig, showing scale and ladybirds — natural size. (From Marlatt.)

Suborder 7. Heteromera. (Darkling, Blister- and Oil-Beetles, Fig. 303.) — The Heteromera contains the darkling ground-beetles (Tenebrionidæ), one of which, the meal-worm, *Tenebrio molitor* (Fig. 303), is quite common in mills and grocery stores and is used as food for ·cage birds. This group also includes the blister- and oil-beetles (Meloidæ); some of these when dried and pulverized have a blistering effect when applied to the human skin.

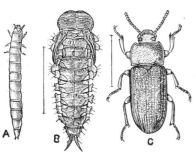

Fig. 303. — Order Coleoptera. Mealworm, *Tenebrio molitor*. **A**, larva. **B**, pupa. **C**, adult. (From the Cambridge Natural History.)

Suborder 8. Rhynchophora. (Snout-beetles, Fig. 304.) — The Rhynchophora are the curculios, weevils, bill-bugs, and snout-beetles. The front of the head is prolonged into a beak or snout, with the mouthparts at the end. *Weevils* (Fig. 304, A) attack many varieties of fruits, nuts, and grain. The *bark-beetles* (SCOLYTIDÆ) are the most destructive of all insects to forest trees, their depredations reaching a total of probably $100,000,000 annually. The genera *Dendroctonus* (Fig. 304, B) and *Tomicus* are the most notorious.

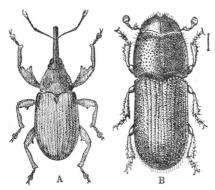

FIG. 304. — Order COLEOPTERA. **A**, cotton-boll weevil. **B**, southern pine beetle, *Dendroctonus frontalis*. (A, from Farmer's Bul. 189; B, from Hopkins, Bul. 83, Bur. Ent., U. S. Dep't. Agric.)

Order 19. Hymenoptera.

— SAW-FLIES, GALL-FLIES, ICHNEUMON-FLIES, ANTS, BEES, WASPS (Figs. 305–312). — Insects possessing four membranous wings with few veins; first abdominal segment fused or partly fused with thorax; mouth-parts both mandibulate and suctorial; female with an ovipositor; metamorphosis complete.

There are about seventy-five hundred species of HYMENOPTERA inhabiting North America. They may be grouped into suborders, superfamilies, families, subfamilies, etc., but because

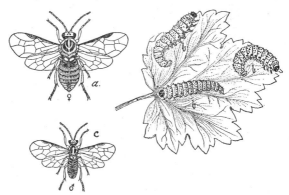

Fig. 305. — Order HYMENOPTERA. Saw-fly, *Nematus ventricosus*. *a*, adult female; *b*, larvæ (currant worms); *c*, adult male. (From Report State Entomologist of Minnesota.)

of the limited space that can be devoted to them in this book, only a few of the most important families will be considered; these are the saw-flies (TENTHREDINIDÆ), the chalcid-flies (CHAL-

CIDIDÆ), the gall-flies (CYNIPIDÆ), the ichneumon-flies (ICH-NEUMONIDÆ, Fig. 308), the bees (APIDÆ), the solitary wasps (EUMENIDÆ), the social wasps (VESPIDÆ), the digger-wasps (SPHEGIDÆ), and the ants (FORMICIDÆ).

The *saw-flies* (TENTHRE-DINIDÆ, Fig. 305) are not gen-erally noticed as adults, but their larvæ, which feed on the leaves of the rose, currant, pear, willow, and larch, are only too well known. The eggs are usually laid in slits made in plant tissue by the saw-like ovipositor of the female. The larvæ possess usually from six to eight pairs of abdominal legs and can thus be dis-tinguished from the larvæ of LEPIDOPTERA, which have not more than five pairs. Some adult saw-flies lay eggs which develop parthenogenetically.

FIG. 306. — Order HYMENOPTERA. Chalcid-fly, *Prospalta murfeldtii*. (From Insect Life.)

The *chalcid-flies* (CHALCIDIDÆ, Fig. 306) are minute parasites which perform a service of inestimable value to man, since they attack the eggs, caterpillars, and adults of many injurious insects. The eggs are laid on or in the host and the larvæ

FIG. 307. — Order HYMENOPTERA. **A**, gall-fly, *Rhodites rosæ*, female. **B**, galls produced by a bug. (A, from the Cambridge Natural History ; B, from Davenport, after Kerner.)

slowly devour its soft parts. One species, *Blastophaga grossorum*, is held responsible for the fertilization of the fig.

The *gall-flies* (CYNIPIDÆ, Fig. 307) are small, dull-colored insects possessing a long ovipositor with which eggs are laid in

plant tissue.   In some way the plant is stimulated so that an
abnormal growth, called a gall, is produced.   The young gall-
fly is protected by the sur-
rounding tissue.   Many species are parthenogenetic, and
only females are known.

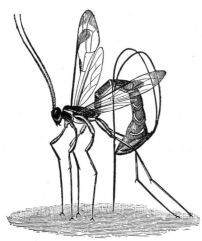

The *bees* (APIDÆ) comprise
a large family, of which the
honey-bee is the best-known
example.   All grades of social
life are exhibited by bees.
The leaf-cutter, *Megachile
acuta*, is a solitary species;
she lays her eggs in leaf-lined
cavities in wood, places pollen
and nectar in the cavities for
the larvæ to feed on, and then
flies away never to return.
The carpenter bee, *Cratina
dupla*, is also a solitary bee,
but she watches her young

FIG. 308. — Order HYMENOPTERA.   Ich-
neumon-fly, *Thalessa lunator*, laying eggs
(oviposition).   (From Sedgwick, after
Riley.)

until they mature.   Certain mining bees, *e.g. Andrena*, lay eggs
in burrows in the ground (Fig. 309, B).   They are solitary bees
but often build their tunnels close together, *i.e.* they have a tendency toward a gregarious habit.
The females of other mining
bees, *e.g. Halictus*, band together and use a single main
burrow from which the individual channels branch off (Fig.
309, A).   These bees therefore
have a tendency toward com-
munity life.   The bumble-bees,
Bombus, live in colonies during
the summer, but these colonies
are temporary, since all members
but the young queens perish in
the autumn.   And finally the

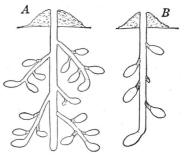

FIG. 309. — Diagrams of nest bur-
rows of short-tongued mining bees.
A, nest of *Halictus*.   **B**, nest of *Andrena*.
(From Hegner, after Kellogg.)

honey-bees, as we have seen, are banded together in permanent
colonies and have a very complex social life.

The *solitary wasps* (EUMENIDÆ) are miners, carpenters, or masons, *i.e.* they dig tunnels in the earth, excavate cavities in wood, or build mud-nests. Like the solitary bees, the Eumenidæ provision their nests, lay their eggs, and then fly away, leaving their young to shift for themselves.

Many of the *digger-wasps* belong to the family SPHEGIDÆ. The mud-daubers are common species. They attach their mud nests to the ceilings of buildings or to the lower surface of stones, and provision them with spiders. The digger-wasps of the West (genus *Ammophila*, Fig. 310) paralyze caterpillars with their sting and place them in their burrows in the ground for the larvæ to live on. The burrows are then carefully filled up with earth and the top made level with the surrounding surface.

FIG. 310. — Order HYMENOPTERA. Solitary digger-wasp, *Ammophila*, putting inchworm into nest burrow. (From Bailey and Coleman, after Peckham.)

The *social wasps* (VESPIDÆ) live in temporary colonies containing females, males, and sexually undeveloped females, called workers. They do not leave their young to live upon food stored up for them, but care for them constantly. The commonest genera

FIG. 311. — Hornet and nest, *Polistes tepidus*. (From Shipley and MacBride.)

are *Polistes* and *Vespa*. The hornet, *Polistes* (Fig. 311), builds a nest of a single layer of cells made out of wood-pulp. This single comb nest is hung by a stalk under the eaves or to the ceiling of

an outbuilding, or porch. Only the females survive the winter,
and new colonies must therefore be established each spring. The
yellow-jacket, *Vespa*, builds a more elaborate nest than that of
Polistes. It consists of a series of combs one above the other,
and is surrounded by a paper covering with an entrance near the
pointed lower end.

The *ants* (FORMICIDÆ) constitute in many ways the most
remarkable group of insects in the world. Their adaptations for
the complex social life that they lead are very wonderful. A
colony, as in the social bees and wasps, contains a queen, males,
and workers. The
workers may be
modified as large or
small workers, or as
soldiers. Ants usu-
ally live in tunnels
in the ground, or in
wood, or in the hol-
low stems of plants.
Beetles and other
insects live in ants'
nests. The honey-

1   2

FIG. 312. — Honey ants and leaf-cutting ants.
(From Brehm.)

ant, *Myrmecocystus* (Fig. 312, *1*) is a peculiar form. Some of the
workers cling to the roof of the mound-like nests and serve as
reservoirs for the storing of a sort of honey until it is needed by
the colony. The leaf-cutter ants (Fig. 312, *2*) of the genus *Atta*
(*Œcodoma*) have a peculiar method of securing food. Certain
workers cut out pieces of leaves and carry them to the nest, where
the other workers pack them into balls on which they cultivate a
fungus, *Rozites gongylophora*. The ants regulate the growth of
this fungus in such a way that it produces white masses which
serve as food for the colony.

d. *The Economic Importance of Insects*

The economic importance of certain insects has been emphasized during our discussion of the orders of insects. A few
species of insects are of considerable value to man. For example,
the honey-bee produces enormous quantities of both honey and
wax; the silkworm supplies us with delicate silk threads; the
bees and many other insects cross-fertilize flowers; the bodies

of the scale insect, *Coccus cacti*, are known as cochineal; predaceous species usually prey upon injurious insects; and many parasitic species attack destructive caterpillars.

On the other hand, the injurious insects are numerous and important. Some of them are responsible for the transmission of certain diseases. For example, the house-fly carries the germs of typhoid, tuberculosis, cholera, and many other diseases on its

TABLE XIII

ANNUAL LOSSES DUE TO INSECT PESTS OF THE UNITED STATES

Product	Value	Percentage of Loss	Amount of Loss
Cereals	$2,000,000,000	10	$200,000,000
Hay	530,000,000	10	53,000,000
Cotton	600,000,000	10	60,000,000
Tobacco	53,000,000	10	5,300,000
Truck crops . . .	265,000,000	20	53,000,000
Sugar	50,000,000	10	5,000,000
Fruits	135,000,000	20	27,000,000
Farm forests . . .	110,000,000	10	11,000,000
Miscellaneous crops .	58,000,000	10	5,800,000
Animal products . .	1,750,000,000	10	175,000,000
Total	5,551,000,000		595,100,000
Natural forests and forest products . .			100,000,000
Products in storage .			100,000,000
Grand total . .			795,100,000

legs, proboscis, and body; the anopheles mosquito transmits the malaria germ; the stegomyia mosquito transmits the yellow fever germ; the rat flea carries plague germs; the body-louse transmits relapsing fever; and the tsetse-fly is responsible for sleeping-sickness.

Millions of dollars are lost every year because of the attacks of insects upon domestic animals. Among these insects are the blood-sucking gnats, buffalo-gnats, horse-flies, gadflies, bot-flies, horn-flies, flesh-flies, ticks, fleas, sucking lice, and bird-lice.

Even more enormous are the losses due to insects that eat the leaves of plants, bore into their stems, suck their juices, or destroy their fruits. Table XIII presents a conservative estimate of these losses. (Marlatt.)

6. Class V. Arachnida

The class ARACHNIDA (Gr. *arachne*, a spider) includes the spiders, ticks, mites, scorpions, and king-crabs. These animals differ markedly from one another, but agree in several important respects: (1) they have no antennæ; (2) there are no true jaws; (3) the first pair of appendages are nippers, termed cheliceræ; and (4) the body can usually be divided into an anterior part, the cephalothorax, and a posterior part, the abdomen. Twelve orders of arachnids are recognized in this book. The first four orders ARANEIDA, SCORPIONIDEA, PHALANGIDEA, and ACARINA contain most of the living species; the last order, EURYPTERIDA, is known only from fossils.

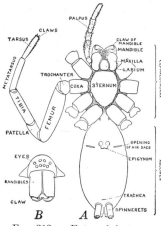

FIG. 313. — External features of a spider. **A**, under surface; all but one leg removed. **B**, front of head, showing eyes and mandibles. (From Emerton.)

a. *The Spiders*

Order 1. Araneida. — SPIDERS. — Since the spiders are the most common of all arachnids, they are used here to illustrate the anatomical and physiological characteristics of the class.

External Features. — Figure 313 shows the principal external features of a spider. The body consists of a *cephalothorax* which is undivided, and an *abdomen* which is usually soft, rounded, and unsegmented.

There are six pairs of *appendages* attached to the cephalothorax. Antennæ are absent; their sensory functions are in part performed by the walking legs. The first pair of appendages are called *cheliceræ* (Fig. 314). They are in many species composed of two parts, a basal "mandible" (Fig. 313, *B*), and a terminal claw. *Poison-glands* (Fig. 314) are situated in the cheliceræ. The poison they secrete passes through a duct and out of the end of the chelicera; it is strong enough to kill insects and to injure larger animals. The second pair of appendages are the *pedipalpi* (Fig. 313, palpus and maxilla); their bases, called "maxillæ," are used as jaws to press or chew the food. The pedipalpi of the male are used as copulatory organs.

Following the pedipalpi are four pairs of *walking legs*. This number easily distinguishes spiders from insects, since the latter possess only three pairs. Each leg consists of seven joints, — (1) coxa, (2) trochanter, (3) femur, (4) patella, (5) tibia, (6) metatarsus, (7) tarsus, — and is terminated by two toothed claws (Fig. 315) and often a pad of hairs (*s*) which enables the spider to run on ceilings and walls. The bases of certain of the legs sometimes serve as jaws.

The *sternum* lies between the legs, and a " *labium* " is situated between the " maxillæ." The *eyes*, usually eight in number, are on the front of the head (Fig. 313, B). The *mouth* (Fig. 314)

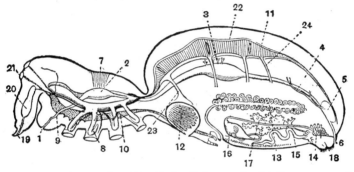

Fig. 314. — Diagram of a spider, *Epeira diademata*, showing the arrangement of the internal organs. *1*, mouth ; *2*, sucking stomach ; *3*, ducts of liver ; *4*, so-called malpighian tubules ; *5*, stercoral pocket ; *6*, anus ; *7*, dorsal muscle of sucking stomach ; *8*, cæcal prolongation of stomach ; *9*, cerebral ganglion giving off nerves to eyes ; *10*, suboesophageal ganglionic mass ; *11*, heart with three lateral openings or ostia ; *12*, lung sac ; *13*, ovary ; *14*, acinate and pyriform silk glands ; *15*, tubuliform silk glands ; *16*, ampuliform silk gland ; *17*, dendriform silk glands ; *18*, spinnerets ; *19*, distal joint of chelicera ; *20*, poison gland ; *21*, eye ; *22*, pericardium ; *23*, vessel bringing blood from lung sac to pericardium ; *24*, artery. (From the Cambridge Natural History.)

is a minute opening between the bases of the pedipalpi (maxillæ); it serves for the ingestion of juices only, since spiders do not eat solid food.

The *abdomen* is connected by a slender waist with the cephalothorax. Near the anterior end of the abdomen on the ventral surface is the *genital opening*, protected by a pair of appendages which have fused together to form a plate called the *epigynum* (Fig. 313). On either side of the epigynum is the slit-like opening of the respiratory organs or *lung books* (Fig. 313; Fig. 314). Some spiders also possess *tracheæ* which open to the outside near the posterior end on the ventral surface (Fig. 313). Just back of the tracheal opening are three pairs of tubercles or *spinnerets* (Fig. 313; Fig. 314), used for spinning threads. The *anus* (Fig. 314) lies posterior to the spinnerets.

Internal Anatomy and Physiology (Fig. 314). — The *food* of the spider consists of juices sucked from the bodies of other animals, principally insects. Suction is produced by the enlargement of the sucking stomach (Fig. 314), due to the contraction of muscles attached to its dorsal surface and to the chitinous covering of the cephalothorax. The *true stomach*, which follows the sucking stomach, gives off five pairs of *cæca* or blind tubes in the cephalothorax. The *intestine* passes almost straight through the abdomen; it is enlarged at a point where ducts bring into it a digestive fluid from the *"liver,"* and again near the posterior end, where it forms a sac, the

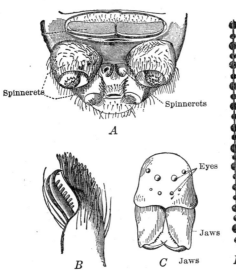

FIG. 315. — Parts of a spider's body. **A**, ventral view of posterior end of abdomen showing three pairs of spinnerets. **B**, foot showing claws and bristles. **C**, front of head showing eyes and jaws. **D**, a thread from a spider's web. (From Warburton.)

"stercoral pocket." Tubes, called *Malpighian tubes*, enter the intestine near the posterior end. The alimentary canal is surrounded in the abdomen by a large digestive gland or "liver." This gland secretes a fluid resembling pancreatic juice and pours it into the intestine through ducts.

The *circulatory system* consists of a heart, arteries, veins, and a number of spaces or sinuses. The *heart* is situated in the abdomen and is surrounded by the digestive glands. It is a muscular, contractile tube lying in a sheath, the pericardium, into which it opens by three pairs of ostia. It gives off posteriorly a caudal artery, anteriorly an aorta which branches and supplies the tissues in the cephalothorax, and three pairs of abdominal arteries. The *blood*, which is colorless and contains mostly ameboid corpuscles, passes from the arteries into sinuses and is carried to the book lungs where it is aërated; it then passes to the pericardium by way of the pulmonary veins, and finally enters the heart through the ostia.

Respiration is carried on by tracheæ and book lungs; the latter are peculiar to arachnids. The *book lungs*, of which there are usually two, are sacs, each containing generally from fifteen to twenty leaf-like horizontal shelves through which the blood circulates. Air entering through the external openings is thus brought into close relationship with the blood. Tracheæ are also usually present, but do not ramify to all parts of the body as in the insects (p. 288, Fig. 242).

The *excretory organs* are the *Malpighian tubules* (Fig. 314), which open into the intestine, and two *coxal glands* in the cephaclothorax. The oxal glands are sometimes degenerate, and their openings are difficult to find; they are homologous with the green glands of the crayfish (p. 252, Fig. 202).

The *nervous system* consists of a bilobed ganglion above the œsophagus (Fig. 314), a subœsophageal ganglionic mass (*10*), and the nerves which arise from them. There are *sensory hairs* on the pedipalps and probably on the walking legs, but the principal sense-organs are the eyes. There are usually eight *eyes* (Fig. 313, B; Fig. 314), and these differ in size and arrangement in different species. Spiders apparently can see objects distinctly only at a distance of four or five inches.

The sexes are separate, and the *testes* or *ovaries* (Fig. 314) form a network of tubes in the abdomen. The spermatozoa are transferred by the pedipalps of the male to the female, and fertilize the eggs within her body. The eggs are laid in a silk cocoon, which is attached to the web or to a plant, or carried about by the female. The young leave the cocoon as soon after hatching as they can run about.

The *spinning organs* of spiders are three pairs of appendages called *spinnerets* (Fig. 313; Fig. 314). The spinnerets are pierced by hundreds of microscopic tubes through which a fluid secreted by a number of abdominal *silk glands* (Fig. 314), passes to the outside and hardens in the air, forming a thread. These threads are used to build nests, form cocoons, spin webs, and for many other purposes. An *orb web*, such as is shown in Figure 316, is spun in the following manner. A thread is stretched across the space selected for the web; then from a point on this thread other threads are drawn out and attached in radiating lines. These

Fig. 316. — Photograph of a spider at the center of its web. (After Burlend.)

threads all become dry and smooth. On this foundation a spiral is spun of sticky thread. The spider stands in the center of the web or retires to a nest at one side and waits for an insect to become entangled in the sticky thread; it then rushes out and spins threads about its prey until all struggles cease.

Many spiders do not spin webs, but wander about capturing insects, or lie in wait for them in some place of concealment. In this group belong the crab-spiders (THOMISIDÆ, Fig. 317, A), jumping-spiders (ATTIDÆ, Fig. 317, B), ground-spiders (DRASSIDÆ), and running spiders (LYCOSIDÆ, Fig. 317, C). The cobweb spiders spin various kinds of nets for capturing insects. The tube-weavers (AGELENIDÆ) build platforms on the grass and hide in a tube at one side; the line weavers (LINYPHIADÆ) spin

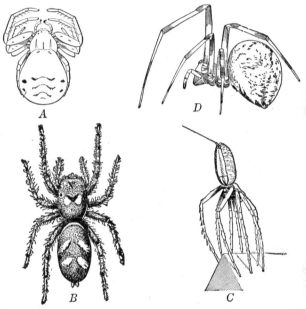

FIG. 317. — **A**, crab-spider, *Thomisus*. **B**, jumping-spider, *Attus*. **C**, young spider, *Lycosa*, preparing for an aerial voyage. **D**, house-spider, *Theridium epidariorum*. (A, B, C, from Davenport, after Emerton; D, from Emerton.)

flat webs with irregular meshes; the round-web spiders (EPEIRIDÆ) builds webs like that shown in Figure 316; and the THERIDIDÆ (Fig. 317, D) build irregular webs in corners and on plants.

b. *Other Arachnida*

Order 2. Scorpionidea. — SCORPIONS. — The scorpions are rapacious arachnids measuring from half an inch to eight inches in length. They live in tropical and subtropical regions, hiding in crevices or in pits in the sand during the daytime, but running

about actively at night.   They capture insects and spiders with
their pedipalpi (Fig. 318), tear them apart with their cheliceræ,
and devour the pieces.   Larger animals are paralyzed by the
sting on the end of the tail.   This sting does not serve as a weapon
of defense unless the scorpion is hard pressed; and is not used, as
is often stated, to sting itself to death, since its poison has no
effect upon its own body.

The scorpion's body (Fig. 318) is more obviously segmented
than that of most of the other arachnids.   There is a *cephalo-*

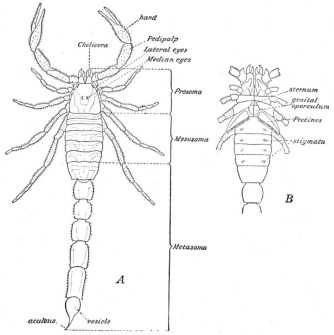

FIG. 318. — Scorpion, *Buthus occitanus.*   **A**, dorsal view.   **B**, ventral view.
(From the Cambridge Natural History, after Kraepelin.)

thorax (prosoma), and an abdomen of two parts — a thick anterior
portion (mesosoma), and a slender tail (metasoma) which is held
over the back when the animal walks.   The dorsal shield of the
cephalothorax bears a pair of median *eyes* and three lateral eyes
on each side.   The sense of sight is, however, poorly developed.
On the ventral surface of the second abdominal segment are two
comb-like appendages called pectines (Fig. 318, B);   these are

probably special tactile organs. *Tactile hairs* are distributed over the body, and the sense of touch is quite delicate. There are four pairs of *lung books* opening by means of *stigmata* (Fig. 318, B) on the under surface of abdominal segments III–VI.

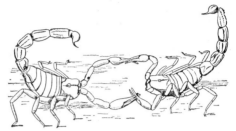

The mating activities of scorpions are very curious, and include a sort of promenade (Fig. 319). Scorpions are viviparous. The young ride

FIG. 319. — The "*promenade à deux*" of the scorpion, *Buthus occitanus*. (From the Cambridge Natural History, after Fabre.)

about upon the back of the female for about a week, and then shift for themselves. They reach maturity in about five years.

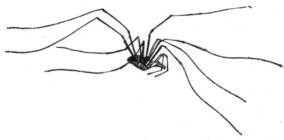

FIG. 320. — Order PHALANGIDEA. Harvestman, *Phalangium opilio*, male. (From Sedgwick's Zoology.)

Order 3. Phalangidea. — HARVESTMEN OR DADDY-LONG-LEGS. —

The harvestmen may be distinguished from spiders by their extremely long legs (Fig. 320), the absence of a waist, and their segmented abdomen. They are able to run rapidly over leaves and grass. Their food consists of small living insects.

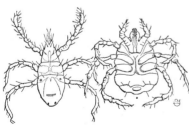

FIG. 321. — Order ACARINA. Harvestmites or "chiggers." *Lepus irritans* on the right; *L. americana* on the left. (From Osborn, after Riley.)

Order 4. Acarina. — MITES AND TICKS.—These are minute arachnids without any external signs of segmentation. Many of them are parasitic and often cause serious diseases.

The family TROMBIDIIDÆ includes the harvest mites or " chiggers " (Fig. 321). These little creatures are transferred by contact from plants to the bodies of man and other animals. They burrow into the skin, with painful results. Treatment with a one or two per cent solution of carbolic acid is the proper remedy. The poultry tick, *Dermanyssus gallinæ* (Fig. 322, A) belongs to

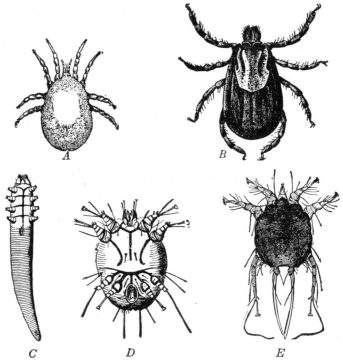

FIG. 322. — Order ACARINA. **A**, poultry tick, *Dermanyssus gallinæ*, young. **B**, cattle tick, *Boophilus annulatus*. **C**, follicle mite, *Demodex folliculorum*. **D**, itch-mite, *Sarcoptes scabiei*. **E**, sheep-scab mite, *Psoroptes communis* var. *ovis* (A, B, E, from Osborn; B, after Packard; C, D, from Sedgwick's Zoology; C, after Mégnin, D, after Gudden.)

the family GAMASIDÆ. It sucks the blood of chickens, and is a pest on poultry farms.

The family IXODIDÆ contains a number of injurious species. The cattle tick, *Boophilus (Margaropus) annulatus* (Fig. 322, B), is perhaps the most important. These ticks cling to the skin of cattle with their strong mouth-parts, and suck the blood of their host. When full grown the females drop to the ground and lay from 2000 to 4000 eggs; these soon hatch, and the young crawl upon a blade of grass and wait for cattle to come past to which they can fasten themselves. The principal injury done by the ticks is the transference of a sporozoan parasite, *Piroplasma bigeminum*, from the blood of one animal to that of another. This parasite produces Texas

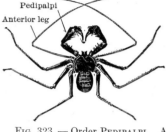

Fig. 323. — Order PEDIPALPI. A South American species, *Admetus pumilio.* (From Sedgwick's Zoology.)

fever, a disease that causes an annual loss of about $100,000,000 in the United States.

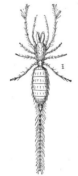

Fig. 324. — Order PALPIGRADI. *Kœnenia mirabilis.* (From the Cambridge Natural History, after Hansen.)

Other members of the order ACARINA that should be mentioned are: (1) the follicle mites, *Demodex folliculorum* (Fig. 322, C), that lives in the sweat-glands and hair follicles of man and some domestic animals, causing what are known as "black-heads"; (2) the itch-mite, *Sarcoptes scabiei* (Fig. 322, D) which burrows beneath the epidermis of man and causes intense itching; and (3) the scab parasite, *Psoroptes communis* (Fig. 322, E), which feeds on the skin of sheep, cattle, and horses, producing scabs.

Order 5. Pedipalpi (Fig. 323). — The members of this order have large, conspicuous pedipalps. They are nocturnal in habit and live under stones and in crevices during the day. They inhabit the warm countries and feed chiefly on insects.

Order 6. Palpigradi (Fig. 324). — One family and two genera belong to this order. They are small (about 1 mm. long) and widely distributed. Several species have been recorded from Texas.

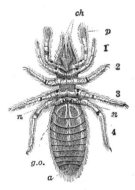

Fig. 325. — Order SOLIFUGÆ. *Rhagodes,* ventral view. *a,* anus; *ch,* cheliceræ; *g.o,* genital operculum; *n,* racket organs; *p,* pedipalp; *1, 2, 3, 4,* walking legs. (From the Cambridge Natural History, after Bernard.)

Order 7. Solifugæ. — The Solifugæ (Fig. 325) are fair sized, hairy arachnids living in warm parts of the globe. About one hundred and seventy species are known.

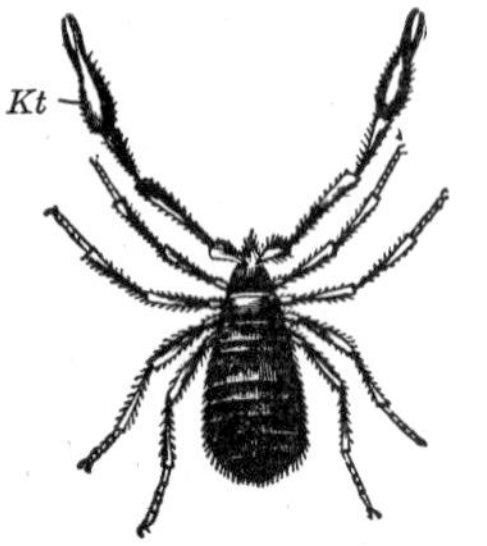

Order 8. Chernetidia (Pseudoscorpionida, Fig. 326.) — These are brownish arachnids from one-eighth to one-fourth of an inch in length. They possess comparatively large pedipalps with which they capture their insect food. Large insects to which they cling often carry them about — a fact that probably accounts for their wide distribution. There is only one family.

Fig. 326.— Order Cher-netidia. *Obisium trom-bidioïdes. Kt,* pedipalp. (From Sedgwick's Zo-ology.)

Order 9. Xiphosura. — King-crabs. — The king-crab or horseshoe crab, *Limulus polyphemus* (Fig. 327), occurs along the Atlantic coast from Maine to Yucatan. It differs from other arachnids in the presence of *gills* (Fig. 327, B, 11–15) and the absence of Malpighian tubules. The king-crabs and a few mites are the only living marine arachnids. *Limulus* is a burrowing animal and lives in the sand. It may be active at night, moving by " short swimming hops, the respiratory appendages giving the necessary

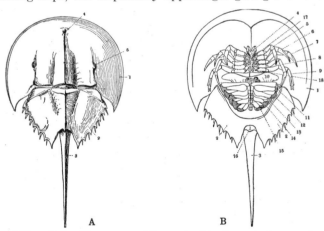

Fig. 327. — Order Xiphosura. King-crab, *Limulus polyphemus.* **A,** dorsal view. *1,* carapace ; *2,* meso- and meta-soma ; *3,* telson ; *4,* median eye ; *5,* lateral eye. **B,** ventral view. *1,* carapace ; *2,* meso- and meta-soma ; *3,* telson ; *4,* chelicera ; *5,* pedipalp ; *6, 7, 8, 9,* 3d to 6th appendages, walking legs ; *10,* genital operculum turned forward to show genital aperture ; *11, 12, 13, 14, 15,* appendages bearing gill books ; *16,* anus ; *17,* mouth ; *18,* chilaria. (From Shipley and MacBride.)

impetus, whilst between each two short flights the animal balances itself for a moment on the tip of its tail." The food of *Limulus* consists chiefly of worms, such as *Nereis* (Fig. 163), and mollusks.

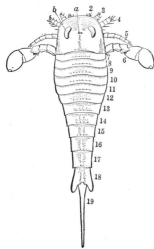

These are caught while burrowing through the sand, are held by the cheliceræ, and chewed by the bases of the walking legs. In the spring the king-crabs come near shore to spawn.

Order 10. Eurypterida (Fig. 328). — The Eurypterida lived

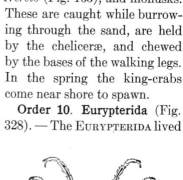

FIG. 328. — Order Eurypterida. *Eurypterus fischeri*, dorsal surface. *a*, ocellus; *b*, lateral eye; *2–6*, appendages of prosoma; *7–12*, segments of mesosoma; *13–18*, segments of metasoma; *19*, tail spine. (From the Cambridge Natural History, after Holm.)

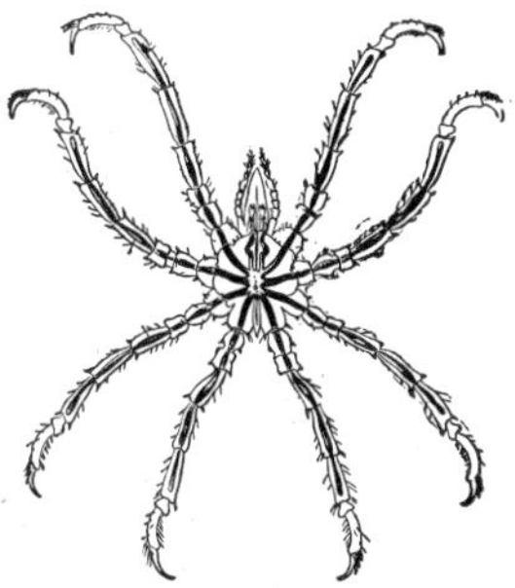

FIG. 329. — Pycnogonida. *Ammothea pyconogonides* (From Sedgwick's Zoology, after règne animal.)

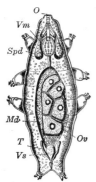

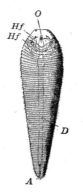

FIG. 330.—Tardigrada. *Macrobiotus schultzei*. *Md*, stomach; *O*, mouth; *Ov*, ovary; *Spd*, salivary glands; *T*, malpighian tubules; *Vm*, pharynx; *Vs*, accessory gland. (From Sedgwick's Zoology, after Greeff.)

FIG. 331. — Pentastomida. *Pentastomum tænioides*. *A*, anus; *D*, intestine; *Hf*, hooks; *O*, mouth. (From Sedgwick's Zoology.)

in both salt water and fresh water during the Silurian and Devonian periods (Table XVII), and are known to us only as fossils. They appear to represent a condition intermediate between *Limulus* and the SCORPIONIDEA.

It is convenient to mention at this point three groups of peculiar animals that are often placed in the class ARACHNIDA: (1) the PYCNOGONIDA (PANTOPODA), (2) the TARDIGRADA, and (3) the PENTASTOMIDA. The PYCNOGONIDA (Fig. 329) are marine animals with small bodies and long legs. They crawl about over seaweeds and cœlenterates, the juices of which they suck. The TARDIGRADA, or "bear-animalcules" (Fig. 330), are minute creatures from 0.3 mm. to 1 mm. in length. They live on tree trunks, and in the débris in ditches. The PENTASTOMIDA (Fig. 331) are parasitic in the noses of flesh-eating vertebrates.

CHAPTER XIV

PHYLUM CHORDATA: INTRODUCTION [1]

The Phylum Chordata (Lat. *chordatus*, having a cord) includes the vertebrate animals (mammals, birds, reptiles, amphibians, fishes, elasmobranchs, and cyclostomes) and a number of marine forms (Figs. 332 to 341) that are not generally known except to zoologists. All of these animals are characterized at some stage in their existence by (1) a skeletal axis, the *notochord*, (2) by *paired slits* connecting the pharynx with the exterior, and (3) by a *central nerve-cord dorsal to the alimentary canal* and containing a cavity or system of cavities, the *neurocœle*. In many respects the chordates differ widely from one another, and it is customary to separate them into four subphyla: —

(1) The Enteropneusta (Gr. *enteron*, intestine; *pneuma*, breathe), containing two orders of worm-like animals of somewhat doubtful systematic position,

(2) The Tunicata (Lat. *tunica*, mantle), or sea-squirts, and a number of other marine forms,

(3) The Cephalochorda (Gr. *kephale*, head; *chorde*, cord), comprising only two families of fishlike animals called lancelets, and

(4) The Vertebrata (Lat. *vertebratus*, jointed).

1. Subphylum I. Enteropneusta

This subphylum is sometimes given the names Hemichorda or Adelochorda. It contains two orders: (1) the Balanoglossida, and (2) the Cephalodiscida. Four families and about ten genera are recognized in the order Balanoglossida,

---

[1] This chapter is designed to give a brief account of the primitive chordates as they exist today, especially of *Amphioxus*, and an introductory account of the vertebrates. A general idea of vertebrate structure can be obtained by reading over this account carefully, which will help one to understand the various types of vertebrates described in subsequent chapters.

but only two genera, *Cephalodiscus* (Fig. 336) and *Rhabdopleura* (Fig. 335), belong to the order CEPHALODISCIDA.

The external features of one of the BALANOGLOSSIDA are shown in Figure 332. Three regions may be distinguished: a *proboscis*, a *collar*, and a *trunk*. Paired lateral *gill-slits* are present in the anterior part of the trunk. The *mouth* opens on the anterior surface of the collar region and the *anus* is situated at the posterior end of the trunk. The proboscis and collar possess cavities which become filled with water through ciliated pores (Fig. 333). When in a swollen condition, the proboscis and collar are forced into the sand or mud, and constitute effective burrowing instruments.

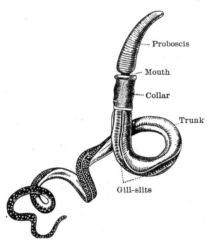

FIG. 332.—*Dolichoglossus kowalevskii.* (From Shipley and MacBride, after Spengel.)

Figure 333 shows diagrammatically the principal internal structures of *Glosso-balanus.* The *notochord* is a supporting organ consisting of a hollow tube of cells; it opens posteriorly into the alimentary canal. The *alimentary canal* is straight. Mud in which the animals live is taken into the mouth and forced slowly through the digestive tube, where nutriment is extracted from the organic matter contained in it — a process similar to digestion in the earthworm

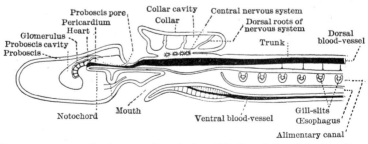

FIG. 333. — Longitudinal section through the middle line of *Glossobalanus.* (From Shipley and MacBride.)

(p. 201). The *gill-slits* or *branchial clefts* open into the anterior portion of the alimentary canal and supply water to the tongue-like respiratory organs.

There is a *dorsal blood-vessel* ending anteriorly in a contractile *heart* which lies in a *pericardial cavity*. A *ventral blood-vessel* is connected with the dorsal blood-vessel in the collar region by two lateral tubes. The other blood-vessels are simply spaces in the tissues. Excretory products appear to be extracted from the blood by the *glomerulus* or *kidney*, which lies on the posterior wall of a cavity in the proboscis. The excretions pass out through the proboscis pore when water is expelled from the proboscis cavity.

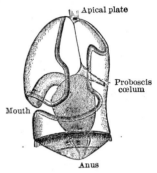

Fig. 334. — *Tornaria* larva of ENTEROPNERUSTA. (From Sedgwick's Zoology, after Metchnikoff.)

The *nervous system* is not concentrated. A layer of nerve-fibers just beneath the ectoderm makes the entire surface sensitive. Thickenings occur along the mid-dorsal and mid-ventral lines of the trunk and around the trunk just posterior to the collar. A *neural tube* is formed by the dorsal thickening. The *cœlom* which arises from the primitive digestive tract, very much as in echinoderms (p. 195, Fig. 150, *A*), is represented by a proboscis cavity (Fig. 333), two collar cavities, and two trunk cavities.

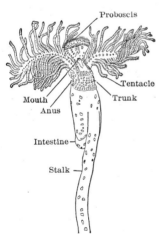

Fig. 335. — *Rhabdopleura*. (From Parker and Haswell, after Lankester.)

The sexes are separate. The *ovaries* or *testes* form a double row in the anterior trunk region, and the germ-cells reach the exterior through pores in the body-wall. In some species each egg develops into a free-swimming larva called a *Tornaria* (Fig. 334). When first discovered, these larvæ were thought to belong to an echinoderm. The resemblance of the *Tornaria* to the larvæ of echinoderms (Figs.

150–151) is quite striking and has led to a rather plausible theory of the origin of the vertebrates (Chap. XXII).

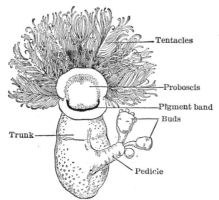

FIG. 336. — *Cephalodiscus dodecalophus*, anterior view. (From Sedgwick's Zoology, after McIntosh.)

Rhabdopleura (Fig. 335) and *Cephalodiscus* (Fig. 336) are colonial ENTEROPNEUSTA inhabiting the deep sea. They have the power of reproducing by means of buds (Fig. 336). *Cephalodiscus* has only one pair of gill-slits; *Rhabdopleura* has none.

2. SUBPHYLUM II. TUNICATA

The TUNICATA or URO-CHORDA (Fig. 337) all live in the sea. They are either free-swimming or attached, are widely distributed, and occur at all levels from near the surface to a depth of over three miles. They range in size from about a hundredth of an inch to over a foot in diameter. Some are brilliantly colored. The adult (Fig. 338) is often saclike and has received the common name "sea-squirt" because when irritated it may eject water through two openings in the unattached end (Fig. 338). The term *tunicata* is applied to members of the group on account of a cuticular outer covering known as a *test* or *tunic*.

The chordate characteristics of tunicates were not recognized until

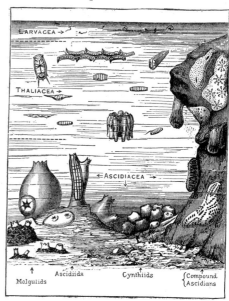

FIG. 337. — Sketch of the chief kinds of TUNICATA found in the sea. (From the Cambridge Natural History.)

the development of the egg and metamorphosis of the larva
were fully investigated (Kowalevsky, 1866). It was then discovered that the typical larva (Fig. 339), which is about a quarter
of an inch long and resembles a frog tadpole, possesses (1) a distinct *notochord*, (2) a *neural tube* in the tail which enlarges in
the trunk, ends in a vesicle (A), and is considered the fore-
runner of the brain of the VERTEBRATA, and (3) a *pharynx* which

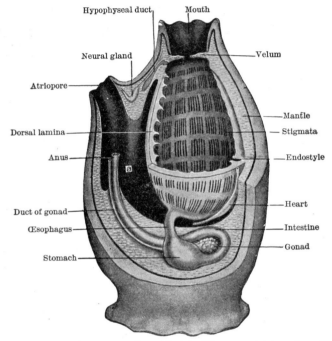

FIG. 338. — Internal anatomy of a typical Ascidian. *a*, atrial cavity. (From
Newman, after Hertwig.)

opens to the exterior by ciliated *gill-slits*. The tail propels the
larva forward by lateral strokes. After a short existence as a
free-swimming organism the larva becomes attached to some
object by three projections on the anterior end (Fig. 339), which
secrete a sticky fluid. It then undergoes a retrogressive metamorphosis during which the tail with the notochord and neural tube
disappear, and other changes take place as shown in Figure 339.

The typical adult tunicate (Fig. 338) is attached by a *stalk* and
surrounded by a *tunic*. At the distal end are two openings; one

is the *mouth,* or branchial aperture, into which a current of water passes; the other is the *atrial orifice* through which the water escapes to the outside. This current of water brings food into the alimentary canal, furnishes oxygen for respiration, and carries away excretory substances. Near the mouth is a velum forming a sensory sieve through which incoming water and food must pass.

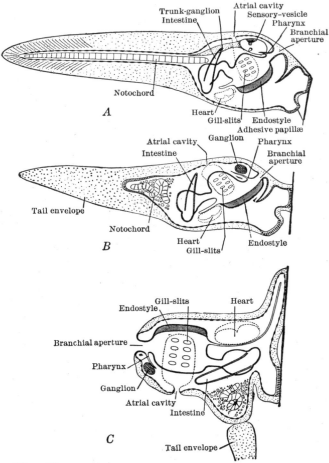

Fig. 339. — Diagram of the metamorphosis of the free, tailed larva into the fixed Tunicate. *A*, stage of free-swimming larva. *B*, recently fixed larva. *C*, older fixed stage. (From Davenport, after Seeliger.)

Microscopic plants and animals are entangled in mucus secreted by a pharyngeal groove or *endostyle* (Fig. 339), which forms a peripharyngeal band. The *alimentary canal* is bent upon itself (Fig. 338), and opens into the *atrial cavity*. A single ganglion, the *brain*, lies between the branchial and atrial tubes. Tunicates are hermaphroditic. The reproductive organs lie near the intestinal loop, and their ducts open near the anus. Many species reproduce asexually by budding.

There are three orders of tunicates (Fig. 337): (1) the ASCIDIACEA, (2) the THALIACEA, and (3) the LARVACEA.

Order 1. Ascidiacea (Fig. 337, lower portion). — The tunicates belonging to this group are either free-swimming or fixed, colonial or solitary. The colonial forms reproduce asexually by budding, as well as sexually. Examples: *Ciona* (Fig. 338), *Cynthia, Molgula, Botryllus, Pyrosoma.*

Order 2. Thaliacea (Fig. 337, central portion).— These are free-swimming, solitary, or colonial forms living near the surface of the sea, *i.e.* pelagic. The commonest genus, *Salpa* (Fig. 340, A), is cylindrical, and its hooplike muscle bands cause it to resemble a barrel. Usually there is an alternation of generations; a solitary individual gives rise asexually to a row of sexual members, each of which produces a

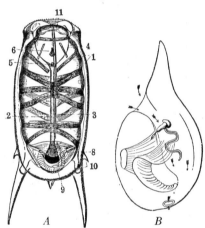

FIG. 340. — **A**, solitary Tunicate, *Salpa democratica*, dorsal view. *1*, muscle bands; *2*, "gill"; *3*, endostyle; *4*, peripharyngeal band; *5*, brain; *6*, ciliated pit; *8*, "nucleus" of stomach, liver, intestine; *9*, stolon; *10*, process of mantle; *11*, mouth. (From Shipley and MacBride, after Brooks.) **B**, *Oikopleura cophocerca* in its test. (From Sedgwick's Zoology, after Fol.)

single egg; the eggs develop into asexual solitary individuals.

Order 3. Larvacea (Fig. 337, upper portion). — The LARVACEA are small pelagic forms which retain the larval condition throughout life. Examples: *Appendicularia, Oikopleura* (Fig. 340, B).

3. Subphylum III. Cephalocorda

This subphylum contains about a dozen species of marine animals of which *Branchiostoma lanceolatus,* commonly known as Amphioxus or the Lancelet, is the form usually studied. Amphioxus is of special interest, since it exhibits the characteristics of the chordates in a simple condition. Furthermore it is probably similar to the ancestors of the Vertebrata.

Amphioxus is several inches long. The semi-transparent body is pointed at both ends and laterally compressed. It is found near the shore, where it burrows in the clean sand with its head or tail, and conceals all but the anterior end. It sometimes leaves its burrow at night and swims about by means of rapid lateral movements of the body. When it ceases to move, it falls on its side.

External Features (Fig. 341). — Although Amphioxus is shaped like a fish, it differs from the latter in many important respects both externally and internally. There are no lateral fins and no

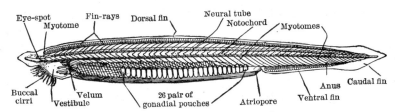

Fig. 341. — An adult specimen of Branchiostoma lanceolatus, seen from the left side as a transparent object. (From Bourne.)

distinct head. Along the mid-dorsal line is a low *dorsal fin* extending the entire length of the body and widening at the posterior end into a *caudal fin.* The caudal fin extends forward on the ventral surface. Both dorsal and ventral fins are strengthened by rods of connective tissue, called *fin-rays.* In front of the ventral fin the lower surface of the body is flattened, and on each side is an expansion of the integument called the *metapleural fold* (Fig. 342).

The *body-wall* is divided into a number (62) of V-shaped muscle segments, the *myotomes* (Fig. 341), these are separated from one another by septa of connective tissue. The myotomes on one side of the body alternate with those on the other side.   The muscle fibers contained in them are longitudinal, and, since they are attached to the connective tissue partitions, are able to produce the lateral movements of the body used in swimming.

The *mouth opening* is at the bottom of a funnel-shaped cavity in the ventral surface near the anterior end, called the *vestibule* (Fig. 341).   The *anus* is situated on the left side of the body in myotome fifty-two.   Just in front of the ventral fin opposite

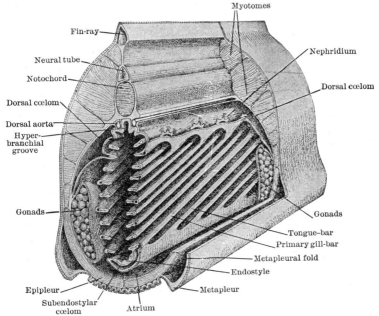

Fig. 342. — Diagram illustrating the anatomy of the pharyngeal region of *Amphioxus*.   (From Bourne.)

myotome thirty-six is the *atriopore*, an opening through which water used in respiration passes to the outside.

Internal Anatomy and Physiology. — *Skeleton.* — Amphioxus has a well-developed axial support, the *notochord* (Figs. 341–342) lying near the dorsal surface and extending almost the entire length of the body.   The notochord is composed of vacuolated cells which are made turgid by their fluid contents and are, therefore, resistant.   Other skeletal structures are the connective

tissue rods which form the fin-rays (Fig. 341), and similar structures that support the *cirri* (Fig. 343) of the *oral hood*.

Digestive System. (Fig. 343). — The food of Amphioxus consists of minute organisms which are carried into the mouth with
the current of water produced by cilia on the gills (compare with
mussel, p. 224). The *mouth* is an opening in a membrane, the
velum, and may be closed by circular muscle fibers which surround
it. Twelve sensory-oral or *velar tentacles* protect the mouth, and,
when folded across it, act as a strainer, thus preventing the entrance of coarse, solid objects. The funnel-shaped *vestibule* is
the cavity of the *oral hood*. The twenty-two ciliated *cirri* which
project from the edge of the oral hood are provided with *sensory
cells*. The inner wall of the oral hood bears a number of ciliated
lobes and is known as the *wheel organ* because its cilia appear to
produce a rotatory movement. Water is forced into the mouth
by the cilia.

The mouth opens into a large, laterally compressed *pharynx*
(Fig. 342). A ciliated dorsal indentation in the pharynx is called
the *hyperbranchial groove* (Fig. 342). A ventral groove, the
endostyle, is also present. The endostyle consists of a median
ciliated region with a glandular portion on either side. The glands
secrete strings of mucus (compare tunicate, p. 349) in which food
particles are entangled. The cilia then drive this mucus forward
by way of two peripharyngeal grooves into the *hyperbranchial
groove*. From here it is carried by the hyperpharyngeal cilia into
the *intestine* (Fig. 343). A ventral finger-shaped diverticulum
of the intestine is known as the *liver*, or *hepatic cæcum*, since it is
supposed to secrete a digestive fluid similar to that produced by the
liver in the vertebrates. The intestine leads directly to the *anus*.

Respiratory System. — The *pharynx* (Fig. 342) is attached
dorsally and hangs down into a cavity called the *atrium* (Figs.
342–343). The atrium is not the cœlom but is lined with an ectodermal epithelium and is really external to the body, as has been
proved by the study of its development. Water which is carried
into the pharynx by way of the mouth passes through the gill-
slits into the atrium and out of the atriopore (Fig. 341; Fig. 343).
The *gill-slits*, sometimes as many as one hundred and eighty, are
separated by *gill-bars* (Fig. 342); these are ciliated and supported by chitinous rods. *Respiration* takes place as the water,
driven by the cilia, flows through the gill-slits.

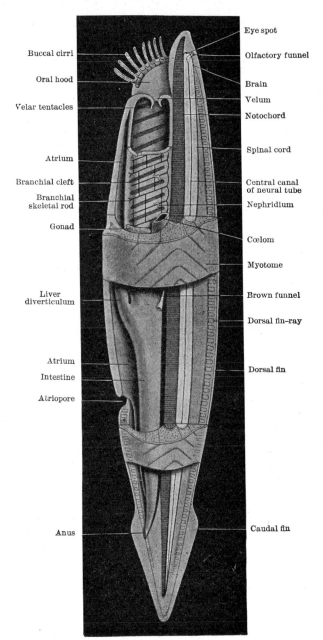

Buccal cirri

Oral hood

Velar tentacles

Atrium

Branchial cleft

Branchial
skeletal rod

Gonad

Liver
diverticulum

Atrium

Intestine

Atriopore

Anus

Eye spot

Olfactory funnel

Brain

Velum

Notochord

Spinal cord

Central canal
of neural tube

Nephridium

Cœlom

Myotome

Brown funnel

Dorsal fin–ray

Dorsal fin

Caudal fin

Fig. 343. — General anatomy of *Amphioxus.* (From Newman, after Parker and Haswell.)

Circulation. — Amphioxus does not possess a heart. The position of the principal blood-vessels and the direction of the blood flow are shown in Figure 344. The *subintestinal vein* collects blood loaded with nutriment from the intestine and carries it forward into the *hepatic portal vein,* and hence to the liver. The *hepatic vein* leads from the liver to the *ventral aorta.* Blood is forced by the rhythmical contractions of the ventral aorta into the *afferent branchial arteries,* which are situated in the gill-bars, and then through the *efferent branchial arteries* into the paired dorsal aortæ. It passes back into the *median dorsal aorta* and finally by way of *intestinal capillaries* into the *subintestinal vein.* The blood is oxygenated during its passage through the branchial

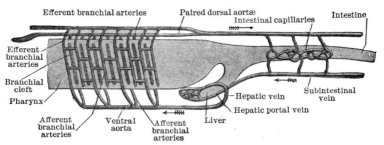

Fig. 344. — Diagram of the vascular system of *Amphioxus.* (From Parker and Haswell.)

arteries. The direction of the blood flow, backward in the dorsal and forward in the ventral vessel, is like that of the vertebrates (p. 363), but just the reverse of that in annelids and arthropods (see pp. 203 and 257).

The Cœlom. — The cœlom arises from five embryonic pouches of the primitive digestive tract as in *Balanoglossus* (p. 346), but is difficult to make out in the adult. The position of the cœlomic cavities is shown in Fig. 343, and Fig. 342.

Excretory System. — The excretory organs are ciliated *nephridia* (Figs. 342–343) situated near the dorsal region of the pharynx. The nephridia connect the dorsal cœlom (Fig. 342) with the atrial cavity. A pair of *brown funnels* (Fig. 343), one on either side and dorsal to the intestine in the region of myotome twenty-seven, may also be excretory organs.

Nervous System. — Amphioxus possesses a *central nerve-cord* (Fig. 343; Fig. 342) lying entirely above the alimentary canal (compare annelids, p. 199, and arthropods, p. 258). It rests on the notochord and is almost as long. A minute *canal* (Fig. 343) traverses its entire length and enlarges at the anterior end into a *cerebral vesicle* which is the only trace of a brain present. An *olfactory pit* opens into this vesicle in young specimens. At the anterior end of the nerve-cord is a mass of pigmented cells forming an *eye-spot*. Two pairs of sensory nerves arise from the cerebral vesicle, and supply the anterior region of the body. The rest of the nerve-cord gives off nerves on opposite sides, but alternating with one another. These nerves are of two kinds: (1) *dorsal nerves* with a sensory function which pass to the skin, and (2) *ventral nerves* with a motor function which enter the myotomes. The *sense-organs* include the olfactory pit, eye-spot, and sensory cells in the ectoderm, on the cirri, and on the velar tentacles.

Reproduction. — In Amphioxus the sexes are separate. The twenty-six pairs of gonads (Fig. 341) project into the atrium. The germ-cells are discharged into the atrial cavity and reach the exterior through the atriopore. Fertilization takes place in the water. The early development of the egg of Amphioxus was described in Chapter III (pp. 84 to 87), and is illustrated in Figure 50. For a detailed description of the embryology of Amphioxus, the student is referred to Willey's *Amphioxus and the Ancestry of the Vertebrates* and to advanced textbooks of zoology.

4. Subphylum IV. Vertebrata: Introduction

The Vertebrata are animals with an axial notochord at some period in their existence. This notochord persists in some of the lower vertebrates, but is modified by an investment of cartilage which becomes segmented and constitutes the *vertebral column*. In the higher vertebrates the vertebral column is made up of a series of bodies called vertebræ, and the notochord disappears before the adult stage is reached. The vertebrates are the lampreys, hags, sharks, rays, chimæras, fishes, frogs, toads, salamanders, lizards, snakes, crocodiles, turtles, birds, hairy quadrupeds, whales, seals, bats, monkeys, and man. Seven classes of vertebrates are recognized.

Class I. Cyclostomata (Gr. *kyklos*, circle; *stoma*, mouth). — Lampreys and Hags (Figs. 352–356). — Cold-blooded, fishlike vertebrates without jaws and lateral fins.

Class II. ELASMOBRANCHII (Gr. *elasmos*, metal plate; *branchia*, gills). — SHARKS, RAYS, and CHIMÆRAS (Figs. 358–367). — Cold-blooded, fish-like vertebrates with jaws, a cartilaginous skeleton, a persistent notochord, and placoid scales.

Class III. PISCES (Lat. *piscis*, fish). — FISHES (Figs. 368–408). — Cold-blooded vertebrates with jaws, and usually with lateral fins supported by fin-rays. They breathe chiefly by gills.

Class IV. AMPHIBIA (Gr. *amphi*, both; *bios*, life). — FROGS, TOADS, and SALAMANDERS (Figs. 409–438). — Cold-blooded, naked vertebrates mostly with pentadactyle (five-fingered) limbs. The young are usually aquatic and breathe by gills; the adults usually lose the gills, and breathe by means of lungs.

Class V. REPTILIA (Lat. *repere*, to crawl). — SPHENODON, CHAMELEONS, LIZARDS, SNAKES, CROCODILES, and TURTLES (Figs. 439–469). — Cold-blooded vertebrates breathing by means of lungs and usually having a scaly skin.

Class VI. AVES (Lat. *avis*, bird). — BIRDS (Figs. 470–509). — Warm-blooded vertebrates with the fore limbs modified into wings and the body covered with feathers.

Class VII. MAMMALIA (Lat. *mamma*, breast). — HAIRY QUADRUPEDS, WHALES, SEALS, BATS, MONKEYS, and MAN (Figs. 510–550). — Warm-blooded vertebrates with a hairy covering at some stage in their existence; the young nourished after birth by the secretion of the mammary glands of the mother.

Plan of Structure. — The vertebrates resemble the other chordates in their *metamerism* and *bilateral symmetry* and in the possession of a *cœlom*, a *notochord*, and *gill-slits* at some stage in their existence, and a *dorsal nerve tube*. They differ from other chordates and resemble one another in the possession of cartilaginous or bony *vertebræ*, usually two pairs of *jointed appendages* containing a central skeleton, a *ventrally situated heart* with at least two chambers, and *red corpuscles* in the blood.

The body of a vertebrate may be divided into a *head, neck* (usually), and *trunk*. In many species there is a posterior extension, the *tail*. Two pairs of *lateral appendages* are generally present, the thoracic (pectoral fins, forelegs, wings, or arms) and the pelvic (pelvic fins, hind legs). The limbs support the body, are locomotory, and usually have other special functions.

A general account of the plan of structure of an ideal vertebrate can be given most clearly with the aid of diagrams showing longitudinal and cross sections through the body (Figs. 345–346). As in Amphioxus, the *nerve-chord* is dorsal but extends in front of the end of the notochord and enlarges into a brain. The *notochord*

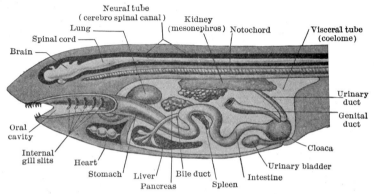

Fig. 345. — Diagrammatic longitudinal section of a vertebrate (female). (From Wiedersheim.)

becomes invested by the vertebræ. The *cœlom* is large. The *alimentary canal* forms a more or less convoluted tube which lies in the body cavity. The *liver, pancreas,* and *spleen* are situated near the alimentary canal. In the anterior trunk region are the

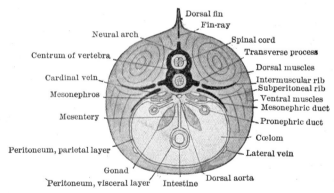

Fig. 346. — Transverse section through the trunk of a vertebrate. (From Parker and Haswell.)

lungs and *heart*. The *kidneys* and *gonads* lie above the alimentary canal.

Integument (Fig. 347). — The outer covering of the vertebrates is the *skin*, consisting of an outer ectodermal layer, the *epidermis*, and an inner mesodermal layer, the *dermis*. The skin is chiefly protective and sensory, but may also carry on respiration and excretion. Excretion takes place by means of glands, which may be simple, as the *mucous glands* of fishes, or complex, as the *sweat*, *oil*, and *mammary glands*. The skin often produces numerous outgrowths such as hair, feathers, nails, hoofs, claws, scales, teeth, and bony plates.

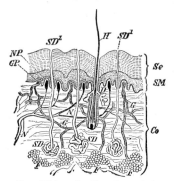

FIG. 347. — Section through human skin. *Co*, dermis; *F*, subcutaneous fat; *GP*, vascular papillæ; *H*, hair with sebaceous glands (*D*); *N*, *G*, nerves; *NP*, sensory papillæ; *Sc*, stratum corneum; *SD*, sweat-glands with their ducts (*SD′*); *SM*, stratum malpighi. (From Wiedersheim.)

Skeleton. — The outgrowths of the integument noted above constitute the *exoskeleton*. The internal supporting framework of the body is the *endoskeleton*. This consists of (1) an *axial portion* comprising the skull and vertebral column, and (2) an *appendicular portion* which supports the appendages.

The *bones* of the endoskeleton are typically formed in and around cartilage. The animal part of the bone is the cartilage; this can be obtained by dissolving out the mineral part, the bone-ash, in hydrochloric acid. The bone-ash consists principally of carbonate and phosphate of lime, and is the residue when a bone is burned. The mineral constituents give the bone rigidity; the cartilage furnishes pliancy and elasticity. Bones support the soft parts, furnish points of attachment for the muscles, and protect certain delicate organs, such as the brain, spinal cord, and eyes.

The *axial skeleton* consists typically of the skull, the vertebræ, and the ribs which may be attached to a ventral bone, the sternum. The *skull* includes a brain case or *cranium*, which protects the brain, and a *visceral skeleton*, which supports the respiratory apparatus and includes the facial bones.

The *vertebral column* serves as a supporting axis for the body. Its structure, however, is such as to allow movement, since it is composed of a number of movable parts, the *vertebræ*. The vertebræ develop from cartilaginous tissue which forms a sheath around the notochord. A typical vertebra consists of a supporting basal portion, the *centrum* (Fig. 346), a dorsal or *neural arch,* which protects the spinal cord, a *neural spine,* which extends dorsally from the center of the neural arch and serves for the attachment of muscles, and a *transverse process* on each side of the centrum to which a rib may be joined.

Four *types of vertebræ* are recognized; (1) *cervical vertebræ* in the neck, (2) *dorsal* or *thoracic vertebræ* which bear ribs, (3) *sacral vertebræ* with which the skeleton of the hind limbs are united, and (4) *caudal vertebræ* posterior to the sacrum.   The *ribs* support the walls of the trunk and may be united with a plate-like breast-bone, the *sternum.* Ribs that are not attached to the sternum are called *false ribs.*

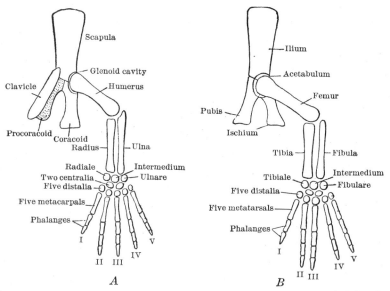

Fig. 348. — Diagrams of **A**, fore limb and girdle, and **B**, hind limb and girdle of a vertebrate. (From Parker and Haswell.)

The *appendicular skeleton* serves to support the appendages and fasten them to the axial skeleton.   The anterior appendages are joined to the *pectoral girdle;* the posterior appendages to the *pelvic girdle.*   The bones of these girdles and of the appendages are shown in Figure 348.   The appendicular skeleton of fishes is usually more simple than that of the higher vertebrates.

Muscular System.[1] — The " flesh " of the vertebrates consists largely of muscle.   Muscular tissue is capable of contraction

[1] A general account of the systems of organs and their functions will be found on pages 76 to 79.

and is responsible for all the movements of an animal. The
muscles are attached to the bones by tendons. The body muscles
are called axial, those of the appendages, appendicular. The
muscles of the internal organs are involuntary, *i.e.* they do not
depend upon the will of the animal (see p. 74).

Digestive System. — The organs of digestion vary considerably
among the vertebrates. The *mouth* opens into a *buccal cavity*
which is usually provided with *jaws* generally bearing teeth. The
teeth are used to hold the food and often to masticate it. In
many cases a fluid from salivary glands enters the buccal cavity
and is there mixed with the food, making it easier to swallow and
digest. Following the buccal cavity is the *pharynx*. In lower
vertebrates and in the embryos of higher forms the pharynx opens
to the outside by *gill-slits*. The *œsophagus* leads from the pharynx
to the stomach. It is usually a narrow tube, but may be enlarged
as in birds, to form a crop for storing and softening food.

The *stomach* varies in shape and structure according to the
kind of food to be digested in it. Its walls contain glands which
secrete digestive ferments or enzymes (p. 202) and hydrochloric
acid; these help dissolve the food so that it can be absorbed. A
circular muscle, called the pyloric sphincter, regulates the passage
of food into the *small intestine*.

Connected with the small intestine by a bile duct is the *liver*.
This organ secretes an alkaline fluid called bile which is poured
into the intestine, where it divides fatty food into particles fine
enough to penetrate the walls of the intestine. Often an enlargement, the *gall-bladder*, is present, in which the bile is stored.
The liver also changes sugar into a substance called *glycogen*,
which is stored up as a reserve for the future needs of the animal.

Another large gland, the *pancreas*, secretes a digestive fluid,
the pancreatic juice, which enters the intestine through the
pancreatic duct. This fluid contains three important ferments;
(1) amylopsin, which forms soluble sugar from starch, (2) trypsin,
which converts proteid into peptones, and (3) steapsin, which
changes fat into soluble fatty acids and glycerin.

The *intestine* is usually longer than the body and therefore
coiled within the abdomen. Through its walls most of the digested food is absorbed into lymphatic tubes and blood capillaries. The absorbent surface is often increased by folds and
small prominences called *villi*. Undigested particles are formed

into *fæces* in the posterior part of the intestine and ejected through the *anus*. In many vertebrates the intestine opens into a terminal sac, the *cloaca*, into which the excretory and reproductive ducts also open.

Circulatory System. — The *blood* into which the digested food passes from the alimentary canal consists of a colorless *plasma* containing passive *red corpuscles* and active, ameboid, *colorless corpuscles*. The color of the red corpuscles is due to the presence of a substance called *hæmoglobin*. The *heart* of vertebrates lies in a part of the cœlom termed the *pericardium*. It consists of at least two chambers: (1) an *auricle* into which the blood is brought by the veins, and (2) a *ventricle* which forces the blood through the arteries.

The smallest blood vessels are called *capillaries*. The exchange of substances between the blood and tissues takes place through the walls of the capillaries. Certain capillaries unite to form *veins*, which carry blood from all parts of the body to the heart. Arterial blood leaves the heart chiefly through the aorta. The *aorta* gives off branches which in turn branch until they end in minute arterial capillaries. The functions of the circulatory system are like those of this system in invertebrates, *i.e.* the transportation of nutriment, oxygen, and waste products from one part of the body to another. In close connection with the circulatory system are a number of spaces and channels comprising the *lymphatic system*. Lymph is a clear fluid containing ameboid cells like the colorless blood corpuscles.

Respiratory System. — Two kinds of respiration may be recognized, (1) *external respiration*, during which oxygen passes into the blood from the air or water and carbon dioxide passes out of the blood, and (2) *internal respiration*, during which the blood supplies oxygen to and takes carbon dioxide from the cells of the body. External respiration is carried on by *gills* in most aquatic vertebrates and by *lungs* in terrestrial vertebrates. Respiration also takes place to some extent through the *skin*. Oxygen unites readily with the hæmoglobin in the red corpuscles. The hæmoglobin is then transported by the blood from the respiratory organs to the capillaries, where it breaks up, the oxygen being absorbed by the tissues. Carbon dioxide from the tissues becomes chemically combined with the sodium in the blood, is carried to the respiratory organs, and discharged to the outside.

Excretory System. — The substances resulting from the oxidation of protoplasm are eliminated by the *kidneys, respiratory organs,* and *skin.* These waste products are carried by the blood. Carbon dioxide is eliminated by the respiratory organs. Nitrogenous waste products are excreted by the kidneys in the form of urea or uric acid. Ducts, called *ureters,* lead from the kidneys either directly to the outside or empty the excretion into a storage vesicle, the *urinary bladder.*

Nervous System. — The nervous system of vertebrates is more complex than that of any other animals. It comprises a *central nervous system* consisting of the *brain* and *spinal cord,*

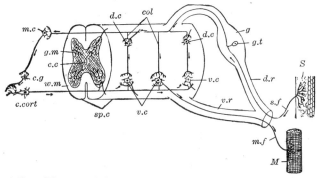

Fig. 349. — Diagram of the spinal cord showing the paths taken by nervous impulses. The direction of the impulses is indicated by arrows. *c.c,* central canal; *col,* collateral fibers; *c.cort,* cell in the cerebral cortex; *c.g,* smaller cerebral cell; *d.c,* cells in dorsal horn of gray matter; *d.r,* dorsal root; *g,* ganglion of dorsal root; *g.c,* ganglion cell in dorsal ganglion; *g.m,* gray matter; *M,* muscle; *m.c,* cell in medulla oblongata; *m.f,* motor fiber; *S,* skin; *s.f,* sensory fiber; *sp.c,* spinal cord; *v.c,* cells in ventral horn of gray matter; *v.r,* ventral root; *w.m,* white matter. (From Holmes, after Parker.)

a *peripheral nervous system* consisting of the *cerebral* and *spinal nerves,* and a *sympathetic system.* The brain is made up of three primary vesicles, a fore-brain, mid-brain, and hind-brain. The fore-brain is thought to correspond to the cerebral vesicle of Amphioxus (Fig. 343). The fore-brain usually gives rise to a pair of cerebral hemispheres, the mid-brain to a pair of optic lobes, and the hind-brain to the cerebellum and medulla oblongata. The spinal cord is a thick tube directly connected with the brain; it passes through the neural arches of the vertebral column.

The *peripheral nervous system* consists of ten to twelve pairs of *cranial nerves* and a number of pairs of *spinal nerves.* The origin, distribution, and function of the cranial nerves are indicated in Table XIV.

The *spinal nerves* arise from the spinal cord in pairs, one on either side in each body segment, and pass out between the ver-

TABLE XIV

THE NUMBER, NAMES, ORIGIN, DISTRIBUTION, AND FUNCTIONS OF THE CRANIAL NERVES OF VERTEBRATES

Number	Name	Origin	Distribution	Function
I	Olfactory	Olfactory lobe of fore-brain	Lining of nose	Sensory
II	Optic	Second vesicle of fore-brain	Retina of eye	Sensory
III	Oculomotor	Ventral region of mid-brain	Muscles of eye	Motor
IV	Trochlearis (patheticus)	Dorsal region of the mid-brain	Superior oblique muscle of eye	Motor
V	Trigeminal (trifacial)	Side of medulla (hind-brain)	Skin of face, mouth, and tongue, and muscles of jaws	Largely sensory
VI	Abducens	Ventral region of medulla	External rectus muscle of eye	Motor
VII	Facial	Side of medulla	Chiefly to muscles of face	Largely motor
VIII	Auditory	Side of medulla	Inner ear	Sensory
IX	Glossopharyngeal	Side of medulla	Muscles and membranes of pharynx, and tongue	Sensory and motor
X	Vagus (pneumogastric)	Side of medulla	Posterior visceral arches, lungs, heart, stomach and intestines	Sensory and motor
XI	Spinal accessory (not present in all vertebrates	Side of medulla	Chiefly muscles of shoulder	Sensory and motor
XII	Hypoglossal (not present in all vertebrates)	Ventral region of medulla	Muscles of tongue and neck	Motor

tebræ. Each nerve has two roots (Fig. 349), a dorsal root and a ventral root. The *dorsal root* possesses a ganglion containing nerve cells. Its fibers carry impulses toward the spinal cord from various parts of the body and are therefore sensory. The fibers of the *ventral root* carry impulses from the spinal cord to the tissues and are therefore motor. The constitution of the nerve cells (neurons) is similar to that of the earthworm (p. 205). The direction of the nervous impulses is indicated by arrows in Figure 349.

On each side of the spinal cord is a chain of ganglia which is connected at various places with the central nervous system. This is known as the *sympathetic nervous system.* These ganglia send nerves chiefly to the alimentary tract, circulatory system, and glandular organs.

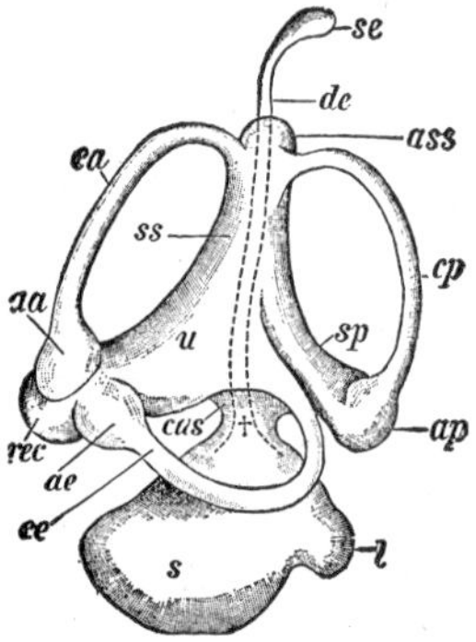

FIG. 350. — Semidiagrammatic figure of the left membranous labyrinth of a vertebrate. *aa, ae, ap,* ampullæ of semicircular canals; *ass,* apex of sinus utriculi superior; *ca, ce, cp,* anterior, external, and posterior semicircular canals; *cus,* utriculosaccular canal; *de, se,* ductus and saccus endolymphaticus; *l,* recessus sacculi; *rec,* recessus utriculi; *s,* sacculus; *sp,* sinus utriculi posterior; *ss,* sinus utriculi superior; *u,* utriculus. (From Wiedersheim.)

Sense-Organs. — Vertebrates possess a number of highly developed sense-organs — nose, eyes, and ears. In addition to these there are many species with sense-cells, single or in groups, scattered over the body. In some of the lower vertebrates these take the form of *lateral line organs* (p. 386) of doubtful function. Usually sense-organs of *taste* occur as pits over the tongue and soft palate.

The sense-organs of *smell* are located in the nose. The nose consists of a pair of cavities at the anterior end of the body. These cavities are lined with folds of mucous epithelium covered with olfactory sense-cells.

The two *ears* of vertebrates arise as cavities of the skin at the sides of the midbrain. They are rather complicated in structure, as indicated in Figure 350. They function as organs of hearing and equilibrium.

The *internal ear* is called the *membranous labyrinth* and is enclosed by cartilage or bone. Within the labyrinth is a fluid called *endolymph;* and between the labyrinth and the surrounding cartilage or bone is a fluid called *perilymph.* The labyrinth is usually constricted into two chambers, (1) a dorsal *utriculus* (Fig. 350) which gives rise to three *semicircular canals*, and (2) a ventral *sacculus* bearing an outgrowth called the *cochlea*. The bases of the semicircular canals are enlarged into *ampullæ* containing cells with long sense hairs which record change of position in any direction and are therefore organs of equilibrium. The cochlea of the sacculus in higher vertebrates is well developed, contains the auditory sense-cells, and is the true organ of hearing.

Sound waves are brought to the cochlea in the ears of higher vertebrates by means of the *middle ear*. This consists of a vibrating membrane, the *tympanum*, which transmits vibrations to the inner ear with the aid of a chain of three bones.

In many vertebrates a funnel-shaped fold of skin, which is supported by cartilage, and called the *pinna* or *external ear*, aids in catching sound waves. In aquatic animals this collecting apparatus is not necessary, since the water carries the sound waves to the tissues which transmit them directly to the inner ear.

The *eyes* are the most complex of the sense-organs of vertebrates. They arise in part from the sides of the fore-brain and in part from the skin and connective tissue. The principal elements of structure and the method of action may be pointed out by means of a diagram of the human eye (Fig. 351). The eye is nearly spherical. It consists of three concentric coats enclosing transparent substances. The outer or *sclerotic coat* is the white of the eye. It is composed of connective tissue and serves as a protective covering. In front of the *lens* the sclerotic coat forms a transparent area called the *cornea*. Beneath the sclerotic coat is the middle coat or *choroid;* this is supplied with blood vessels and contains a great deal of black pigment which prevents light from entering except through the cornea. The choroid coat is separated from the sclerotic coat and perforated just in front of the lens; the opening is the *pupil*, and a part of the choroid surrounding the pupil is the *iris*. The inner coat, the *retina*, is the most important, since it is the sensitive layer, being an expansion of the *optic nerve*. It lines the cavity back of the lens. The lens is biconvex and transparent. It is attached to the choroid coat by a *suspensory ligament* and separates the small anterior cavity, filled with a fluid called *aqueous humor*, from the large posterior cavity, filled with a jelly-like substance called *vitreous humor*.

The eye is like a camera in certain respects. With the aid of the lens an image is formed on the sensitive retina of the

objects in front of the cornea. The eye is accommodated for
recording images of distant and near objects by changes in the
convexity of the lens caused by its own elasticity, and the pull
exerted upon it by the elastic choroid coat and the *ciliary
muscles.* In viewing near objects the ciliary muscle counteracts

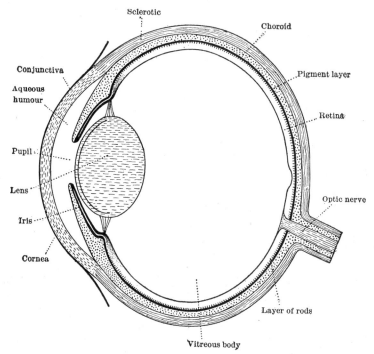

Fig. 351. — Structure of the eye of a vertebrate.   (From Kerr.)

the pull of the choroid coat and allows the lens to assume a more
convex shape, whereas distant objects are made distinct by the
flattening of the lens.

The eye is moved by six muscles; four straight (*rectus*) and
two oblique. Folds of skin, the *eyelids*, protect the eye in higher
vertebrates. There may be three eyelids: an upper and a lower
lid which act vertically, and a lateral lid (nictitating membrane)
which moves outward from the inner angle of the eye. In some
reptiles the eyelids are transparent and fused over the eye.
Terrestrial vertebrates have *lacrymal glands* in connection with

the eye, the secretion from which keeps the surface of the eyeball moist and washes away foreign particles.

Reproductive System. — The sexes of vertebrates, with few exceptions, are separate. The reproductive organs arise in close connection with the excretory organs, and the excretory ducts may serve to carry germ-cells to the exterior. Fertilization takes place in some AMPHIBIA and most fishes after the eggs are extruded. In other vertebrates fertilization is internal. Most vertebrates lay eggs, *i.e.* are *oviparous*, but many of them, especially mammals, bring forth their young alive, *i.e.* are *viviparous*.

5. GENERAL CONSIDERATIONS

The Variety and Unity of Animal Life. — Thus far we have studied representatives of ten phyla of animals each of which was divided into from several to many Classes, Orders, Families, etc. Besides this a number of groups have been described briefly that cannot at present be placed with certainty in their proper places in the zoological series. All these animals differ from one another in their morphology sufficiently to be recognizable. Differences occur in size, symmetry, habitat, geographical distribution, reproduction, protective devices, organs of locomotion, of capturing food, of digestion, and of the other physiological processes, and in many other ways. There are, however, many characteristics in which large numbers of them resemble one another. All of them consist of protoplasm and are built up of one or more cells; cellular division by mitosis is common to them all as a form of cell multiplication; certain fundamental physiological processes are necessary such as digestion, assimilation, respiration, excretion, secretion; growth is an invariable characteristic; reproduction in kind is obligatory for the maintenance of the various races; genetic continuity of chromosomes has been demonstrated in many species; an ontogenetic development takes place in the higher forms including cleavage, gastrulation, and organogeny; and in all groups the processes of organic evolution have been in operation for many centuries and may still be in operation, bringing about the modifications which account for the wonderful variety of animal life now existing on the earth.

A survey of the phyla of invertebrates with the following subjects in mind is suggested as an excellent method of demonstrating the variety and unity in animal life and of forming generalizations before proceeding to a detailed study of the vertebrates.

The Cell Theory	Oögenesis
Morphology	Spermatogenesis
Physiology	Fertilization
Cell Division	Parthenogenesis
The Origin of Metazoa	Asexual Reproduction
Symmetry	Embryology
Metamerism	Origin of Germ Cells and Somatic Cells
Metagenesis	Classification
Homology	Biogenetic Law
Germ Layers	Regeneration, Autotomy and Grafting
The Cœlom	Polymorphism
Organology	Metamorphosis
Methods of Nutrition	Symbiosis and Parasitism
Organ Physiology	Animal Habitats
Spontaneous Generation	Geographical Distribution.
Sexual Reproduction	

Animal Ecology. — Some idea has been presented of where animals live in Chapter I (pp. 5–7) and in connection with the various groups of invertebrates. This subject of animal habitats or the relations of animals to their environment has been organized into the science of animal ecology, which deals with the relations of individuals or species to their physical environment, to other individuals of the same species, to individuals of other species and to plants. Some of the most interesting associations among animals are known as commensalism, symbiosis, and parasitism. A commensal is an animal that lives at the table of another, feeding on scraps but not injuring its companion, *e.g.* the remora fish is a commensal associated with a shark which is its host (p. 421, Fig. 400). Other examples of this type of relation may be found among the animals already described. Symbiosis is a more rigid relationship in which the two associated organisms are often mutually beneficial and, in fact, sometimes cannot live independently of each other. An excellent example of this type is that of certain termites, or white ants (p. 305), which feed on dead wood. This wood they are unable to utilize unless certain flagellate protozoans are present in their digestive tract; these protozoans digest the wood, part of which they use as their food and the rest of which furnishes nutriment for the termite hosts. Another example, that does not involve the dependence of the symbionts is that of the hermit crab and sea-anemone (p. 272). In parasitism one of the associated animals, the parasite, lives on or within the body of another, its host, inflicting upon the latter some degree of injury. The parasite does not kill its host outright as a predaceous animal does its prey, but allows it to live while continually using it as a protection and a source of food supply. Many examples of parasitism have been described in the preceeding pages among the invertebrates.

A study of the relations of animals to their environment reveals many ways in which they are adapted for life in the particular habitat in which they flourish. These adaptations involve all the organs and physiological processes that make up the activities of the animal, and different animals are adapted to similar conditions in different ways. Thus aquatic insects and fish are able to move and breathe under water but the methods by which these activities are accomplished are very different. A review of the morphology and behavior of any animal will show how wonderfully it is adapted to life in its particular environment. Each species of animal, however, is not adapted to a certain habitat to the exclusion of other species, but many species of animals and plants may live in one habitat. Associations of animals in one habitat are known as animal communities and an attempt has been made by students of ecology to classify these communities. Thus we may recognize various types of fresh-water communities; of salt-water or marine communities, including communities of the open sea, of the sea bottom and of the sea shore; and of terrestrial communities, which include forests with broad thin leaves, evergreen forests, grassland, and desert. It is a comparatively simple matter to determine what species of animals occupy a certain habitat, but it is more difficult to work out the actual physiological relations between the animal and the various factors in its environment, and only a beginning has been made in this direction.

Migration. — Many animals migrate at more or less definite seasons of the year and for various reasons. For example, many fish migrate long distances to lay their eggs. The chinook salmon lives in the sea along the Pacific coast from Monterey Bay, California, and China, north to Bering Straits. It enters the fresh-water streams to spawn, especially the Sacramento, Columbia, and Yukon rivers. The ascent takes place in the spring and summer, beginning in February or March in Columbia River. The salmon do not feed during this migration, but swim at first slowly and then more rapidly until they reach the small, clear mountain streams often more than a thousand miles from the sea. Spawning occurs from July to December, according to the temperature of the water, which apparently must be below 54° Fahrenheit. The eggs are deposited upon the gravelly bottoms of the streams, after which both males and females die; consequently an individual spawns only once in its lifetime. The eggs hatch in about seven weeks, and the young remain on the spawning ground for six weeks. They then float slowly downstream and may be four or five inches long when they reach the sea.

The remarkable powers of locomotion possessed by birds enable them to move from one part of the country to another with comparative ease. As a result, when winter approaches in temperate regions most of the birds gather together in flocks and migrate to the warmer southern countries. Those that remain in one locality throughout the year, like the great horned owl and English sparrow, are called permanent residents; those that pass through on their way south in the autumn and on their way north in the spring, like most of the warblers, are called migrants; and those that leave in the autumn and return the following spring, remaining with us to nest, we call summer residents. (See page 553.)

Geographical Distribution. — As a result of the adaptation of animals to a definite type of habitat each species is restricted by its morphology and physiology to those parts of the world in which the proper type of habitat exists. Thus each species of animal is rather definitely restricted to certain regions on the earth's surface. The study of this subject is known as zoogeography. The facts of geographical distribution have led to the formulation of the three following laws: (1) the law of definite habitats, (2) the law of dispersion, and (3) the law of barriers and highways.

The Law of Definite Habitats. — Among the most important physical factors that determine the habitat of an animal are temperature, water, light, and food. The continent of North America has been divided by scientists into definite regions, according to the sum total of the temperature during the season of growth; and regions of a certain temperature, though widely separated, are liable to support similar kinds of animals. Winter is met by northern animals in one of four ways: (1) by dying, *e.g.* adult butterflies, (2) migrating, *e.g.* birds, (3) hibernating, *e.g.* bears, (4) remaining active, *e.g.* rabbits. Animals living in tropical regions pass the summer in many cases in a torpid condition, and are said to be æstivating.

A certain amount of water is necessary for life, as the bodies of animals are made up of from 55 to 95 per cent water. Animals living in dry climates have thick skins, and thus evaporation is prevented.

Light plays a leading rôle in the lives of animals; many species require it, but others shun it as much as possible, principally in order to escape their enemies.

And finally, food conditions are most effective, since carnivorous animals, *e.g.* lions, must live where they may obtain flesh; herbivorous animals, *e.g.* deer, must live where suitable vegetation abounds; and omnivorous animals, *e.g.* man, where both flesh and vegetation of certain sorts exist.

The Law of Dispersion. — Animals tend to migrate from the region of their birth. It is supposed that every animal produces a greater number of offspring than can be supported in its particular habitat, and since parents and offspring cannot occupy the same area, some individuals must either migrate or die.

The Law of Barriers and Highways. — Animals are confined to certain habitats by barriers and are prevented from entering a new region by mountains or lakes, by lack of food, and by the interference of other animals. Common barriers are mountains, bodies of water, open country for forest animals, and forests for prairie-inhabiting species. The reverse of a barrier is a highway. Apparently there are routes of migration which are especially favored.

Cosmopolitan Groups of Animals. — Some species of animals have wide ranges, *e.g.* some are found inhabiting practically every large land area on the earth's surface. This is true of many birds and of the bats among the mammals.

Restricted Groups of Animals. — In a number of cases certain species are restricted to very limited areas. The mountain goat is found only in the higher Rocky and Cascade mountains of Alaska. Islands are famous for the presence of restricted species. Darwin's descriptions of the animals he found in the Galapagos Islands read like fairy tales.

Discontinuous   Distribution. — Whenever   a   species   occurs   in two widely separated regions, it is safe to conclude that the distribution must once have been continuous.   Examples of discontinuously distributed animals are rare.   Tapirs inhabit tropical America and nowhere else except the Malay Archipelago.

CHAPTER XV

SUBPHYLUM VERTEBRATA: CLASS I. CYCLOSTOMATA [1]

THE CYCLOSTOMATA (Fig. 352) are vertebrates that have a superficial resemblance to eels, but differ from them as well as from all other vertebrates in many important respects. They are without functional jaws and lateral appendages, and have only one olfactory pit. Cyclostomes are commonly known as

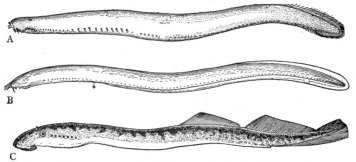

FIG. 352. — CYCLOSTOMES. **A**, *Bdellostoma dombeyi.* Light apertures along side are mucous pits; dark apertures are branchial openings. **B**, *Myxine glutinosa.* Left common branchial aperture is at *. **C**, *Petromyzon marinus.* (From Dean.)

hags and lampreys. There are two subclasses, the MYXINOIDEA or hagfishes, and the PETROMYZONTIA or lampreys; the former are all marine; the latter are found both in salt water and fresh water. They usually feed on the mucus, blood, and even the internal organs of fishes, which they attack with their rasping mouth.

1. THE LAMPREY — PETROMYZON

Petromyzon marinus, the sea lamprey (Fig. 352, C), inhabits the waters along the Atlantic coast of North America, the coasts of Europe, and the west coast of Africa. It swims about near

---

[1] The cyclostomes are interesting chordates but a general idea of the group is all that time usually allows in a beginning course. This chapter is therefore included for reference only.

the bottom by undulations of its body, or, when in a strong current, progresses by darting suddenly forward and attaching itself to a rock by means of its suctorial mouth. In the spring the lamprey ascends the rivers to spawn.

External Features. — The lamprey reaches a length of about three feet. Its body is nearly cylindrical, except at the posterior end, where it is laterally compressed. There is no exoskeleton. The *skin* is soft and is made slimy by secretions from *epidermal glands*. It is mottled greenish brown in color. A row of segmental sense pits, the *lateral line*, lies on each side of the body and on the head. The *mouth*

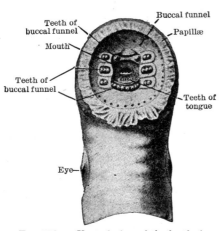

FIG. 353. — Ventral view of the head of *Petromyzon marinus*. (From Parker.)

(Fig. 353), lies at the bottom of a suctorial disc, the *buccal funnel*, and is held open by a ring of cartilage (Fig. 354). Around the mouth are a number of *papillæ* (Fig. 353), and horny *teeth*. Just beneath the mouth is a piston-like *tongue* which also bears teeth. On each side of the head is an *eye*, and, posterior to the eye, seven *gill-slits* (Fig. 352, *C*). Between the eyes on the dorsal surface is a single opening, the *nasal aperture* (Fig. 355). The *anus* opens on the ventral surface near the posterior end; just behind it is the *urinogenital aperture* in the end of a small papilla. There are two *dorsal fins* and one *caudal fin* (Fig. 352, C).

The Skeleton (Fig. 354). — The *notochord* of *Petromyzon* persists as a well-developed structure in the adult (Fig. 355; Fig. 354). In the trunk region the notochord is supplemented by small cartilaginous *neural arches* (Fig. 354). Cartilaginous *rays* hold the fins upright. The organs in the head are supported by a cartilaginous skull and a cartilaginous branchial basket.

The *skull* is very simple. Its principal parts, as shown in Figure 354, are an *annular cartilage* which holds the mouth open, two *labial cartilages* which form a rooflike support for the buccal funnel, a *lingual cartilage* supporting the tongue, an *olfactory capsule*, two *auditory capsules*, and a *cranial roof*. The *branchial basket* is a cartilaginous framework which supports the gill-sacs and the walls of the pericardium.

The Muscular System. — The muscles of the body-wall are zigzag *myotomes* (Fig. 355). The tongue is moved by large muscles, and the buccal funnel is supplied with a number of radiating muscles.

The Digestive System. — *Petromyzon* lives on the blood of other animals. The expansion of the buccal funnel (Fig. 355) causes the mouth to act like a sucker and enables the animal to

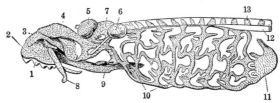

FIG. 354. — Lateral view of skull of *Petromyzon marinus*. *1*, horny teeth; *2*, annular cartilage; *3*, anterior labial cartilage; *4*, posterior labial cartilage; *5*, nasal capsule; *6*, auditory capsule; *7*, dorsal portion of trabeculæ; *8*, lateral distal labial cartilage; *9*, lingual cartilage; *10*, branchial basket; *11*, cartilaginous cup supporting pericardium; *12*, sheath of notochord; *13*, anterior neural arches fused together. (From Shipley and MacBride, after Parker.)

cling to stones or to fasten itself to fishes such as shad, sturgeon, cod, and mackerel. With its rasp-like tongue a hole is made in the flesh of the victim and the blood sucked out.

The *mouth* opens into a *buccal cavity* (Fig. 355). Two tubes lead posteriorly from the latter, a dorsal *œsophagus* and a ventral *respiratory tube*, guarded by a fold called the *velum*. There is no distinct *stomach*. The œsophagus is separated from the *intestine* only by a valve. A fold in the intestine called the *typhlosole* (see also p. 202) forms a sort of *spiral valve*. A *liver* is present, but there is usually no bile duct in the adult.

The Circulatory System. — *Petromyzon* possesses a heart, a number of veins and arteries, and many lymphatic sinuses (Fig. 355). The *heart* lies in the *pericardium*, and consists of a *ventricle* which forces the blood into the arteries and an *auricle* which receives the blood from the veins. A *renal portal system* is absent.

The Respiratory System. — Respiration is carried on by means of seven pairs of *gill pouches* (Fig. 355), which open to the outside

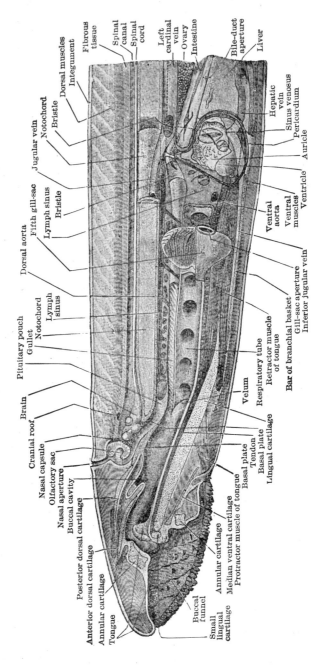

Fibrous tissue
Spinal canal
Spinal cord
Left cardinal vein
Ovary
Intestine
Bile-duct aperture
Liver
Dorsal muscles
Integument
Bristle
Notochord
Jugular vein
Hepatic vein
Sinus venosus
Pericardium
Auricle
Fifth gill-sac
Lymph sinus
Bristle
Dorsal aorta
Ventricle
Ventral aorta
Ventral muscles
Notochord
Lymph sinus
Gullet
Pituitary pouch
Retractor muscle of tongue
Respiratory tube
Gill-sac aperture
Inferior jugular vein
Bar of branchial basket
Brain
Velum
Cranial roof
Nasal capsule
Olfactory sac
Nasal aperture
Buccal cavity
Basal plate
Tendon
Basal plate
Lingual cartilage
Posterior dorsal cartilage
Anterior dorsal cartilage
Annular cartilage
Tongue
Annular cartilage
Median ventral cartilage
Protractor muscle of tongue
Buccal funnel
Small lingual cartilage

Fig. 355. — *Petromyzon marinus.* Dissection of female. The cartilaginous parts and sheath of notochord are dotted. (From Parker.)

by the *gill-slits* and internally to the *respiratory tube*. Each gill pouch contains numerous *gill lamellæ*. Water is taken into the gill-sacs through the gill-slits, and discharged by the same openings.

The Nervous System. — The *brain* (Fig. 355) of the adult lamprey is very primitive and in many respects similar to that of the embryos of higher vertebrates. It is remarkable because of its thin membranous roof and the small band-like cerebellum. The *spinal cord* is flat, and lies on the floor of the neural canal.

The Sensory Organs. — Organs of taste, smell, hearing, and sight are present in the lamprey. The end organs of *taste* are situated between the gill pouches on the pharyngeal wall. The organ of *smell* is an *olfactory sac* (Fig. 355) which lies in the *nasal capsule*, and opens by a *nasal aperture* on the dorsal surface between the eyes. The olfactory sac gives off ventrally a tube of unknown function, called the *hypophysis* or *pituitary body*.

The *auditory organs* of *Petromyzon*, which lie in the *auditory capsule* (Fig. 354), have only two semicircular canals instead of the usual number, three (Fig. 350). The hagfish has only one. The *eyes* of the lamprey are poorly developed.

The Urinogenital System. — The excretory and reproductive systems are so closely united in the lamprey that it is customary to treat them together as the urinogenital system. The *kidneys* lie along the dorsal wall of the body-cavity, and each pours its secretions by means of a duct, called the *ureter*, into the *urinogenital sinus*, and thence to the outside through the *urinogenital aperture*. The sexes are separate, but eggs are sometimes present in the testis of the male. The single *gonad* (Fig. 355), fills most of the abdominal cavity. The germ-cells break out into the cœlom, make their way through two genital pores into the urinogenital sinus, and then pass out through the urinogenital aperture into the water, where fertilization occurs.

Development. — The eggs produce larvæ known as Ammocœtes. The larva differs in many respects from the adult, and apparently represents a stage of development intermediate between Amphioxus and a primitive vertebrate. As in Amphioxus, food particles are drawn into the mouth by means of a current of water produced by cilia. An endostyle, which represents the thyroid gland of the adult, secretes mucus which entangles the food and carries it into the alimentary canal.

The Ammocœtes lies buried in mud and sand, and probably keeps its skin free from bacteria, fungi, and other parasitic growths by means of an integumentary secretion. In the winter of the third or fourth year the larval lamprey undergoes a metamorphosis during which the structure and habits of the adult are acquired.

Relationships. — The hagfishes and lampreys are the lowest vertebrates. Many of their structures, such as the cranium and vertebral column, are very primitive, but others are apparently highly specialized. The absence of jaws and of limbs may be due to degeneration.

Economic Importance. — The flesh of the lamprey is used as food both in Europe and America. The number of lampreys, however, has decreased so much within recent years that their value as food is now almost negligible. Fishermen charge the lamprey with destroying numbers of food fishes, which are attacked just beneath the pectoral fins. The flesh is torn with their rasping teeth and the blood sucked out of the body.

2. Cyclostomata in General

Subclass I. Myxinoidea. — The Hagfishes. — One family, the Myxinidæ, belongs to this subclass. The Myxinidæ are all marine, and are represented by three genera: (1) *Bdellostoma* (Fig. 352, A) and (2) *Paramyxine* in the Pacific, and (3) *Myxine* (Fig. 352, B) in the Pacific, Atlantic, and North Sea. These hagfishes differ from the lampreys in a number of characters: (1) the nasal aperture is terminal; (2) the pituitary body opens into the pharynx; (3) there are four tentacles on either side of the mouth; (4) the oral sucker is absent, and there is only a single large tooth; (5) there are no neural arches in the trunk, and the branchial basket is poorly developed; and (6) the gills may open by a single common pore on each side (*Myxine*).

The hagfishes live in the mud of the sea bottom down to a depth of nearly three hundred and fifty fathoms. They are very destructive to fishes, especially those caught on lines or in nets, boring their way into the body and eating out the soft parts. Cod and flounders are the fish usually attacked.

Subclass II. Petromyzontia. — The Lampreys.—The lampreys all resemble *Petromyzon* in general structure. There is a single family, PETROMYZONTIDÆ, and a number of genera. *Petromyzon* inhabits the rivers and seas of America, Europe, and Asia; *Lampetra* and *Ichthyomyzon* live in North American streams and lakes; *Mordacia* and *Geotria* in South America and Tasmania.

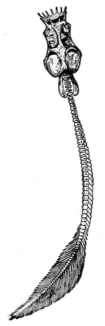

Lampetra wilderi, the brook lamprey of North America, breeds in the spring. Stones are moved by means of the buccal funnel until a space is cleared on the bottom where a number of individuals congregate

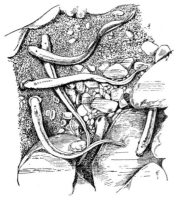

FIG. 356. — *Lampetra wilderi*, in the act of spawning. (From Shipley and MacBride, after Dean and Sumner.)

FIG. 357. — *Palæospondylus gunni*, a Devonian Cyclostome. (From Dean, after Traquair.)

(Fig. 356). A male clings to the head of a female for a moment, winds his tail about her body, and discharges spermatozoa over the eggs when they are extruded. The adults die soon after spawning; they probably take no food, and are therefore not injurious to fishes.

A fossil vertebrate, *Palæospondylus gunni* (Fig. 357), was probably closely allied to the cyclostomes. It was found in the Devonian rocks of Scotland and is about an inch long.

CHAPTER XVI

SUBPHYLUM VERTEBRATA: CLASS II. ELASMO-BRANCHII [1]

THE elasmobranchs are the sharks, dogfish sharks, and rays or skates. They resemble the true fishes (PISCES, Chapter XVII) in external form, but differ from them so widely in structure that they are placed in a class by themselves.[2] The elasmobranchs exhibit a number of structural advances over the cyclostomes; there are paired fins, a lower jaw, gill arches, and placoid scales. Among the peculiarities which separate the elasmobranchs from the true fishes (PISCES) are the absence of membrane bones, of an air bladder, and of true scales, and the presence of skeletal characteristics which are not found in true fishes. Two subclasses of living elasmobranchs are recognized: the SELACHII or sharks and rays, and the HOLOCEPHALI or chimæras.

1. THE DOGFISH SHARK — SQUALUS ACANTHIAS

The common dogfish shark (Fig. 358) is abundant in the waters off the coast of New England and northern Europe. It is widely used for laboratory study, and detailed accounts of

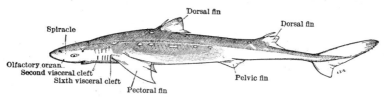

FIG. 358. — The dogfish shark, *Acanthias*. (From Kerr.)

its anatomy may be found in several laboratory manuals. It will suffice here to point out certain of its more prominent characteristics.

---

[1] The dogfish shark furnishes excellent material for laboratory work in vertebrate anatomy. If time allows the study of only one vertebrate type, however, the frog is recommended, and this chapter should then be used for reference purposes. /

[2] See Jordan, *Guide to the Study of Fishes*, Vol. I. pp. 506–511.

External Features.[1] — The body is fusiform and about two and one half feet long. There are two *dorsal fins* (Fig. 359) each with a *spine* (not shown in Fig. 359) at the anterior end, two *pectoral fins*, and two *ventral fins*. The ventral fins in the male possess cartilaginous appendages, known as *claspers*. The tail is *heterocercal* (see Chap. XVII). The *mouth* is a transverse slit on the ventral surface of the head. On either side above the mouth is an *eye*, and in front an *olfactory organ*. Anterior to each pectoral fin are six *gill-slits*, the first of which is situated just back of the eye and modified as a *spiracle*. Between the ventral fins is the *cloacal opening*.

The surface is covered with *placoid scales* or *dermal denticles* (Fig. 360) which form shagreen. They represent a primitive exoskeletal structure and have been the starting-point for the development of the scales and bony plates of the true fishes.

Over the jaws they are modified as *teeth* with their points directed backward, and are used for holding and tearing prey. A placoid scale consists of a bony basal plate with a

[1] Figure 359 shows the anatomy of a shark which differs slightly from that of the dogfish shark.

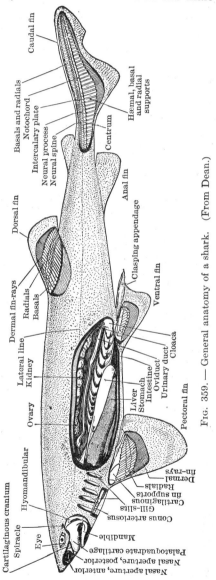

Fig. 359. — General anatomy of a shark. (From Dean.)

spine in the center composed of dentine and covered with enamel.

The Skeleton. — The skeleton is *cartilaginous*. The *axial skeleton* consists of the vertebral column, skull, and visceral arches. The *vertebræ* (Fig. 359) are hour-glass-shaped (amphicœlous), and the *notochord* persists in the lenticular spaces between them. The *skull* is much more highly developed than that of the cyclostomes. It is composed principally of the *cranium* or brain case, two large anterior *nasal capsules*, and two posterior *auditory capsules*. The *visceral skeleton* comprises the *jaws*, the *hyoid arch*, and five *branchial arches*. The *appendicular skeleton* consists of the skeletons of the fins and those of the *pectoral* and *pelvic girdles* which support them.

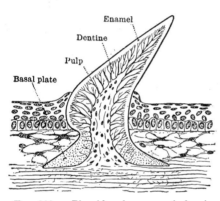

FIG. 360. — Placoid scale, as seen in longitudinal section. (From Kerr.)

The Digestive System. — The *alimentary canal* is longer than the body. Following the *mouth* (Fig. 359) is a large *pharynx* into which open the spiracles and gill-clefts. The pharynx leads into the short, wide *œsophagus* which opens into the U-shaped *stomach*. The hinder end of the stomach is provided with a sphincter, or circular muscle marking it off from the *intestine*. The latter is provided interiorly with a spiral fold of mucous membrane, called the *spiral valve*, which furnishes a large surface for absorption and prevents the too rapid passage of food. The *liver* is large, and consists of two long lobes; its secretion, the bile, is stored up in a *gall-bladder* and emptied through the bile-duct into the intestine. A *pancreas* and *spleen* are also present.

The Circulatory System (Fig. 361). — As in the cyclostomes and most of the true fishes, the heart contains venous blood only. This is pumped through the *ventral aorta* and thence into the *afferent branchial arteries*, becoming oxygenated in the capillaries of the gills. It then passes into the *efferent branchial arteries*, which carry it to the *dorsal aorta*. The dorsal aorta supplies the various parts of the body as shown in Figure 361. Veins carry the blood back to the heart, opening into the *sinus venosus*. Other veins, called the *hepatic portal system*, transport the blood from the alimentary canal, pancreas, and spleen to the liver. A third system, the *renal portal system*, conveys the blood from the hinder portion of the body to the kidneys.

The Respiratory System. — Respiration is carried on by means of *gills*. These are folds of mucous membrane well supplied with blood-vessels and borne by the hyoid arch and first four branchial arches. They are supported both by these arches and by gill-rays. Water entering the mouth passes between the branchial arches and out through the gill-slits (Fig. 359), thus bathing the gills and supplying oxygen to the branchial blood-vessels.

The Nervous System.—The *brain* (Fig. 362) is more highly developed than that of the cyclostomes. It possesses two remark-

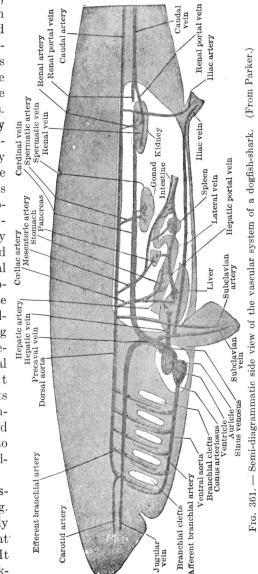

Fig. 361. — Semi-diagrammatic side view of the vascular system of a dogfish-shark. (From Parker.)

ably large *olfactory lobes,* a *cerebrum* of two hemispheres, a pair of *optic lobes,* and a cerebellum which projects backward over the *medulla oblongata.* There are ten pairs of *cranial nerves* (Fig. 362 and Table XIV). The *spinal cord* is a dorsoventrally flattened tube with a narrow central canal; it is protected by the vertebral column. *Spinal nerves* arise from its sides in pairs.

The Sense-organs. — The *olfactory sac* (Fig. 362) is characteristically large in elasmobranchs. The *ears* (Fig. 350) are membranous sacs each with three semicircular canals; they lie within the auditory capsules. The *eyes* (Fig. 362) are well developed. Along each side of the head and body is a longitudinal groove, called the *lateral line* (Fig. 359), and on the head are also *mucous canals* which open on the dorsal and ventral surfaces and end in ampullæ at the anterior end of the snout. These structures are supposed to be sensory in function.

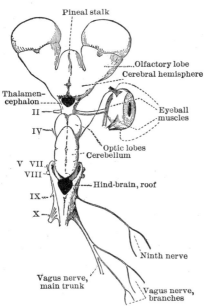

Fig. 362. — Brain of a dogfish shark, *Scyllium catulus,* dorsal view. (From Shipley and MacBride.)

The Urinogenital System. — The dogfish shark possesses two ribbon-like *kidneys* (Fig. 359), one on either side of the dorsal aorta Their secretion is carried by small ducts into a larger duct, the *ureter,* which empties into a *urinogenital sinus;* it then passes out of the body through the *cloacal aperture.* A series of yellowish gland-like bodies, called *suprarenals,* are associated with the kidneys.

The spermatozoa of the male arise in two testes and are carried by the *vasa deferentia* into the urinogenital sinus. During *copulation* they are transferred to the oviducts of the female with the aid of the *claspers.*

The eggs of the female arise in the single *ovary* (Fig. 359), which is attached to the dorsal wall of the abdominal cavity. They break out into this cavity and enter the funnel-like openings of the *oviducts*. When they reach an expanded portion, called the *oviducal gland*, they receive a horny covering which protects them from injury after they are laid.

2. ELASMOBRANCHS IN GENERAL

The chief characteristics of the elasmobranchs are the presence of a cartilaginous skeleton, a persistent notochord, placoid scales, a spiral valve in the intestine, and claspers in the male; and the

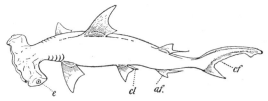

FIG. 363. — Hammerhead shark, *Sphyrna tudes*. *af.*, anal fin; *cf*, caudal fin; *cl*, clasper; *e*, eye. (From Lankester's Treatise, after Day.)

absence of a gill-cover or operculum, pyloric cæca, and an airbladder. The mouth is a transverse aperture on the ventral side of the head.

SUBCLASS I. SELACHII. — There are two distinct types of elasmobranchs belonging to this subclass: (1) *sharks*, which are slender and cylindrical and have the gill-slits on the side; and

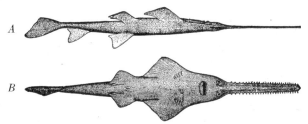

FIG. 364. — Sawfish, *Pristis pectinatus*. *A*, side view. *B*, ventral view. (From Dean; *A*, after Goode.)

(2) *rays*, which are flattened dorso-ventrally and have the gillslits underneath.

Order 1. Squali. — SHARKS AND DOGFISH SHARKS. — The sharks and dogfish sharks resemble in general the common horned dogfish shark (Fig. 358). Most sharks are under eight feet in length, and although carnivorous and voracious, very seldom attack man. They feed principally on small fish, squids, and CRUSTACEA. The great white shark, *Carcharodon carcharias*, occurs in all warm seas. It reaches a length of over thirty feet and has earned the name of man-eater by occasionally devouring a human being. One of the most peculiar sharks is the hammerhead, *Sphyrna tudes* (Fig. 363), which is also found in warm seas. Its head is shaped like the head of a mallet, with an eye (*e*) at either end.

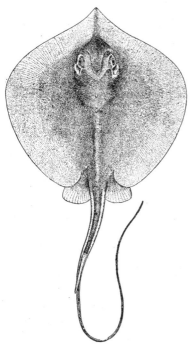

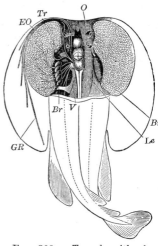

FIG. 366. — *Torpedo* with electric organ, *EO*, and brain exposed, dorsal view. *Br*, branchial sacs; *GR*, sensory canal tubes of the skin; *Le*, electric lobe of brain; *O*, eye; *Tr*, trigeminal nerve; *V*, vagus nerve. (From Sedgwick's Zoology, after Gegenbaur.)

FIG. 365. — Sting-ray, *Dasyatis sabina*, dorsal view. (From Jordan and Evermann.)

Order 2. Raji. — RAYS OR SKATES. — The rays or skates are flattened dorso-ventrally and adapted for living on the bottom. Some of them are only slightly flattened, whereas others are broader than long. The sawfish, *Pristis pectinatus* (Fig. 364), lives in tropical seas and is abundant in the Gulf of Mexico. It reaches a length of from ten to twenty feet. The saw of a large specimen is about five feet long; it is used as a weapon of defense, and dangerous sidewise strokes can be made with it.

The sting-ray, *Dasyatis sabina* (Fig. 365), lives half buried in the sand along the coast of Florida. There is a barbed spine on its whip-like tail which makes a painful wound if driven into the hand or naked foot. The torpedo (Family TORPEDINIDÆ, Fig. 366) is interesting because of the presence of modified bundles of muscles (Fig. 366, *EO*) lying on either side of the head which are capable of storing up electrical energy and discharging it. The discharge of these electric organs is sufficient to paralyze large animals; they thus may serve as weapons of offense and defense.

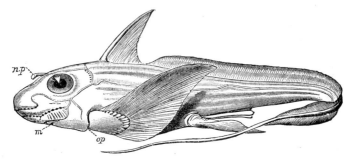

Fig. 367. — *Chimæra monstrosa*, male. *m*, mouth ; *n.p*, frontal clasper : *op*, operculum. (From the Cambridge Natural History.)

SUBCLASS II. HOLOCEPHALI. — The members of this subclass differ from the SELACHII in a number of minor structural characters. There is a single family, the CHIMÆRIDÆ, containing three genera. The species shown in Figure 367 is the sea-cat of the North Atlantic.

3. THE ECONOMIC IMPORTANCE OF ELASMOBRANCHS

Many destructive species belong to the elasmobranchs. The smooth dogfish shark, *Mustelus canis*, is an important enemy of the lobster. It is estimated that the minimum number of lobsters destroyed by these dogfish sharks in Buzzards Bay during one year is about 640,000. The sand-shark, *Carcharias littoralis*, devours large numbers of valuable fishes, including menhaden, flounders, and scup. The horned dogfish shark, *Squalus acanthias* (Fig. 358), is the most serious destructive agency with which fishermen have to contend. It devours valuable food fishes, drives away or destroys schools of squid used by the fishermen for bait, and robs and injures nets and other fishing gear. Experts estimate the damage from dogfish sharks to marketable fish and fishing gear owned in Massachusetts at not less than $400,000 per year. They suggest that dogfish sharks be converted into oil and fertilizer so as to make it profitable for fishermen to capture them and thus bring about a decrease in their numbers.

CHAPTER XVII

SUBPHYLUM VERTEBRATA: CLASS III. PISCES [1]

THE PISCES are the true fishes. The class includes the common fishes and the lung-fishes. They are aquatic animals and are, therefore, adapted to life in the water. The respiratory organs of fishes are gills. Usually a dermal exoskeleton of scales or bony plates furnishes a protective covering for the body. Living fishes are grouped into two subclasses.

Subclass I. TELEOSTOMI. — Fishes with a skeleton consisting wholly or partially of bone, usually with scales (never placoid scales), and a well-developed operculum covering the gills.

Subclass II. DIPNOI. — Fishes with a skeleton of cartilage and bone, a single or double lung, and an operculum covering the gills.

1. A BONY FISH — THE PERCH

External Features. — The yellow perch, *Perca flavescens* (Fig. 368), inhabits the fresh-water streams and lakes of the northeastern United States, and ranges west to the Mississippi Valley. Its body is about a foot long and is divisible into *head, trunk,* and *tail.* There are two *dorsal fins,* a *caudal fin,* a single median *anal fin* just posterior to the anus, two lateral *ventral fins,* and two lateral *pectoral fins.* On each side of the body is a *lateral line.* The head bears a *mouth* with well-developed *jaws* armed with *teeth,* a pair of lateral *eyes,* a pair of *nasal apertures* in front of each eye, and *gill-covers* or *opercula* beneath which are the *gills.* The *skin* is provided with a number of *dermal scales* which are arranged like the shingles on the roof of a house, and protect the fish from mechanical injury.

---

[1] Fish are seldom used for laboratory dissection, but the description of the perch will be found of importance for comparative purposes. The general account presents facts about some of the more common or interesting species and furnishes material for the study of the biological relations of aquatic organisms.

Locomotor Organs. — The body of the perch, and of most other fishes, is spindle-shaped and offers little resistance to the water through which the animal swims (Fig. 369). It is kept at the

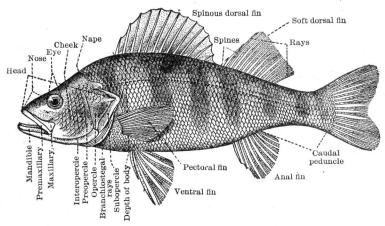

FIG. 368. — Diagram of a perch, *Perca flavescens*. (After Forbes.)

same weight as the amount of water it displaces by means of an *air-bladder*. The fish is thus able to remain stationary without muscular exertion. The principal locomotor organ is the *tail*.

FIG. 369. — Front view of a fish (Spanish mackerel). (From Dean.)

By alternating contractions of the muscular bands on the sides of the trunk and tail, the tail with its caudal fin is lashed from one side to the other, moving in a curve shaped like a figure 8 as shown in Figure 370. Similar movements are employed in sculling a boat, and the method of progress is analogous to the action of the screw of a steamer. During the flexions and extensions of the tail, the trunk is curved in such a way as to bring about the most effective extension or forward stroke and a weak flexion or noneffective stroke.

The *fins* are integumentary expansions supported by bony or cartilaginous rays. The paired lateral fins (pectoral and ventral) are used as oars in swimming, but only when the fish is moving slowly. They also aid the caudal fin in steering the animal, for, although the course is altered largely by the pointing of the head and tail in the desired direction, the lateral fins assist in swerving the body to one side or the other, either by executing more powerful strokes on one side, or by the expansion of one fin and the folding back of the other. These methods are like those used in steering a rowboat with oars. Movement up or down results from holding the lateral fins in certain positions — obliquely backwards with the anterior edge higher for the ascent, and obliquely forwards for the descent.

Fishes must maintain their *equilibrium* in some way, since the back is the heaviest part of the body and tends to turn them over. The dorsal, anal, and caudal fins increase the vertical surface of the body (Fig. 369) and, like the keel of a boat, assist the animal in maintaining an upright position. The paired lateral fins are also organs of equilibration, acting as balancers; if both pectoral fins are removed, the anterior end of the fish sinks downward; if a pectoral or both pectoral and ventral fins are removed from one side, the fish turns toward that side; and if all four lateral fins are cut off, the fish turns completely over with the ventral surface upward.

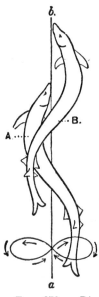

FIG. 370. — Diagram to illustrate the mode in which the tail of an ordinary fish is used in swimming. (From the Cambridge Natural History, after Pettigrew.)

The Skeleton. — The *exoskeleton* of the perch includes scales and fin-rays. The *scales* develop in pouches in the dermis. They are arranged in oblique rows and overlap like the shingles on the roof of a house, thus forming an efficient protective covering. The posterior edge of each scale which extends out from under the preceding scale is toothed, and therefore rough to the touch. Scales of this kind are called *ctenoid scales* (Fig. 371, *A*). The *fin-rays* support the fins. Those of the first dorsal fin (Fig. 372), and at the anterior edge of the anal and ventral fins, are unjointed and unbranched *spines*. The caudal and pectoral fins and most of the anal and ventral fins are supplied with jointed, and usually branched, *soft fin-rays*.

The *endoskeleton* (Fig. 372) consists principally of bones, and includes the skull, vertebral column, ribs, pectoral girdle, and the interspinal bones or pterygiophores which aid in supporting the unpaired fins. The body of the fish is to a considerable extent supported by the surrounding water; consequently, the bones do not need to be so strong as those of land animals, like birds and mammals, which must support the entire weight of the body.

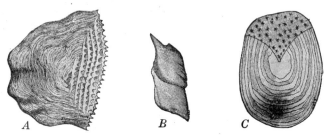

FIG. 371. — Scales. *A*, ctenois. *B*, ganoid. *C*, cycloid. (From the Cambridge Natural History; A, B, after Günther; C, after Parker and Haswell.)

The *vertebræ* (Fig. 372) are simple and comparatively uniform in structure. They are called *amphicœlous* vertebræ because the centrum has concave anterior and posterior faces. A typical vertebra has a cylindrical supporting *centrum*, a *neural arch* through which the spinal cord extends, a *neural spine* for the attachment

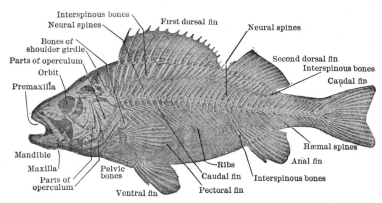

FIG. 372. — Skeleton of perch. (From Schmeil.)

of muscles, and short ventral projections, the *parapophyses*, to which the ribs are attached. The centrum of one vertebra is connected with those of the preceding and following vertebræ by ligaments. The spaces between the centra contain the remains of the notochord.

Ribs (Fig. 372) are attached by ligaments to the centra or parapophyses of the abdominal vertebræ and serve as a protecting framework for the body-cavity and its contents. There is no sternum. *Intermuscular bones* are also attached to some of the vertebræ. In the caudal region *hæmal arches* and *hæmal spines* extend down from the centrum, and the caudal artery and caudal vein pass through these arches. The extreme posterior portion of the vertebral column is modified so as to furnish a support for the caudal fin.

The *skull* of the perch (Fig. 372) consists of a large number of parts, some of bone, others of cartilage. As in *Petromyzon*, these parts may be grouped into the cranium and the visceral skeleton. The *cranium* is originally of cartilage, but becomes strengthened by the addition of membrane bones, which are dermal ossifications. The cranium protects and supports the brain, auditory organs, and olfactory sacs, and furnishes orbits for the eyes.

The *visceral skeleton*, which is represented in *Petromyzon* by the branchial basket (Fig. 354, *10*), is, in the perch, composed of *seven arches* more or less modified. The first or *mandibular arch*, forms the jaws. The *upper jaw* consists principally of two pairs of bones, the *premaxillæ* (Fig. 372) and the *maxillæ*. The premaxillæ bear teeth. The *lower jaw* or *mandible* also bears teeth. The second or *hyoid arch* is modified as a support for the gill-covers. Arches three to seven support the gills and are known as *gill-arches*. The first four of these bear spine-like ossifications, the *gill-rakers*, which act as a sieve to intercept solid particles, and keep them away from the gills.

The *appendicular skeleton* is represented in the perch by a *pectoral girdle* only (Fig. 372). This consists of a number of bones which lie just behind the head on either side and furnish a firm foundation for the attachment of the muscles that move the pectoral fins. The fin-rays of the pectoral fin articulate with the girdle by means of four rod-like bones, the *pterygiophores* or radials, and a number of small cartilages. There is no pelvic girdle. The ventral fins articulate with a flat bone, the *basipterygium* (Fig. 372), which is probably formed by the fusion of interspinal bones (pterygiophores).

The Muscular System. — The principal muscles are those used in locomotion, in respiration, and in obtaining food. The movements of the body employed in swimming are produced by four longitudinal bands of muscles, one heavy band on either side along the back and a thinner band on either side of both trunk and tail. These are arranged in zigzag myotomes. Weaker muscles move the gill-arches, operculum, hyoid, and jaws.

The Digestive System. — The aquatic insects, mollusks, and small fishes that constitute a large part of the food of the perch are captured by the jaws and held by the many conical teeth. *Teeth* are borne on the mandibles and premaxillæ, and on the roof of the mouth. They are not used to masticate the food. A rudimentary *tongue* projects from the floor of the mouth cavity; it is not capable of independent movement, but functions as a *tactile organ*. The *mouth cavity* is followed by the *pharynx*, on either side of which are four *gill-slits*. Food passes directly to the stomach through a short *œsophagus*.

Digestion is begun in the *stomach* by the fluid secreted by its walls. The partially digested food then passes through the pyloric valve into the *intestine*. Three short tubes, called *pyloric cæca*, open into the intestine and increase its secreting surface. The *liver* lies in the anterior part of the body-cavity; its secretion, the bile, is stored in the gall-bladder and then passed into the intestine through the bile-duct. About the *intestine*, which curves slightly in the body-cavity, is a mass of *fat*. Undigested substances pass out through the *anus*. A large red gland, the *spleen*, is situated near the anterior end of the intestine; it has no duct.

The Circulatory System. — The *blood* of the perch contains oval nucleated *red corpuscles* and *ameboid white corpuscles*. The *heart* lies in a portion of the cœlom, the *pericardium*, beneath the pharynx. *Circulation* in the perch is similar to that in the dog-fish shark (Fig. 361). Blood is carried into the thin-walled *auricle* from the veins through the *sinus venosus*. It passes into the muscular *ventricle* and is forced by rhythmical contractions into the *ventral aorta* and thence by *afferent branchial arteries* into the gills. The aërated blood is collected by the *efferent branchial arteries* and conveyed to the *dorsal aorta*. Various parts of the body are supplied by branches from the dorsal aorta. Oxygen is supplied to the tissues by the *arterial capillaries*, and waste substances are taken up by the *venous capillaries* and transported to the excretory organs. *Veins* carry the blood back to the heart. Circulation is much slower in fishes than it is in the higher vertebrates.

The Respiratory System. — The perch breathes with four pairs of *gills* supported by the first four gill-arches. Each gill bears a double row of *branchial filaments* (Fig. 373) which are abundantly supplied with capillaries. The afferent branchial artery (Fig. 373, *K*; Fig. 361) brings the blood from the heart to the gill-filaments; here an exchange of gases takes place. The carbonic acid gas with which the blood is loaded passes out of the gill, and a supply of oxygen is taken in from the continuous stream of water which enters the pharynx through the mouth and bathes the gills on its way out through the gill-slits.

The oxygenated blood is collected into the efferent branchial artery (Fig. 373, *3*; Fig. 361) and carried about the body. The gills are protected from external injury by the gill covering or *operculum* (Fig. 372) and from solid particles which enter the mouth by the *gill-rakers* (p. 395). Because oxygen is taken up by the capillaries of the gill-filaments, a constant supply of fresh water is necessary for the life of the fish. If deprived of water entirely, respiration is prevented, and the fish dies of suffocation.

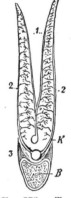

FIG. 373. — Transverse section through a branchial arch (*B*), with two gill filaments. *1*, afferent branchial vessel; *2*, efferent branchial vessel. (From Schmeil.)

The *air-bladder* is a comparatively large, thin-walled sac lying in the dorsal part of the body-cavity. It is filled with gas and is a *hydrostatic organ* or " float "; in certain fishes it may also aid in respiration. The gas contained in it is a mixture of oxygen and nitrogen, and is derived from the blood-vessels in its walls. The air-bladder decreases the specific gravity, making the body of the fish equal in weight to the amount of water it displaces. The fish, therefore, is able to maintain a stationary position without muscular effort. The amount of gas within the air-bladder depends upon the pressure of the surrounding water, and in some way is regulated by the fish according to the depth. If a fish is brought to the surface from a great depth, the air-bladder, which was under considerable pressure, is suddenly relieved, and therefore expands, often forcing the gullet out of the mouth.

The Excretory System. — The *kidneys* lie just beneath the backbone in the abdominal cavity. They extract urea and other waste products from the blood. Two thin tubes, the *ureters*, carry the excretory matter into a *urinary bladder*, where it is stored for a time and then expelled through the *urinogenital opening* just posterior to the anus.

The Nervous System. — The brain of the perch is more highly developed than that of *Petromyzon* or *Squalus*. The four chief divisions are well marked, — the cerebrum, optic lobes, cerebellum, and medulla oblongata. The brain gives off *cranial nerves* to the sense-organs and other parts of the anterior portion of the body. The *spinal cord* lies above the centra of the vertebral column and passes through the neural arches of the vertebræ. *Spinal nerves* arise from the sides of the spinal cord.

Sense-organs. — The principal organs of sense are the eyes, ears, and olfactory sacs. The mucous membrane of the mouth is the seat of the sense of *taste*, but this sense is not well developed. The integument, especially that of the lips, serves as an organ of *touch*. *Lateral line organs* are also present, but their function is not certain.

The two *olfactory sacs* lie in the anterior part of the skull and open by a pair of apertures in front of each eye. They are not connected with the mouth cavity, and take no part in respiration. The inner surface is thrown up into folds which are covered with sense-cells. Water flows in and out through the external openings.

The *ear* consists of the membranous labyrinth only. As in *Petromyzon* and *Squalus*, the sound waves are transmitted by the bones of the skull to the fluid within the labyrinth. Three semicircular canals (Fig. 350, *ca, ce, cp*) are present, and the sacculus (*s*) contains concretions of carbonate of lime, called earstones or *statoliths*. The ear is both an organ of hearing and an organ of equilibrium.

The *eye* of the perch differs in several respects from that of terrestrial vertebrates. The *eyelids* are usually absent in fishes, since the water keeps the eyeball moist and free from foreign objects. The *cornea* is flattened and of about the same refractive power as the water. The *lens* is almost spherical. The *pupil* is usually larger than that of other vertebrates and allows the entrance of more light rays; this is necessary, since semi-darkness prevails at moderate depths. When at rest the eye focuses at about fifteen inches. To focus on distant objects the lens is moved back. Fishes cannot see in air.

The Reproductive System. — The sexes are separate. The *ovaries* or *testes* lie in the body-cavity. The germ-cells pass through the repro-ductive ducts and out of the urinogeni-tal opening. Perch migrate in the spring from the deep waters of lakes and ponds, where they spend the winter, to the shallow waters near shore. The female lays about a hun-dred thousand eggs in a long ribbon-like mass. The male fer-tilizes the eggs by depositing sperma-tozoa (milt) over them. Very few of the eggs develop be-cause of the numer-ous animals, such as other fishes and aquatic birds, which feed upon them.

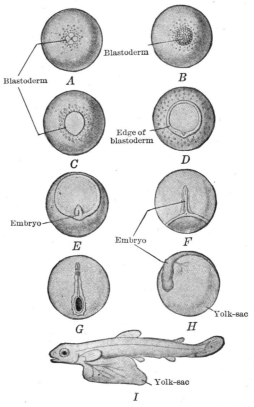

Fig. 374. — Nine stages in the development of a fish (*Salmo fario*). *A–H*, before hatching; *I*, shortly after hatching. (From Parker and Haswell; *A–G*, after Henneguy.)

Development. — The young perch hatches from the egg in from two to four weeks, depending upon the temperature of the water. The egg passes through stages similar to those shown in Figure 374. A large part of the egg consists of yolk. A protoplasmic accumulation which forms a slight projection at one end is called the *germinal disc*. The fusion nucleus, resulting from the union of the egg nucleus and the nucleus brought into the egg by the spermatozoon, soon divides, and two cells are formed. *Cleavage* of the germinal disc continues (Fig. 374, *A*, *B*) and the *blastoderm* produced gradually grows around the yolk (*C–G*). The *embryo* (*E*) appears as a thickening of the edge of the blastoderm. This grows in size (*F*, *G*) at the expense of the yolk. After a time the head and tail become free from the yolk, and the young fish breaks out of the egg membranes (*I*). The young fish lives at first upon the yolk in the yolk-sac (*I*), but is soon able to obtain food from the water. This consists of small crustaceans; insects are added after a time, and still later larger crustaceans, mollusks, and small fishes.

Economic Importance. — The perch is perhaps the best pan-fish among American fresh-water fishes. In many localities it is taken largely for market. It is not a good game-fish, but has one advantage — it is easy to catch. The perch has been introduced successfully into several small lakes in Washington, Oregon, and California. It can be artificially propagated, but other fishes, such as whitefish, lake trout, and pike-perch are of commercial importance and are, therefore, preferred for propagative purposes to the yellow perch.

2. An Abridged Classification of Living Fishes

The classification of fishes is attended with many difficulties, since it is as yet impossible to determine the relationships of many of the groups. That adopted in this book is a simplified arrangement of the classifications used in some of the recent publications. Synonyms are placed in parentheses after some of the names. There are about twelve thousand species of fishes known from the entire world. Of these Jordan and Evermann in their large four-volume work on the *Fishes of North and Middle America* have described one hundred and ninety-eight families and thirty-three hundred species from the waters of North America north of the Isthmus of Panama.

Besides the living fishes there are a great many species known only as fossils; in fact, a number of orders, suborders, and families contain nothing but fossil forms. These will be considered later (p. 427).

SUBCLASS I. TELEOSTOMI. THE TRUE FISHES.

Order 1. Crossopterygii. The Polypteridæ.

Order 2. Chondrostei. The Paddle-fishes and Sturgeons.

Family POLYODONTIDÆ. The Paddle-fishes.

Family ACIPENSERIDÆ. The Sturgeons.

Order 3. Holostei. The Garpikes and Bowfins.

Family AMIIDÆ. The Bowfins.

Family LEPISOSTEIDÆ. The Garpikes.

Order 4. Teleostei. The Bony Fishes.

Suborder 1. Cypriniformes (OSTARIOPHYSI). The Carp, Minnows, Suckers, and Catfishes.

Family CYPRINIDÆ. The Carp, Minnows, and Suckers.

Subfamily CATOSTOMINÆ. The Suckers.

Subfamily CYPRININÆ. The Carp and Minnows.

Family SILURIDÆ. The Catfishes.

Suborder 2. Clupeiformes (ISOSPONDYLI, MALACOPTERYGII). The Herrings, Trouts, Salmons, etc.

Family ELOPIDÆ. The Tarpons.

Family CLUPEIDÆ. The Herrings.

Family SALMONIDÆ. The Whitefishes, Trouts, and Salmons.

Suborder 3. Esociformes (HAPLOMI). The Pikes, Cave-fishes, and Flying-fishes.

Family ESOCIDÆ. The Pikes.

Family AMBLYOPSIDÆ. The Cave-fishes.

Family EXOCŒTIDÆ. The Flying-fishes.

Suborder 4. Anguilliformes (APODES). The Eels.

Family ANGUILLIDÆ. The True Eels.

Family LEPTOCEPHALIDÆ. The Conger Eels.

Suborder 5. Symbranchiformes (SYMBRANCHII). The SYMBRANCHIDÆ and AMPHIPNOIDÆ.

Suborder 6. Gasterosteiformes (CATOSTEOMI, HEMIBRANCHII, LOPHOBRANCHII). The Sticklebacks, Pipefishes, and Sea-horses.

Family GASTEROSTEIDÆ. The Sticklebacks.

Family SYNGNATHIDÆ. The Pipe-fishes and Sea-horses.

Suborder 7. Notacanthiformes (HETEROMI). Mostly Deep-sea Fishes.

Suborder 8. Mugiliformes (PERCESOCES). The Silver-sides and Mullets.

Suborder 9. Acanthopterygii. The Spiny-rayed Fishes.
Family SERRANIDÆ. The Sea-basses.
Family DIODONTIDÆ. The Porcupine Fishes.
Family PERCIDÆ. The Perches.
Family CENTRARCHIDÆ. The Sunfishes and Basses.
Family ECHENEIDIDÆ. The Remoras.
Family LOPHIIDÆ. The Anglers.
Family SCOMBRIDÆ. The Mackerels.
Family XIPHIIDÆ. The Swordfishes.
Family PLEURONECTIDÆ. The Flounders.
Family GADIDÆ. The Codfishes.
SUBCLASS II. DIPNOI. THE LUNG-FISHES.
Family CERATODONTIDÆ. The Australian Lung-fishes.
Family LEPIDOSIRENIDÆ. The South American and
African Lung-fishes.

3. THE ANATOMY AND PHYSIOLOGY OF FISHES IN GENERAL

External Features. — *Form of the Body.* — The body of the
majority of fishes is spindle-shaped and laterally compressed,
as in the perch — a form that offers slight resistance to progress
through the water (Fig. 369). Variations in form are correlated
with the habits of the fish. For example, the flatfishes, or
flounders, have thin bodies and are adapted for life on the
sea bottom; they are laterally compressed and swim on one
side or the other; the eels have a long cylindrical body which
enables them to enter holes and crevices; and the globe-fishes
when disturbed inflate themselves with air, becoming almost
spherical, in which condition they float in the water. The shape
of the head differs considerably among the fishes; in the angler-
fish it is enormous; in the garpike it is long and pointed; and
that of the paddle-fish extends forwards as a thin paddle-like
structure. Many fishes, like the sea-horse (Fig. 398) and some
deep-sea species, are so curiously shaped as to show little resemblance to our common fishes.

Fins and Tail. — Fins arise in the embryo as median and
lateral folds of the integument (Fig. 375, *A*) which are at first
continuous. Later, parts of the folds disappear and the isolated
dorsal, caudal, anal, ventral, and pectoral fins persist (Fig. 375,
B). There is a theory that the paired fins arise from gill-arches,

but this method of origin seems less probable than that just described.

The *ventral fins* of fishes vary considerably in position, probably because their skeletal parts are held only by muscles. In

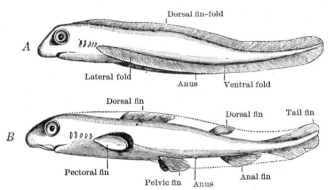

FIG. 375. — Diagram showing *A*, the undifferentiated condition of the paired and unpaired fins in the embryo, and *B*, the manner in which the permanent fins are formed from the continuous folds.   (From Wiedersheim.)

the perch (Fig. 368) they are situated beneath the pectoral fins and are said to be ventral; in the fresh-water dogfish (Fig. 384) they are just in front of the anus and are called abdominal; and in certain other species they are in the throat region and are said to be jugular in position. In most fishes the fins are supported, as in the perch, by cartilaginous rods and bony spines; this type of appendage is called an *ichthyopterygium*. In a few fishes (*e.g. Polypterus*, Fig. 380) the pectoral fins have a median axis, which may be jointed, and bears rays about the edge; this is termed an *archipterygium* (Fig. 376). The fingered appendage (*cheiropterygium*) of higher vertebrates may have arisen from the latter type.

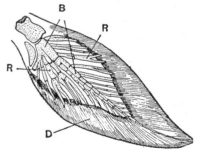

FIG. 376. — Archipterygial pectoral fin of a lung-fish, *Neoceratodus*. *B*, basal; *D*, dermal; *R*, radial. (From Dean, after Howes.)

The shape of the *caudal fin* and the terminal portion of the tail differs in the main groups of fishes, and is therefore of importance in classification. The most primitive condition is exhibited by very few if any living fishes, except in the embryo or early larval stages. It is termed *protocercal* or *diphycercal*, and is symmetrical both externally and in internal structure (Fig. 377, *A*). The second type, or *heterocercal* tail, is not symmetrical, and the vertebral column extends into the dorsal lobe; this condition exists in the sturgeons (Fig. 382) and many others. The stroke of the asymmetrical heterocercal tail forces the anterior part of the body downward. This type is therefore of advantage to and characteristic of those fishes that have a ventrally situated mouth and feed on the bottom. The third type, or *homocercal* tail, is externally symmetrical but internally unsymmetrical (Fig. 377, *B*). The stroke of the homocercal tail

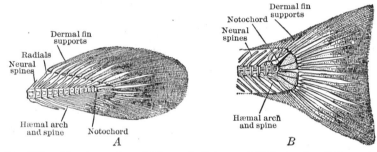

Fig. 377. — Two types of caudal fins. *A*, diphycercal (*Polypterus*). *B*, homocercal. *D*, dermal fin supports. (From Dean; A, after Agassiz; B, after Ryder.)

forces the fish straight forward. It is characteristic of fishes with a terminal mouth and is the type possessed by most bony fishes.

Fins are normally used in locomotion through the water, but may be modified for other purposes. For example, the pectoral fins of the flying fishes (Fig. 394) are used somewhat like the wings of an aëroplane to sustain the fish in the air during its leap from the water; the pectoral fins of the African goby serve the purpose of feet, enabling the fish to move about on the ground in search of food; and the first dorsal fin of the sucker-fish, *Remora* (Fig. 400), forms a sucker for the attachment of its possessor to a shark or turtle.

Scales. — The scales of fishes form a protecting exoskeleton. They are of three principal types: (1) ganoid, (2) cycloid, and (3) ctenoid. *Ganoid* scales are usually rhombic in shape (Fig. 371, *B*). They have a superficial covering of dentine called ganoin. Ganoid scales occur in most of the CHONDROSTEI and HOLOSTEI, and these are often called ganoid fishes. Cycloid and ctenoid scales are arranged in overlapping rows as described for the perch (p. 434). *Cycloid* scales (Fig. 371, *C*) are nearly circular with concentric rings about a central point. *Ctenoid* scales (Fig. 371, *A*) are similar to cycloid scales, but the part which extends out from under the neighboring scales bears small spines. In many fishes the scales develop into large protective spines, or may fuse to form bony plates.

Color. — The general impression is that fishes are not brightly colored, but many of them, especially in tropical waters, are exceedingly brilliant. The colors are due to pigments within special dermal cells, called chromatophores, or to reflection and iridescence resulting from the physical structure of the scales which contain crystals of guanin (iridocytes, Fig. 378). The pigments are red, orange, yellow, or black, but other colors may be produced by a combination of chromatophores; for example, yellow and black when blended give brown. Usually the colors are arranged in a definite pattern consisting of transverse or longitudinal stripes, and spots of various

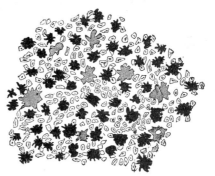

FIG. 378. — Chromatophores in skin of upper side of a freshly killed flounder, *Pleuronectes flesus*. Black bodies represent black chromatophores; gray bodies, yellow; small gray plates, iridocytes. (From the Cambridge Natural History, after Cunningham and MacMunn.)

sizes. Coral-reef fishes have long been famous for their brilliant colors, and many fresh-water fishes of the temperate zone exhibit bright hues distributed so as to form striking and intricate patterns (*e.g.* the rainbow darter).

The contraction and expansion of the chromatophores of certain fishes result in changes in coloration. These changes "are due to incident light reflected from surrounding surfaces, acting through the visual organs and the nervous system on the differently colored chromatophores." (Bridge.) The changes are therefore dependent upon the color of the fish's environment, and are often such as to conceal the animal, being consequently protective. The change is slow in many fishes, but may be quite rapid, as in the flounder. Male fishes are often more brightly colored than the females, especially during spawning activities.

The Skeleton. — The skeleton differs among the fishes chiefly in the relative amount of bone and cartilage. Both the TELEO-STOMI and DIPNOI possess skeletons which consist to a greater or less extent of bones preformed in cartilage, and membrane bones which are developed as dermal ossifications. The *vertebræ* are usually amphicœlous, as in the perch, and bear neural arches; some of them in the trunk region bear ribs; others in the tail bear hæmal arches. There is no sternum.

The *cranium* is independent of the visceral arches. It is complicated in the teleosts by the addition of numerous membrane bones. The *visceral skeleton* consists of seven arches; five of them are usually gill-arches. The lower jaw articulates with the upper jaw and not directly with the cranium. The bones contained in the gill-cover or operculum develop from the hyoid arch.

The Digestive System. — The food of our common fishes consists of vegetation, insect larvæ, crustaceans, mollusks, and other smaller fishes. Some fishes are voraciously carnivorous, and, like the sharks, attack animals larger than themselves; others are herbivorous to a considerable extent, feeding on seaweeds and other vegetation; and still others act as scavengers or swallow mud from which both living and dead organisms are obtained.

Fishes are ultimately dependent upon microscopic organisms, as is illustrated by the following example: —

" On the morning of July 23 there was taken a large specimen (squeteague) whose stomach contained an adult herring. In the stomach of the herring were found two young scup (besides many small crustacea), and in the stomach of one of these scup were found copepods, while in the alimentary tract of these last, one could identify one or two of the diatoms (unicellular plants) and an infusorian test among the mass of triturated material which formed its food." (Peck.)

Most fishes possess *teeth* on the jaws, roof of the mouth, or gill-arches. These are used principally for holding food, but in some cases for mastication. The most primitive type of tooth is a simple pointed cone. Some fishes have front teeth for capturing prey and back teeth for crushing; and in others the teeth are all modified for crushing. Teeth that are lost or worn away are generally replaced.

The *alimentary canal* is usually similar to that of the perch. Gastric glands in the walls of the stomach secrete digestive juices. The intestine often possesses blind pouches, the pyloric cæca, which increase the secretory surface.

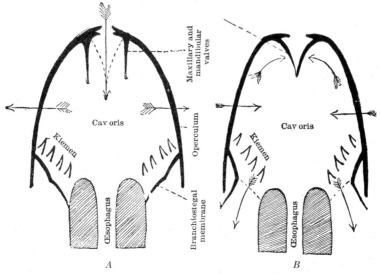

Fig. 379. — Diagram illustrating the mechanism of respiration in teleosts. *A*, phase of inspiration. *B*, phase of expiration. (From Wiedersheim, after Dahlgren.)

The Circulatory System. — Circulation in fishes is essentially like that already described (Fig. 361). Lymph spaces and lymph capillaries are situated in various parts of the body; they collect blood plasma from the tissues and transport it to the veins.

The body of the fish contains several *ductless glands* which may be considered under the circulatory system. The functions of these glands are not well known. The extirpation of them results in serious disturbances, and, in some cases, death. They secrete substances (internal secretions) directly into the blood or lymph. The *thyroid* is homologous to the endostyle of tunicates (p. 351) and Amphioxus (p. 354). It lies in the branchial region and is paired. The thymus is situated dorsally in the branchial region. The *spleen* is a large gland usually lying near the stomach, colorless blood corpuscles are formed in it, and old red corpuscles are destroyed by it. The *suprarenal bodies* are situated close to the kidneys.

The Respiratory System. — Respiration takes place in the *gills*, and, in the DIPNOI and some teleosts, also to some extent in the *air-bladder*. During respiration in teleosts the walls of the mouth act like a pump (Fig. 379). In *inspiration* (*A*) the oral cavity (*cav oris*) is enlarged by the raising of the opercular apparatus, and water is therefore drawn into it through the mouth. Folds of mucous membrane (branchiostegal membranes) prevent water from entering through the opercular aperture. *Expiration* (*B*) results from the contraction of the opercular apparatus; the branchiostegal membrane is opened and water passes out through the gill-slits. The exit of water by way of the mouth is prevented by valves of mucous membrane (maxillary and mandibular valves).

4. GENERAL ACCOUNT OF SOME OF THE PRINCIPAL GROUPS OF FISHES

SUBCLASS I. TELEOSTOMI. — To the TELEOSTOMI belong the majority of fishes. The four orders of living forms are unequal in number of species, most of which belong to the TELEOSTEI.

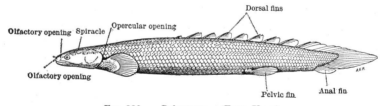

FIG. 380. — *Polypterus.* (From Kerr.)

Order 1. Crossopterygii. — Most of the CROSSOPTERYGII are extinct, and the order contains only one family and two genera of living forms. One species, *Polypterus senegalus* (Fig. 380), lives in the Nile. It is of special interest to morphologists because it presents many structural features characteristic of ancient crossopterygians.

Order 2. Chondrostei. — This order contains the sturgeons and paddle-fishes. These have a skeleton largely of cartilage, a heterocercal tail, ganoid scales (Fig. 371, *B*), and abdominal pelvic fins.

The family POLYODONTIDÆ contains two species of paddle-fishes, *Polyodon spathula* (Fig. 381) of the Mississippi Valley, and *Psephurus gladius* of the Yang-tse-Kiang in China. *Polyodon* reaches a length of six feet and a weight of one hundred

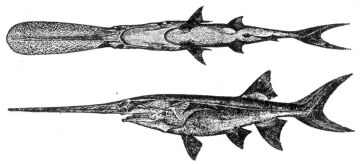

FIG. 381. — The paddle-fish, *Polyodon spathula*. (From Dean, after Goode.)

and sixty pounds, but the specimens usually taken weigh no more than fifty pounds. Its large, paddle-shaped snout is regarded as a sense-organ, and its use is still unknown. The food of *Polyodon* consists largely of minute plants and animals, of which enormous numbers are devoured. The paddle-fish is good to eat, but its roe, from which caviar is made, is more valuable than its flesh.

The family ACIPENSERIDÆ contains two genera of sturgeons, *Acipenser* and *Scaphirhynchus*. They inhabit the seas, lakes, and rivers of Europe, Asia, and America. Sturgeons possess a

FIG. 382. — The common sturgeon, *Acipenser sturio*. (From Dean, after Goode.)

cephalic prolongation or rostrum which bears on its ventral surface a number of tactile filaments called barbels. The scales form five longitudinal rows of bony scutes between which are smaller ossifications. The mouth lacks teeth. The common sturgeon, *Acipenser sturio* (Fig. 382), lives along the Atlantic coast and ascends the rivers of northern Europe and the United

States. *Acipenser rubicundus* is the sturgeon of the rivers and lakes of the middle west. It feeds on the bottom, using its snout for stirring up the mud and its barbels for locating snails, crayfishes, and insect larvæ. Sturgeon flesh is a valued article of food, the eggs are made into caviar, and the air-bladders furnish isinglass.

Order 3. Holostei. — Most of the Holostei are extinct; only two of the eight families have living representatives, namely the Lepisosteidæ or garpikes, and the Amiidæ or bowfins. These fishes are called bony ganoids, since the skeleton is bony and the scales are often ganoid. In some the scales are cycloid (Fig. 371). The tail is diphycercal or homocercal, with a tendency toward the heterocercal type, and the ventral fins are abdominal. The living species of garpikes and bowfins are known only from America.

The garpikes belong to the genus *Lepisosteus*. There are three common species, the long-nosed garpike, the short-nosed

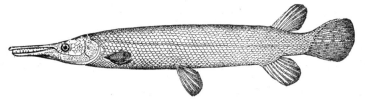

Fig. 383. — The alligator gar, *Lepisosteus tristœchus*. (From Jordan and Evermann.)

gar, and the alligator gar (Fig. 383). The long-nosed gar, *Lepisosteus osseus*, is common in the lakes and rivers of the United States. It is about four feet long. The body is slender with an extended beak, at the end of which are the nostrils. Its heavy ganoid scales effectively protect it from every other living creature in the water. Garpikes are voracious, devouring minnows, young fish, and other aquatic animals, and where they occur in large numbers are very harmful to the fishing industry.

Amia (Amiatus) calva, the mudfish, fresh-water dogfish, or bowfin (Fig. 384), is the only existing representative of the family Amiidæ. It inhabits the sluggish waters of the Great Lakes region and the Mississippi Valley. The body is about a foot and one half long, is dark olive in color, and bears, in the male, a black spot at the base of the caudal fin. It is very voracious, feeding on fish, crayfishes, mollusks, and other aquatic animals. The breeding season is in April, May, or June, according to the latitude. The male clears a space in the vegetation of a quiet inlet in which the eggs are laid, and then guards the nest (Fig. 384) during the hatching period of from eight to ten days, and while the young remain in the nest — about nine days more. The male

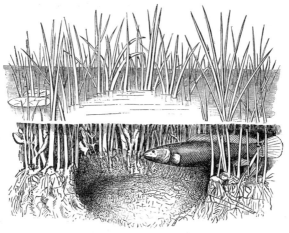

FIG. 384. — The fresh-water dogfish or bowfin, *Amia* (*Amiatus*) *calva*, and its nest. (From the Cambridge Natural History, after Dean.)

accompanies the young when they leave the nest, and continues to guard them until they reach a length of about four inches.

Order 4. Teleostei. — This order contains the majority of living species, the bony fishes. The skeleton is extensively ossified; the tail is usually homocercal (Fig. 377, *B*); and the scales are cycloid or ctenoid (Fig. 371). Space will allow a few notes on only about one-eighth of the families of fishes included in the order.

Family CYPRINIDÆ. — The Carp, Minnows, and Suckers.

Subfamily CATOSTOMINÆ. — The Suckers. Most of the suckers are inhabitants of the fresh waters of North America; two of the seventy or more species occur in Asia. Their mouths are usually very protractile and possess fleshy lips. They feed on the bottom, eating vegetation, worms, insect larvæ, and other soft-bodied animals. In the spring suckers swim upstream to spawn. The sucker is barely edible, but is nevertheless an important commercial fish. The common or white sucker, *Catostomus commersoni* (Fig. 385), is very widely distributed. This subfamily includes, besides the suckers, the red-horses, buffaloes, quillbacks, and fresh-water mullets.

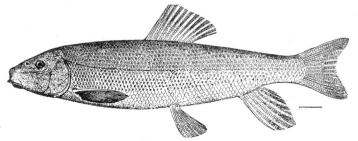

FIG. 385. — The common sucker, *Catostomus commersoni.* (From Jordan and Evermann.)

Subfamily CYPRININÆ. — There are about two hundred genera and a thousand species of fishes belonging to this subfamily. About two hundred and twenty-five species occur in the United States. They are mostly small, but should not be mistaken for young fish on that account. The chubs, hornyheads, fall-fish, and squaw fish are common in various parts of the

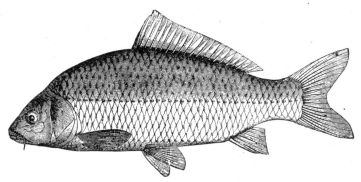

FIG. 386. — The German carp. (From Dean, after Goode.)

country. The German carp (Fig. 386) was introduced into North America in 1872, and is now firmly established in our waters. It will live in muddy ponds and streams, is prolific, grows rapidly, and is edible, although not very good. Since its introduction it has been accused of driving away other fishes, of making clear lakes muddy, of eating wild celery and grasses on which ducks feed, and of devouring the eggs of other fishes.

Family SILURIDÆ. — The Catfishes. These are mostly fresh-water fish, about thirty species of which are known from the United States. The body of the catfish is naked; the head bears

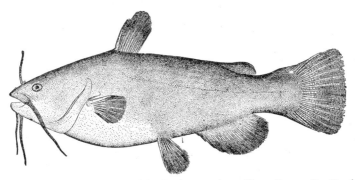

FIG. 387. — The bullhead or catfish, *Ameiurus melas*. (From Dean, after Goode.)

eight barbels; and there is a short, fatty, adipose fin back of the dorsal fin. The bullhead or horned pout, *Ameiurus nebulosus*, is a common fish in the ponds and streams of the North and East. The black bullhead, *Ameiurus melas* (Fig. 387), is found chiefly west of the Mississippi River. The bullhead is tenacious of life and can live out of water for some time. The blue or

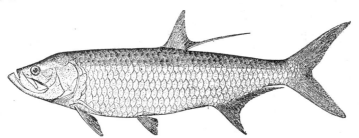

FIG. 388. — The tarpon, *Tarpon atlanticus*. (From the Cambridge Natural History, after Goode.)

Mississippi catfish, *Ictalurus furcatus*, is a valuable food-fish It inhabits the sluggish waters of the streams of the Mississippi Valley and Gulf States, and is the largest member of the family, sometimes reaching a length of five feet and attaining a weight of over one hundred pounds. Another large species is the channel or spotted catfish, *Ictalurus punctatus*. It occurs in the

Great Lakes region and Mississippi Valley, and prefers clear, flowing water.

Family ELOPIDÆ. — The Tarpons. There are four or five species of tarpons inhabiting the tropical seas. The common tarpon, *Tarpon atlanticus* (Fig. 388), is a famous game-fish on the coast of Florida, and is called the " silver king."

Family CLUPEIDÆ. — The Herrings. The members of this family are mostly salt-water forms. They are not game-fishes, but about ten species are of commercial value. The common herring, *Clupea harengus* (Fig. 389), is " the most important of the food-fishes in the Atlantic." (Jordan and Evermann.) Herring swim about the North Atlantic in immense shoals, often covering half a dozen square miles and containing as many as

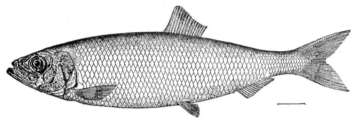

FIG. 389. — The herring, *Clupea harengus.* (From Jordan and Evermann.)

three billion individuals. On the New England coast herring are smoked, salted, pickled, packed as sardines, or serve as bait for cod-fishing.

Family SALMONIDÆ. — The Whitefishes, Salmons, and Trouts. Many of our most important food and game fishes belong to this family, such as the mountain trout, rainbow-trout, and steelhead trout of the West, the lake-trout and common whitefish of the Great Lakes, the brook trout of the East, the Atlantic salmon of Europe and North America, and the quinnat or chinook salmon, the blueback or sockeye salmon, and the silver or coho salmon of the Pacific. These fishes are easily reared, and millions of their eggs or young are distributed each year by the United States Bureau of Fisheries (see Table XV).

The common whitefish, *Coregonus clupeiformis* (Fig. 390), occurs throughout the Great Lakes region. During the winter it prefers deep water, but in the spring it migrates to the shallow water to secure insect larvæ which become abundant at that time. It migrates to shallow water again in the autumn to spawn. The mouth is on the under side, and the crustaceans, mollusks, and other animals used as food are picked up from the bottom. The eggs are laid over honeycomb rock, and, since many of them are covered by sediment or fall prey to mud-puppies, yellow perch, crayfishes, and other enemies, very few reach the adult stage. Because of this fact the government each year gathers, rears, and distributes millions of whitefish eggs.

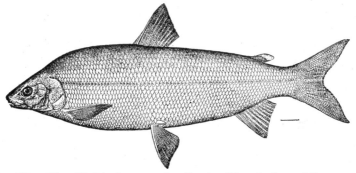

FIG. 390. — The whitefish, *Coregonus clupeiformis*. (From Jordan and Evermann.)

Whitefishes are captured in deep water by means of gill-nets which hold the fish just behind the gill-covers. The average weight is about four pounds, but they may become as heavy as twenty pounds.

The lake-trout, *Cristivomer namaycush*, is another important food-fish of the Great Lakes region. It is the largest of our trouts, averaging about eighteen pounds, but occasionally attaining a weight of over one hundred pounds. Lake-trout are captured usually in gill-nets. They are omnivorous, but show special preference for lake herring. The spawning season ranges from September to November, according to the latitude. Millions of eggs are cared for and distributed by the government each year.

The brook or speckled trout, *Salvelinus fontinalis*, is one of our most beautiful and well-known game-fishes. It prefers clear, cool streams with a swift current and a gravelly bottom.

The mountain or cut-throat trout, *Salmo clarkii*, is a large species inhabiting the streams and lakes of the Rocky Mountain region. The rainbow-trout, *Salmo irideus*, is also a Western species. It is a good game-fish and takes the fly readily. In

weight it averages about two or three pounds. The steelhead
or salmon trout, *Salmo gairdneri*, is found in the streams along
the Pacific coast. Like the salmon it migrates upstream to
spawn. Its average weight is about eight pounds. Thousands
of steelhead trout are taken each year for canning purposes,
especially in the Columbia River. They are also considered
excellent game-fish.

The chinook or quinnat salmon, *Oncorhynchus tschawytscha*
(Fig. 391), is the most important commercial fish of the family.

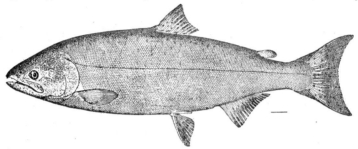

Fig. 391. — Quinnat salmon (female). *Oncorhynchus tschawytscha*. (From
Jordan and Evermann.)

It lives in the sea along the Pacific coast " from Monterey
Bay, California, and China, north to Bering Straits." It enters
the fresh-water streams to spawn, especially the Sacramento,
Columbia, and Yukon rivers. The adults are captured by gill-
nets and other devices as they ascend the rivers, and are considered the most important of all commercial fishes. The
government is artificially propagating the chinook salmon, otherwise its numbers would soon be materially decreased.

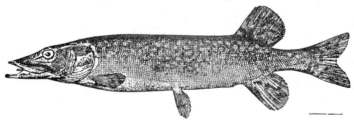

Fig. 392. — The pike, *Esox lucius*. (From Jordan and Evermann.)

Family ESOCIDÆ. — The Pikes. There is one genus with
seven species of pikes; all of them occur in North America. The
common pike or pickerel, *Esox lucius* (Fig. 392), inhabits " all

suitable fresh waters of northern North America, Europe, and Asia." It is extremely voracious, feeding on other fishes, frogs, aquatic birds, and many other aquatic animals. The pike is an excellent game-fish, but its flesh is not very good. The muskallunge, *Esox masquinongy*, resembles the pike in form and habits. It is found in the Great Lakes region and is a king among fresh-water game-fishes, reaching a length of over seven feet and a weight of almost a hundred pounds.

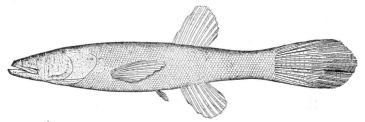

Fig. 393. — A cave-fish, *Amblyopsis spelæus*. (From Lankester's Treatise, after Jordan and Evermann.)

Family AMBLYOPSIDÆ. — The Cave-fishes. There are six species of cave-fishes known from the subterranean streams of the cave region of Indiana, Kentucky, and Missouri. They are small fish, but are of special interest because the eyes of some of them are rudimentary and covered with a thick skin. *Amblyopsis spelæus* (Fig. 393) is common in the river Styx of the Mammoth Cave.

Family EXOCŒTIDÆ. — The Flying-fishes (Fig. 394). There are about sixty-five species in this family, inhabiting warm

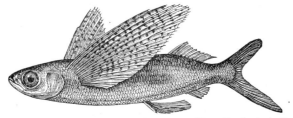

Fig. 394. — A flying fish, *Exocœtus callopterus*. (From Lankester's Treatise, after Günther.)

seas. Some of them are able to leave the water, and, rising in the air a few feet, " fly " a distance of from a few rods to more than an eighth of a mile. It seems probable that the pectoral fins do not force the fish forward, but simply sustain the body in the air.

Family ANGUILLIDÆ. — The Eels. The true eels should not be confused with the lamprey eels of the class CYCLOSTOMATA

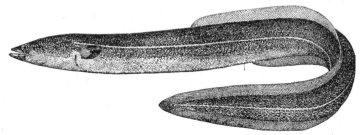

FIG. 395. — The common eel, *Anguilla rostrata.* (From Jordan and Evermann.)

(p. 375). The single species of eel, *Anguilla rostrata* (Fig. 395), in North America occurs in the streams of the Atlantic coast. It is long and slender, and its scales are inconspicuous. The

FIG. 396. — The Eastern stickleback, *Gasterosteus bispinosus.* Above, nest with eggs, and male entering. Below, male depositing milt on the eggs. (From Davenport.)

dorsal, caudal, and anal fins are continuous. The eels enter the sea in the autumn to spawn, after which they die. The eggs are deposited on mud-banks usually near the mouths of rivers. The young develop in the sea and then migrate up the rivers. Eels are considered by many a good article of food, and are therefore of commercial value.

Family GASTEROSTEIDÆ. — The Sticklebacks. These are small fishes famous for their nest-building habits. The common

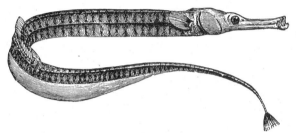

FIG. 397. — The pipe-fish, *Syngnathus acus*. (From Lankester's Treatise, after Günther.)

Eastern stickleback, *Gasterosteus bispinosus* (Fig. 396), has two large spines preceding the dorsal fin. The nest is built of sticks fastened together with threads secreted by a gland in the male. The female lays eggs in the nest; the male then enters and fertilizes them, after which he guards them from intruders.

Family SYNGNATHIDÆ. — The Pipe-fishes and Sea-horses. The pipe-fishes (Fig. 397) are extremely thin, with a tubular snout, abbreviated fins, and a covering of bony armor. Their food is captured by inserting the snout into the cavities in sponges and corals, and by picking off minute animals from the branches of seaweeds. The sea-horses (Fig. 398) are small species that do not look much like fish, the head reminding one of the head of a horse. They swim by means of the dorsal fin, holding themselves in a vertical position as in Figure 398. They cling to objects with their prehensile tail.

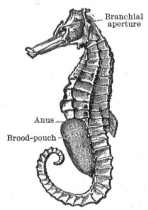

FIG. 398. — The sea-horse, *Hippocampus guttulatus*, male. (From the Cambridge Natural History.)

The eggs are carried in a brood pouch of the male until they hatch.

Family SERRANIDÆ. — The Sea-basses. This is a large family containing over four hundred species, mostly marine. The white lake bass, *Roccus chrysops*, is a fresh-water species of the Great Lakes region. The striped bass, *Roccus lineatus*, is a fine game-fish occurring along the coast of eastern North America. It has also been successfully introduced along the coast of California.

FIG. 399. — The porcupine fish, *Diodon maculatus*. *A*, normal; *B*, inflated. (From Lankester's Treatise, after Günther.)

The jewfish or black sea-bass, *Stereolepis gigas*, is the giant game-fish of the California coast. It can be taken with a sixteen-ounce rod, and there are many records of specimens captured by this method weighing over three hundred pounds.

Family DIODONTIDÆ. — The Porcupine-fishes. These inhab-itants of tropical seas are covered with movable spines, hence their name. They live on the bottom among seaweeds and corals, and when disturbed inflate their bodies by swallowing air (Fig. 399). They then float belly upward, in which condi-tion they are not easily injured by their enemies.

Family PERCIDÆ. — The Perches.   The perch family contains
a large number of small fresh-water fishes, most of which are of
little economic importance.   The yellow perch, *Perca flavescens*,
was chosen as a type of the class (pp. 391–400).   The wall-eyed
pike or pike-perch, *Stizostedion vitreum,* is another well-known and
valuable species.   It is common in the Great Lakes region and is
extensively propagated by the Bureau of Fisheries (see Table XV).

Family CENTRARCHIDÆ. — The Basses, Crappies, and Sunfishes.   These fishes inhabit the fresh waters of North America.
There are about thirty species, most of which are good game-
fishes and also excellent for the table.   Some of the most common species are the crappie, *Pomoxis annularis,* the rock-bass,
Ambloplites rupestris, the bluegill, *Lepomis pallidus,* the common sunfish or pumpkin-seed, *Eupomotis gibbosus,* the small-
mouthed black bass, *Micropterus dolomieu,* and the large-
mouthed black bass, *Micropterus salmoides.*   The small-mouthed
black bass is considered " inch for inch and pound for pound,
the gamest fish that swims." (Henshall.)   The male bass in
May or June makes a nest by clearing away a place near shore
where there are good-sized stones.   Eggs are then laid and fertilized, and the male guards them during the hatching period of
five or six days.   The male continues to protect the young
until they reach a length of an inch and a quarter.   Black bass
are successfully propagated in artificial ponds by the Bureau
of Fisheries (see Table XV).

Family ECHENEIDIDÆ. — The   Remoras   (Fig.   400).   This
family contains about a dozen species of peculiar fishes that live

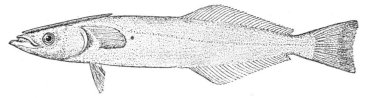

FIG. 400. — A sucking fish, *Remora brachyptera.*   (From the Cambridge Natural
History, after Goode.)

in tropical, warm seas.   The first dorsal fin is modified to form
a sucker by means of which the fish attaches itself to sharks,
turtles, whales, other large aquatic animals, and floating objects
such as boats.   They are able to swim, but prefer to be carried

about by other animals. Their food consists of other fish and probably of the scraps obtained when the shark, or other animal to which the individual is attached, has a meal.

Family LOPHIIDÆ. — The Anglers. Living on the bottom of the Atlantic, Indian, and Pacific oceans are about a dozen species of extremely large-mouthed fishes known as anglers.

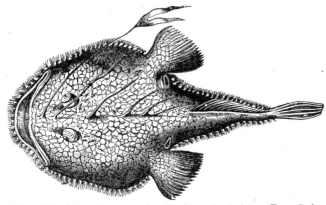

FIG. 401. — The fishing-frog or angler, *Lophius piscatorius*. (From Sedgwick's Zoology, after Cuvier.)

Lophius piscatorius, the fishing-frog or goose-fish (Fig. 401), occurs on the coast of North America. It is said to lie on the bottom with its mouth open and to use its long first dorsal ray, which is inserted on the snout, as a bait to attract other fishes into its mouth cavity. It reaches a length of over three feet and has a mouth more than a foot wide.

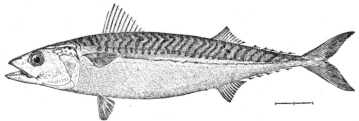

FIG. 402. — The mackerel, *Scomber scombrus*. (From Jordan and Evermann.)

Family SCOMBRIDÆ. — The Mackerels. There are about sixty species of food-fishes belonging to this family, fifteen of which inhabit the salt waters of North America. The common mackerel, *Scomber scombrus* (Fig. 402), occurs in the North

Atlantic, swimming about in enormous schools. It feeds on small aquatic animals, such as CRUSTACEA, and furnishes food for other fishes. It is also a valuable food-fish for man. The Spanish mackerel, *Scomberomorus maculatus*, is also a common food-fish of the North Atlantic. The tuna, *Thunnus thynnus*, is called the tunny or horse-mackerel on our eastern coast, but is the tuna of California. They are eagerly sought with hook and line, and many have been landed by this means that weighed over one hundred pounds.

Family XIPHIIDÆ. — The Swordfishes. The single species, *Xiphias gladius*, belonging to this family is widely distributed in salt waters. It reaches a maximum weight of about six hundred pounds, and its prolonged upper jaw makes it a formidable foe. Sometimes fishing boats are pierced and sunk by the sword of large individuals. The food of the swordfish consists of squids, mackerel, menhaden, and other fish, and it in turn is a valuable article of food for man.

Family PLEURONECTIDÆ. — The Flounders. These are flat-fishes known as flounders, halibuts, soles, plaice, and turbots.

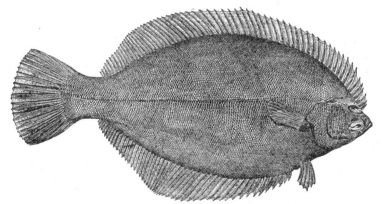

FIG. 403. — The flounder, *Pseudopleuronectes americanus*. (From Dean, after Goode.)

They are flattened from side to side, and thus adapted for life on the sea bottom. Frequently they are colored on the upper surface so as to resemble the sand or other material surrounding them. The young flatfish resembles an ordinary fish when it hatches, but it soon begins to broaden laterally and swim on its side, while the eye on the lower side moves around to the upper side. The common halibut, *Hippoglossus hippoglossus*, and the winter flounder, *Pseudopleuronectes americanus* (Fig. 403), are important American food-fishes.

Family GADIDÆ. — The Codfishes. Many of our most important food-fishes, the pollacks, codfishes, haddocks, and hakes, belong to this family. The common codfish is *Gadus callarias*

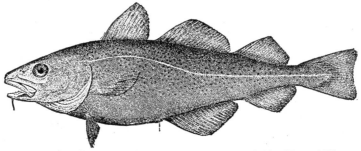

Fig. 404. — The cod, *Gadus callarias*. (From the Cambridge Natural History, after Goode.)

(Fig. 404). " From the earliest settlement of America the cod has been the most valuable of our Atlantic coast fishes. Indeed, the codfish of the Banks of Newfoundland was one of the principal inducements which led England to establish colonies in America." (Jordan and Evermann.)

SUBCLASS II. DIPNOI. THE LUNG-FISHES. — The lung-fishes, of which there are only three living genera, are said to be intermediate between the fishes and amphibians. They possess

Fig. 405. — The Australian lung-fish, *Neoceratodus fosteri*. (From Sedgwick, after Günther.)

certain structural features not found in other fishes, but characteristic of AMPHIBIA. On the other hand, they are in many respects like the HOLOCEPHALI and CROSSOPTERYGII. Among their important characters are their acutely lobate, paired fins (Fig. 405), an opening between the nasal sac and the mouth cavity, a persistent, unconstricted notochord, and an air-bladder which opens into the pharynx and functions as a lung.

Family CERATODONTIDÆ. — The Australian lung-fish, *Neocera-todus fosteri* (Fig. 405), is the only living species belonging to this family. It lies on the bottom of stagnant pools and feeds on worms, mollusks, crustáceans, and other small animals that it gathers from the vegetation. Occasionally it comes to the surface in order to change the air in its single lung. Because of this lung it can exist in water unfit for fishes that breathe entirely with gills. Such an environment may have led to the evolution of lung-breathing AMPHIBIA from gill-breathing fishes.

Family LEPIDOSIRENIDÆ. — This family contains two genera of living fish. The three species of the genus *Protopterus* (Fig.

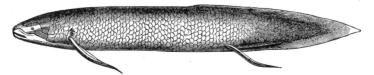

FIG. 406. — The African lung-fish, *Protopterus annectens*. (From Sedgwick's Zoology, after Claus.)

406) are found in the marshes of Central Africa. They feed on crustaceans, worms, insects, and frogs, and breathe with a pair of lungs. During the dry summer season they burrow about eighteen inches into the mud, where a cocoon of slime is secreted, and the fish remains inactive, breathing with its lungs, and living on fat stored in the kidneys and gonads, until the rainy season comes again.

The second genus of this family, *Lepidosiren*, has but a single species, *Lepidosiren paradoxa* (Fig. 407), confined to the marshes

FIG. 407. — The South American lung-fish, *Lepidosiren paradoxa*. (From Shipley and MacBride, after Kerr.)

and swamps of South America. It feeds on algæ, mollusks, and other plants and animals, and comes to the surface to change the air in its lungs. Like the African lung-fish, it hibernates in the mud during the dry season.

5. Deep-sea Fishes

Many families of fishes contain deep-sea species, and about thirty families of teleosts are known only from specimens taken in the sea at depths of over a thousand fathoms. At this depth conditions are quite different from those near the surface. There is probably no sunlight below two hundred fathoms; the temperature is always a few degrees above the freezing-point; the pressure is a ton or more to the square inch, whereas it is only about fifteen pounds at the surface; and there is no vegetation, so that the inhabitants of the depths must be carnivorous or live on organisms that sink toward the bottom.

Fig. 408. — A deep-sea fish, *Stomias boa*. The white dots are the luminous organs. (From Parker and Haswell, after Filhol.)

Fishes meet these conditions in various ways and are often curiously modified. Some have very large eyes so as to catch as many rays of light as possible; these eyes probably serve in connection with phosphorescent organs. Others have small or rudimentary eyes and are blind; they depend upon tactile organs instead of eyes. Many have large mouths with long, sharp teeth, and enormous stomachs. The phosphorescent organs are variously distributed over the body (small circular areas in Fig. 408). Some of them consist of a cup of secretory cells covered by a cellular lens. The secretion is luminous, and in certain cases acts as a lure; in others it probably enables the fish to see in the dark abyss of the ocean.

6. Fossil Fishes

A large number of species of fish are known only from their fossil remains. The earliest fish remains consist of spines and scales from the lower Silurian or Ordovician strata of the earth's crust, which were laid down probably twenty-five million years ago (see Table XVII). The slightly younger Devonian age is called the " Age of Fishes " because of the predominance of fishes over the other animals that lived at that time. A considerable portion of the Teleostomi are fossils; four of the five families of the Crossopterygii; five of the seven families of the Chondrostei; six of the eight families of the Holostei; and about fifteen families of the Teleostei are fossil forms. In the Dipnoi there are two families of fossil and two of living species. The study of fossil fishes is very important because of the light these prehistoric forms shed upon the affinities of modern species.

7. The Economic Importance of Fishes

Fishes furnish an important article of food for man, and many of them provide a means of recreation because of the difficulty of hooking them and the desperate struggles they make before they can be captured. Most game-fishes are also useful as food, but this is not always the case; for example, the tarpon which occurs on our Atlantic coast is the greatest of game-fishes, but is not ordinarily eaten by man. A few species are injurious because of the number of food-fishes and other valuable animals they destroy.

CHAPTER XVIII

SUBPHYLUM VERTEBRATA: CLASS IV. AMPHIBIA [1]

THE common amphibians are the frogs, toads, and salamanders. They spend part or all of their existence in the water or in damp places. Most of them lay their eggs in the water, and the larvæ, which breathe with gills, are known as tadpoles or pollywogs. Some amphibians are often confused with reptiles (especially with the lizards) because of their similarity of form, but almost all reptiles possess scales, whereas amphibians have usually a smooth, slimy skin without scales except in a few rare species. There are two orders of extinct amphibia and three orders of living forms. The latter are as follows: —

Order 1. APODA. — The APODA or CŒCILIANS are legless, worm-like amphibians inhabiting tropical and subtropical regions.

Order 2. CAUDATA. — These are amphibians with tails. They include the mud-puppies, sirens, and salamanders.

Order 3. SALIENTIA. — The tailless AMPHIBIA, frogs and toads, belong to this order.

1. THE FROG

The leopard frog, *Rana pipiens*, lives in or near fresh-water lakes, ponds, and streams, and is distributed over the North American continent except on the Pacific slope. The frog *leaps* on land and *swims* in the water. The hind legs are large and powerful. When the frog is on land they are folded up, and a sudden extension propels the body through the air. Likewise in swimming the hind legs are alternately folded up and extended, and during their backward stroke the toes are spread apart so as to offer more resistance to the water. Frequently

[1] The frog is perhaps the most important of all vertebrates for laboratory study and is here treated in more detail than any other species. As in previous chapters the classification and review of orders and families are intended for general reading or reference.

frogs float on the surface with just the tip of the nose exposed and with the hind legs hanging down. When disturbed in this position, the hind legs are flexed, a movement which withdraws the body, the fore legs direct the frog downward, and then the hind legs are extended, completing the dive.

Frogs *croak* mostly during the breeding season, but also at other times of the year, especially in the evening or when the atmosphere becomes damp. Croaking may take place either in air or under water. In the latter case the air is forced from the lungs, past the vocal cords, into the mouth cavity, and back again.

The principal *enemies* of frogs are snakes, turtles, cranes, herons, other AMPHIBIA, and man. The excellence of frogs' legs for the table has resulted in widespread destruction, and this has been augmented by the capture of great numbers for use in scientific investigations. Tadpoles fall a prey to aquatic insects, fishes, and water-fowl, and very few of them reach maturity.

External Features. — The body of the frog may be divided into the *head* and *trunk*. The *eyes* usually protrude from the head, but are drawn into their orbits when the frog closes its eyelids. Behind each eye is a *tympanic membrane* covering the eardrum. A pair of *nostrils* or external nares are situated on the dorsal surface near the end of the snout. Just in front of the eyes in some specimens is a light area, called the *brow spot*, which, in the embryo, was connected with the brain. The *mouth* of the frog extends from one side of the head to the other. The *anus* is situated at the posterior end of the body.

The *fore legs* are short and serve to hold up the anterior part of the body. The *hands* possess four digits and the rudiment of a fifth, the thumb. In the male the inner digit is thicker than the corresponding digit of the female, especially during the breeding season. The *hind legs* are folded together when the frog is at rest. They are long and powerful. The five toes are connected by a *web*, making the foot an efficient swimming organ.

The *skin* is smooth and loose; it contains large black pigment spots and a lesser amount of green and golden pigments. The skin consists, as in other vertebrates (Fig. 347), of two layers, an outer *epidermis* and an inner *dermis*. It is furnished with a large number of *mucous glands* which secrete the fluid that makes the surface of the body slimy, and a smaller number of *poison glands,* which secrete a whitish fluid of use probably for defensive purposes.

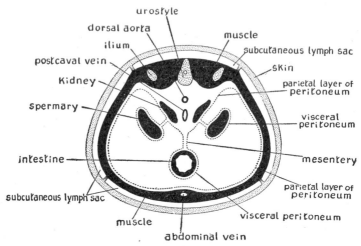

FIG. 409. — Diagram of a cross section of the body of a frog showing the course of the peritoneum by a dotted line. (From Newman, after Parker and Parker.)

General Internal Anatomy. — The body of the frog is supported by a *bony skeleton,* is moved by *muscles,* and contains a well-developed *nervous system.* If the body-wall is slit open in the ventral middle line from the posterior end of the body to the angle of the jaw, the organs in the body-cavity or *cœlom* will be exposed.

The *heart* lies within the sac-like *pericardium;* it is partially surrounded by the three lobes of the reddish brown *liver.* The two *lungs* lie one on either side near the anterior end of the abdominal cavity. Coiled about within the body-cavity are the *stomach* and *intestine.* The *kidneys* are flat reddish bodies attached to the dorsal body-wall. The two *testes* of the male are small ovoid organs suspended by membranes and lying at the sides of the alimentary canal. The *ovaries* and *oviducts* of the female occupy a large part of the body-cavity during the breeding season. The *cœlom* is lined with

FIG. 410. — Three stages of the movement of the tongue of a frog, *Rana esculenta.* (From the Cambridge Natural History.)

a mesodermal membrane, the *peritoneum* (Fig. 409). The reproductive organs and alimentary canal are suspended by double layers of peritoneum called *mesenteries*.

The Digestive System. — The *food* of the frog consists principally of living worms and insects. These are usually captured

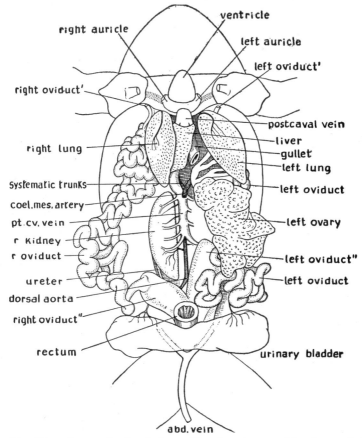

FIG. 411. — Organs of a female frog. The alimentary canal has been cut off at the gullet and rectum, and most of the liver has been removed. The right ovary and fat body are also removed and the ventricle of the heart turned forward. (From Newman, after Parker and Haswell.)

by the *extensile tongue*, which can be thrown forward as shown in Figure 410. The object adheres to the tongue, which is covered with a sticky secretion, and is then drawn into the mouth. No attention is paid to objects that are not moving. Large insects are pushed into the mouth with the forefeet.   If the object swallowed is undesirable, it can be ejected through the mouth.

The *mouth cavity* is large (Fig. 412).   The *tongue* lies on the floor of the cavity with its anterior end attached to the jaw and its forked posterior end lying free.   When a lymph space beneath the tongue is filled, the tongue is thrown forward for capturing insects (Fig. 410).   The *teeth* are conical in shape and are borne by the upper jaw and by two bones of the roof of the mouth called vomers (Fig. 412).   They are used only for holding food and not for masticating it. New teeth replace those that become worn out.

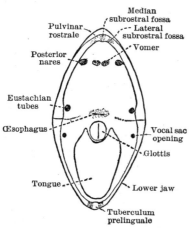

Fig. 412. — Mouth of the frog widely opened.   (From Holmes.)

The *œsophagus* opens into the mouth cavity by a horizontal slit (Fig. 412); it is a short distensible tube leading directly to the stomach.   The *stomach* is crescent-shaped and lies mostly on the left side of the body; it is large at the anterior or *cardiac end,* but constricted at the posterior or *pyloric end* where it joins the small intestine.   The walls of the stomach are thick, consisting of four layers: (1) the outer thin *peritoneum;* (2) a tough *muscular layer;* (3) a spongy layer, the *submucosa;* and (4) an inner folded mucous layer, the *mucosa.*   The mucosa is made up of *glands* lying in connective tissue.   Near the cardiac end the glands are longer than at the pyloric end.

The anterior portion of the *small intestine* is known as the *duodenum;* this leads to the much-coiled *ileum,* which widens into the *large intestine.*   The alimentary canal, as well as the urinary bladder and reproductive ducts, open into a sac-like cavity called the *cloaca.*   The inner layer of the intestine, the mucosa, is much folded; it consists of ordinary absorptive cells and goblet cells.

The *digestive glands* are the pancreas and liver.   The *pancreas* lies between the duodenum and the stomach.   It is a much-branched tubular gland which secretes an alkaline digestive fluid and empties it into the common bile-duct. The *liver* is a large three-lobed reddish gland which secretes an alkaline digestive fluid called *bile*. This fluid is carried by bile capillaries into the *gall-bladder*, where it is stored until food enters the intestine, when it passes into the duodenum through the common *bile-duct*.

Digestion begins in the stomach. The alkaline fluid secreted by the mucosa layer of the œsophagus and the acid gastric juice secreted by the glandular walls of the stomach digest out the protein portion of the food by means of a *ferment*, called *pepsin*, which changes proteids into soluble peptones. The food then passes through the pyloric constriction into the intestine. Here it is attacked by the pancreatic juice and the bile. The pancreatic juice contains three ferments: (1) *trypsin*, which converts proteids into peptones; (2) *amylopsin*, which converts starch into sugar; and (3) *steapsin*, which splits up fats into fatty acid and glycerin. The bile emulsifies fats and converts starch into sugar. The intestinal wall produces a secretion which probably aids in converting starch into sugar.

Absorption begins in the stomach, but takes place principally in the intestine. The food substances which have been dissolved by the digestive juices are taken up by the mucosa layer, passed into the blood and lymph, and are then transported to various parts of the body. The undigested particles of food pass out of the intestine into the cloaca and are then discharged through the anus as fæces.

The absorbed food is used by the frog to build up new protoplasm to take the place of that consumed in the various life activities, and to increase the size of the body. Food is stored up in the liver as *glycogen*, a carbohydrate similar to starch and often called " animal starch." When needed by the body, this glycogen is changed into dextrose by enzymes produced by the liver, and slowly passed into the blood. During the winter the hibernating frog lives largely on the glycogen stored up in the liver in the autumn.

The Respiratory System. — *Respiration* takes place to a considerable extent through the *skin* both in water and in air, but is carried on principally by the *lungs*. As shown in Figure 413, air passes through the nostrils or *external nares* (Fig. 413) into the *olfactory chamber*, and then through the internal or *posterior nares* (Fig. 413; Fig. 412) into the *mouth cavity*. The external nares are then closed (Fig. 413), the floor of the mouth is raised, and the air is forced through the *glottis* (Fig. 413; Fig. 412) into a short tube, the *larynx*, and thence into the *lungs*. Air is expelled from the lungs into the mouth cavity by the contraction of the muscles of the body-wall.

The air in the mouth cavity is changed by throat movements. The glottis remains closed, while the floor of the mouth is alternately raised and lowered. Air is thus drawn in and expelled through the nares.

The *lungs* are pear-shaped sacs with thin, elastic walls. The area of their inner surface is increased by folds which form

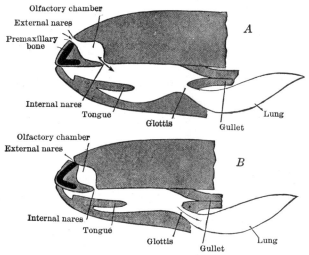

Fig. 413. — Diagram to illustrate the respiratory movements of the frog. In *A* the floor of the mouth is depressed, the nares are open, and air rushes through them into the buccal cavity. In *B*, the floor of the mouth is raised, the nares are closed, and air is forced from the buccal cavity into the lungs. (From Holmes, after Parker.)

minute chambers called *alveoli*. Blood capillaries are numerous in the walls of these alveoli.

The *larynx* is strengthened by five cartilages. Across it are stretched two elastic bands, the *vocal cords*. The croaking of the frog is produced by the vibrations of the free edges of the vocal cords due to the expulsion of air from the lungs. The laryngeal muscles regulate the tension of the cords, and hence the pitch of the sound. Many male frogs have a pair of *vocal sacs* which open into the mouth cavity (Fig. 412); they serve as resonators to increase the volume of sound.

The Circulatory System. — The circulatory system of the frog consists of a heart, arteries, veins, and lymph spaces. The *blood* is a *plasma* containing three kinds of *corpuscles,* — red corpuscles, white corpuscles, and spindle cells. The blood plasma carries food and waste matter in solution. It *coagulates* under certain conditions, forming a *clot* of fibrin and corpuscles, and a liquid called *serum.* The power of coagulation

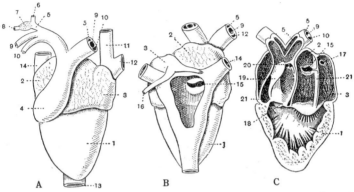

Fig. 414. — Heart of the frog. **A**, ventral view. **B**, dorsal view. **C**, ventral wall removed. *1*, ventricle; *2*, right auricle; *3*, left auricle; *4*, truncus; arteriosus; *5*, carotid arch; *6*, lingual artery; *7*, carotid gland; *8*, carotid artery; *9*, systemic arch; *10*, pulmocutaneous arch; *11*, innominate vein; *12*, subclavian vein; *13*, vena cava inferior; *14*, vena cava superior; *15*, opening of sinus venosus into right auricle; *16*, pulmonary vein; *17*, aperture of entry of pulmonary vein; *18*, semi-lunar valves; *19*, longitudinal valve; *20*, point of origin of pulmocutaneous arch. (From Shipley and MacBride, after Howes.)

is of decided benefit, since the clot soon closes a wound and thus prevents loss of blood.

The *red corpuscles* (erythrocytes) are elliptical, flattened cells containing a substance called *hæmoglobin.* Hæmoglobin combines with oxygen in the capillaries of the respiratory organs and gives it out to the tissues of the body. The *white corpuscles* (leucocytes) are ameboid in shape, vary in size, and are capable of independent movement. They are of great value to the animal, since they engulf small bodies, such as bacteria, thereby frequently preventing the multiplication of pathogenic organisms and consequently helping to overcome germ diseases. White corpuscles also aid in the removal of broken-down tissue. The *spindle cells* are usually spindle-shaped. In the springtime they develop into red corpuscles. Blood corpuscles arise principally in the marrow of the bones. They also increase in numbers by division while in the blood-vessels. Some white corpuscles are probably formed in the spleen, a gland in which worn-out red corpuscles are destroyed.

The *heart* (Fig. 414, Fig. 415) is the central pumping station of the circulatory system. It is composed of a conical, muscular *ventricle* (Fig. 414), two thin-walled *auricles*, one on the right (2), the other on the left (3), a thick-walled tube, the *truncus arteriosus* (4), which arises from the base of the ventricle, and a thin-walled, triangular sac, the *sinus venosus* (Fig. 414, B), on the dorsal side.

The *arteries* (Fig. 415) carry blood away from the heart. The truncus arteriosus (Fig. 414; Fig. 415) divides as shown in Figure 413, A, and each branch gives rise to three arteries.

(1) The *common carotid* (Fig. 414, A; Fig. 415) divides into the lingual or external carotid (Fig. 415), which supplies the tongue and neighboring parts, and the internal carotid, which gives off the palatine artery to the roof of the mouth, the cerebral carotid to the brain, and the ophthalmic artery to the eye. Where the common carotid branches is a swelling called the carotid gland (Fig. 414, A); this body impedes the blood flow in the internal carotid artery.

(2) The *pulmocutaneous artery* (Fig. 414, A ; Fig. 415) branches, forming the pulmonary artery, which passes to the lungs, and the cutaneous artery. The latter gives off the auricularis, which is distributed to the lower jaw and neighboring parts, the dorsalis, which supplies the skin of the back, and the lateralis, which supplies the skin of the sides. Most of these branches carry blood to the respiratory organs — lungs, skin, and mouth.

(3) The third branches or *systemic arches* (Fig. 414, A ; Fig. 415) after passing outward and around the alimentary canal unite to form the dorsal aorta (*d.ao*). As shown in Figure 415, each systemic arch gives off an occipito-vertebral artery, which divides, one branch, the occipital, supplying the jaws and nose, the other, the vertebral, supplying the vertebral column, and a subclavian artery, which is distributed to the shoulder, body-wall, and arm. The dorsal aorta gives off the cœliaco-mesenteric artery ; this divides, forming the cœliac, which supplies the stomach, pancreas,

and liver, and the anterior mesenteric, which is distributed to the intestine, spleen, and cloaca. Posterior to the origin of the cœliaco-mesenteric, the dorsal aorta gives off four to six urinogenital arteries which supply the kidneys, reproductive organs, and fat bodies. A small posterior mesenteric artery arises near the posterior end of the dorsal aorta and passes to the rectum,

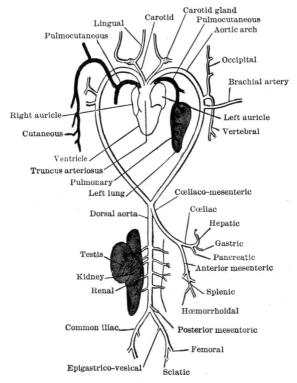

Fig. 415. — Diagram of the arterial system of the frog, ventral view. (From Holmes, after Howes.)

and in the female to the uterus. The dorsal aorta finally divides into two common iliac arteries, which are distributed to the ventral body-wall, the rectum, bladder, the anterior part of the thigh (femoral artery), and other parts of the hind limbs (sciatic artery).

The *veins* (Fig. 416) return blood to the heart. The blood from the lungs is collected in the pulmonary veins and poured into the left auricle. The rest of the venous blood is carried to the sinus venosus by three large trunks, the two anterior venæ cavæ and the posterior vena cava. The anterior venæ cavæ receive blood from the external jugulars which collect blood from the tongue, thyroid, and neighboring parts, the innominates which

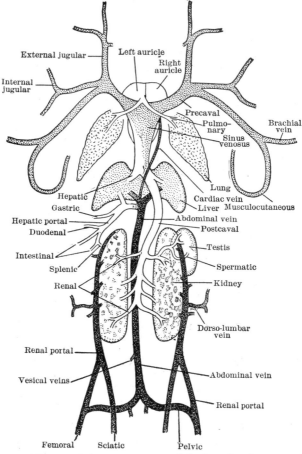

Fig. 416. — Diagram of the venous system of the frog, dorsal aspect. (From Parker and Haswell.)

collect blood from the head by means of the internal jugulars and from the shoulder by means of the subscapulars, and the subclavians which collect blood from the fore limbs by means of the brachial and from the side of the body and head by means of the musculocutaneous veins. The posterior vena cava receives blood

from the liver by means of two hepatic veins, from the kidneys
by means of four to six pairs of renal veins, and from the reproductive organs by means of spermatic or ovarian veins.

The veins which carry blood to the kidneys constitute the
renal portal system. The renal portal vein receives the blood from
the hind legs by means of the sciatic and femoral veins, and blood
from the body-wall by means of the dorso-lumbar vein.

The liver receives blood from the *hepatic portal system*. The
femoral veins from the hind limbs divide, and their branches unite
to form the abdominal vein. The abdominal vein also collects
blood from the bladder, ventral body-wall, and heart. The portal
vein carries blood into the liver from the stomach, intestine, spleen,
and pancreas.

Circulation takes place in the following manner: The sinus
venosus contracts first, forcing the impure venous blood into
the right auricle (Fig. 414, C, *15*). Then both auricles contract,
and the oxygenated blood brought into the left auricle by the
pulmonary veins is forced into the left part of the ventricle,
and the impure blood from the right auricle is forced into the
right side of the ventricle. The ventricle then contracts and
the impure blood is forced out first, passing principally into the
pulmocutaneous arteries and thence to the lungs and skin, and
the oxygenated blood is forced out later through the carotid
and systemic arteries to the other parts of the body. The blood
is prevented from flowing back, and the oxygenated blood and
impure blood are distributed as stated above, by means of *valves*
(Fig. 414, C, *18, 19*).

The blood that is thus forced through the arteries makes its
way into tubular blood-vessels that become smaller and smaller
until the extremely narrow *capillaries* are reached. Here food
and oxygen are delivered to the tissues, and waste products are
taken up from the tissues. The renal portal system carries
blood to the kidneys, where urea and similar impurities are taken
out. The hepatic portal system carries blood to the liver, where
bile and glycogen are formed. The blood brought to the lungs
and skin is oxygenated and then carried back to the heart. The
passage of blood through the capillaries can easily be observed
in the web of the frog's foot or in the tail of the tadpole.

The *lymph spaces* in the frog's body are very large. They
communicate with one another and with the veins. Four lymph

hearts, two near the third vertebra and two near the end of the vertebral column, force the lymph by pulsations into the internal jugular and transverse iliac veins. The lymph is colorless and contains colorless corpuscles.

The Excretory System (Fig. 417). — A certain amount of substance resulting from the breaking down of living matter is excreted by the skin, liver, and intestinal walls, but most of it is taken from the blood in the *kidneys*, passes through the *ureters*, and then by way of the *cloaca* into the bladder (10), where it is stored until expelled from the body through the anus. The *kidney* is composed of connective tissue containing a large number of *uriniferous tubules*, each of which begins in a *Malpighian body*, consisting of a coiled mass of blood-vessels, the *glomerulus*, and

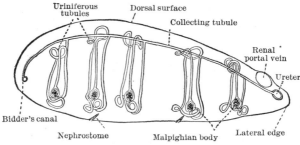

FIG. 417. — Diagram of a cross-section of the kidney of the frog. (From Holmes.)

an enclosing membrane called *Bowman's capsule*. The excretions are carried by the uriniferous tubules to a collecting tubule and thence into the ureter. Ciliated funnels, called *nephrostomes*, occur in the ventral portion; these are in the young frog connected with the renal tubules, but open into branches of the renal vein in the adult. Renal arteries (Fig. 415) and the renal portal vein (Fig. 416; Fig. 418) bring blood into the kidney. Blood leaves the kidney by way of the renal veins (Fig. 416).

The Reproductive System. — The sexes are separate. The male can be distinguished from the female by the greater thickness of the inner digit of his fore legs. The *spermatozoa* of the male arise in the *testes*, pass through the *vasa efferentia* (Fig. 418) into the kidneys, then by way of *Bidder's canal* (Fig. 417) to the ureter (Fig. 417); and thence out through the anus.

The eggs arise in the ovaries of the female (Fig. 418), break out into the body-cavity, make their way into the coiled *oviduct* through a small opening, and pass down into the thin-walled, distensible *uterus*. The glandular wall of the oviduct secretes the gelatinous coats of the eggs. The fertilization and development of the eggs will be described later (pp. 453–456).

Just in front of each reproductive organ is a yellowish, glove-shaped *fat-body* (Fig. 418) which serves to store up nutriment.

Glands. — Besides the liver and pancreas, there are a number of glands in the body of the frog that are of great importance because of their secretions. These glands have no ducts, but

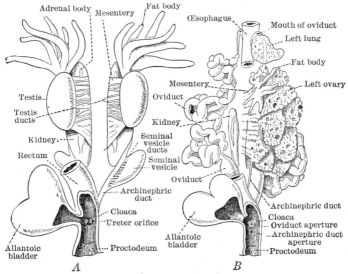

Fig. 418. — Urinogenital organs of the frog. *A*, male. *B*, female. (From Shipley and MacBride, after Howes.)

empty their products directly into the body; they are therefore called *ductless glands*, and their products are called *internal secretions*. Internal secretions are also produced by other organs, *e.g.* the liver forms sugar and urea.

The *spleen* is a reddish body situated above the anterior end of the cloaca. In it old blood corpuscles are destroyed and new colorless corpuscles are probably formed.

The two *thyroid glands* are situated one on either side of the hyoid. Their secretions contain a large amount of iodin. The function of the thyroid is not certain in the frog. In man its atrophy causes a disease called cretinism.

The two *thymus glands* lie one behind each tympanum, beneath the depressor mandibulæ muscle. Their function is not certain.

The *adrenal bodies* are long, thin glands lying on the ventral surface of the kidneys. They secrete adrenalin, a substance necessary for the life of the animal. When adrenalin is extracted and then injected into the blood of a mammal, it causes a contraction of the blood-vessels and therefore raises the blood pressure.

The Skeleton. — The skeleton of the frog consists principally of bone. The *axial portion* comprises the skull and vertebral column. The *appendicular portion* consists of the pectoral and pelvic girdles and the bones of the limbs which they support.

The cartilage and bones of the skull may be grouped into two main divisions: (1) the brain case and auditory and olfactory capsules, which constitute the *cranium;* and (2) the jaws and hyoid arch, which constitute the *visceral skeleton.*

Cranium. — A large part of the cranium consists of cartilage (dotted in Fig. 419). The bones are either ossifications of the cartilage (the exoccipitals, prootics, and ethmoid), or are developed from membranes and invest the cartilage and cartilage bones. The spinal cord passes through a large opening, the *foramen magnum* in the posterior end of the cranium. On either side of this opening is a convexity of the exoccipital bones, called the *occipital condyle,* which articulates in life in a concavity of the first vertebra, and enables the frog to move its head.

The cranial bones of the dorsal side are the *prootics* (Fig. 419) which enclose the inner ears, the *frontoparietals* which form most of the roof of the cranium, the *sphenethmoid* which forms the posterior wall of the nasal cavity, and the *nasals* which lie above the nasal capsules. The ventral surface of the cranium discloses the central, dagger-shaped *parasphenoid* and the *vomers* which bear the vomerine teeth.

The Visceral Skeleton. — The jaws and hyoid, which constitute the visceral skeleton, are also preformed in cartilage and then strengthened by ossifications. The *upper jaw* or maxillary arch consists of a pair of *premaxillæ* (Fig. 419), a pair of *maxillæ,* and a pair of *quadratojugals.* The maxillæ and premaxillæ bear teeth. The *lower jaw* or mandibular arch consists of a pair of cartilaginous rods (Meckel's cartilages) invested by a pair of *den-*

tary bones, and a pair of *angulo-splenials*. The jaws are attached to the cranium by a suspensory apparatus consisting of the *squamosals* (Fig. 419), the *pterygoids*, and the *palatines*.

The *visceral arches* are represented in the adult by the *hyoid* and its processes. The cartilaginous *basilingual plate* lies in the floor of the mouth cavity. The *hyoid arches* curve upward and

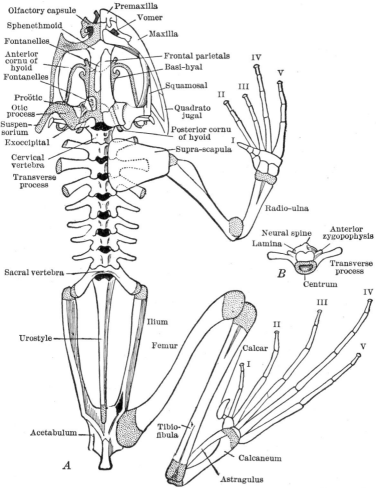

Fig. 419. — Skeleton of *Rana temporaria*. The left limbs, left shoulder girdle, and the membrane bones of the left side of the skull are removed. Cartilaginous parts dotted; names of cartilage bones in thick, those of membrane bones in italic capitals. (From Parker and Haswell.)

join the prootics on either side.   Two ossified posterior processes, the *thyrohyals*, help support the larynx.

The Vertebral Column   (Fig. 419). — The vertebral column consists of nine *vertebræ* and a blade-like posterior extension, the *urostyle*.   The vertebræ consist of a basal *centrum*, which is concave in front and convex behind (procœlous type), and a

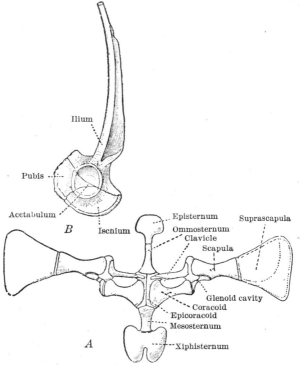

Fig. 420. — Skeleton of the frog. **A**, pectoral girdle. **B**, pelvic girdle, side view.
(From Bourne, after Ecker.)

neural arch (Fig. 419) through which the spinal cord passes. The neural arch possesses a short, *dorsal spine*, a *transverse process* on each side (except on the first vertebra, *av*), and a pair of articulating processes, called *zygapophyses*, at each end.   The vertebræ are held together by ligaments, and move on one another by means of the centra and zygapophyses. The vertebral column thus serves as a firm axial support which also allows bending of the body.

The Appendicular Skeleton. — The *pectoral girdle* and *sternum* (Fig. 420) support the fore limbs, serve as attachments for the muscles that move the fore limbs, and protect the organs lying within the anterior portion of the trunk. They are composed partly of bone and partly of cartilage. The suprascapulæ lie above the vertebral column, and the rest of the girdle passes downwards on either side and unites with the sternum in the ventral, middle line. The principal parts are the *suprascapulæ* (Fig. 420, A), the *scapulæ*, the *clavicles*, the *coracoids*, the *epicoracoids*, the *ommosternum, episternum, mesosternum,* and *xiphisternum.* The end of the long bone of the fore limb (*humerus*) lies in a concavity in the scapula and coracoid called the *glenoid fossa.*

The *pelvic girdle* (Fig. 420, B) supports the hind limbs. It consists of two sets of three parts each, the *ilium*, the *ischium*, and the *pubis*. The pubis is cartilaginous. The anterior end of each ilium is attached to one of the transverse processes of the ninth vertebra. Where the parts of each half of the pelvic girdle unite, there is a concavity, called the *acetabulum*, in which the head of the long leg bone (femur) lies.

The *fore limbs* (Fig. 419) consist of a *humerus* which articulates with the glenoid fossa of the pectoral girdle at its proximal end and with the *radio-ulna* at its distal end. The bone of the forearm (radio-ulna) consists of the radius and ulna fused. The *wrist* contains six bones: the *ulnare, radiale, intermedium,* and three *carpals.* The *hand* is supported by five proximal *metacarpal* bones, followed in digits II and III by two *phalanges,* and in digits IV and V by three phalanges.

The *hind limbs* (Fig. 419) consist of (1) a *femur* or thigh bone, (2) a *tibio-fibula* (the tibia and fibula fused) or leg bone, (3) four *tarsal* bones, — the *astragalus*, the *calcaneum*, and two smaller bones, — (4) the four *metatarsals* of the foot, (5) the *phalanges* of the digits, and (6) the *prehallux* or calcar of the accessory digit.

The Muscular System (Fig. 421). — Muscles are usually attached by one or both ends to bones either directly or by means of a *tendon*, which is an inelastic band of connective tissue. The two ends of a muscle are designated by different terms: the *origin* is the end attached to a relatively immovable part; the *insertion* is the movable end. A muscle which bends· one part upon another, as the leg upon the thigh, is a *flexor;* one that straightens out a part, as the extending of the foot, is an *extensor;* one that draws a part back toward the median line is an *adductor;* one that pulls a part forward toward the median line is an *abductor;*

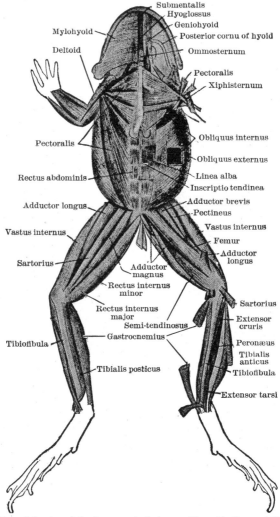

Fig. 421. — Muscles of the frog, ventral view. (From Parker and Haswell.)

one that lowers a part is a *depressor;* one that raises a part is a *levator;* and one that rotates one part on another is a *rotator.* The movements of an organ depend on the origin and insertion of the muscles and the nature of the articulations of its bones with each other and with other parts of the body.

The muscles of the hind limb are usually selected for study to illustrate the methods of action of muscles in general. Table XVI gives the name, origin, insertion, and action of the principal muscles of the hind limb, and Figure 421 shows most of them as seen from the ventral side.

TABLE XVI

THE NAME, ORIGIN, INSERTION, AND ACTION OF THE PRINCIPAL MUSCLES OF THE HIND LIMB OF THE FROG

NAME	ORIGIN	INSERTION	ACTION
Sartorius (Fig. 421)	Ilium, just in front of pubis	Just below head of tibia	Flexes leg; draws leg forward and ventrally
Adductor magnus	Pubis, ischium, and tendon of semimembranosus	Distal end of femur	Bends thigh ventrally, adducts or abducts femur according to position of latter
Adductor longus	Ventral part of ilium	Joins adductor magnus	Abducts thigh; draws thigh ventrally.
Triceps femoris	From three heads, one acetabulum, two ilium	Upper end of tibio-fibula; tendon of gastrocnemius	Extends and abducts leg
Gracilis major	Posterior margin of ischium	Proximal end of tibia; head of tibio-fibula	Adducts thigh; flexes or extends leg according to position of latter
Gracilis minor	Tendon behind ischium	Joins tendon of gracilis major	Same as gracilis major
Semimembranosus	Dorsal half of ischium	Proximal end tibio-fibula	Same as gracilis major
Ileo-fibularis	Behind dorsal crest of ilium	Proximal end of fibula	Draws thigh dorsally; flexes leg
Semitendinosus	Two points on ischium	Proximal end of tibia	Adducts thigh; flexes leg

TABLE XVI — *Continued*

Name	Origin	Insertion	Action
Pyriformis	Tip of uro-style	Near proximal end of femur	Pulls urostyle to one side; draws femur dorsally
Iliacus externus	Outer side of dorsal crest of ilium	Head of femur, posterior side	Rotates femur forward
Iliacus internus	Ventral border of ilium	Proximal half of femur	Draws thigh forward
Gastrocnemius	Distal end of femur; tendon of triceps	By broad tendon on sole of foot	Flexes leg; extends foot
Tibialis posticus	Posterior side of tibio-fibula	Proximal end of astragalus	Extends foot when flexed; flexes foot when fully extended
Tibialis anticus longus	Distal end of femur	Proximal end of astragalus and calcaneum	Extends leg; flexes foot
Peroneus (*per*)	Distal end of femur	Distal end femur; head of calcaneum	Extends leg and foot; flexes foot
Extensor cruris	Distal end of femur	Anterior surface of tibio-fibula	Extends foot
Tibialis anticus brevis	Distal third of tibio-fibula	Proximal end of astragalus	Flexes foot

The following are a few of the muscles of the other parts of the body: The *rectus abdominis* (Fig. 421) extends along the ventral side of the trunk; the *obliquus externus* covers most of the sides of the trunk; the *transversus* lies beneath the obliquus externus and serves to contract the body-cavity; the *pectoralis major* moves the fore limbs; and the *submaxillary* raises the floor of the mouth cavity during respiration.

The Nervous System. — Three main divisions may be distinguished in the nervous system of the frog: (1) the *central*, consisting of the brain and spinal cord; (2) the *peripheral*, consisting of the cerebral and spinal nerves; and (3) the *sympathetic*. It will be sufficient in this place to point out certain selected points concerning the nervous system of the frog, since general accounts of nervous tissue (p. 77), nervous activity (pp. 205–207), and the nervous system of vertebrates (pp. 364–366) have already been given.

The Brain. — The brain (Fig. 422) has two large *olfactory lobes* which are fused together, two large *cerebral hemispheres*,

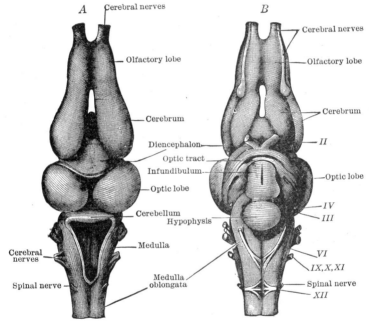

FIG. 422. — Brain of the frog. **A**, dorsal aspect. **B**, ventral aspect. I–XII, nerves. (From Davenport, after Wiedersheim.)

two large *optic lobes*, a well-developed *midbrain*, a very small *cerebellum*, and a *medulla oblongata*, which is produced by the broadening of the spinal cord. The *optic chiasma*, the *infundibulum*, and the *hypophysis* are visible only on the ventral surface of the brain.

The *functions* of the different parts of the frog's brain have been partially determined by experiments in which the parts were removed and the effects upon the animals observed. It is not certain what the functions of the cerebral hemispheres are in the frog. They are the seat of intelligence and voluntary control in higher animals. When the midbrain is removed along with the cerebral hemispheres, the frog loses the power of spontaneous movement. When the optic lobes are removed, the spinal cord becomes more irritable; this shows that these lobes have an inhibiting influence on the reflex activity of the spinal cord. The cerebellum apparently has no important function in the frog. Many activities are still possible when everything but the medulla is removed. The animal breathes normally, snaps at and swallows food, leaps and swims regularly, and is able to right itself when thrown on its back. Extirpation of the posterior region of the medulla results in the early death of the frog. The brain as a whole controls the actions effected by the nerve-centers of the spinal cord. " The higher centers of the brain are comparable to the captain of a steamer who issues orders to the man running the engine when to start and when to stop, and who has his hand on the wheel so as to guide the course of the vessel." (Holmes.) Cranial nerves I to X (see p. 365, Table XIV) are present in the frog.

The Spinal Cord. (Fig. 423). — The spinal cord extends backward from the medulla and ends in the urostyle. It is surrounded by two membranes, an outer dura mater and an inner pia mater. The cord is composed of a central mass of gray matter (Fig. 349) consisting mainly of nerve-cells, and an outer mass of white matter made up chiefly of nerve-fibers. A median fissure occurs both in the dorsal and in the ventral side of the cord, and a central canal lies in the gray matter and communicates anteriorly with the cavities of the brain.

The Spinal Nerves. — The relation of the spinal nerves to the spinal cord and the paths taken by nervous impulses are indicated in Figure 349. There are ten pairs of spinal nerves in the frog (Fig. 423). Each arises by a dorsal (Fig. 349) and a ventral root (see p. 364) which spring from the horns of the gray matter of the cord. The two roots unite to form a trunk, which passes out between the arches of adjacent vertebræ. The largest nerves are the brachial (Fig. 423), which are composed of the second and branches from the first and third pairs of spinal nerves, and are distributed to the fore limbs and shoulder, and the sciatics, which arise from plexuses composed of the seventh, eighth, and ninth spinal nerves, and are distributed to the hind limbs.

The Sympathetic System. (Fig. 423). — This system consists of two principal trunks, which begin in the prootic ganglion and extend posteriorly, one on either side of the vertebral column. Each trunk is provided with ten ganglionic enlargements at the

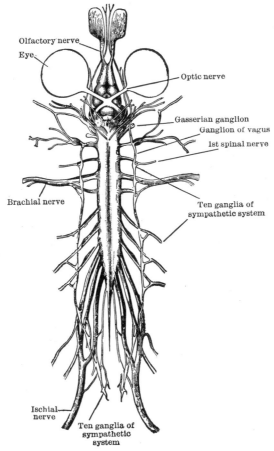

Olfactory nerve

Eye

Optic nerve

Gasserian ganglion

Ganglion of vagus

1st spinal nerve

Brachial nerve

Ten ganglia of sympathetic system

Ischial nerve

Ten ganglia of sympathetic system

FIG. 423. — Nervous system of the frog. (From Sedgwick's Zoology, after Ecker.)

points where branches from the spinal nerves unite with it. The nerves of the sympathetic system are distributed to the internal organs which are thus intimately connected.

Sense-organs. — The principal sense-organs are the *eyes, ears,* and *olfactory organs.* There are many smaller structures on the surface of the tongue, and on the floor and roof of the mouth, which probably function as organs of *taste*. In the skin are also many sensory nerve endings which receive contact, chemical, temperature, and light stimuli.

The Olfactory Organs. — The olfactory nerves (Fig. 423) extend from the olfactory lobe of the brain (Fig. 422) to the nasal cavities (Fig. 412), where they are distributed to the epithelial lining. The importance of the sense of smell in the life of the frog is not known.

The Ear. — The *inner ear* of the frog lies within the *auditory capsule* and is protected by the prootic (Fig. 419) and exoccipital bones. It is similar in structure to that shown in Figure 350, page 356, and is supplied by branches of the auditory nerve. There is no external ear in the frog. The *middle ear* is a cavity which communicates with the mouth cavity through the Eustachian tube (Fig. 411), and is closed externally by the tympanic membrane.

A rod, the *columella*, extends across the cavity of the middle ear from the tympanic membrane to the inner ear. The vibrations of the tympanic membrane produced by sound waves are transmitted to the inner ear through the columella. The sensory end organs of the auditory nerve are stimulated by the vibrations, and the impulses carried to the brain give rise to the sensation of sound. The inner ears serve also as organs of *equilibration*. Frogs from which they are removed cannot maintain an upright position.

The Eye. — The eyes of the frog resemble those of man in general structure and function (Fig. 351, pp. 367–369), but differ in certain details. The *eyeballs* lie in cavities (orbits, Fig. 419) in the sides of the head. They may be rotated by six muscles and also pulled into the orbit. The *upper eyelid* does not move independently. The *lower eyelid* consists of the lower eyelid proper fused with the third eyelid or *nictitating membrane*. The *lens* is large and almost spherical. It cannot be changed in form nor in position, and is therefore fitted for viewing distinctly objects at a certain definite distance. Movements are noted much oftener than form. The amount of light that enters the eye can be regulated by the contraction of the *pupil*. The *retina* of the eye is stimulated by the rays of light which pass through the pupil, and the impulses which are carried through the optic nerve to the brain give rise to sensations of sight.

Behavior. — The activities of the frog are such as to enable it to exist within the confines of its habitat. The ordinary movements are those employed in leaping, diving, crawling, burrowing, and maintaining an upright position. These and most of its other activities may be resolved into a series of reflex acts, although they are commonly said to be instinctive. Instinct is " the faculty of acting in such a way as to produce certain ends, without foresight of the ends, and without previous education in the performance." (James.)

Some of the movements of the frog are due to internal causes, but many of them are the responses to external stimuli. Frogs are sensitive to light, and experiments have shown that both the eyes and skin are stimulated by it. The reaction to light causes the animal to orient its body so that it faces the source and is in line with the direction of the rays. Nevertheless, frogs tend to congregate in shady places. Frogs also seem to be stimulated by contact (thigmotropism, p. 36), as shown by their tendency to crawl under stones and into crevices. The desire for shade may, however, have some influence upon this reaction. The temperature modifies the responses both to light and to contact.

Investigators who have studied the behavior of frogs have come to the conclusion that they are very stupid animals. It is possible to teach them certain things, and habits once formed are not easily changed. For example, Yerkes found that a frog could learn to follow a path in a labyrinth after about one hundred trials. If we consider the power to learn by individual experience as evidence of the presence of mind, then we must attribute a primitive sort of mind to the frog.

Development. — Frogs lay their eggs in water in the early spring. The male clasps the female firmly with his fore legs just behind her fore legs. After the male has been carried about by the female for several days, the eggs pass from the uterus out of the cloaca and are fertilized by the spermatozoa of the male, which the latter discharges over them as they are extruded. The male then loses the clasping instinct and leaves the female.

The jelly which surrounds and protects the eggs soon swells up through the absorption of water. *Cleavage* takes place as indicated in Figure 424. Some of the cells, called *macromeres* (Fig. 425, A), are large because of a bountiful supply of *yolk;* others, the *micromeres*, are smaller. A *blastula* (A) is formed by the appearance of a cavity, the *blastocœl*, near the center of the egg. *Gastrulation* is modified in the frog's egg because of the amount of yolk present. The dark side of the egg gradually grows over the lighter portion until only a circular area of the latter, called the *yolk plug*, is visible. This gastrula contains two germ-layers, an outer *ectoderm* (C) and an inner *entoderm* (C). A third layer, the *mesoderm* (C), soon appears between the other two, and splits into two, an inner *splanchnic* layer, which forms the supporting tissue and musculature of the alimentary canal, and an outer *somatic* or *parietal* layer, which forms the connective tissue, muscle,

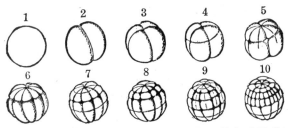

Fig. 424. — Segmentation of the frog's egg.   (From Sedgwick's Zoology, after Ecker.)

and peritoneum of the body-wall. The cavity between these two mesodermal layers is the *cœlom*.

Soon after gastrulation a groove called the *primitive* or *medullary groove* (Fig. 425, B) appears, on either side of which is a *medullary fold*. The medullary folds grow together at the top, forming·a tube which later develops into the brain and spinal cord of the embryo. The medullary groove lies along the median dorsal line, and the embryo now lengthens in this direction. The region where the yolk plug was situated lies at the posterior end. On either side near the anterior end two *gill-arches* appear, and in front of each of these a depression arises which unites with its fellow and moves to the ventral surface, becoming the *ventral sucker* (E). An invagination soon appears just above the ventral sucker; this is the *stomodæum* which develops into the mouth.

The invagination (*proctodæum*, E) which becomes the anus appears beneath the tail at the posterior end. On either side above the mouth a thickening of the ectoderm represents the beginning of the *eye*, and just above the gills (E), appear the invaginations which form the vesicles of the inner ears. The markings of the muscle segments show through the skin along the sides of the body and tail.

The embryo moves about within the egg by means of cilia, but these soon disappear after hatching. The tadpole, after breaking out of the egg membranes, lives for a few days on the yolk in the alimentary canal, and then feeds on algæ and other vegetable matter. The external gills grow out into long, branching tufts. Four pairs of *internal gills* are formed later, and, when

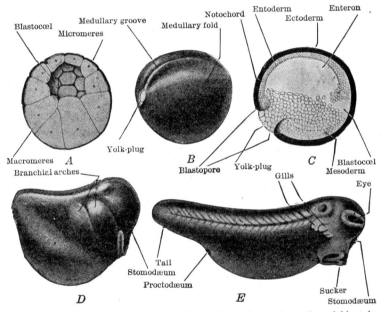

Fig. 425. — Development of the embryo of the frog. **A**, section of blastula. **B**, formation of medullary groove. **C**, section of egg in stage **B** to show germ-layers. **D**, older embryo. **E**, newly hatched tadpole. (From Parker and Haswell; A, D, after Ziegler's models; B, C, E, after Marshall.)

the external gills disappear, these function in their stead, the water entering the mouth, passing through the gill-slits, and out of an opening on the left side of the body, called the *spiracle*.

The hind limbs appear first (Fig. 426, 10). Later the fore limbs break out (11). The tail decreases in size as the end of the larval period approaches and is gradually resorbed (12, 13, 14). The gills are likewise resorbed, and the lungs develop to take their place as respiratory organs. Finally the form resembling that of the adult frog (15) is acquired.

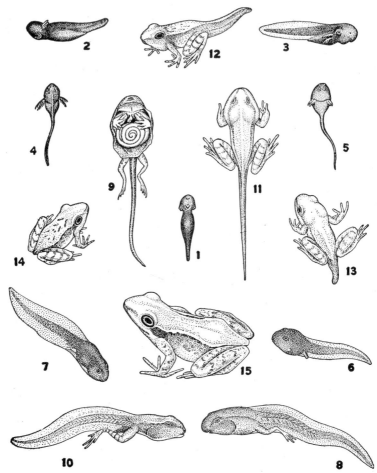

Fig. 426. — Larval development of the frog and metamorphosis. *1*, tadpole just hatched, dorsal aspect; *2, 3*, older tadpoles, side view; *4, 5*, later stages, dorsal views showing external gills and development of operculum; *7*, older stage, right side, showing hind leg and anus; *8* and *10*, lateral view of two later stages showing development of hind legs; *9*, dissection of tadpole to show internal gills, spiral intestine, and anterior legs developed within operculum; *11*, advanced tadpole just before metamorphosis; *12, 13, 14*, stages in metamorphosis, showing gradual resorption of tail; *15*, juvenile frog after metamorphosis. (From Newman after Leuckart-Nitsche wall chart.)

2. A Brief Classification of Living Amphibia[1]

There are about one thousand different species of AMPHIBIA — a number very much smaller than that of the other principal classes of vertebrates. Approximately forty of these belong to the order APODA, one hundred to the CAUDATA, and nine hundred to the SALIENTIA.

Order 1. Apoda (GYMNOPHIONA, Fig. 427). — CŒCILIANS. — Worm-like AMPHIBIA without limbs or limb-girdles; usually with small scales embedded in the skin; tail short or absent.

Family CŒCILIIDÆ. — With the characters of the order. Examples: *Dermophis, Cæcilia, Gymnopis, Siphonops, Ichthyophis* (Fig. 427).

Order 2. Caudata (URODELA, Figs. 428–433). — Tailed AMPHIBIA. AMPHIBIA with a tail; without scales; usually two pairs of limbs; the adults with or without external gills and gill slits.

Suborder 1. Proteida (Fam. PROTEIDÆ, Fig. 428). — MUDPUPPIES. — Tailed AMPHIBIA with two pairs of limbs; three pairs of external gills and two pairs of gill-openings persistent; no eyelids.

Family PROTEIDÆ. — With the characters of the suborder. Examples: *Necturus, Proteus, Typhlomolge.*

Suborder 2. Meantes (Fam. SIRENIDÆ, Fig. 429). — SIRENS. — Tailed AMPHIBIA without hind limbs; three pairs of external gills and three pairs of gill-openings persistent; no eyelids.

Family SIRENIDÆ. — With the characters of the suborder. Examples: *Siren, Pseudobranchus.*

Suborder 3. Mutabilia (Fam. SALAMANDRIDÆ, Figs. 430–433). — SALAMANDERS. — Tailed AMPHIBIA with two pairs of limbs; without gills and generally without gill-openings in adult; usually with movable eyelids.

Superfamily 1. AMPHIUMOIDEÆ. — MUTABILIA with two pairs of small limbs; sometimes one pair of gill-openings; vertebræ amphicœlous; without eyelids.

---

[1] I am indebted to Dr. Alexander G. Ruthven for the main divisions of this classification.

Family CRYPTOBRANCHIDÆ. — With the characters of the
superfamily. Examples: *Cryptobranchus* (Fig. 430),
Amphiuma.

Superfamily 2. SALAMANDROIDEÆ. — MUTABILIA without
gills or gill-openings in the adult; with movable eyelids;
vertebræ usually opisthocœlous. The families are distinguished from one another principally by the position of
the teeth and the number of toes.

Family 1. SALAMANDRIDÆ. — Examples: *Salamandra, Triton*
(Fig. 431), *Diemyctylus.*

Family 2. AMBYSTOMIDÆ. — Examples: *Ambystoma* (Fig.
432), *Chondrotus.*

Family 3. PLETHODONTIDÆ. — Examples: *Plethodon, Spelerpes, Desmognathus* (Fig. 433).

Order 3. **Salientia** (ANURA, Figs. 434–436). — TAILLESS AM-
PHIBIA. AMPHIBIA without a tail; without scales; two
pairs of limbs; without external gills or gill-openings in
adult.

Suborder 1. *Aglossa.* — SALIENTIA without a tongue; Eustachian tubes open by single aperture; no distinct tympanic membrane; vertebræ opisthocœlous.

Family AGLOSSIDÆ. — With the characters of the suborder. Examples: *Pipa* (Fig. 434), *Xenopus.*

Suborder 2. *Linguata* (PHANEROGLOSSA). — FROGS and TOADS.
SALIENTIA with a tongue; Eustachian tubes open by two
apertures.

Family 1. PELOBATIDÆ. — Spade-foot toads. Examples:
Pelobates, Scaphiopus.

Family 2. BUFONIDÆ. — TOADS. Examples: *Bufo, Rhino-
phrynus.*

Family 3. HYLIDÆ. — TREE-FROGS. Examples: *Acris, Chorophilus, Hyla, Nototrema* (Fig. 435).

Family 4. CYSTIGNATHIDÆ. Examples: *Hemiphractus, Hy-
lodes, Paludicola.*

Family 5. ENGYSTOMATIDÆ. Examples: *Engystoma, Phry-
niscus, Hypopachus.*

Family 6. RANIDÆ. — TRUE FROGS. Examples: *Rana,
Phyllobates, Oxyglossus.*

Suborder 3. Costata (DISCOGLOSSIDÆ). — SALIENTIA with a tongue; Eustachian tubes open by two apertures; with short ribs.

Family DISCOGLOSSIDÆ. — With the characters of the suborder. Examples: *Discoglossus, Alytes, Bombinator.*

3. REVIEW OF THE ORDERS AND FAMILIES OF LIVING AMPHIBIA

Order 1. Apoda. — The single family, CŒCILIIDÆ, of this order includes about forty species of wormlike or snakelike legless AMPHIBIA. They inhabit the tropical regions of America, Africa, India, Burma, and northern Australasia, but none occurs in the United States. They burrow in moist ground with their strong heads, and, as a result of living in darkness, their eyes are small and concealed under the skin or maxillary bones. A sensory tentacle which can be protruded from between the eyes and the nose aids the animal in crawling about. They feed on small invertebrates. Most of the cœcilians lay eggs, but some are viviparous. *Ichthyophis glutinosa* (Fig. 427),

FIG. 427. — A legless amphibian, *Ichthyophis glutinosa*, female guarding her eggs. (From the Cambridge Natural History, after Sarasin.)

which lives in India, Ceylon, and the Malay Islands, and is about one foot long, has been more carefully studied than any other species.

Order 2. Caudata. — The tailed AMPHIBIA differ so widely from one another that it has been found necessary to recognize three suborders.

FIG. 428. — The "mud-puppy," *Necturus maculosus*. (From Mivart.)

Suborder 1. Proteida. — This suborder contains a single family, PROTEIDÆ, the mud-puppies, and three genera, *Necturus, Typhlomolge,* and *Proteus,* with one species each. *Necturus maculosus* (Fig. 428) is confined to the rivers and lakes of the northern and eastern part of the United States, west of the Alleghanies. It breathes by means of bushy red gills which extend out from in front of the fore legs. The food of *Necturus* consists chiefly of crustaceans, frogs, worms, insects, and small fishes. During the day the mud-puppy lies concealed in a dark place, but at night it swims or crawls about with wavy movements of the body.

Proteus anguinus is a protean about one foot long, which has been found only in the caves of Austria. It is white, but if exposed to the light may become dark and ultimately black. It has rudimentary eyes.

Typhlomolge rathbuni is a blind protean that came up with the water of an artesian well one hundred and eighty-eight feet deep, in Texas. It probably feeds on the crustaceans in underground streams, since four species of these, all new to science, came up along with the amphibians.

Suborder 2. Meantes. — This suborder also contains a single family, SIRENIDÆ, the sirens, and two genera, *Siren* and *Pseudobranchus*, with one species each. *Siren lacertina* (Fig. 429), the

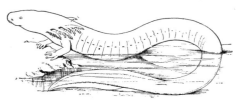

FIG. 429. — The "mud-eel," *Siren lacertina.*
(From the Cambridge Natural History.)

"mud-eel," burrows in the mud of ditches and ponds, and swims by undulations of the body. It has three pairs of gill-slits and four toes, and reaches a length of two and one half feet. It inhabits the ponds and rivers from Texas to North Carolina. *Pseudobranchus striatus* has but one pair of gill-slits and only three toes. It has been found in Georgia and Florida.

Suborder 3. Mutabilia. — Family CRYPTOBRANCHIDÆ. — There are three genera, *Cryptobranchus*, *Megalobatrachus*, and *Amphiuma*. *Cryptobranchus alleghaniensis*, the hellbender (Fig. 430), occurs only in the streams of the eastern United States. It reaches a length of from eighteen to twenty inches. Its food consists of worms and small fish. *Megalobatrachus maximus* is the giant salamander of Japan, the largest of all the AMPHIBIA. It feeds on fishes, amphibians, worms, and insects, and may reach a length of over five feet. *Amphiuma means*, the Congo

" snake," is long and eel-shaped, and possesses two widely separated pairs of small legs. It occurs in the marshes and muddy streams of the southeastern United States, and feeds on crayfishes, mollusks and small fish.

Family SALAMANDRIDÆ. — This family contains the true salamanders and the newts or tritons. " Of the twenty-five species, only two are American, four are eastern Asiatic, and of the remaining nineteen, two are Algerian, while the rest live in Europe or in Asia Minor." (Gadow.) The two American species are *Diemyctylus viridescens* and *Triton torosus*.

FIG. 430. — The "hellbender," *Cryptobranchus*. (From Davenport, after the Standard Natural History.)

Diemyctylus viridescens, the crimson-spotted newt, is common in the ponds of the northern and eastern portions of the United States. It is about three and one-half inches long and has a row of crimson spots on either side. Its food consists principally of insect larvæ, worms, and small mollusks. The eggs are laid in April, May, or June, and a sort of " nest " of aquatic vegetation is constructed for each egg. The young live for a time on land under stones and logs, but return to the water after several years, becoming aquatic adults.

Triton torosus, the newt of western North America, is a large species reaching a length of six inches. It feeds on earthworms.

The common fire salamander of Europe is *Salamandra maculosa*, a species about six inches long. It is black, with bright yellow spots, and the glands of the skin secrete a poisonous substance. The enemies of salamanders are supposed to be " warned " by the conspicuous colors and will not attack this poisonous species.

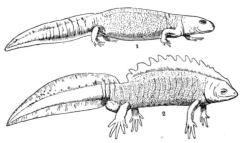

FIG. 431. — *Triton cristata*. 1, female; 2, male as he appears during the breeding season. (From Shipley and MacBride, after Gadow.)

Pronounced sexual dimorphism, *i.e.* differences between the male and female of the same species, is exhibited by *Triton cristatus* (Fig. 431), the European crested newt. The male is conspicuously colored and develops a high serrated crest during the breeding season.

Family AMBYSTOMIDÆ. — A common member of this family is *Ambystoma tigrinum* (Fig. 432). This species occurs from New York to California and south to central Mexico, and reaches a length of from six to nine inches. It is dark colored and marked with yellow spots. The larval form, called axolotl, was for a long time considered a separate species because the external gills persisted in the adult. Later it was discovered (1865) that if forced to breathe air the axolotls would shed their gills and become air-breathing salamanders of the species *Ambystoma tigrinum*.

FIG. 432. — The axolotl stage of the tiger salamander, *Ambystoma trigrinum*. (From the Cambridge Natural History.)

Family PLETHODONTIDÆ. — All except one species of the eight genera belonging to this family are confined to America. *Desmognathus fuscus* (Fig. 433), the dusky salamander, is a species four or five inches long that lives under stones and in other dark, moist places. The eggs of this species are laid in two long strings which the female takes care of in some place of concealment by winding them about her body. *Typhlotriton spelæus* is a blind species found in a cave in Missouri. The slimy salamander, *Plethodon glutinosus*, is common from Ohio to the Gulf of Mexico. It gives off a great quantity of slime when irritated. *Autodax lugubris* is an inhabitant of the western United States. It lays its eggs in holes in the branches of live-oak trees. *Spelerpes bilineatus* occurs in the Atlantic states. The only European species of the family PLETHO- DONTIDÆ is *Spelerpes fuscus*.

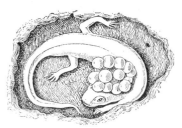

Order 3. Salientia. — Most of the AMPHIBIA, about nine hundred species of frogs and toads, belong to this order. They resemble one another very closely and are classified according to the characteristics of certain internal structures.

FIG. 433. — A lungless salamander, *Desmognathus fuscus;* female with eggs in a hole underground. (From the Cambridge Natural History, after Wilder.)

In North America there are seven families and about fifty-six species. Some of them (toads and tree-frogs) live on land, but others (water frogs) spend a large part of their time in the water. The terrestrial species possess only slightly webbed hind feet or no webs at all. They crawl or hop on land, burrow in the earth, or climb trees. Dark, moist hiding places are usually required, and most of them take to water only during the breeding season.

Suborder 1. Aglossa. — There are only a few toads in this suborder; all of them are tongueless and belong to the family AGLOSSIDÆ. *Pipa americana* inhabits the northern portion of South America; *Hymenochirus bættgeri* and *Xenopus lævis* are confined to Africa.

The Surinam toad, *Pipa americana* (Fig. 434), has a peculiar method of carrying its eggs. They are placed on the back of the female during copulation, are held there by a sticky secretion, and are gradually enveloped by the skin. Within the epidermal pouches thus formed the eggs develop and the tadpole stage is passed; then the young toad escapes as an air-breathing terrestrial animal.

Suborder 2. Linguata. — Most of the frogs and toads are included in the six families of this suborder.

Family 1. PELOBATIDÆ. — There are about twenty species, called spade-foot toads, in this family. One genus, *Scaphiopus*, with four species, occurs in North America. The spade-foot toads are burrowing AMPHIBIA, and usually have thick hind feet provided with a sharp spur for digging. The spade-foots of eastern North America belong to the species *Scaphiopus holbrookii*. They are seldom seen or heard except during the breeding season, when they come out of their burrows in great numbers and seek ponds in which to deposit their eggs.

Family 2. BUFONIDÆ. — This family includes over one hundred species of toads, most of which belong to the genus

FIG. 434. — The Surinam toad, *Pipa americana*. (From Mivart.)

Bufo. About fifteen species of this genus have been reported from North America.

Bufo americanus, the common toad of the northeastern United States, possesses a rough, warty skin, but does not cause the appearance of warts upon the hands of those who handle it, as is often supposed. Toads secrete a milky, poisonous fluid by means of glands in the skin, which protects them from many animals that would otherwise be important enemies. During the day they remain concealed in some dark, damp place, but at night they sally forth and hop about, feeding upon worms, snails, and especially insects, which they capture with their sticky tongue, as in the case of the frog (p. 430, Fig. 410). The value of toads as destroyers of insects injurious to vegetation is considerable. Kirkland has estimated that one toad is worth $19.44 in a single season because of the cutworms it devours.

During the winter toads hibernate in some sheltered nook, but as soon as conditions are favorable in the spring (about May 1) they emerge from their winter's home and proceed to water to deposit their eggs. At this time the males utter their sweet, tremulous calls. The eggs are laid in long strings. They develop very much like those of the frog (pp. 453–456).

Family 3. HYLIDÆ. — The tree-frogs are arboreal amphibians with adhesive discs on their toes and fingers which usually enable them to climb trees. They are provided with large vocal sacs and have a correspondingly loud voice. Of the more than

FIG. 435. — Brooding tree-frog, *Nototrema*, female, from Venezuela. In posterior part of trunk is opening of brood-pouch. (From Davenport's Zoology.)

one hundred and eighty species belonging to the family, fifteen occur in North America, and about one hundred and thirty in Central and South America. The North American species belong to the genera *Hyla*, *Acris*, *Chorophilis*, and *Smilisca*.

Hyla versicolor is the common tree-frog. It is about two inches long and has the power of slowly changing its color from white to stone-gray or brown and from white to green. These changes usually produce such a perfect harmony between the frog and its surroundings that the animal becomes practically invisible. The eggs are laid in May. They are attached in groups to plants at the surface of the water.

Hyla pickeringii, the spring peeper, has the discs on the fingers and toes so small that they are scarcely discernible.

Acris gryllus is called the cricket-frog. *Chorophilus nigritus*, the swamp tree-frog, has fingers and toes with minute discs. The brooding tree-frog, *Nototrema* (Fig. 435), of Venezuela, has a pouch with an opening in the hinder part of the trunk in which the eggs are placed and the young are reared.

Family 4. CYSTIGNATHIDÆ. — This family contains almost as many species (over one hundred and fifty) as the family HYLIDÆ, but only three species occur in North America. *Lithodytes latrans* and *Syrrophus marnockii* have been recorded from Texas, and *Lithodytes ricordii* from Florida. Most of the *Cystignathidæ* occur in Mexico and Central and South America. They form a comparatively heterogeneous group and are not easily defined.

Family 5. ENGYSTOMATIDÆ. — The narrow-mouthed toads as a rule inhabit the tropics. Only three of the seventy or more species are found in the United States. *Engystoma carolinense* ranges from South Carolina to Florida and west to Texas. Like other members of the family, its head is narrow and pointed and is thus adapted for the capture of ants and other small insects.

Family 6. RANIDÆ. — The true frogs occur in all parts of the globe except Australia, New Zealand, and southern South America. Only one genus, *Rana*, and about seventeen species are found in North America. Of these *Rana pipiens* (pp. 428–456) is the most common.

Rana catesbiana, the bullfrog, is found all over the United States east of the Rocky Mountains. It is the largest of the family in this country, often reaching a length of six or eight inches. Bullfrogs usually remain in or near water. They possess a deep, bass voice like that of a bull, and when a number are engaged in a noctural serenade they can be heard for a considerable distance. Their food consists of worms, insects, mollusks, other frogs, young water-fowl, etc. The eggs are deposited in ponds from the last of May until July. The tadpoles do not become frogs the first year as do those of the leopard-frog, but transform during the second or even the third year.

Rana clamitans, the green frog, is common in the ponds of eastern North America. It is little more than half as long as the bullfrog, from which it may be distinguished by the presence of two glandular folds of skin along the sides of the back.

Rana sylvatica, the eastern wood-frog, is not restricted to the vicinity of water, but usually lives in damp woods. It is found throughout the northeastern United States.

Rana palustris, the pickerel frog, inhabits the brooks and ponds of eastern North America, and is often found also in fields and meadows. It reaches a length of three inches.

Suborder 3. Costata. — The five genera and eight species of Salientia included in this suborder all belong to the single family Discoglossidæ. Only one species occurs in North America; this is the American discoglossoid toad, *Ascaphus truei,* of which only a single specimen from Humptulips, Washington, is known. An interesting European species is the obstetrical toad, *Alytes obstetricans* (Fig. 436). The male of this toad carries the egg strings with him wound about his hind limbs, and when the tadpoles are ready to emerge, takes to the water and allows them to escape.

Fig. 436. — The obstetrical frog, *Alytes obstetricans;* male, with string of eggs. (From Sedgwick's Zoology, after Claus.)

4. General Remarks on Amphibia

Color and Color Change. — The pigments in the skin of Amphibia are diffuse or granular. The latter are usually brown, black, yellow, or red and are contained in cells called chromatophores. The power of changing its colors is possessed by most Amphibia, but especially by the frogs. These are supplied with black pigment cells, interference cells, golden pigment cells, and sometimes red pigment cells.

The black chromatophores are branching cells which may spread out or contract, as shown in Figure 437. When expanded the pigment covers a larger area and consequently gives the skin a darker color. The yellow pigment is contained in spherical golden cells. The green color results from the reflection of light from granules of guanin in the skin through the golden cells. Most of the color changes are due to changes in the concentration of the black and yellow pigments.

Color changes are brought about by direct stimulation of the pigment cells or indirectly through the central nervous system.

Light is an important stimulus; it acts both directly and through the central nervous system. In a bright light the skin of the frog becomes light in color, whereas in the dark it changes to a darker hue. Temperature is another important factor. The pigment becomes more concentrated if the temperature is raised, and the skin changes to a lighter color. An expansion of the pigment and a darker color result from subjection to cold. Changes in the circulation, in the moisture of the frog's habitat, and in the chemical composition of the animal's environment affect the chromatophores and consequently produce changes in color.

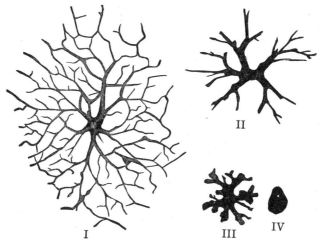

FIG. 437. — Pigment cells from the frog, in different states of extension. (From Holmes, after Verworn.)

In many cases the color changes are such as to cause the frog to resemble more closely its surroundings, and hence to conceal it.

Regeneration. — The power of regenerating lost parts is remarkably well developed in many AMPHIBIA. For example, the hand of a two-year-old axolotl was cut off, and in twelve weeks a complete hand was regenerated in its place (Barfurth). *Triton* has been observed to regenerate both limbs and tail. The SALIENTIA are apparently unable to regenerate lost parts to any considerable extent, except in the early stages. As a general rule, the younger tadpoles regenerate limbs or tail more readily than older specimens. There is a distinct advantage in the possession of the power of regeneration, since amphibians no doubt often escape from their enemies with mutilated limbs or tail, but are not seriously inconvenienced by the loss, as new parts rapidly grow out.

Breeding Habits. — Most AMPHIBIA are oviparous, and their eggs, as in the leopard-frog, are fertilized by the male after extrusion. In some of the CAUDATA and in the APODA, however, the eggs are fertilized before they are laid. A few species of CAUDATA bring forth their young alive; for example, the fire salamander, *Salamandra maculosa*, of Europe.

Several curious brooding habits have already been referred to; for example, the obstetrical toad (p. 467), the Surinam toad (p. 464), and the dusky salamander (p. 463). The " marsupial " frogs of the genus *Nototrema* should also be mentioned. They have a permanent pouch on the back in which the eggs develop. These frogs belong to the family *Hylidæ* and inhabit the tropical forest region of South America.

Hibernation. — Many AMPHIBIA bury themselves in the mud at the bottom of ponds in the autumn, and remain there in a dormant condition until the following spring. During this period of hibernation the vital processes are reduced; no air is taken into the lungs, since all necessary respiration occurs through the skin; no food is eaten, but the physiological activities are carried on by the use of nutriment stored in the body; and the temperature decreases until only slightly above that of the surrounding medium. The temperature of all cold-blooded vertebrates — cyclostomes, elasmobranchs, fish, amphibians, and reptiles — varies with the surrounding medium. Frogs cannot, however, be entirely frozen, as is often stated, since death ensues if the heart is frozen. In warm countries many AMPHIBIA seek a moist place of concealment in which to pass the hotter part of the year. They are said to æstivate.

Poisonous Amphibia. — The poison-glands of the leopard-frog (p. 430) and of the common toad (p. 464) have already been mentioned. Certain salamanders and newts are also provided with poison-glands. The poison acts upon the heart and the central nervous system. It has no effect upon the skin of individuals of the same species, but if inoculated into the blood it poisons even the individual that produces it. As a means of defense the poison is very effective, since an animal that has once felt the effects of an encounter with a poisonous amphibian will not soon repeat the experiment. Some of the most poisonous species, for example, *Salamandra maculosa*, are said to be warningly colored.

Prehistoric Amphibia. — Two orders of amphibians, the STEGOCEPHALIA and MICROSAURIA are known only from fossils. The STEGOCEPHALIA are salamander-like extinct animals (Fig. 438) that lived in the Carboniferous, Permian, and Triassic periods. They were probably fresh-water or terrestrial creatures. They possessed large, bony dermal plates on the dorsal surface of the skull and often on other parts of the body. Some of the STEGOCEPHALIA are called LABYRINTHODONTS because the dentine of their teeth is much folded.

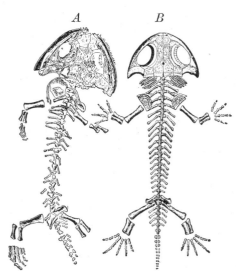

FIG. 438. — STEGOCEPHALIA. *Branchiosaurus amblystomus*. **A**, skeleton of adult. **B**, restoration of larva with branchial arches. (From Sedgwick's Zoology, after Credner.)

MICROSAURIA are small extinct animals probably belonging to the AMPHIBIA, though they are often placed with the reptiles.

The Economic Importance of the Amphibia.—The AMPHIBIA are practically all beneficial to man. Many of them are so rare as to be of little value, but the frogs and toads are of considerable importance. Frogs have been and are now used extensively for laboratory dissections and for physiological experiments and investigations. They seem in fact to have been "especially designed as a subject for biological research."

Frogs' legs are eagerly sought as an article of food. New York, Maryland, Virginia, Indiana, Ohio, Missouri, and California furnish the largest number for market. Frog hunters obtain an annual price of about $50,000 for their catch. "Frog farms" are now carried on profitably in Wisconsin, California, and several other states. Small frogs are often used as fish bait.

Frogs and toads are widely recognized as enemies of injurious insects. The toads are of special value, since they are accustomed to live in gardens where insects are most injurious (see p. 464). In France the gardeners even buy toads to aid them in keeping obnoxious insects under control.

CHAPTER XIX

SUBPHYLUM VERTEBRATA: CLASS V. REPTILIA [1]

THE reptiles constitute one of the most interesting, but generally least known, classes of the VERTEBRATA. They are cold-blooded; usually covered with scales and frequently with bony plates; and breathe with lungs. The popular notion that reptiles are slimy is erroneous. Contrary also to general belief, very few reptiles, at least in the United States, are dangerous to man, but the majority of them are harmless and many even beneficial. The reptiles that are living to-day are but a remnant of vast hordes that inhabited the earth's surface in prehistoric times. In fact, of the twenty orders of reptiles now recognized by herpetologists, only four possess living representatives, and one of these includes only one nearly exterminated species confined to New Zealand. The four orders of living reptiles are as follows: —

ORDER 1. TESTUDINATA (CHELONIA). — Turtles and Tortoises.

ORDER 2. RHYNCHOCEPHALIA. — One lizard-like reptile confined to New Zealand.

ORDER 3. CROCODILINI. — Crocodiles, Alligators, Gavials, and Caimans.

ORDER 4. SQUAMATA. — Chameleons, Lizards, and Snakes.

1. THE TURTLE

The turtle has been selected as a type of the REPTILIA. It will not be discussed in detail, as was the frog, but only the more important points regarding its external and internal anatomy and physiology will be mentioned.

---

[1] The reptiles are seldom used for laboratory work except in advanced courses, but occupy an important position in the vertebrate series. It is suggested that a comparison of the morphology and physiology of this group be made with those of the amphibians and birds. The classification and review of the orders and families of reptiles are intended for general reading and reference.

External Features. — The *shell* of the turtle is broad and flattened, and protects the internal organs. Even the head, limbs, and tail can be more or less completely withdrawn into the shell. The *neck* is long and very flexible. The *head* is flattened dorso-ventrally and triangular in shape. The *mouth* is large, but, instead of teeth, horny plates form the margin of the jaws. The *nostrils*, or external nares, are placed close together near the

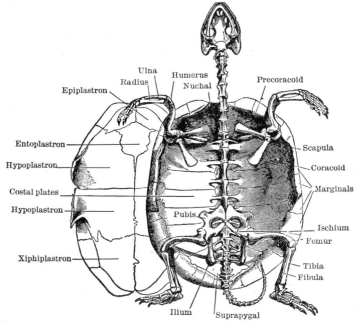

Fig. 439. — Skeleton of a turtle, *Cistudo lutaria*, ventral aspect ; plastron removed to one side. (From Zittel.)

anterior end of the snout. The *eyes*, situated one on each side of the head, are each guarded by three *eyelids:* (1) a short, thick, opaque upper lid; (2) a longer, thin lower lid; and (3) a transparent nictitating membrane, which moves over the eyeball from the anterior corner of the eye. Just behind the angle of the jaw on either side is a thin *tympanic membrane*. The *limbs* usually possess five *digits* each; most of the digits are armed with large *claws*, and connected one with another by a more or less complete *web*. The *skin* is thin and smooth on the head, but thick, tough, scaly, and much wrinkled over the exposed parts of the body.

Internal Anatomy and Physiology. — *The Skeleton.* — Since the life of the turtle is influenced so strongly by the skeleton, this system will be described first.

The *exoskeleton* (Fig. 439) consists of a convex dorsal portion, the *carapace*, and a flattened ventral portion, the *plastron;* these are usually bound together on each side by a bony bridge. Both carapace and plastron are usually covered by a number of symmetrically arranged *epidermal plates* forming a *shield;* the plates do not correspond either in number or arrangement to the bony plates beneath them. The number and shape of the plates vary

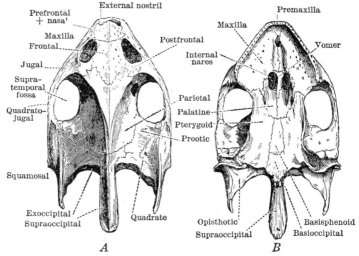

Fig. 440. — Skull of a turtle, *Trionyx gangeticus.* *A*, dorsal; *B*, ventral aspect. (From Zittel.)

according to the species, but are usually constant in individuals of the same species. The horny shields of the " Hawk's-bill Turtle " (Fig. 447) furnish the tortoise-shell of commerce. Beneath the shields are a number of *bony plates* formed by the dermis and closely united by sutures (Fig. 439).

The *endoskeleton* may, as in other vertebrates, be divided into an axial portion and an appendicular portion. The *skull* (Fig. 440) is very firm. It is devoid of teeth. The premaxillæ, maxillæ, and dentary bones possess sharp edges which are covered with horn, and form a *beak.* The quadrate bone is stationary; no transverse bone is present as in other reptiles; there is one occipital condyle, and only one sphenoidal bone, the basisphenoid. The supraoccipital has a prominent crest.

There are comparatively few *vertebræ* (Fig. 439) — usually eight cervical, ten thoracic, two sacral, and a variable number of caudal. The vertebræ of the neck move very freely upon one another by cup and ball joints. The thoracic or trunk vertebræ bear *ribs* which are closely united with the carapace. They lack transverse and articulating processes.

The *pectoral* and *pelvic girdles* (Fig. 439) are peculiarly situated within instead of outside of the ribs. They serve, in fact, as braces to keep the plastron and carapace apart. The *limbs* are almost typically pentadactyl.

The Digestive System. — Turtles feed on both plants and animals; some are entirely vegetarian. The animals preyed upon are water-fowl, small mammals, and many kinds of invertebrates. The flexible neck enables the turtle to rest on the bottom and reach out in all directions for food. The jaws of the snapping-turtle, *Chelydra serpentina,* are powerful enough to amputate a finger, or even, in large specimens, a hand.

The *digestive organs* are simple. The broad, soft *tongue* is attached to the floor of the mouth cavity; it is not protrusible. The two *posterior nares* are situated in the anterior part of the roof of the mouth. At the base of the tongue is a longitudinal slit, the *glottis,* and a short distance back of the angle of the jaw are the openings of the Eustachian tubes. The *pharynx* is thin-walled and very distensible; it leads into the more slender and thicker-walled *œsophagus.* The *stomach* opens by a *pyloric valve* into the *small intestine;* this is separated from the *large intestine* by the *ileocæcal valve.* The terminal portion of the alimentary canal is the *rectum;* it opens into the *cloaca.* There is no intestinal cæcum.

The *liver* discharges bile into the intestine through the bile-duct. Several pancreatic ducts lead from the *pancreas* to the intestine.

The Circulatory System. — The *heart* (Fig. 441) consists of two *auricles,* and a single *ventricle* which is divided into two by a per-forated septum. The venous blood from the body is carried by the postcaval vein and the two precaval veins into the sinus venosus and thence into the right auricle. From here it passes into the right side of the ventricle, and, when the latter contracts, is forced

out through the pulmonary artery, which sends a branch to each
lung, and through the left aorta which conveys blood to the viscera
and into the dorsal aorta.

The blood which is purified in the lungs is returned by the
pulmonary veins to the left auricle and thence into the left side
of the ventricle. This blood is pumped out through the right
aortic arch, which merges into the dorsal aorta. Because the
septum dividing
the ventricle into
two parts is per-
forated, the blood
that ¦ enters the
right aortic arch is
a mixture of puri-
fied blood from
the left auricle and
venous blood from
the right auricle.

Recent work in-
dicates that cer-
tain species of
turtles have a well
developed renal
portal system; the

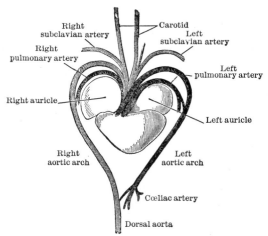

Right
subclavian artery
Right
pulmonary artery

Carotid
Left
subclavian artery

Left
pulmonary artery

Right auricle

Left auricle

Right
aortic arch

Left
aortic arch

Cœliac artery

Dorsal aorta

FIG. 441. — Heart and arteries of a turtle, *Chelydra*.
(From Gegenbaur.)

hepatic portal system shows an advance in development over the
condition as described in the frog (p. 439).

The Respiratory System. — Turtles breathe by means of *lungs*.
Air enters the mouth cavity by way of the nasal passages. The
glottis opens into the *larynx*, through which the air passes into the
trachea or windpipe. The larynx is supported by the *hyoid apparatus*. The trachea divides, sending one *bronchus* to each lung.
The lungs are more complicated than those of AMPHIBIA. The
bronchi branch a number of times, and the lung cavity is broken
up into many spaces, thus increasing the respiratory surface.

The shell of the turtle prevents the expansion and contraction
of the lungs by means of abdominal or thoracic muscles. Air
is therefore drawn in and expelled partly by the hyoid apparatus
and partly by alternately extending and drawing in the neck
and appendages. The air is thus pumped into the lungs or else
swallowed.

Many aquatic turtles possess a pair of thin-walled sacs (Fig. 442), one on either side of the cloaca, which are alternately filled with water and emptied through the anus. They have walls plentifully supplied with blood-vessels, and act as auxiliary breathing organs (compare sea-cucumber, p. 191, and nymph of dragon-fly, p. 305).

The Urinogenital Organs (Fig. 442). — *Excretion* is carried on by the two *kidneys.* Their secretions pass through the *ureters* into the cloaca, are stored in the *urinary bladder*, and then make their exit through the anus.

The sexes are separate. The *male organs* are a pair of *testes* and a pair of *vasa deferentia* through which the spermatozoa pass to the grooved copulatory organ, or *penis*, attached to the front wall of the cloaca. The *female organs* are a pair of *ovaries* and a pair of *oviducts;* the latter open into the cloaca.

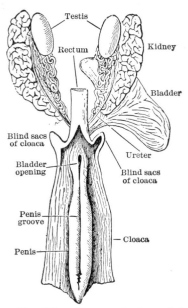

FIG. 442. — Cloaca and urinogenital organs of a turtle, *Chelydra serpentina.* (From Gegenbaur.)

Turtles are *oviparous.* The eggs, which are white, round or oval, and covered by a more or less hardened shell, are laid in the ground a few inches from the surface.

The Nervous System. — The *brain* (Fig. 443) is more highly developed than in the AMPHIBIA. The *cerebral hemispheres* are larger, and a distinction can be made between the superficial gray layer and the central white medulla. The *cerebellum* is also larger, indicating an increase in the power of correlating movements.

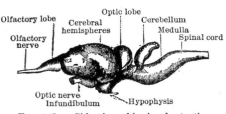

FIG. 443. — Side view of brain of a turtle. (From Wiedersheim.)

Sense-organs. — The *eye* is small. It has a round pupil and an iris which is usually dark in terrestrial forms, but often colored in aquatic turtles. The sense of *hearing* is fairly well developed, and turtles are easily frightened by noises. The sense of *smell* enables the turtle to distinguish between various kinds of food both in and out of the water. The skin over many parts of the body is very sensitive to *touch*.

2. A Brief Classification of Living Reptilia [1]

The four thousand or more species of living reptiles may be grouped into four orders: (1) the TESTUDINATA, containing about two hundred and twenty-five species of turtles and tortoises; (2) the RHYNCHOCEPHALIA, represented by a single New Zealand species; (3) the CROCODILINI, containing about twenty-three species of crocodiles, gavials, and alligators; and (4) the SQUAMATA, containing about three thousand seven hundred species of lizards, chameleons, and snakes. In most cases the orders, families, and subfamilies of reptiles are indicated by means of structural characters, such as the position of the teeth, the shape and arrangement of the bones of the skull, and the form of the vertebræ. Since these cannot be determined by the beginning student, they are mostly omitted from the following paragraphs.

Order 1. Testudinata (CHELONIA). — TURTLES and TORTOISES. — Reptiles with the body incased in a bony capsule; jaws without teeth; quadrate bone immovable; usually pentadactyl appendages.

Superfamily 1. CRYPTODIRA. — TESTUDINATA with the carapace covered with horny shields; neck bends in S-shaped curve in a vertical plane; pelvis not fused with the carapace.

Family 1. CHELYDRIDÆ. — SNAPPING-TURTLES. — CRYPTODIRA with small plastron; tail long; limbs, neck, and head large and cannot be withdrawn into shell; snout with hooked beak. Examples: *Chelydra*, *Macrochelys* (Fig. 444).

Family 2. KINOSTERNIDÆ. — MUSK- and MUD-TURTLES. — CRYPTODIRA possessing a nuchal plate with costiform processes underlying the marginals; eight bones in the plastron. Examples: *Kinosternon*, *Aromochelys*.

[1] I am indebted to Dr. Alexander G. Ruthven for the main divisions of this classification.

Family 3. DERMATEMYDIDÆ. — FRESH-WATER TURTLES of Southern Mexico and Central America. CRYPTODIRA with nuchal plate as in KINOSTERNIDÆ; nine bones in plastron. Examples: *Dermatemys, Staurotypus, Claudius.*

Family 4. PLATYSTERNIDÆ. — CRYPTODIRA without costiform processes on nuchal plate. Examples: *Platysternum* (a single species, *P. megacephalum*, in Burma, Siam, and China).

Family 5. TESTUDINIDÆ. — TORTOISES and most TURTLES. — CRYPTODIRA without costiform processes on nuchal plate; lateral temporal arch usually present; no parietosquamosal arch. Examples: *Testudo* (Fig. 446), *Chrysemys* (Fig. 445), *Emys.*

Superfamily 2. CHELONIIDEA (CHELONIDÆ + ATHECA). — SEA-TURTLES. — MARINE TESTUDINATA with paddle-shaped limbs.

Family 1. CHELONIIDÆ. — Four species inhabiting tropical and semitropical seas (Fig. 447).

Family 2. DERMOCHELYIDÆ. — The leathery turtle of tropical and semitropical seas (Fig. 448).

Superfamily 3. PLEURODIRA. — TESTUDINATA with neck bending laterally; pelvis fused with the shell.

Family 1. PELOMEDUSIDÆ. — FRESH-WATER TURTLES. — PLEURODIRA with neck completely retractile within the shell; carapace without nuchal shield; plastron of eleven bones. Examples: *Pelomedusa, Podocnemis, Sternothœrus.*

Family 2. CHELYDIDÆ. — FRESH-WATER TURTLES. — PLEURODIRA with neck not completely retractile within the shell; plastron of nine bones. Examples: *Hydraspis, Emydura.*

Superfamily 4. TRIONYCHOIDEA. — TESTUDINATA with soft, leathery skin, without horny shields.

Family 1. CARETTOCHELYDIDÆ. — TRIONYCHOIDEA with paddle-shaped limbs; neck not retractile. Example: *Carettochelys* (one species *C. insculpta* from New Guinea).

Family 2. TRIONYCHIDÆ. — SOFT-SHELLED TURTLES. — TRIONYCHOIDEA with digits broadly webbed; head and neck retractile, bending in vertical plane. Examples: *Trionyx* (Fig. 449), *Emyda.*

Order 2. Rhynchocephalia. — One genus of New Zealand lizard-like reptiles. Vertebræ biconcave, often containing remains of the notochord; immovable quadrate bone; parietal organ present. Example: *Sphenodon* (Fig. 450).

Order 3. Crocodilini. — CROCODILES, ALLIGATORS, GAVIALS, and CAIMANS. — Reptiles with procœlous vertebræ; nostril single, at end of snout; anterior appendages with five digits, posterior with four and traces of a fifth; anal opening a longitudinal slit.

Family 1. GAVIALIDAE. — GAVIALS. — CROCODILINI with long, slender snout. Example: *Gavialis* (Fig. 451).

Family 2. CROCODILIDAE. CROCODILES, ALLIGATORS, and CAIMANS. — CROCODILINI with broad, rounded snout. Examples: *Crocodilus, Alligator, Caiman* (Fig. 451).

Order 4. Squamata. — CHAMELEONS, LIZARDS, and SNAKES. —. Reptiles usually with horny epidermal scales; vertebræ usually procœlous; quadrate bones movable.

Suborder 1. Rhiptoglossi. — CHAMELEONS. — SQUAMATA with body laterally compressed; tail prehensile; tongue vermiform, projectile; well-developed limbs; digits in groups of two and three, for grasping (see Fig. 452).

Family 1. CHAMÆLEONTIDÆ. — CHAMELEONS. — With characters of the suborder. Examples: *Chamæleon* (Fig. 452), *Brookesia, Rhampholeon.*

Suborder 2. Sauria (LACERTILIA). — LIZARDS. — SQUAMATA with transverse anal opening; paired copulatory organs; at least a vestige of a pectoral arch; usually well-developed limbs; rami of lower jaw united. (Only ten of the twenty families are listed below.)

Family 1. GECKONIDÆ. — GECKO. — SAURIA with four legs; eyes usually without movable lids; tongue protrusible; many with adhesive digits for climbing. Examples: *Gecko* (Fig. 453), *Gymnodactylus, Sphærodactylus.*

Family 2. AGAMIDÆ. — OLD-WORLD LIZARDS. — SAURIA with well-developed limbs; eyes with complete lids; tongue broad and short; teeth usually differentiated into incisors, canines, and molars (heterodont), and always situated on the edge of the jaw (acrodont). Examples: *Draco* (Fig. 454), *Gonycephalus, Calotes.*

Family 3. IGUANIDÆ. — NEW-WORLD LIZARDS. — SAURIA resembling AGAMIDAE, but usually with teeth similar (homodont) and fastened in a groove (pleurodont). Examples: *Anolis, Sceloporus, Phrynosoma* (Fig. 457), *Iguana* (Fig. 456).

Family 4. ANGUIDÆ. — OLD and NEW-WORLD LIZARDS. SAURIA with teeth in a groove; anterior part of tongue thin, and retractile into posterior part; limbs present or absent; body protected by bony plates.

Family 5. HELODERMATIDÆ. — BEADED LIZARDS. — SAURIA with grooved teeth; poisonous; tongue bifid, protractile; limbs short but strong. Example: *Heloderma* (Fig. 459).

Family 6. VARANIDÆ. — MONITORS. — SAURIA with tongue long, smooth, deeply bifid and retractile; tail long; limbs well developed. Example: *Varanus.*

Family 7. TEIIDÆ. — NEW-WORLD LIZARDS. — SAURIA with tongue long and bifid, with scale-like papillæ; limbs normal or reduced. Examples: *Ameiva, Cnemidophorus.*

Family 8. AMPHISBÆNIDÆ. — WORM LIZARDS. — Vermiform SAURIA with short tail; limbs absent (except in *Chirotes*); girdles reduced; eyes and ears concealed; skin divided into regular rings. Examples: *Amphisbæna, Monopeltis, Lepidosternon.*

Family 9. LACERTIDÆ. — TYPICAL OLD-WORLD LIZARDS. — SAURIA with well-developed, pentadactyl limbs, with sharp claws; tail long, brittle; tongue long, bifid, with papillæ or folds. Examples: *Lacerta, Acanthodactylus, Eremias.*

Family 10. SCINCIDÆ. — SKINKS. — SAURIA with tongue scaly, and only slightly nicked; limbs may be reduced or absent; strongly developed bony plates on head and body. Examples: *Mabuia, Lygosoma, Eumeces.*

Suborder 3. Serpentes (OPHIDIA). — SNAKES. — Elongated SQUAMATA without limbs; anal opening transverse; copulatory organs paired; without movable eyelids, tympanic cavity, urinary bladder and pectoral arch; rami of lower jaw connected by ligament. (Four of the nine families and several of the subfamilies are not included in the following list.)

Family 1. TYPHLOPIDÆ. — BURROWING SNAKES. — SER-
PENTES with reduced eyes covered by scales; without
teeth in lower jaw; pelvis represented by vestiges.
Examples: *Typhlops, Helminthophis.*

Family 2. GLAUCONIIDÆ. — BURROWING SNAKES. — SER-
PENTES resembling the TYPHLOPIDÆ; lower jaw toothed;
vestiges of pelvis and hind limbs. Examples: *Glauconia, Anomalepis.*

Family 3. BOIDÆ. — PYTHONS and BOAS. — SERPENTES
usually large, with vestiges of pelvis and hind limbs;
ventral scales transversely enlarged; eyes functional
and free.

Subfamily 1. PYTHONINÆ. PYTHONS. — Examples: *Loxo-
cemus, Liasis, Python* (Fig. 460).

Subfamily 2. BOINÆ. — BOAS. — Examples: *Epicrates,
Boa, Ungalia.*

Family 4. COLUBRIDÆ. — HARMLESS and POISONOUS
SNAKES. — SERPENTES with facial bones movable; both
jaws toothed.

Series **A**. AGLYPHA. — COLUBRIDÆ with solid teeth, not grooved
or tubular. Non-venomous.

Subfamily 1. COLUBRINÆ. — TYPICAL HARMLESS SNAKES.
— Examples: *Thamnophis* (Fig. 461), *Zamenis, Elaphe.*

Series **B**. OPISTHOGLYPHA. — COLUBRIDÆ with grooved fangs in
the rear of the upper jaw. Venomous.

Subfamily 2. HOMALOPSINÆ. — RIVER SNAKES. — Examples: *Hypsirhina, Homalopsis.*

Subfamily 3. DIPSADOMORPHINÆ. — Examples: *Tantilla,
Philodryas, Oxyrhopus.*

Series **C**. PROTEROGLYPHA. — COLUBRIDÆ with fangs in the
front of the upper jaw. Venomous.

Subfamily 4. HYDRINÆ. — SEA-SNAKES. — Examples:
Hydrophis, Distira, Platurus.

Subfamily 5. ELAPINÆ. — COBRAS and CORAL-SNAKES. —
Examples: *Naja* (Fig. 462), *Elaps, Denisonia.*

Family 5. VIPERIDÆ. — THICK-BODIED POISONOUS SNAKES.
— Poisonous SERPENTES with a pair of large perforated
fangs.

Subfamily 1. VIPERINÆ. — TRUE VIPERS. — Examples:
Vipera, Atractaspis.

Subfamily 2. CROTALINÆ. — PIT-VIPERS. — Examples: *Crotalus* (Fig. 466), *Agkistrodon* (Figs. 463 and 464), *Lachesis.*

3. REVIEW OF THE ORDERS AND FAMILIES OF LIVING REPTILES

Order 1. Testudinata. — TURTLES and TORTOISES. — The TESTUDINATA are reptiles with a short, stout body provided with a shell — a structural feature that distinguishes them from other animals as effectively as wings and feathers do the birds. They are without teeth; the neck is very flexible; and the limbs are fitted for creeping, running, or swimming. The position of the pectoral and pelvic girdles within instead of outside of the ribs is peculiar. They all deposit eggs in sand or earth, where they are left to develop. Some turtles are carnivorous; others are herbivorous.

America is the richest of all countries in TESTUDINATA. Three of the eleven families — DERMATEMYDIDÆ, KINOSTERNIDÆ, and CHELYDRIDÆ — are now restricted to North and Central America. Most of the land and freshwater turtles hibernate in the earth during the winter, but in warmer countries they sleep during the hotter months (æstivate).

Family CHELYDRIDÆ. — SNAPPING-TURTLES. — Only three species belong to this family. *Chelydra serpentina*, the

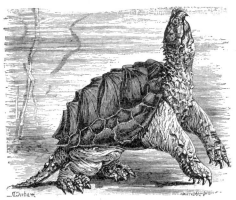

FIG. 444. — The alligator turtle, *Macrochelys lacertina.* (From Gadow.)

common snapping-turtle, inhabits fresh-water ponds and streams of North America east of the Rocky Mountains and southward to Ecuador. It is a voracious, carnivorous animal feeding on fish, frogs, water-fowl, etc., and does not hesitate to attack man with its formidable beak, often inflicting severe wounds. The plastron is very small and offers little protection for the body. *Chelydra rossignonii* is a native of Mexico and Guatemala, differing only slightly from *C. serpentina*.

The alligator snapping-turtle, *Macrochelys lacertina* (Fig. 444), lives in the streams of the southeastern United States. It is the largest North American turtle, attaining a weight of one hundred and forty pounds and a length of shell of twenty-eight inches. It has "a head as large as that of a bull-terrier and jaws that can chop up an ordinary broom handle," and a bad temper as well. The flesh of the snapping-turtle is a regular article of food in certain localities.

Family KINOSTERNIDÆ. — MUSK- and MUD-TURTLES. — These are all confined to America. There are three species of musk-turtles belonging to the genus *Aromochelys*, and eleven species of mud-turtles of the genus *Kinosternon*.

The common musk-turtle, *Aromochelys odoratus*, is an inhabitant of the muddy streams of the eastern United States. It has a carapace three or four inches long, a large head, and broadly

FIG. 445.—The painted terrapin, *Chrysemys picta*. (From Gadow.)

webbed feet. It is voracious and carnivorous. The disagreeable odor it emits when captured has given it its name.

The common mud-turtle, *Kinosternon pennsylvanicum*, shares the habitat of the musk-turtle, and resembles the latter in size and in habits.

Family TESTUDINIDÆ. — TURTLES, TERRAPINS, and TORTOISES. — There are twenty-two genera and about one hundred and ten species in this family. Space will permit a brief discussion of only six or eight of these.

The painted terrapin, *Chrysemys picta* (Fig. 445), inhabits the ponds and sluggish rivers of eastern North America. It loves to sun itself upon a log or protruding rock, from which it slides off into the water when disturbed. It feeds on aquatic insects, tadpoles, fishes, and water-plants. The shells of the painted terrapin are beautifully colored and are often carefully cleaned and then varnished, in which condition they make very pretty ornaments.

The diamond-back terrapin, *Malacoclemmys palustris*, is famous as an article of food. It lives in the salt marshes of the Atlantic coast. Persistent persecution by market hunters has caused a great decrease in the number of these animals and a corresponding increase in their value. The price has risen from twenty-five cents for a large specimen to seventy dollars per dozen for small ones (Hornaday).

The spotted or pond turtle, *Clemmys guttatus*, is abundant in the ponds, marshes, and streams of the eastern United States. Like the painted terrapin, they may often be seen in groups sunning themselves on floating logs. They feed on dead fish, insect larvæ, and probably water-plants. The western pond turtle, *Clemmys marmorata*, is the only common fresh-water turtle along the Pacific coast.

Blanding's turtle, *Emys blandingii*, is a fresh-water form common in the Middle States. Its carapace measures about eight inches in length and its plastron is hinged so that it can be partially closed. This species is not as aquatic as the TESTUDINIDÆ already described, but is often found wandering about on wet ground. Unlike the more aquatic turtles, it can eat out of water. *Emys orbicularis* is the European pond turtle.

Terrapene carolina is the common box turtle. The plastron of this species, and of the five other species belonging to the genus *Terrapene*, is hinged transversely near the

FIG. 446. — A giant tortoise, *Testudo abingdoni*. (From Gadow.)

center so that the shell can be closed completely when the animal is in danger. *Terrapene carolina* has a highly arched carapace about five inches in length. It occurs in the Northeastern states and is terrestrial in habits, living in dry woods and feeding on berries, tender shoots, earthworms, and insects.

The gopher tortoise, *Gopherus polyphemus*, lives in burrows in dry, sandy areas of the southeastern United States. It is a slow-moving, herbivorous, terrestrial animal. The common Greek tortoise of southern Europe belongs to the genus *Testudo*.

The giant tortoises (Fig. 446) are interesting not only because of their great size, but also because they are living representatives of the fauna of past ages. Six species inhabit the Galapagos Islands off the west coast of South America; four species occur in the Aldabra Islands of the Indian Ocean, and four species inhabit the Mauritius-Rodriguez Group of islands. Some of those captured on the Galapagos Islands weigh over three hundred pounds and are probably over four hundred years old. These giant tortoises live on cacti, leaves, berries, and coarse grass. They have been persecuted for food and for scientific purposes so persistently that extermination in a wild state seems certain within a few years.

Family CHELONIIDÆ. — SEA-TURTLES. — These are the giant water turtles. They inhabit tropical and semitropical seas and come to land only to lay their eggs on sandy beaches. Their limbs are modified as paddles for swimming. The two species of loggerhead turtles belong to the genus *Thalassochelys*. Some individuals have a carapace four feet in length and weigh five hundred pounds.

FIG. 447. — The hawk's-bill turtle, *Chelonia imbricata*, young. (From Gadow.)

The green turtle, *Chelonia mydas*, so called because of the green color of its fat, is almost as large as the loggerhead. It is famous as an article of food, and is common in the markets of the large cities of the eastern United States. It feeds largely on aquatic vegetation and probably eats fish, and other animals also.

The hawk's-bill or tortoise-shell turtle, *Chelonia imbricata* (Fig. 447), has the shields of its carapace arranged like the shingles on a roof. These shields, of which a large specimen yields about eight pounds, are the " tortoise " shell of commerce. The shields are detached either after the turtles have been killed and immersed in boiling water or after the living animals have been suspended over a fire. In the latter case the animals are liberated and allowed to regenerate a new covering of shields. The regenerated shields, however, are not, as supposed, of commercial value. Hawk's-bill turtles are smaller than the loggerhead and green turtles, reaching a weight of about thirty pounds and a carapace length of thirty inches. They are carnivorous, feeding largely on fish and mollusks.

Family DERMOCHELYIDÆ. — LEATHERY TURTLE. — The single species of this family, *Sphargis coriacea* (Fig. 448), is the largest of all living turtles, sometimes attaining a weight of a thousand pounds. It has a leathery covering over the shell instead of horny shields. It inhabits tropical and semitropical seas and goes to land only to deposit its eggs. The limbs are modified as flippers for swimming. The flesh is not used for food.

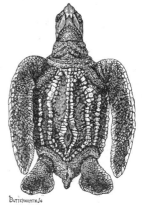

Family CHELYDIDÆ. — This is one of the families of turtles, the members of which bend the neck laterally. They are all fresh-water, semiaquatic species and are found in South America, Australia, and New Guinea.

FIG. 448. — The leathery turtle, *Sphargis coriacea*, young. (From Gadow.)

Family TRIONYCHIDÆ. — SOFT-SHELLED TURTLES. — The six genera and about twenty-four species belonging to this family inhabit fresh-water ponds and streams in various parts of North America, Africa, Asia, and the East Indies. The four species occurring in North America are members of the genus *Trionyx*. They are thoroughly aquatic and have large, strongly webbed feet. The body is flat; the neck is long and very flexible; the nose terminates in a small proboscis; and the shell is leathery, without shields, and with only a few scattered bones.

Trionyx ferox (Fig. 449) is the southern soft-shelled turtle of North America,

FIG. 449. — The soft-shelled turtle, *Trionyx ferox*. (From Gadow.)

occurring in muddy-bottomed streams and ponds of Georgia, Florida, and Louisiana. In the Central United States the common species is the spiny soft-shelled turtle, *Trionyx spinifer*. These turtles are voracious and carnivorous, feeding on fish, frogs, young water-fowl, and mollusks. When attacked they are very vicious. The shell as well as other parts of the animals are used as food and are regularly sold in the markets.

Order 2. Rhynchocephalia. — There is only a single living representative of this order — *Sphenodon punctatum* (Fig. 450). This reptile, which formerly inhabited all of the main islands of

Fig. 450. — *Sphenodon punctatum*. (From Gadow.)

New Zealand, is now restricted to some small islets in the Bay of Plenty, and will probably soon be entirely exterminated. It is about two feet long and resembles a lizard in form. It lives in burrows, is nocturnal, and feeds on other live animals.

One of its most striking peculiarities is the presence of a well-developed parietal organ or pineal eye in the roof of the cranium, which has all the characters of a simple eye. It is also the only reptile without a copulatory organ. Numerous skeletal characteristics are like those possessed by some of the oldest fossil reptiles, and the ancestors of living reptiles were apparently much like this queer relic of past ages.

Order 3. Crocodilini. — Crocodiles, Alligators, Gavials, and Caimans (Fig. 451). These reptiles are lizard-like in form, but have the jaws extended into a long snout. The nostrils are at the end of the snout and the eyes protrude from the head so that the crocodilians can float at the surface with only these parts above the water. The skin is thick and leathery, covered with horny epidermal scales, and with dorsal, and sometimes ventral bony plates somewhat like those in the shell of the turtles. The nostrils and ears are provided with valves and are closed when the animal is under water.

The limbs are well developed. There are five digits on the fore limbs and four more or less webbed digits on the hind limbs.

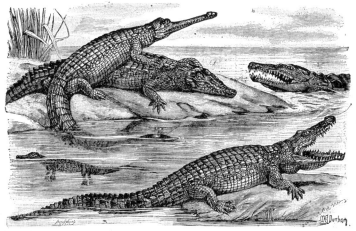

FIG. 451. — CROCODILINI. A long-snouted gavial (*Gavialis gangeticus*) on top of an American crocodile (*Crocodilus americanus*). A Nile crocodile (*Crocodilus niloticus*) in the foreground. A "mugger" (*Crocodilus palustris*) in the right upper corner. Notice peculiar floating attitude of young. (From Gadow.)

The tail is a laterally compressed swimming organ. The anus is a longitudinal slit. Two pairs of musk glands are present, — one on the throat, and one in the cloaca.

Some of the peculiarities of the internal structures are as follows: The vertebræ are mostly procœlous; all of the cervical and trunk vertebræ and some of the caudal vertebræ bear ribs, a number of which are attached by two heads; there is a sternum, but no clavicles; the teeth are conical and are shed at intervals, being replaced by others which grow up beneath them; they are set in sockets (thecodont) on the premaxillæ, maxillæ, and dentary bones; the tongue is flat and non-protrusible, but can be raised and lowered, serving as a valve to prevent water from entering the œsophagus when the mouth is opened under water; palatal folds separate the upper air-passage from the lower food-passage; there are no salivary glands, no intestinal cæcum, and no bladder; the lungs are partitioned off from the rest of the organs in the body-cavity by a membrane which assists in respiration and is analogous to the diaphragm of mammals; the ventricle of the heart is completely divided into two by a septum, whereas that of other reptiles is only partially divided; the cerebellum is more highly developed than in the other reptiles; the penis resembles that of the turtles (see Fig. 442).

Family GAVIALIDÆ. — Two of the twenty-one species of living CROCODILINI belong to this family. *Gavialis gangeticus*, the Indian gavial, lives in northern India, and *Tomistoma schlegeli*, the Malayan gavial, lives in Borneo and Sumatra. The Indian gavial (Fig. 451) reaches a length of twenty feet or more, and has a very long, slender snout. It inhabits the Ganges and Brahmaputra rivers and their territories. The food of the gavial consists principally of fish; man is seldom if ever attacked.

Family CROCODILIDÆ. — This family contains four genera — *Crocodilus*, *Osteolœmus*, *Caiman*, and *Alligator*. *Crocodilus americanus*, the American crocodile (Fig. 451), is an inhabitant of Florida, Mexico, and Central and South America. It has a triangular head becoming very narrow toward the snout. It attains a length of fourteen feet. In Florida the crocodile digs burrows in the bank in which to hide; the openings are entirely or partly under water. The American crocodile is not dangerous to man.

The African crocodile, *Crocodilus niloticus* (Fig. 451), is one of the few man-eating species, and has probably destroyed more human beings than any other kind of wild animal in the dark continent. Formerly it was held sacred by the Egyptians, and many specimens were preserved as mummies.

The other nine species of the genus *Crocodilus* live in various parts of the world — *C. intermedius*, the Orinoco crocodile, in Venezuela; *C. rhombifer*, the Cuban crocodile, in Cuba; *C. moreletti*, the Guatemala crocodile, in Guatemala and Honduras; and the others in Africa, Australia, Siam, Java,

India, Malaysia, or Madagascar. The salt-water crocodile, *C. porosus*, which occurs in India and Malaysia, is a man-eating species.

The five species of caimans occur in Central and tropical South America. The spectacled caiman, *Caiman sclerops*, ranges from southern Mexico southward into Argentina. It reaches a length of eight feet. The largest American crocodile is the black caiman, *Caiman niger*, of the upper Amazon. Some of these animals are said to be twenty feet long.

There are two species of the genus *Alligator;* the American alligator, *A. mississippiensis*, inhabits the southeastern United States; and the Chinese alligator, *A. sinensis*, is found only in China. The American alligator has a broad, blunt snout, and is stouter, less active, and less vicious than the crocodiles. It attains a length of sixteen feet, but most of the large specimens have been killed for their hides, so that probably none now exist in the wild state over twelve feet long. The habits of the alligator are similar to those of the crocodile. The nest is a mound of earth and rotting vegetation. From twenty to forty eggs are deposited in this nest and left to hatch without any assistance from the parents.

The Chinese alligator inhabits the Yangtse-Kiang River of China. It is only six feet long.

Order 4. Squamata. — CHAMELEONS, LIZARDS, and SNAKES. These animals resemble one another rather closely in structure. They are all protected by horny, epidermal scales, and often by dermal plates of bone. The horny layer of the skin is cast off periodically. The anus is a transverse slit and there are two copulatory organs in the male. The legless lizards and snakes have undoubtedly evolved from ancestors with limbs. In all the living Squamata the limbs, when present, are adapted for walking on land.

Suborder 1. Rhiptoglossi. — CHAMELEONS. — A number of different kinds of SQUAMATA are called Chameleons, but the true Chameleons belong to the single family CHAMÆLEONTIDÆ of the suborder RHIPTOGLOSSI. There are fifty species, all of which live in Africa and Madagascar; two of them also occur in Spain, India, and Ceylon. The three genera are *Chamæleon* (Fig. 452) with forty-five species, *Brookesia* with three species, and *Rhampholeon* with two species.

The Chameleons differ from other SQUAMATA both in external features and in internal structure. The body is laterally compressed; the tail is prehensile, is not brittle, and cannot be regenerated if lost; the limbs are long and slender, and the digits are grouped so that two are permanently opposed to the other three; the head usually bears a prominent crest; no tympanum and tympanic cavity are present; the pectoral girdle lacks clavicles and interclavicles; the eyelids are united into a single fold with a small central opening; the eyes are moved separately, causing the animal to squint. The tongue is club-shaped and covered by a sticky secretion; it can be projected by muscles and by the inflow of blood to a distance of over six inches, and is used like that of the frog (p. 430, Fig. 410) for capturing live insects which constitute its entire food. The skin is covered with granules; it is shed several times a year, coming off in large flakes when the body is rubbed against stones or the limbs of trees.

FIG. 452. — The chameleon, *Chamæleon vulgaris.* (From Gadow.)

One of the features that has made the chameleons famous is the power of rapidly changing their colors. This is brought about with the aid of chromatophores (see p. 467) and is apparently partly under the control of the animal and partly due to external stimuli, such as light and temperature.

A few chameleons are viviparous, but most of them deposit their eggs in the ground. In northern Africa the animals become fat in the autumn and hibernate in the ground during the winter.

The common chameleon of North Africa, Syria, and Asia Minor is *Chamæleon vulgaris* (Fig. 452). It is usually greenish in color and reaches a length of from eight inches to a foot, about half of which consists of the tail.

Suborder 2. Sauria. — LIZARDS. — The lizards constitute a very diversified group of reptiles. They usually have an elongated body and four well-developed limbs that are used for running, clinging, climbing, or digging. Some have no limbs or only vestiges, but the pectoral and pelvic girdles are always present and there is usually a trace of a sternum. The tail is generally long; it is easily broken off, but a new organ is soon regenerated, which, however, does not possess vertebræ. The eyelids are movable except in some of the degenerate burrowing forms in which the eyes have become concealed beneath the skin. The skin is covered with small scales.

Lizards are in most cases oviparous, and the eggs are protected by a parchment-like shell. They feed largely on insects, worms, and other small animals, but many are exclusively vegetarian. The more than fifteen hundred and twenty-five species of lizards are placed in two hundred and fifty-seven genera and twenty families. Only eight of these families are reviewed in the following paragraphs.

Family GECKONIDÆ. — GECKOS (Fig. 453). — This is a large family containing forty-nine genera and about two hundred

FIG. 453. — Geckos, *Hemidactylus turicus* (left) ; *Tarentola mauritanica* (right). (From Gadow.)

and seventy species. Geckos inhabit all the warmer parts of the globe, are harmless, and usually nocturnal. Many of them have lamellæ under the toes (Fig. 453), which enable them to climb over trees, rocks, walls, and ceilings. Three species occur in North America — the reef geckos, *Sphærodactylus notatus*, of Florida, Cuba, and the Bahamas, the tubercular gecko, *Phyllodactylus tuberculosus*, of Lower California, and the cape gecko, *P. unctus*, also of Lower California.

The genus *Sphærodactylus* contains, besides reef geckos, seventeen species inhabiting Central and South America and the West Indies. The reef gecko is about three inches long. It has been reported from Key West, Florida. *Phyllodactylus* is another large genus; its twenty-five species occur in tropical South America, Africa, Australia, and islands in the Mediterranean.

Family AGAMIDÆ. — OLD WORLD LIZARDS. — These lizards can be readily distinguished by the position of their teeth, which are set on the edges of the jawbones (acrodont dentition) and not in grooves or sockets. There are thirty genera and about two hundred species in the family.

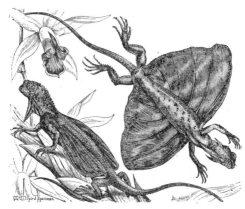

FIG. 454. — The flying dragon, *Draco volans*.
(From Gadow.)

The flying-dragon, *Draco volans* (Fig. 454), is a species whose sides are expanded into thin membranes supported by ribs. These membranes are employed as a parachute when leaping from tree to tree, and are folded when not in use. It is about ten inches long and inhabits the Malay Peninsula, Sumatra, Java, and Borneo. Members of the genus *Calotes* have the power of changing their colors rapidly. Another interesting genus is *Chlamydosaurus*, which includes the frilled lizard, *C. kingi* (Fig. 455). This species inhabits Queensland and northern Australia and reaches a length of about three feet. The skin at the sides of the neck is expanded into a sort of frill, and when the animal is irritated, this frill is extended by means of rib-like horns of the hyoid apparatus.

Family IGUANIDÆ.— NEW WORLD LIZARDS. — All but three of the forty-eight genera be-

FIG. 455. — The frilled lizard, *Chlamydosaurus kingi*, at bay. (From Gadow.)

longing to this family are confined to America. The habits of
these lizards vary considerably. Some are arboreal; others terrestrial; and still others semiaquatic. The anoles, often called
chameleons, the iguanas, the swifts, and the horned "toads" are
the best-known groups.

The genus *Anolis* contains over one hundred species. These
are mostly small, with a long, slender tail. They have the power
of changing color rapidly and are popularly called "chameleons."
They are enabled to run about on smooth, vertical surfaces by
lamellæ under the central portion of each toe. *Anolis carolinensis*,
the American "chame-
leon," is common in
the southeastern
United States and in
Cuba.

The iguanas range
from the southwestern
United States south-
ward through tropical
South America. The
marine iguana, *Am-
blyrhynchus cristatus*,
lives on the Galapagos
Islands. Colonies of
these iguanas, many

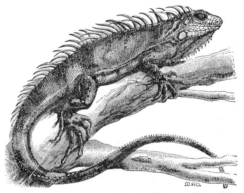

Fig. 456. — The common iguana, *Iguana tuberculata*.
(From Gadow.)

of the individuals being over four feet long, inhabit the seacoast
and feed on seaweed. The common iguana, *Iguana tuberculata*
(Fig. 456), reaches a length of six feet. It inhabits tropical
America and is a favorite article of food. It loves to bask in
the sun, lying stretched out on a stone fence or the limbs of a
tree. The food of this iguana consists largely of insects, but it
will also take small animals, and certain kinds of vegetation.

The swifts belong to the genera *Uta* and *Sceloporus*. They
are common in western North America, Mexico, and Central
America. Most of them are small, and, as their popular name
implies, very active. The sixteen species of small-scaled swifts
are included in the genus *Uta*. They live in the arid regions of the
Southwestern states and are all terrestrial. The genus *Sceloporus*
contains about thirty-five species of spiny swifts. The scales on
the dorsal surface of the body terminate in sharp, spine-like points.

The horned "toads" (genus *Phrynosoma*, Fig. 457) occur in the western United States and in Mexico. They live in hot, dry regions, many of them inhabiting the deserts, where they run about in search of insects for food. They are viviparous.

FIG. 457. — The horned "toad," *Phrynosoma coronatum*. (From Gadow.)

Horned "toads" can be kept very easily in captivity if placed in a warm, dry place and fed on meal worms.

Family ANGUIDÆ. — OLD AND NEW WORLD LIZARDS. — These lizards have a deep fold on each side of the body. Most of them have poorly developed limbs or none at all. The glass "snakes," *Ophisaurus apus* of Europe, and *O. ventralis* of America, have no limbs and move, as do snakes, by lateral undulations. They can be distinguished from true snakes by the presence of movable eyelids and an ear opening. Their name is due to the extreme brittleness of the tail. Another species, called the "blind-worm" or "slow-worm," *Anguis fragilis* (Fig. 458), inhabits Europe, western Asia, and Algeria.

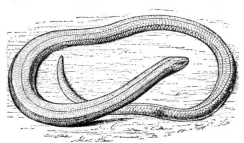

FIG. 458. — A limbless lizard, *Anguis fragilis*, the "slow-worm" or "blind-worm." (From Shipley and MacBride.)

It looks like a large, brightly colored worm, but is not blind, since it has well-developed eyes.

Family HELODERMATIDÆ. — BEADED LIZARDS. — The two species included in this family are the gila monster, *Heloderma suspectum*, of Arizona and New Mexico, and the beaded lizard, *H. horridum*, of Mexico and Central America. The gila monster (Fig. 459) is the only poisonous lizard of the United States.

It has a stout body and is conspicuously colored with bright red and black. A large specimen measures a foot and one half in length. Gila monsters possess grooved fangs on the lower jaw, and, when fighting, viciously grasp their prey and throw themselves on their back, thus allowing the poison to flow down into the wound.

FIG. 459. — The Gila monster, *Heloderma suspectum.* (From Gadow.)

The bite is fatal to small animals and dangerous to man.

Family AMPHISBÆNIDÆ. — WORM LIZARDS. — These are limbless, burrowing lizards resembling worms in appearance. There are about ten genera and sixty species known from both the Old and New Worlds. Of these only one, the Florida worm lizard, *Rhineura floridana*, is found in the United States. This species is restricted to the Florida peninsula. It is about eight inches long.

Family LACERTIDÆ. — TYPICAL OLD-WORLD LIZARDS. — There are seventeen genera and about ninety-six species of lizards that are included in this family. They all possess well-developed limbs, and a long, fragile tail. The green lizard, *Lacerta viridis*, is a species common in central and southern Europe. *Lacerta vivipara* of Europe is viviparous.

Family SCINCIDÆ. — SKINKS. — The skinks are found in many parts of the globe. In North America there are two genera and fifteen species. *Eumeces quinquelineatus*, the five-lined or blue skink, is the species common in the Eastern and Central states. The young are black with a longitudinal yellow stripe on the back and two on either side, and a blue tail. The females " retain dull stripes through life, but the males become uniform, dull olive-brown on the body and bright red about the head." This color change has been the cause of several specific and common names. The length of this skink is about nine inches.

Suborder 3. Serpentes. — SNAKES. — The snakes resemble the lizards and chameleons in many of their anatomical features. They differ from them in at least four respects: (1) the right and left halves of the lower jaw are not firmly united, but are connected by an elastic band; (2) there is no pectoral girdle; (3) the urinary bladder is absent; and (4) the brain case is closed anteriorly.

Snakes are covered with scales; those on the head are so regular as to be of importance in classification. On the ventral surface in front of the anus is a single row of broad scales, called abdominal scutes, to which the ends of the ribs are attached. The outer, horny layer of the skin is shed a number of times during the year. Appendages are entirely absent except in a few species, like the python, which possess a pair of short spur-like projections one on either side of the anus, — vestiges of the hind limbs. The eyelids are fused over the eyes, but there is a transparent portion which allows the animal to see. When the skin is being shed, the snake is partially blind.

There is no tympanic membrane, and the sense of hearing is very slightly developed. The tongue is a slender, deeply notched protrusible structure that can be thrust out even when the mouth is closed, because of the presence of grooves in the jaws. It is very sensitive to vibrations and probably serves as an organ of hearing. The prevalent idea that the tongue can inflict an injury is erroneous. The teeth are sharp and recurved. They are adapted for forcing the food into the throat. In the venomous snakes certain teeth are grooved or tubular, and serve to conduct poison into any object bitten.

The bones of the skull are so arranged that the jaws are extremely mobile. The snake is on this account able to swallow objects four or five times the diameter of its neck. When swallowing, the glottis is pulled forward, thus preventing the snake from choking. The vertebræ are very numerous — there may be over four hundred — and a large number of ribs are also present.

Movement on land is accompanied by lateral undulations of the body. The body is drawn forward by pressing the rough posterior edges of the abdominal scutes against the substratum. Snakes cannot move forward on a smooth surface. Most species are able to swim, and this, of course, is the normal method of locomotion of the aquatic forms.

The majority of snakes are oviparous, but some of them bring forth their young alive. The idea that they swallow their young in order to protect them and then spew them out again when the danger has passed is erroneous.

The tropics are more plentifully supplied with snakes than are the temperate zones. Snakes are, however, found in many places not inhabited by lizards. Madagascar seems to be the only large country in warm and temperate latitude not inhabited by dangerous snakes. As in the other groups of vertebrates, the serpents are found in almost every kind of habitat; some species live in salt water, others in fresh water; some are arboreal; and many live underground.

Only four of the nine families of SERPENTES occur in North America. With a few exceptions those described below are found in the United States.

Family GLAUCONIIDÆ. — BLIND SNAKES. — Two species of these small, burrowing reptiles occur in the United States —

Glauconia dulcis, the Texas blind snake, in Texas and New Mexico, and *G. humilis*, the California blind snake, in Arizona, and southern California. They dig long tunnels in the earth and feed on worms and insect larvæ.

Family BOIDÆ. — PYTHONS and BOAS. — The members of the

FIG. 460. — The python, *Python molurus*, devouring a mammal. (From Gadow.)

family BOIDÆ are constrictors. They live almost exclusively upon birds and mammals which they squeeze to death in their coils (Fig. 460). None of them is venomous and only a few are large enough to be dangerous to man. The largest species on record is the regal python, *Python reticulatus*, of Burma, which attains a length of thirty feet. The anaconda or water boa, *Eunectes murinus*, of South America averages about seventeen feet in length.

Not all of the BOIDÆ are large. Many of them are of moderate size or even small. Four species are found in North America, but they are comparatively rare and confined to the South-western states. There is only one " boa-constrictor " with several varieties. It belongs to the genus *Boa* and its specific name is *constrictor*. It is a native of tropical South America and reaches a length of eleven feet. Boa-constrictors are docile in captivity and therefore preferred by snake " charmers."

Family COLUBRIDÆ. — This family contains about 90 per cent of all living snakes and is so large that it is usually divided into three series.

Series A. AGLYPHA. — The snakes placed in this series have solid teeth, and no grooved nor perforated fangs. They are all non-venomous and are found in every country inhabited by snakes. Half a dozen of the most common species found in the United States are briefly described below.

The common garter-snake or striped snake, *Thamnophis sirtalis* (Fig. 461), is usually provided with three longitudinal yellow stripes, one on the back and one on either side. Every portion of North America is inhabited

FIG. 461. — The garter-snake, *Thamnophis sirtalis*. (From Gadow.)

by a species or variety of this genus. The garter-snakes are so difficult to classify that our description must be only a general one. The species *T. sirtalis* possesses nineteen rows of scales on the body, and certain peculiarities in the scales (shields) on the chin. The garter-snakes are the most abundant of our harmless snakes. They are the first to appear in the spring and the last to hibernate in the autumn. Their food consists largely of frogs, toads, fishes, and earthworms. The young are brought forth alive, usually in August, and become mature in about one year.

The common water-snake, *Natrix fasciatus* variety *sipedon*, belongs to a genus whose species and varieties are abundant in the United States, Europe, and Asia. They are semiaquatic serpents, living in swampy places or in the vicinity of ponds and streams. The water is usually selected by them as an avenue of escape when disturbed. The variety *sipedon* of the eastern United States is pale brownish or reddish in color, with wavy cross bands of brown; these break up into blotches on the hinder part of the body. The length of an adult is usually about three feet six inches. Like the garter-snake, the water-snake is viviparous and about twenty-five young are produced in August or September. The water-snake is often erroneously called " water-moccasin."

The black-snake, *Zamenis constrictor*, is a slender, long-tailed snake of the eastern United States which reaches a length of six feet. West of the Mississippi it gives way to a color variety, *Z. constrictor* variety *flaviventris*, called the " blue " racer. In the East the black-snake is slaty black except the chin and throat, which are milky white. In Michigan and adjoining states it is bluish green above and immaculate white beneath. Contrary to popular belief, this reptile does not attack snakes larger than itself, has no power to squeeze its prey to death, and is unable to hypnotize birds and squirrels. Its prey is almost always smaller than itself, and is swallowed while still alive, often being held down by a portion of the body during the process. Black-snakes prefer dry and open situations, especially at the edge of meadows. They are partial to birds' eggs and young, but also devour mice, frogs, and various other small animals. Their eggs to the number of a dozen or more are deposited in June or July, usually under a stone or in soft, moist soil.

The king-snakes belong to the genus *Ophibolus*. They are of various sizes, are constrictors, and have received their common name because they prey on other snakes. Of the seven species occurring in the United States, the milk-snake, *O. doliatus* variety *triangulus*, the scarlet king-snake or " coral-snake," *O. doliatus* variety *coccineus*, and the common king-snake, *O. getulus*, are of special interest.

The milk-snake derives its name from its supposed habit of

stealing milk from cows. This is not true, since rats and mice are its principal articles of food. The color of this variety is gray above, with brownish saddle-shaped blotches on the back, and smaller blotches on the sides. It averages about three feet in length, and is oviparous.

The scarlet king-snake or " coral-snake " is a small variety about a foot long. It is ringed with bright bands of scarlet, yellow, and black, causing it to resemble the venomous coral-snake, *Elaps fulvius* (see p. 503).

The common king-snake or chain-snake is a heavy-bodied constrictor of the eastern United States. Other snakes, both harmless and venomous species, and field mice, are squeezed to death and devoured by it. King-snakes are immune to venom and do not hesitate to attack rattlesnakes, water-moccasins, and copperheads. The length of an average adult is about five feet.

The hog-nosed snakes of the genus *Heterodon* are represented in North America by three species popularly known as " puff-adders," " spreading vipers," or " blow snakes." The common hog-nosed snake, *Heterodon platyrhinus*, inhabits dry, sandy places over most of the United States east of the Rocky Mountains. The snout is turned up at the end, whence its common name. It is non-venomous and entirely harmless, but when disturbed throws itself into a defiant attitude, dilates its neck like a cobra, and makes a hissing sound. If this does not frighten away the enemy, the snake may suddenly open its mouth, and appear to be injured and to lose strength. " Then a convulsion seemingly seizes the snake, as it contorts its body into irregular undulations, ending in a spasmodic wriggling of the tail, when the reptile turns on its back and lies limp and to all appearances dead.

" So cleverly and patiently does the snake feign death that it may be carried about by the tail for half an hour or more, hung over a fence rail where it dangles and sways to a passing breeze, or tied in a knot and thrown in the road, and to all of this treatment there is no sign of life except from one condition. In spite of this remarkable shamming, the snake may be led to betray itself if placed upon the ground on its crawling surface. Then like a flash it turns upon its back again and once more becomes limp and apparently lifeless. It appears, according to this creature's reasoning, that a snake to look thoroughly dead should be lying upon its back. This idea is persistent, and the experiment may be repeated a dozen times or more.

" Should the observer retreat some distance away, while the reptile lies thus, or he seek near-by concealment, the craftiness of the animal may be realized. Seeing nothing further to alarm, the serpent raises its head slightly and surveys its surroundings, and if there is no further sign of the enemy, it quickly rolls over upon its abdomen and glides away as fast as its thick body will carry it. But at such a moment a move on the observer's part would send the reptile on its back again, with ludicrous precipitation." (Ditmars.)

Series B. OPISTHOGLYPHA. — The opisthoglyphs are COLU-BRIDÆ which possess grooved teeth in the rear of the upper jaw. They are all poisonous, but very few are dangerous to man. The subfamily HOMALOPSINÆ contains about twenty-three species of fish-eating, river snakes of the East Indies. The subfamily DIPSADOMORPHINÆ contains about two hundred and seventy-five species of slender, long-tailed snakes of cosmopolitan distribution. They are terrestrial, subterrestrial, arboreal, or semiaquatic in habits. The opisthoglyphs of the United States are found only in the southern part. They are moderate or small in size, few in number, and not very dangerous.

Series C. PROTEROGLYPHA. — The proteroglyphs are COLU-BRIDÆ which possess fixed, tubular fangs in the anterior part of the upper jaw. As in the case of the opisthoglypha, they are all venomous. Many of them are the most dangerous of all poisonous reptiles. There are two subfamilies.

The HYDRINÆ, or sea-snakes, are true sea-serpents. They inhabit the Indian Ocean and the western, tropical Pacific, and one species occurs along the western coast of tropical America. They reach a length of from three to eight feet or more, and most of them are very poisonous. The tail, and sometimes the body, is laterally compressed — an adaptation for swimming.

The subfamily ELAPINÆ contains twenty-nine genera and about one hundred and fifty species of poisonous snakes. They are most abundant in Australia and New Guinea, but occur also in India, Malaysia, Africa, and America. The single genus *Elaps* of the New World contains about twenty-eight species of coral-

snakes. Two of these are found in the United States, the harlequin or coral snake, *Elaps fulvius*, and the Sonoran coral-snake,
E. euryxanthus.

The harlequin snake of the southeastern United States averages about two and a half feet in length. Its body is ringed by
broad cross bands of scarlet and blue-black, separated by narrow bands of yellow. It can easily be distinguished from the
harmless scarlet king-snake (p. 501), since in the latter the yellow
bands are bordered by the black ones. The harlequin snake
burrows in the ground, and feeds chiefly upon lizards and snakes.
It is oviparous. Most writers consider this snake dangerous

only to small animals, but its fangs are
capable of injecting a venom more
virulent than that of the rattlesnake.

The cobra-de-capello, *Naja tripudians* (Fig. 462), of India, China, and
the Malay Archipelago, is the most
notorious relative of the harlequin
snake. The cobra is very vicious;
when disturbed it raises the anterior
part of the body from the ground,
spreads its neck (hood) with a hiss,
and strikes at once. In India the
bare-legged natives are killed in large

Fig. 462. — The cobra, *Naja
tripudians.* (From Gadow.)

numbers by cobras; for example, in
1908, 21,880 were killed by snake bites,
most of them probably the bites of this species. There are nine
other species of cobras — seven confined to Africa, one in the
Philippine Islands, and one, the king cobra, inhabiting the same
countries as the cobra-de-capello.

Family VIPERIDÆ. — THICK-BODIED POISONOUS SNAKES. —
The viperine snakes are often termed solenoglyphs to distinguish
them from the three series of the family COLUBRIDÆ. Their fangs
are tubular, firmly attached to the movable maxillary bones,
and folded flat against the roof of the mouth when the jaws are
closed. The two subfamilies of viperine snakes are the VIPERINÆ,
or true vipers, of the Old World, and the CROTALINÆ, or pit-vipers,
of both the New World and Old World.

The pit-vipers are easily recognized by the presence of a deep
pit on each side of the head between the eye and the nostril.

The function of this pit is not known. There are four genera and about seventy species. Those found in the United States are the copperhead, water-moccasin, and fifteen species of rattlesnakes.

The water-moccasin, *Agkistrodon piscivorus* (Fig. 463), occurs in the swamps of the Atlantic coast south of North Carolina, and in the Mississippi Valley from southern Illinois and Indiana southward. The length of an average specimen is four feet, but a length of over five feet is sometimes attained. The moccasin is one of

FIG. 463. — The water-moccasin, *Agkistrodon piscivorus*. (From Gadow.)

the most poisonous of all snakes. It feeds upon cold-blooded animals such as frogs, and also upon small birds and mammals. The young are brought forth alive.

The copperhead snake, *Agkistrodon contortrix* (Fig. 464), is another very venomous snake. Its range extends from southern Massachusetts to northern Florida and west to Texas. In the southern part of its range the copperhead prefers to live on the plantations, but in the North it is found in or near thick forests. An average specimen measures about two and a half feet in length.

FIG. 464. — The copperhead, *Agkistrodon contortrix*. (From Gadow.)

The rattlesnakes are easily distinguished by the rattle at the end of the tail. This consists of a number of horny, bell-shaped segments loosely held together. Each segment was once the end of the tail; it was shed when the skin was shed, but was held by the newly developed end of the tail. Rattles are therefore added as often as the skin is shed, and, since this happens several times per year, and also since rattles are often detached and lost, it is obvious that the number of rattles is no indication of the age of the snake. Usually before striking, the rattlesnake vibrates the end of the tail rapidly, producing a sort of buzzing noise, which, to the wise, serves as a warning.

The poison apparatus of the rattlesnake is shown in Figure 465. The poison is secreted by a pair of glands (Fig. 465, A, S) lying above the roof of the mouth. These glands open by poison ducts (Gc) into the poison-fangs (†). The poison-fangs are pierced by a canal, which opens near the end (za), and are enclosed by a pouch of mucous membrane (zf). When the jaws are closed (Fig. 465, B), the fangs lie back against

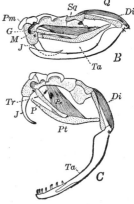

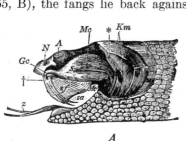

Fig. 465. — Poison apparatus of the rattlesnake. **A**, A, eye; Gc, poison-duct entering poison-fang at †; Km, muscles of mastication, cut at *; Mc, Mc', constrictor muscle; N, nasal opening; S, fibrous poison-sac; z, tongue; za, opening of poison-duct; zf, pouch of mucous membrane enclosing poison-fangs. **B**, position of apparatus when mouth is closed. **C**, position when mouth is opened widely. Di, digastric muscle; G, groove or pit characteristic of Crotaline snakes; J, poison-fang; M, maxillary; P, palatine; Pe, sphenopterygoid muscle; Pm, premaxillary; Pt, pterygoid; Q, quadrate; Sq, squamosal; Ta, insertion of anterior temporal muscle; Tr, ectopterygoid. (A, from Parker and Haswell, after Wiedersheim; B, C, from Gadow.)

the roof of the mouth. When the snake bites, the digastric muscle (Fig. 465, C, Di) opens the jaws; the sphenopterygoid muscle (Pe) contracts, pulls the pterygoid bone (Pt) forward and pushes the ectopterygoid bone (Tr) against the maxillary bone (M). The maxillary bone is thus rotated, and the poison-fang (J) is erected. The poison-glands are so situated that the opening of the jaws and erection of the fangs squeezes the poison out of them, through the fangs, and into the object bitten. There are several pairs of small fangs lying just behind the functional ones, which are held in reserve to replace those that are lost in struggles with prey or are normally shed.

Rattlesnakes are most abundant both as regards the number of species and the number of individuals in the deserts of the south-western United States, but almost every part of this country is inhabited by one or more species. The diamond-back rattlesnake, *Crotalus adamanteus*, is the most deadly and largest rattlesnake, measuring sometimes over eight feet in length. It inhabits the pine swamps and hummock lands of the southeastern United States. A nearly allied species is the Texas rattlesnake, *Crotalus atrox* (Fig. 466). This species inhabits the subarid and desert regions of Texas and the Southwest. These snakes are nocturnal in habit, and prefer the common rabbit as food. Their bite is usually fatal to man within an hour.

FIG. 466. — The Texas rattlesnake, *Crotalus atrox*. (From Shipley and MacBride, after Baird and Girard.)

Other species that should be mentioned are the timber, or banded rattlesnake, *Crotalus horridus*, of the eastern United States; the horned rattlesnake, *Crotalus cerastes*, inhabiting the deserts of the southwestern United States; and the massasauga, *Sistrurus catenatus*, which is a rather common species in the central United States.

4. THE POISONOUS SNAKES OF NORTH AMERICA

As the preceding discussion shows, there are only twenty-two species of poisonous snakes in the United States; namely, the harlequin snake, the Sonoran coral-snake, the copperhead, the water-moccasin, seven unimportant opisthoglyphs (p. 503), and fifteen species of rattlesnakes. It is important for any one who spends much time in the country to be able to distinguish between these poisonous snakes and the non-poisonous species. This can easily be done by means of the following key, which was prepared by Professor Alexander G. Ruthven.

Key to the Venomous and Non-venomous Snakes of the United States

A. Pupil of eye vertical.
   B. A pit between the eye and nostril. — Pit-vipers (venomous).
      C. Tail terminating in a rattle . . . Rattlesnakes.
      CC. Tail not terminating in a rattle. — Moccasin and copper-head.
   BB. No pit between eye and nostril. — Non-venomous or opisthoglyph and not dangerous to man.
AA. Pupil of eye round.
   B. Body ringed with red, black, and yellow, the black rings bordered by the yellow ones. — Coral-snakes (venomous).
   BB. Body not ringed with red, black, and yellow, or if so the yellow rings bordered by the black ones. — Non-venomous or opisthoglyph and not dangerous to man.

Notwithstanding the fear of snakes possessed by most people, very few are bitten by poisonous species in this country, and of these probably not more than two per year die.

Snake Venom. — Venom is a highly complex physiological product elaborated by the poison-glands. Among its powers are the dissolution of various body cells and the destruction of the bactericidal property of the blood. Venoms are albuminoid. They are capable of producing in the blood an antidote or neutralizing substance, called an antibody. It is thus possible, as in the case of smallpox, tetanus, etc., to obtain an antibody (an antivenin) which, when injected into the blood, will counteract the effects of the venom. Unfortunately each kind of venom requires a special sort of antivenin, so that it is impracticable as a rule to carry antivenin into the field.

The best method of procedure when bitten by a poisonous snake is to apply a ligature between the wound and the heart so as to prevent the blood from carrying the venom toward the heart. This ligature should not be kept on more than half an hour, since, as stated above, the venom destroys the bactericidal power of the blood, and gangrene will set in rapidly about the wound if fresh blood is not supplied. After the ligature is in place, the wound should be incised deeply in all directions, and a solution of potassium permanganate injected freely into the tissues about the wound. This treatment should serve to destroy most of the venom before it travels far in the system. Sucking the poison from the wound is a common practice, but there is danger of poison finding its way into the blood through slight abrasions of the lips or mouth, and, besides, this procedure is of no value. It also seems certain that the drinking of large quantities of alcohol is not only useless, but of considerable detriment.

5. THE ECONOMIC IMPORTANCE OF REPTILES

The economic importance of the various kinds of reptiles has been emphasized during the discussion of the orders and families. It will therefore suffice here to give a brief summary of the subject.

The food of reptiles consists of both animals and plants. The animals eaten belong to practically all classes. Many of the snakes live almost entirely upon birds and mammals. Frogs, fish, and other reptiles are favorite articles of food. Most of the smaller species of reptiles feed upon worms and insects. In general it may be stated that reptiles do very little damage because of the animals and plants they destroy for food, but are often of considerable benefit, since they kill large numbers of obnoxious insects and other forms.

The turtles and tortoises rank first as food for man. Especially worthy of mention are the green turtle (p. 486), the diamond-back terrapin (p. 484), and the soft-shelled turtle (p. 487). In some parts of this country it would seem possible to establish turtle farms that would utilize land useless for other purposes, and would be commercially successful. Certain lizards, such as the iguana of tropical America, form a valuable addition to the food supply in various localities.

The skins of the crocodilians are used rather extensively for the manufacture of articles that need to combine beauty of surface with durability. The alligators in this country have decreased so rapidly because of the value of their hides that they will be of no great economic importance unless they are consistently protected or grown on farms. Of less value are the skins of certain snakes. Tortoise-shell, especially that procured from the horny covering of the carapace of the hawk's-bill turtle (p. 486, Fig. 447), is widely used for the manufacture of combs and ornaments of various kinds.

As previously stated, the poisonous snakes of the United States are of very little danger to man. In tropical countries, especially India (p. 504), venomous snakes cause a larger death-rate than that of any other group of animals. The Gila monster, which is one of the few poisonous lizards, and the only one inhabiting the United States, very seldom attacks man, and probably never inflicts a fatal wound.

6. Prehistoric Reptiles

Sixteen of the twenty orders of reptiles are known only from their fossil remains embedded in the earth's crust. Three of these

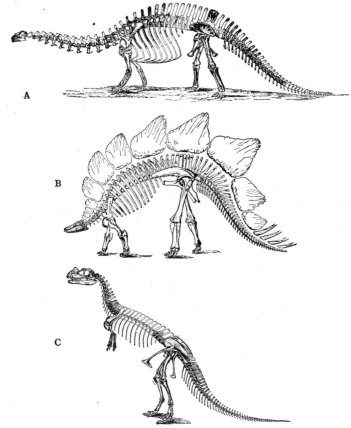

Fig. 467. — Fossil reptiles. **A**, *Brontosaurus excelsus*. **B**, *Stegosaurus ungulatus*. **C**, *Ceratosaurus nasicornis*. (A, B, from Sedgwick's Zoology, after Marsh; C, from Zittel, after Marsh.)

orders will serve to give a general idea of the nature of the extinct reptiles.

Order Dinosauria. — The DINOSAURIA were extremely large reptiles that probably lived in swamps or in the neighborhood of water during Triassic, Jurassic, and Cretaceous times. Remains have been found in America, Europe, Asia, Africa, and Australia, and footprints have been discovered in the sandstone

FIG. 468. — A fossil reptile, *Ichthyosaurus communis.* Caudal fin not shown. (From Parker and Haswell, after Owen.)

of the Connecticut Valley. Some species measured over one hundred feet in length. Both herbivorous and carnivorous forms existed.

Brontosaurus (Fig. 467, A) was about sixty feet long; was herbivorous; and had four limbs about equally well developed. Its remains have been found in Wyoming and Colorado. *Stegosaurus* (Fig. 467, B) reached a length of about twenty-eight feet

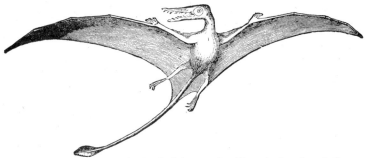

FIG. 469. — Restoration of a fossil, flying reptile, *Rhamphorhynchus phyllurus.* (From Sedgwick's Zoology, after Woodward.)

and was also herbivorous. It possessed huge triangular plates along the back. Remains have been discovered in Wyoming and Colorado. *Ceratosaurus* (Fig. 467, C) was a carnivorous dinosaur with a comparatively large head. The character of its skeleton indicates that it walked about on its hind limbs and rested on its tail, much like a kangaroo. Remains have been found in Colorado.

Order Ichthyosauria. — The ICHTHYOSAURS (Fig. 468) were fish-eating, aquatic reptiles. Their bodies were admirably adapted for life in the water, and they have been called the " whales " of the Mesozoic Era. The remains of ICHTHYOSAURS occur in North America, Europe, Asia, Africa, and Australia.

Order Pterosauria. — The PTEROSAURIA were reptiles of the Mesozoic Era which had the fore limbs modified for flight. They resemble birds in certain skeletal characters, but differ from them in others. *Rhamphorhynchus* (Fig. 469) possessed teeth and a long tail. *Pteranodon* is the largest form known; it had a skull two feet long, and a spread of wing of twenty feet. Teeth are absent, and the tail is short.

CHAPTER XX

SUBPHYLUM VERTEBRATA: CLASS VI. AVES [1]

THE class AVES contains the birds. Birds are easily distinguished from all other animals, since they alone possess *feathers*. The ten thousand or more species of birds are grouped into two subclasses: (1) ARCHÆORNITHES, which contains the fossil form *Archæopteryx;* and (2) NEORNITHES, which contains four orders of extinct forms and seventeen orders with living representatives.

1. THE PIGEON

The common pigeons have been derived from the blue rock pigeon, *Columba livia* (Fig. 470), which ranges from Europe through the Mediterranean countries to central Asia and China. Since pigeons are easily obtained and of moderate size, they are usually selected as a type of the class AVES for laboratory study.

External Features. — The body of the pigeon is spindle-shaped, and therefore

FIG. 470. — The blue rock pigeon, *Columba livia.* (From Brehm.)

adapted for movement through the air. Three regions may be recognized, — head, neck, and trunk. The *head* is prolonged in

[1] Birds offer excellent opportunities for the study of adaptation to an aërial existence as shown by the development of feathers, wings, air sacs, hollow bones and skeletal rigidity. Adaptations to various habitats are exhibited by wings, feet, and bills. Everyone should know something regarding the nests, eggs, and habits of our common birds and of their economic relations to man. Much of this chapter was prepared for this purpose.

front into a pointed, horny *beak*, at the base of which is a patch
of naked, swollen skin, the *cere*. Between the beak and the cere
are the two oblique, slit-like *nostrils* (Fig. 471). On either side is
an *eye* which is provided with upper and lower *lids*, and with a
well-developed third eyelid, or *nictitating membrane*. The third
eyelid can be drawn across the eyeball from the inner angle outward. Below and behind each eye is an external *auditory aperture*
which leads to the tympanic cavity.

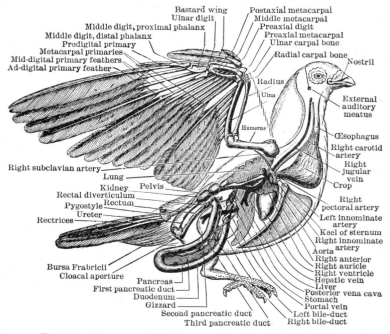

Fig. 471. — Anatomy of the pigeon. (From Marshall and Hurst.)

The *neck* is long and flexible. At the posterior end of the trunk
is a projection which bears the tail feathers. The two *wings* can
be folded close to the body or extended as organs of flight. The
hind limbs are covered with horny epidermal *scales*, and their
digits are each provided with a horny *claw*.

Feathers. — Feathers are peculiar to birds. They arise, as do
the scales of reptiles, from dermal papillæ with a covering of epidermis, and become enveloped in a pit, the feather follicle. A
typical feather (Fig. 472, *A*) consists of a stiff axial rod, the scapus

or *stem;* the proximal portion is hollow, and semitransparent, and is called the *quill* or calamus; the distal portion is called the *vane,* and that part of the stem passing through it is the *shaft* or rachis. The vane is composed of a series of parallel *barbs,* and each barb bears a fringe of small processes, the *barbules,* along either side. The barbules on one side of the barb bear *hooklets* which hold together the adjacent barbs. The whole structure is thus a pliable, but nevertheless resistant, organ wonderfully adapted for use in flight.

The three principal kinds of feathers are: (1) the *contour feathers* or pennæ like that just described; these possess a stiff shaft and firm vanes, and since they appear on the surface, determine to a large degree the contour of the body. (2) The *down feathers* or plumulæ possess a soft shaft and a vane without barbs; they lie beneath the contour feathers and form a

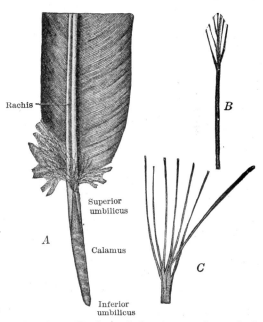

FIG. 472. — Feathers of the pigeon. A, proximal portion of a contour feather. B, filoplume. C, nestling down. (From Parker and Haswell.)

covering for the retention of heat. The barbs of some down feathers arise directly from the end of the quill, and no shaft is present (Fig. 472, C). (3) The *filoplumes* (B) possess a slender, hair-like shaft and very few or no barbs.

Only certain portions of the pigeon's body bear feathers; these *feather tracts* are termed *pterylæ,* and the featherless spaces are known as *apteria.* The feather tracts differ in different species of birds; those of the pigeon are shown in Figure 473.

Birds shed their old feathers, *i.e. molt,* usually in the fall, and acquire a complete new set which are formed within the follicles and from the papillæ of those that are cast off.   There may be a partial molt in the spring, when the bird assumes its breeding plumage.   At this time the plumage often changes color; this is caused probably either by an actual chemical change in the pigment, or by the breaking off of the tips of the feathers.

The Skeleton. — The principal differences between the skeleton of a pigeon and that of a reptile are those that are made necessary by the methods of locomotion of the former.   The hind limbs and pelvic girdle are modified for *bipedal locomotion;* the fore limbs and pectoral girdle are modified for *flight;* the skeleton of the trunk is rigid; the *sternum* has a distinct crest for the attachment of the large muscles that move the wings; short projections, called *uncinate processes*, which extend backward from some of the ribs, make the thoracic framework more firm; and the bones

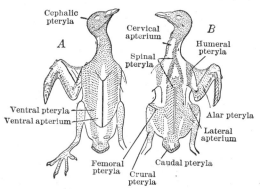

Cephalic pteryla
Cervical apterium
A
B
Spinal pteryla
Humeral pteryla
Ventral pteryla
Ventral apterium
Alar pteryla
Lateral apterium
Femoral pteryla
Caudal pteryla
Crural pteryla

Fig. 473. — Feather tracts of the pigeon.   *A*, ventral; *B*, dorsal.   (From Nitzsch.)

are very light, many of them containing *air-cavities*.   The skeleton of the common fowl (Fig. 474) is larger and more easily studied than that of the pigeon, and is similar to the latter in most respects.

The *skull* is very light, and most of the bones in it are so fused together that they can be distinguished only in the young bird. The *cranium* is rounded; the *orbits* are large; the *facial bones* extend forward into a beak; the *quadrate* is movable and connects the lower jaw with the squamosal of the cranium; there is but *a single occipital condyle* for articulation with the first vertebra; and *no teeth* are present.

The *cervical vertebræ* are long and move freely upon one another by saddle-shaped articular surfaces, making the neck very flexible. This enables the bird to use its bill for feeding, for nest building, and for many other purposes.   The vertebræ of the trunk are almost completely fused together into a rigid skeletal axis which is necessary to support the body while in flight.   There are four or five free caudal vertebræ followed by a terminal pygostyle consisting of five or six fused vertebræ. The *pygostyle* (Fig. 471) supports the large tail feathers (rectrices, Fig. 471), and the free caudal vertebræ allow the movements of the tail which enable the

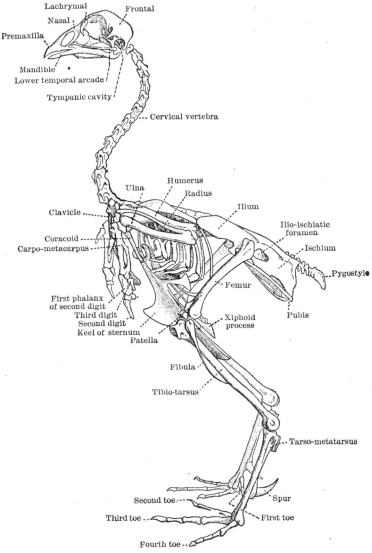

Fig. 474. — Skeleton of the common fowl, male. (From Shipley and MacBride.)

bird to use this organ as a rudder while flying and as a balancer while perching.

There are two cervical *ribs* and five thoracic ribs on each side. The second cervical and first four thoracic ribs bear each an *uncinate process* which arises from the posterior margin and overlaps the succeeding rib, thus making a firmer framework. The thoracic ribs are connected with the *sternum* or *breastbone*. The sternum is united in front with the coracoid (Fig. 474) of the pectoral girdle and bears on its ventral surface a large crest or *keel* (*carina*) to which the muscles that move the wings are attached.

The *pectoral girdle* consists of a pair of blade-like *scapulæ*, the shoulder-blades, which lie above the ribs one on either side of the vertebral column in the thorax. The *coracoids* (Fig. 474) connect the sternum with the anterior end of the scapulæ at the shoulders. A concavity in these bones at their junction furnishes the articular surface for the long wing bone (humerus), and is called the *glenoid cavity*. The two *clavicles* connect proximally with the shoulder and are fused together distally, forming a V-shaped *furcula* or " wishbone." The clavicles are homologous to the collar-bones of man, and serve to brace the shoulders.

The fore limb or *wing* of the pigeon (Fig. 471) is greatly modified. There are but three digits, and only one of these is well developed. The distal row of carpal bones and the three metacarpals are fused together forming a *carpo-metacarpus* (Fig. 471); this adds to the rigidity of the wing. The arm contains, as in other vertebrates, a single bone, the *humerus*, with a convex head which lies in the glenoid cavity. The fore arm possesses two bones, the *radius* and *ulna*. The wrist contains two *carpal bones;* the other carpal bones are fused with the three *metacarpals*, forming the *carpo-metacarpus*, as stated above. Besides the carpo-metacarpus, the hand possesses a *preaxial digit* with two small bones, which supports a small tuft of feathers and is known as the *bastard wing;* a middle digit with three *phalanges;* and a *postaxial digit* containing a single phalanx.

The *pelvic girdle* consists of the *ilia* (Fig. 474), the *ischia*, and the *pubes*, as in nearly all of the vertebrates above the fishes. These bones are firmly fused together and united with the posterior part of the vertebral column in the trunk which is called the *sacrum*. At their junction on either side is a concavity, the *acetabulum*, in which the head of the thigh-bone fits.

The *hind limbs* are used for bipedal locomotion. The thigh is concealed beneath the feathers. The *femur* (Fig. 474) is the short, thick, thigh-bone. In the leg are the slender *fibula,* and the long, stout *tibiotarsus* which consists of the tibia fused with the proximal row of tarsal bones. The *ankle-joint* is between the tibiotarsus and the *tarso-metatarsus;* the latter represents the distal row of tarsal bones and the second, third, fourth, and fifth metatarsals fused together. The *foot* possesses, besides the tarso-metatarsus, four *digits;* the first is directed backwards and is called the *hallux;* and the other three are directed forwards. Each digit bears a terminal *claw.* The tarso-metatarsus of the fowl bears a backwardly directed *spur.*

The Muscular System. — The muscles of the neck, tail, wings, and legs are especially well developed. Those that produce the downward stroke of the wings, the *pectoral muscles,* are the largest; they weigh about one-fifth as much as the entire body; they take their origin from the sternum and its keel, and constitute what is popularly known as the " breast " of the bird. Connected with the leg muscles is a mechanism which enables the bird to maintain itself upon a perch even while asleep. If the hind limb is bent, a pull is exerted on a tendon which flexes all of the toes and bends them automatically round the perch. When resting, the mere weight of the body bends the hind limb and consequently causes the toes to grasp the perch and hold the bird firmly in place.

The Digestive System. — Pigeons feed principally upon vegetable food, such as seeds. The *mouth* cavity opens into the *œsophagus* (Fig. 471), which enlarges into a *crop;* here the food is macerated. The *stomach* consists of two parts, an anterior *proventriculus* with thick glandular walls, which secretes the gastric juice, and a thick muscular *gizzard,* which grinds up the food with the aid of small pebbles swallowed by the bird. The *intestine* forms a U-shaped loop, the *duodenum,* which leads into the coiled small intestine, or *ileum,* and finally passes into the *rectum* at a point where two blind pouches, the *cæca,* are given off. The alimentary canal leads into the *cloaca* into which the urinary and genital ducts also open. The cloaca opens to the outside by means of the *anus.* In young birds a thick glandular pouch, the bursa Fabricii, lies just above the cloaca.

The two *bile ducts,* one from each lobe of the liver, discharge the bile into the duodenum. There is *no gall-bladder*. The *pancreas* pours its secretions into the duodenum through three ducts. There is a *spleen*, paired *thyroids, adrenal bodies*, and, in young pigeons, paired *thymus glands* (see p. 442).

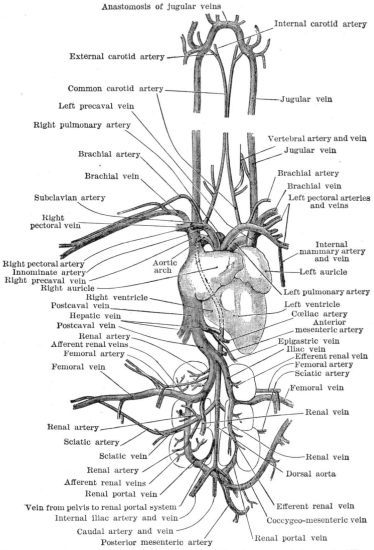

Anastomosis of jugular veins
Internal carotid artery
External carotid artery
Common carotid artery
Left precaval vein
Right pulmonary artery
Jugular vein
Vertebral artery and vein
Jugular vein
Brachial artery
Brachial vein
Brachial artery
Brachial vein
Subclavian artery
Left pectoral arteries and veins
Right pectoral vein
Internal mammary artery and vein
Right pectoral artery
Aortic arch
Innominate artery
Right precaval vein
Left auricle
Right auricle
Right ventricle
Left pulmonary artery
Postcaval vein
Left ventricle
Hepatic vein
Cœliac artery
Postcaval vein
Anterior mesenteric artery
Renal artery
Epigastric vein
Afferent renal veins
Iliac vein
Femoral artery
Efferent renal vein
Femoral vein
Femoral artery
Sciatic artery
Femoral vein
Renal vein
Renal artery
Sciatic artery
Renal vein
Sciatic vein
Renal artery
Dorsal aorta
Afferent renal veins
Renal portal vein
Efferent renal vein
Vein from pelvis to renal portal system
Internal iliac artery and vein
Coccygeo-mesenteric vein
Caudal artery and vein
Renal portal vein
Posterior mesenteric artery

FIG. 475. — The heart and chief blood-vessels of the pigeon, ventral aspect. (From Parker and Haswell, after Parker.)

The Circulatory System (Fig. 475). — The *heart* of a bird is comparatively large. It is composed of two entirely separated muscular *ventricles* and two thin-walled *auricles*. The *right auricle* receives impure, venous blood from the *right precaval*, the *left precaval*, and the *postcaval veins*. This blood passes from the right auricle into the *right ventricle*, and is then pumped through the *pulmonary artery*, which divides into right and left pulmonary arteries, leading to the right and left lungs respectively.

The *left auricle* (Fig. 475) receives the blood which returns, after being aërated in the lungs, through four large *pulmonary veins*. It passes from the left auricle into the left ventricle, and is then pumped through the *right aortic arch*, which gives off the *innominate arteries* and then continues as the *dorsal aorta*.

Contrasting the circulatory system of the pigeon with that of the turtle, it should be noted that the venous blood and arterial blood are not allowed to mingle in the heart of the pigeon. The *renal portal system* of the pigeon has almost completely disappeared, the blood being taken from the posterior part of the body directly to the heart, and not through the renal capillaries, as in all lower vertebrates. The *jugular veins* of the pigeon are united just under the head by a cross vein; this enables blood to pass back to the heart from the head when the neck becomes momentarily twisted so that one of the jugular veins is stopped up.

The Respiratory System. — The two *lungs* in birds are assisted by a remarkable system of *air-sacs*. During *inspiration*, the relaxation of the thoracic and abdominal muscles allows the elastic expansion of the thorax and abdomen. Air enters the mouth cavity through the *nostrils*, as in reptiles; it then passes through the *glottis* into the *trachea* or windpipe, which divides, sending a branch (*bronchus*) to each lung. The bronchi communicate with nine large thin-walled *air-sacs*, which lie principally along the sides and dorsal surface of the body-cavity. During *expiration*, the muscles of the thorax and abdomen contract, forcing the air from the air-sacs, through the lungs and trachea, and out of the nostrils. At each inspiration practically all of the air in the lungs is renewed.

The *air-sacs* enable the bird to breathe easily when in flight, since air is forced into them during the rapid progress through the atmosphere and out of them by the compression of the pectoral muscles, which lower the wings. In man, violent movements interfere with the alternate inspiration and expiration of air.

The *trachea* is held open by partially ossified *cartilaginous rings*. Where the trachea divides into the two bronchi, it enlarges to form the vocal organ, or *syrinx*, a structure peculiar to birds. Extending forward from the angle of bifurcation of the trachea is a flexible valve which is vibrated when air is forcibly expelled from the lungs, thus producing a sound. A number of muscles are able to alter the tension of this valve and consequently the number of its vibrations and the pitch of the note produced.

The Excretory System. — The *kidneys* are a pair of three-lobed bodies situated as shown in Figure 471. Each discharges its secretion, the urine, through a duct, the *ureter*, into the *cloaca*. There is *no urinary bladder*, but the urine passes directly out of the anus with the fæces.

The Reproductive System. — In the *male* are a pair of oval *testes*. From each testis a duct, the *vas deferens*, passes back and opens into the cloaca; it dilates at its distal end to form a *seminal vesicle*. The spermatozoa pass through the vasa deferentia, are stored in the seminal vesicles, and, when *copulation* takes place, are discharged into the cloaca, and transferred by contact to the cloaca of the female. There is *no copulatory organ*.

The right *ovary* of the *female* disappears during development and only the left ovary persists in the adult. The ova break out of the ovary and enter the *oviducts*. During their passage through the oviducts the *albuminous substance*, known as the " white " of the egg, is secreted about them by the walls of the middle portion. The double, parchment-like *shell-membrane* is then secreted about the egg, and finally the *shell* is added by the posterior part of the oviduct a short time before deposition.

Fertilization takes place about forty-one hours before the eggs are laid. Two eggs are laid by pigeons at a sitting, the first usually between four and six P.M., and the second between one and two P.M., two days later. They are kept at a temperature of about 100° F. by the sitting bird for usually fourteen days. At the end of this *period of incubation*, the young birds have developed to such a stage that they are able to break through the shell, *i.e.* they *hatch*. They are at first covered with fine down, but soon acquire a covering of contour feathers. During their early life as nestlings they are fed upon " pigeon's milk," a secretion from the crop of the adult.

The Nervous System. — The *brain* of the pigeon (Fig. 476) is very short and broad. The *cerebellum* is comparatively large, as are also the *optic lobes*, showing that birds have well-developed powers of coordination and of sight. The *olfactory lobes*, on the other hand, are very small, indicating poorly developed olfactory organs.

The Sense-organs. — The *bill* and *tongue* serve as *tactile organs*. Tactile nerves are also present at the base of the feathers, especially those of the wings and tail. Birds are unable to distinguish delicate odors, and on the whole their sense of *smell* is very poor. The sense of *taste* is also very poorly developed, but is nevertheless present, as can easily be proved if a bad-tasting morsel of food is presented to a bird.

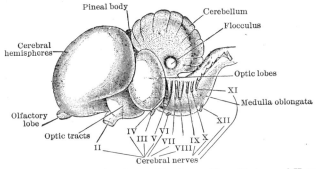

Fig. 476. — The brain of the pigeon, side view. (From Parker and Haswell.)

The *cochlea* of the *ear* is more complex than that of reptiles. The *Eustachian tubes* open by a single aperture on the roof of the pharynx. Birds have acute and discriminating powers of hearing — a power correlated with their singing ability.

The *eyes* of birds are very large, and have a *biconvex shape*. They are surrounded by bony *sclerotic plates*, and contain a fan-shaped, highly vascular, pigmented structure called the *pecten*, which is suspended in the vitreous humor. The function of the pecten is uncertain; it may have some connection with the nutrition of the eyeball, or with the process of *accommodation*. The latter process is remarkably well developed in birds, since their eyes are equally adapted both for far and near vision, and a bird can fly rapidly among the branches of a tree without striking a branch, or can swoop down to the ground from a great height in the air, changing from far-sighted to near-sighted vision in an instant.

2. A Brief Classification of Birds

The birds form a more homogeneous class of vertebrates than the reptiles and cannot be separated into a few well-defined groups. There are comparatively few fossil birds known to man; in fact, only one subclass, containing a single genus, and four orders, are not represented by living forms. The structural differences that distinguish the orders, families, genera, and species are, for the most part, so slight as to make it impossible to state them in a brief and clear manner.

More than twelve thousand species of birds have been described, and no two authorities agree as to their classification. The following arrangement is adapted from Knowlton's *Birds of the World*.

CLASS AVES. BIRDS. — Warm-blooded vertebrates with feathers; usually with fore limbs adapted for flight; the adults of existing species without teeth.

SUBCLASS I. ARCHÆORNITHES. — Ancient, reptile-like, fossil birds. Only three specimens of the single genus *Archæopteryx* are known.

SUBCLASS II. NEORNITHES. — RECENT BIRDS. — There are four orders containing only extinct forms, and seventeen orders containing living representatives.

Order 1. Hesperornithiformes. — Fossil, toothed-birds from America, with teeth set in a groove. Example: *Hesperornis* (Fig. 478).

Order 2. Ichthyornithiformes. — Fossil, toothed-birds from America, with teeth set in separate sockets. Example: *Ichthyornis* (Fig. 479).

Order 3. Struthioniformes. — OSTRICHES. — Flightless, terrestrial birds with naked head, neck, and legs; feet with two toes; without pygostyle; no keel on sternum. Example: *Struthio*, African Ostrich (Fig. 480).

Order 4. Rheiformes.— RHEAS.— Flightless, terrestrial birds with partially feathered head and neck; feathers without aftershaft; feet with three toes. Example: *Rhea*, American Ostrich (Fig. 481).

Order 5. Casuariiformes. — CASSOWARIES and EMEUS. — Flightless terrestrial birds with very small wings; feathers with large aftershaft. Examples: *Casuarius*, Cassowary; *Dromæus*, Emeu (Fig. 482).

Order 6. Crypturiformes. — TINAMOUS. — Flying, terrestrial birds, with short tail; no pygostyle. Example: *Tinamus* (Fig. 483).

Order 7. Dinornithiformes. — MOAS. — Flightless, terrestrial birds, with enormous hind limbs; wing bones absent; all extinct. Example: *Palapteryx* (Fig. 484).

Order 8. Æpyornithiformes. — ELEPHANT-BIRDS. — Flightless, terrestrial birds, with enormous hind limbs; sternum and wings small; eggs very large; all extinct. Example: *Æpyornis.*

Order 9. Apterygiformes. — KIWIS. — Flightless terrestrial birds; feathers hair-like and without aftershaft; all small in size. Example: *Apteryx* (Fig. 485).

Order 10. Sphenisciformes. — PENGUINS. — Flightless marine birds, with small, scale-like feathers; wings modified as paddles for swimming; one family. Example: *Spheniscus* (Fig. 486).

Order 11. Colymbiformes. — LOONS and GREBES. — Aquatic birds with webbed or lobed toes; feet far back; body carried upright; two suborders and two families. Examples: *Gavia,* Loon (Fig. 487); *Dytes,* Grebe.

Order 12. Procellariiformes. — ALBATROSSES and PETRELS. — Marine birds with webbed toes; powers of flight, great; sheath of bill of several pieces; three families. Examples: *Diomedea,* Albatross (Fig. 488); *Procellaria,* Petrel (Fig. 489).

Order 13. Ciconiiformes. — STORK-LIKE BIRDS. — Aquatic or marsh-birds with feet adapted for wading; four suborders, one superfamily, and thirteen families. Examples: PELECANIDÆ, Pelicans; PHALACROCORACIDÆ, Cormorants; ANHINGIDÆ, Snake-birds; ARDEIDÆ, Herons (Fig. 490); IBIDIDÆ, Ibises; PHŒNICOPTERIDÆ, Flamingos (Fig. 491).

Order 14. Anseriformes. — GOOSE-LIKE BIRDS. — Aquatic birds with beak covered by a soft, sensitive membrane and edged with horny lamellæ; two suborders and two families. Examples: PALAMEDEIDÆ, Screamers; ANATIDÆ, Swans, Geese, and Ducks (Fig. 492).

Order 15. Falconiformes. — FALCON-LIKE BIRDS. — Carnivorous birds with curved beak, hooked at the end; feet adapted for perching and provided with strong, sharp claws; three suborders and four families. Examples: CATHARTIDÆ, American Vultures; GYPOGERANIDÆ, Secretary-birds; FALCONIDÆ, Falcons; BUTEONIDÆ, Eagles, Hawks, Vultures, etc. (Figs. 493–495).

Order 16. Galliformes. — Fowl-like Birds. — Terrestrial or arboreal birds with feet adapted for perching; four suborders and seven families. Examples: Phasianidæ, Turkeys, Quails, Pheasant, etc.; Opisthocomidæ, Hoactzin.

Order 17. Gruiformes. — Crane-like Birds. — Mostly marsh birds; seven families. Examples: Rallidæ, Rails; Gruidæ, Cranes.

Order 18. Charadriiformes. — Plover-like Birds. — Terrestrial, arboreal, or marine birds; four suborders and twelve families. Examples: Charadriidæ, Plovers (Fig. 496), Snipes, and Curlews; Laridæ, Gulls and Terns (Fig. 497); Alcidæ, Auks (Fig. 498); Columbidæ, Pigeons (Fig. 470).

Order 19. Cuculiformes. — Cuckoo-like Birds. — Arboreal birds with first and fourth toes directed backwards; fourth toe may be reversible; two suborders and four families. Examples: Cuculidæ, Cuckoos (Fig. 499); Psittacidæ, Cockatoos and Parrots.

Order 20. Coraciiformes. — Roller-like Birds. — Arboreal birds with short legs; seven suborders and eighteen families. Examples: Coraciidæ, Rollers; Alcedinidæ, Kingfishers (Fig. 500); Strigidæ, Owls (Fig. 501); Caprimulgidæ, Goat-suckers; Trochilidæ, Humming-birds; Micropodidæ, Swifts (Fig. 502); Picidæ, Woodpeckers (Fig. 503).

Order 21. Passeriformes. — Sparrow-like Birds. — More than half of all the birds known belong to this order. There are two suborders, four superfamilies, and sixty-four families. The twenty-five North American families are as follows: —

Family	Common Name
1. Tyrannidæ	Tyrant Flycatchers (Fig. 504, A)
2. Cotingidæ	Cotingas
3. Alaudidæ	Larks
4. Motacillidæ	Wagtails
5. Turdidæ	Thrushes, Bluebirds, etc.
6. Mimidæ	Thrashers, Mocking-birds, etc. (Fig. 504, H)
7. Cinclidæ	Dippers
8. Troglodytidæ	Wrens (Fig. 504, G)
9. Chamæidæ	Wren-Tits
10. Sylviidæ	Warblers, Kinglets, and Gnatcatchers
11. Hirundinidæ	Swallows (Fig. 504, E)
12. Bombycillidæ	Waxwings (Fig. 504, F)

F<small>AMILY</small>	C<small>OMMON</small> N<small>AME</small>
13. P<small>TILOGONATIDÆ</small>	Silky Flycatchers
14. L<small>ANIIDÆ</small>	Shrikes
15. V<small>IREONIDÆ</small>	Vireos
16. S<small>ITTIDÆ</small>	Nuthatches
17. P<small>ARIDÆ</small>	Titmice
18. C<small>ORVIDÆ</small>	Crows, Jays, etc. (Fig. 504, B)
19. S<small>TURNIDÆ</small>	Starlings
20. C<small>ERTHIIDÆ</small>	Creepers
21. C<small>ŒREBIDÆ</small>	Honey Creepers
22. M<small>NIOTILTIDÆ</small>	Wood Warblers
23. T<small>ANAGRIDÆ</small>	Tanagers
24. I<small>CTERIDÆ</small>	Blackbirds, Orioles, etc. (Fig. 504, C)
25. F<small>RINGILLIDÆ</small>	Finches, Sparrows, etc. (Fig. 504, D)

3. A R<small>EVIEW</small> <small>OF</small> <small>THE</small> O<small>RDERS</small> <small>AND</small> F<small>AMILIES</small> <small>OF</small> B<small>IRDS</small>

It is, of course, impossible in the limited space that can be devoted to birds in this book to give anything more than a brief survey of the subject. Most of the families that are considered are represented by living species inhabiting the United States.

S<small>UBCLASS</small> I. A<small>RCHÆORNITHES</small>. — The single genus, *Archæopteryx* (Fig. 477), belonging to this subclass is known from a feather and two fairly complete skeletons that were found in the lithographic slates of Solenhofen, Bavaria, of the Upper Jurassic period. *Archæopteryx* was about the size of a crow. It possessed teeth embedded in sockets, fore limbs with three clawed digits (Fig. 477, I, II, III) and separate metacarpal bones, and a lizard-like tail with large feathers (rectrices) on either side. The bird-like characteristics predominate over the reptilian features so that this curious creature is placed in the class A<small>VES</small>, although it is a connecting link between the birds and the reptiles.

S<small>UBCLASS</small> II. N<small>EORNITHES</small>. — R<small>ECENT</small> B<small>IRDS</small>.

Order 1. Hesperornithiformes. — There are three species of fossil birds in this order. *Hesperornis regalis* (Fig. 478), the best-known species, was nearly four feet in length. It possessed teeth set in a groove, strong hind limbs with webbed feet, which were used like oars, and a sternum without a keel. The entire anatomy indicates that *Hesperornis* was a flightless, swimming and diving bird which lived upon fishes and other aquatic animals. The remains of this and the two other species probably belonging to this order were found in the Cretaceous deposits of Kansas.

Order 2. **Ichthyornithiformes.** — Of the dozen or more species of fossil birds included in this order, *Ichthyornis victor* (Fig. 479) from the Cretaceous deposits of Kansas, is the best known. This bird had teeth set in sockets, a keeled sternum, and well-developed

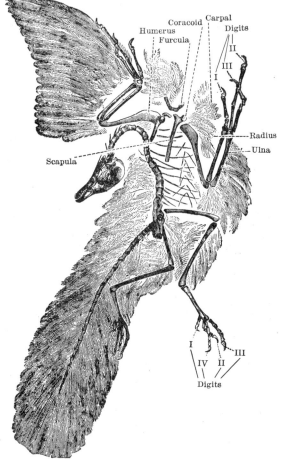

Fig. 477. — *Archæopteryx lithographica.* (From Zittel, after Steinmann and Doderlein.)

wings. It was about the size of a pigeon, was a strong flier, and probably fed upon fish.

Order 3. **Struthioniformes.** — Ostriches. — The ostriches are the largest living birds, attaining a height of more than eight feet, and a weight of over three hundred pounds. Four species are

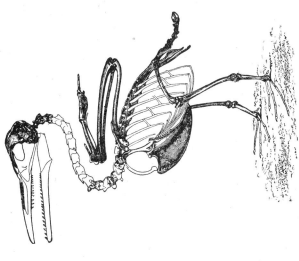

Fig. 479. — *Ichthyornis victor.*   (From Zittel, after Marsh.)

Fig. 478. — *Hesperornis regalis.*   (From Zittel, after Marsh.)

recognized by some authorities. The ostriches or camel birds of North Africa, *Struthio camelus* (Fig. 480), live in desert regions

and travel about in groups, usually of from four to twenty. They are very suspicious and flee from any signs of danger. They do not stick their heads in the sand and think themselves hidden, as commonly reported. Their speed is remarkable, reaching sixty miles an hour, and their single strides may measure more than twenty-five feet. They are omnivorous, feeding upon many kinds of plants and animals. The nest is a hollow in the sand, and several females lay their eggs in a single nest. Each egg weighs from three to four pounds. The males do most of the incubating. The young, which appear in six or seven weeks, run about as soon as they emerge from the shell.

FIG. 480. — Ostrich, *Struthio camelus*. (From Evans.)

Ostrich feathers are now procured almost entirely from domesticated birds. Ostrich farming is now successfully carried on in California, Arizona, Arkansas, North Carolina, and Florida. The feathers are clipped without pain to the birds; those from a single adult weigh about one pound.

Order 4. Rheiformes. — RHEAS. — These are the New-world ostriches (Fig. 481). There are three species inhabiting the pampas of South America. They are smaller than the true ostriches, but their habits are quite similar.

FIG. 481. — Rhea, *Rhea americana*. (From Evans.)

Order 5. Casuariiformes. — CASSOWARIES and EMEUS. — The two families in this order contain ostrich-like birds; the DRO-MÆIDÆ or emeus (Fig. 482), which are, next to the ostriches, the largest of living birds, are confined to Australia; the CASUARIIDÆ or cassowaries inhabit New Guinea and neighboring islands. The cassowaries usually possess a bony, helmet-like knot on the head, and have brightly colored lobes on the head and neck; these are absent in emeus.

FIG. 482. — Emeu, *Dromæus novæhollandiæ*. (From Evans.)

Order 6. Crypturiformes. — TINA-MOUS. — About forty species of tina-mous are known. They resemble game-birds in appearance and are called partridges by the natives of southern Mexico and Central and South America, where they live. The powers of flight of the tinamous are not well developed. In size they range from a length of six inches to that of the rufous or great tinamou, *Rhynchotus rufescens* (Fig. 483), of Brazil, which is fourteen inches long. Tinamous are solitary birds, but may band together into coveys. They make a nest by scratching a hollow in the earth and lining it with grasses, leaves, and feathers. The eggs number from five to a dozen or more to a setting; they are incubated by the male.

FIG. 483.—Great tinamou, *Rhynchotus rufescens*. (From Evans.)

Order 7. Dinornithiformes. — MOAS (Fig. 484). — The moas have probably become extinct within the past five hundred years. The remains of these peculiar birds have been found in great numbers in caves and refuse heaps in New Zealand, to which country they appear to have been confined. Twenty or thirty species are known from these remains. They ranged in size from that of a turkey to nearly ten feet high. They were flightless, but possessed enormous hind limbs.

Order 8. Æpyornithiformes. — ELEPHANT-BIRDS. — These birds have probably become extinct within the past five centuries. They inhabited Madagascar, were flightless, and possessed hind limbs more enormous even than those of the moas. Many of their eggs have been found in the sand near the seashore; they are more than thirteen inches in length and nine inches wide, and have a capacity of over two gallons.

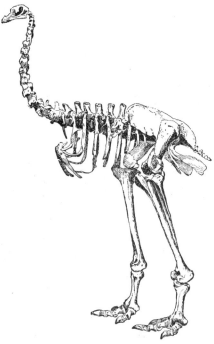

FIG. 484. — Moa, *Palapteryx elephantopus*. (From Zittel, after Owen.)

Order 9. Apterygiformes. — KIWIS. — These wingless birds of New Zealand belong to the single genus *Apteryx* (Fig. 485) and to five or six species. They are about the size of a common fowl; their wings are aborted, and they lack tail-feathers. In habit, they are nocturnal, feeding upon worms, which they probe for with their long beaks, and also upon vegetable matter. The nest is made in a hole in the ground, and one or two large eggs are laid.

Order 10. Spheniseiformes. — PENGUINS. — The penguins, of which about twenty living species are known, are confined to the rocky and barren islands of the Antarctic region. They are adapted for life in the water; the fore limbs are modified as paddles for swimming; the feet are webbed; the cold water can be shaken

FIG. 485. — Kiwi, *Apteryx australis*. (From Evans.)

entirely from the feathers; and a layer of fat just beneath the skin serves to keep in the bodily heat. They feed on fishes and other marine animals. On shore they stand erect (Fig. 486), side

Fig. 486. — Penguins or rock-hoppers, *Eudyptes chrysocome*. (From Evans, after Thomson.)

by side. They nest in colonies, laying the one or two eggs either among the rocks or in a burrow.

Order 11. Colymbiformes. — LOONS and GREBES.

FAMILY GAVIIDÆ. — LOONS or DIVERS (Fig. 487). — The one genus, *Gavia*, and five species of loons inhabit the northern half of the northern hemisphere. They are large birds with strong powers of flight, and with an ability to swim and dive that is not surpassed by any other species. Loons are awkward on land. The two eggs are laid in a slight depression in the ground, near water.

FAMILY PODICIPE-DIDÆ. — GREBES. —

Fig. 487. — Loon. (From Evans.)

The grebes are smaller than the loons, but are excellent swimmers and divers. There are about twenty-five species in the family,

distributed throughout the world, chiefly about fresh waters.   The
six to eight eggs are laid in a nest consisting usually of a mass
of floating rushes.

Order 12.   Procellariiformes. — ALBATROSSES and PETRELS.
— These are marine
birds with tubular ex-
ternal nostrils, fully
webbed toes, and long,
narrow wings.   They
are strong fliers, gre-
garious, and come to
land rarely except to
lay their eggs.   There
are about fifteen spe-
cies of albatrosses; six
of these have been re-
ported   from   North
America.   The wandering albatross, *Diomedea exulans* (Fig. 488),
is over three and a half feet in length, and has a spread of wing
of over ten feet.

FIG. 488. — Wandering albatross, *Diomedea exulans*.
(From Evans.)

FIG. 489. — Stormy Petrel, *Procellaria pelagica*.   (From Evans.)

The petrels, fulmars, and shearwaters, of which there are about
seventy species, belong to the family PROCELLARIIDÆ.   The fulmars are large gull-like birds.   The common fulmar, *Fulmarus
glacialis*, is abundant. in the North Atlantic.   It lays its single

white egg on crags over the sea. The shearwaters are very restless birds that inhabit all oceans. The common Atlantic shearwater is *Puffinus major*. The stormy petrels are small birds under ten inches in length. The common stormy petrel, *Procellaria pelagica* (Fig. 489), is known from the Atlantic and Mediterranean coasts of Europe, Africa, and North America.

Order 13. Ciconiiformes. — Stork-like Birds. — This order includes the tropic birds, cormorants, anhingas, pelicans, gannets, man-o'-war birds, herons, bitterns, boatbills, shoebills, hammerheads, storks, ibises, spoonbills, and flamingos. Most of these

Fig. 490. — Great blue heron spreading its wing. (Photo by Hegner.)

birds have long legs, long, slender necks, elongated bills, and feet fitted for wading or swimming.

The pelicans (Family Pelecanidæ) possess a huge membranous pouch between the branches of the lower jaw, with which they scoop up small fish (Fig. 507, g). The cormorants (Family Phalacrocoracidæ) comprise the majority of the species in the order. They are almost cosmopolitan and very sociable. In China and a few other countries these birds are trained to catch fish and are of considerable value to their owners. The common cormorant, or shag, *Phalacrocorax carbo*, occurs on the Atlantic coast of Europe and North America and breeds on the rocky shores of Labrador and Newfoundland.

The herons and bitterns (Family ARDEIDÆ) possess long legs fitted for wading, broad wings, and short tails. They are found in the warmer regions of the globe and feed chiefly on fishes. The great blue heron, *Ardea herodias* (Fig. 490), is a large species occurring in all parts of North America. It is about four feet long and has an extent of wings of about six feet. Its large flat nest is built of coarse sticks usually in the top of a high tree; four to six greenish blue eggs are laid.

FIG. 491.—Flamingo, *Phœnicopterus roseus*. (From Evans.)

The seven species of flamingos (Family PHŒNICOPTARIDÆ, Fig. 491) inhabit the tropics; one of them occurs in Florida. They are gregarious birds, congregating in thousands on mud flats where they build their conical mud nests. They are rosy vermilion in general color.

Order 14. Anseriformes. — GOOSE-LIKE BIRDS. — These birds are either adapted for swimming, with short legs and fully webbed front toes, or for wading, with large feet and a short decurved bill. Their young are entirely covered with down and can swim or run about soon after hatching, *i.e.* are precocious. The screamers (Family PALAMEDEIDÆ) are all natives of South America. The family ANATIDÆ contains about two hundred and ten species of duck-like birds which are aquatic or semi-aquatic in habits, and cosmopolitan in distribution.

There are five North American subfamilies of the ANATIDÆ: (1) the swans, CYGNINÆ; (2) the geese, ANSERINÆ; (3) the river-ducks, ANATINÆ; (4) the sea-ducks, FULIGULINÆ; and (5) the mergansers, MERGINÆ.

The most beautiful of all our ducks is the wood-duck, *Aix sponsa* (Fig. 492). This bird ranges over the entire United States. Its favorite haunts are the smaller streams, lakes, and ponds. The eggs, from six to fifteen in number, are laid in cavities in the trunks or limbs of trees. The wood-duck is one of our game-birds that is decreasing so rapidly in numbers that it seems on the verge of extinction, and drastic action must be taken by the federal and state governments if this species is not to vanish entirely.

Order 15. Falconi-formes. — FALCON-LIKE BIRDS. — These diurnal birds of prey possess, in most cases, powerful wings, a stout, hooked bill with a cere at the base, and strong toes armed with sharp claws. The order is divided into the CATHARTIDÆ, or American vultures, the GYPOGERANIDÆ, or secretary-birds, the

FIG. 492. — Wood-duck, *Aix sponsa.* (From Brehm.)

FALCONIDÆ, or falcons, and the BUTEONIDÆ, or eagles, hawks, kites, etc.

The nine or ten species of American vultures are weaker than the other FALCONIFORMES. They live on carrion and are valuable in warm countries as scavengers. The species occurring in the United States are the turkey-vulture or turkey-buzzard, *Cathartes aura,* the black vulture or carrion crow, *Catharista urubu,* and the California vulture, *Gymnogyps californianus.* The California vulture and the condor, *Sarcorhamphus gryphus* (Fig. 493), which lives in the Andes Mountains, are two of the largest of flying birds.

The secretary-bird, *Gypogeranus secretarius,* of South Africa, is the only

FIG. 493. — Condor, *Sarcorhamphus gryphus.* (From Evans.)

representative of the family GYPOGERANIDÆ. Its common name was suggested by the resemblance of some plumes on its head to a bunch of quills stuck behind the ear of a clerk. Secretary-birds feed on frogs, toads, insects, and snakes.

The FALCONIDÆ are the falcons, tropical goshawks, and caracaras. About seventeen species of the genus *Falco* are found in North America. The white gyrfalcon, *F. islandus*, inhabits the Arctic regions; the prairie-falcon, *F. mexicanus*, occurs in the western United States; the duck-hawk, *F. peregrinus anatum*, ranges over both North and South America; the pigeon-hawk, *F. columbarius columbarius*, is a North American species; and the sparrowhawk, *F. sparverius sparverius*, inhabits North America east of the Rocky Mountains. All of these birds are of medium size and active. The wings are long and pointed, and the bill has a pronounced notch and tooth.

FIG. 494. — Red-tailed hawk about to sit on her eggs. The nest was in a birch tree 40 feet from the ground. The bird is taking her own picture by sitting on a string which was attached to the shutter of a camera placed in a near-by tree. (Photo by Hegner.)

The two species of caracaras that reach the United States are known as carrion-buzzards. Audubon's caracara, *Polyborus cheriway*, is found in Florida. It lives largely on carrion, but also captures frogs, lizards, and snakes.

The BUTEONIDÆ are the kites, buzzards, eagles, hawks, ospreys, old-world vultures, and harriers. Common North American representatives of these groups are the swallow-tailed kite, *Elanoides forficatus*, which occurs in the warm temperate regions; the osprey, or fish-hawk, *Pandion haliaëtus carolinensis*, inhabiting temperate and tropical America; the bald eagle, *Haliaëtus leucocephalus*, generally distributed in North America; the red-shouldered hawk, *Buteo lineatus;* Swainson's hawk, *Buteo swainsoni;* the marsh-hawk, or harrier, *Circus hudsonius;* the red-tailed hawk, or buzzard, *Buteo borealis* (Fig. 494); the Cooper's hawk, *Accipiter cooperi* (Fig. 495); and the goshawk, *Astur atricapillus.*

Order 16. Galliformes. — FOWL-LIKE BIRDS. — This is a widely distributed group containing seven families, only two of which have North American representatives: (1) the CRACIDÆ or curassows and guans, with one species in Texas; and (2) the PHASIANIDÆ, or turkeys, partridges, etc.

The PHASIANIDÆ are the true game-birds, and are known as bob-whites, quail, grouse, partridges, ptarmigan, chickens, hens, and turkeys. Among the best-known species inhabiting the United States are the wild turkey, *Meleagris gallopavo silvestris,* which is the largest American game-bird and a native species, but now nearly extinct; the bob-white, or quail, *Colinus virginianus;* the ruffed grouse, *Bonasa umbellus;* the willow ptarmigan, *Lagopus,* of the Arctic regions; and the prairie-chicken, *Tympanuchus americanus.*

FIG. 495. — Cooper's hawk, *Accipiter cooperi.* (From Fisher, Yearbook U. S. Dep't. Agric., 1894.)

The game-birds are, as a rule, terrestrial, but many of them roost or feed in trees. Their nests are usually made on the ground in grass or leaves, and generally a large number of eggs, from six to eighteen, are laid. The members of one family often remain together as a " covey," and in some species the coveys unite to form large flocks.

Order 17. Gruiformes. — CRANE-LIKE BIRDS. — The seven families belonging to this order contain mostly wading birds with incompletely webbed front toes. The families RALLIDÆ and GRUIDÆ are represented by North American species.

The RALLIDÆ are the rails, gallinules, and coots. The rails are seldom seen, spending most of their time among the reeds and rushes in marshes. The king-rail, *Rallus elegans*, of eastern North America, is a large species, being about eighteen inches in length. The gallinules also inhabit marshes. The Florida gallinule, *Gallinula galeata*, is a common form. The coots are frequently called mud-hens, and sometimes hell-divers, because of their ability to dive quickly. There is only one common species, *Fulica americana*.

The GRUIDÆ are the cranes, courlans, and trumpeters. The cranes are large birds with long legs and neck. They live in grassy plains and marshes. The whooping-crane, *Grus americana*, meas-

Fig. 496. — Killdeer plover standing over her nest and four eggs among the pebbles near a small stream. (Photo by Hegner.)

ures about four and a half feet in length, and has a spread of wings of about eight feet. It breeds in central North America, making a nest of grasses and weed stalks on marshy ground.

Order 18. Charadriiformes. — PLOVER-LIKE BIRDS. — Five of the twelve families in this order have North American representatives: (1) the CHARADRIIDÆ, plovers, snipes, and curlews; (2) the JACANIDÆ, jacanas; (3) the LARIDÆ, gulls, terns, and skimmers; (4) the ALCIDÆ, auks; and (5) the COLUMBIDÆ, pigeons.

The CHARADRIIDÆ are the turnstones, oyster-catchers, lapwings, true plovers, dotterels, avocets, stilts, phalaropes, sandpipers, curlews, whimbrels, woodcock, snipe, and dowitchers. The killdeer (Fig. 496), which may be taken as an example of this enormous family, occurs throughout temperate North America. It lives in the vicinity of water. The four eggs are laid in a hollow in the ground, and the young are able to run about as soon as hatched.

The JACANIDÆ are tropical marsh-birds, with very long toes and claws enabling them to walk over lily pads without sinking. The Mexican jacana, *Jacana spinosa*, reaches Texas.

The LARIDÆ are known as gulls, terns, skimmers, kittiwakes, noddies, skuas, and jægers. The American herring-gulls, *Larus argentatus*, are about two feet long. They breed along the

FIG. 497. — Common tern, *Sterna hirundo*. (From Davenport, after Fuertes.)

Atlantic coast and also in the interior from Minnesota northwards. Their nests are built on the ground of grasses, seaweed, etc., and two or three eggs are laid. The terns, or sea-swallows (Fig. 497), are as a rule smaller and slimmer than the gulls. They frequent the shores of both fresh and salt water, feed upon fish, and nest in colonies. The black skimmer, *Rynchops nigra*, is found along our Atlantic coast. It flies along the surface of the water with its lower mandible immersed, and literally skims small aquatic animals from the top.

The ALCIDÆ are the puffins, auklets, murrelets, murres, guillemots, and true auks. They spend a large part of their existence at sea. Most of them are strong fliers, and excellent swimmers and divers, but very awkward on land. They feed on fish, crustaceans, and other small marine animals, and nest in colonies, usually on rocky shores. The puffins, or sea-parrots, are grotesque-looking birds with enormous beaks that are grooved and brightly colored.

The murres possess bills which are narrow and without grooves.

The true auks are North American birds represented by three species. The great auk, or garefowl, *Plautus impennis* (Fig. 498), became extinct in 1844, when the last one appears to have been killed. They were destroyed for their feathers, and their eggs were used as food. " All that remains to-day of the Great Auk are about seventy skins, sixty-five eggs, and some twenty-five more

FIG. 498. — Great auk, *Plautus impennis*. (From Evans, after Hancock.)

or less perfect but composite skeletons, that is, skeletons made up from the bones of many different individuals." (Knowlton.)

The COLUMBIDÆ are the pigeons or doves (Fig. 470) of which twelve of the three hundred known species occur in North America. The passenger-pigeon, *Ectopistes migratorius*, is another bird that is practically extinct, although flocks were seen a century ago that contained over two billion birds. The mourning-dove *Zenaidura macroura*, is common and often mistaken for the passenger-pigeon. It makes a flimsy nest of a few twigs and lays two white eggs. The young are naked when born and are fed by regurgitation.

FIG. 499. — Yellow-billed cuckoo, *Coccyzus americanus*. (From Judd, Bul. 17, Bur. Biol. Survey, U. S. Dep't. Agric.)

Order 19. Cuculiformes. —

CUCKOO-LIKE BIRDS. — This order contains the cuckoos, plantaineaters, lories, nestors, cockatoos, and parrots. The cuckoos (Family CUCULIDÆ) are mostly tropical birds. The majority of them do not build a nest, but lay their eggs in the nests of other birds. This is not true, however, of the North American species. The black-billed and yellow-billed cuckoos (Fig. 499) of this country are long, slender birds of solitary habits and with the peculiar vocal powers which have given them their common name.

The American species of parrots, about one hundred and fifty in number, are included in the family PSITTACIDÆ. Only one species, the Carolina paroquet, *Conuropsis carolinensis*, occurs in the United States. Parrots and paroquets live in forests and feed on fruits and seeds. They have shrill voices, but can, with few exceptions, be taught to talk. The African parrot, *Psittacus erythacus*, learns to talk most readily.

Fig. 500. — Belted kingfisher. (Photo by Hegner.)

Order 20. Coraciiformes. — ROLLER-LIKE BIRDS. — The birds placed in this order may be grouped into seven suborders, and about eighteen families. They include the rollers, motmots, kingfishers, bee-eaters, hornbills, hoopoes, oil-birds, frogmouths, goatsuckers, humming-birds, swifts, colies, trogons, puff-birds, jacamars, barbets, honey-guides, toucans, woodpeckers, wrynecks, and owls.

There are about two hundred species and subspecies of king-fishers (ALCEDINIDÆ), three of which occur in North America. The belted kingfisher, *Ceryle alcyon* (Fig. 500), breeds from Florida to Labrador. Its five to eight white eggs are laid at the end of a horizontal hole about six feet deep dug by the birds usually in the bank of a stream. The kingfisher captures small fish by hovering over a stream and then plunging into the water and securing the unsuspecting prey in its bill.

The owls (STRIGIDÆ) are the nocturnal birds of prey. They possess large, rounded heads, strong legs, feet armed with sharp claws, strong bills with the upper mandible curved downward, large eyes directed forward and surrounded by a radiating disc of feathers, and soft, fluffy plumage which renders them noiseless during flight. Owls feed upon insects, mice, rats, and other small mammals, birds, and fish. The indigestible parts of the food are cast out of the mouth in the form of pellets. Most species are beneficial to man.

The screech owl (Fig. 501) is one of the most common North American species. It nests in hollow trees. Four to six white eggs are laid. Its food consists principally of mice and insects.

The goatsuckers (CAPRIMULGIDÆ) are represented in North America by thirteen species, of which the whippoorwill and night-

hawk are the best known. The whippoorwill, *Antrostomus vociferus*, inhabits the woods and thickets of eastern North America. It is most active after sundown and early in the morning, when it captures its insect food while on the wing. The two eggs are laid on the leaves in the woods. The night-hawk, *Chordeiles virginianus*, has a range similar to that of the whippoorwill. During the day it perches on

FIG. 501. — Screech owl. (Photo by Hegner.)

a limb, fence post, or on the ground, but in the evening it mounts into the air after its insect prey. The two eggs are laid on the bare ground, usually on a hillside or in an open field; often they are deposited on the gravel roofs of city buildings.

The humming-birds (TROCHILIDÆ), which are confined to the New World, have been appropriately called feathered gems, or, according to Audubon, " glittering fragments of the rainbow." Only seventeen of the five hundred or more species occur in the United States, and only one, the ruby-throated humming-bird, *Trochilus colubris*, is found east of the Mississippi River. This beautiful little bird is only three and three-quarters inches in length. It hovers before flowers, from which it obtains nectar, small insects, and spiders. The nest, which is saddled on the limb of a tree, is made of plant down and so covered with lichens as to resemble its surroundings very closely. Two tiny white eggs are laid. The young are fed by regurgitation.

The swifts (MICROPODIDÆ) resemble the swallows superficially, but their anatomy shows that there is no real resemblance between the two groups. Of the one hundred species and sub-species of swifts, four are inhabitants of North America, and one, the chimney-swift *Chætura pelagica* (Fig. 502), breeds commonly in eastern North America. This species formerly made its nest in hollow trees, but now usually frequents chimneys. When in the open air it is always on the wing, catching insects or gathering twigs from the dead branches of trees for its nest. The twigs are glued together with saliva and firmly fastened to the inside of the chimney, forming a cup-shaped nest.

FIG. 502. — Chimney swift sitting on nest which was attached to the inside of a chimney twenty feet from the top. (Photo by Hegner.)

Certain species of swifts inhabiting China make nests entirely of a secretion from the salivary glands, producing the edible birds'-nests of the Chinese.

The woodpeckers (PICIDÆ), comprising about three hundred and fifty species, are found in wooded regions almost everywhere except in the Australian region and Madagascar. About fifty species occur in North America. The downy (Fig. 503), hairy, and red-headed woodpeckers, the flicker, and the yellow-bellied sapsucker are the best known. Woodpeckers use their chisel-shaped bills for excavating holes in trees, at the bottom of which their eggs are laid, or for digging out grubs from beneath the bark. Most of them are of great benefit because of the insects they destroy, but the yellow-bellied sapsucker is harmful, since it eats the cambium of trees and sucks sap.

Order 21. Passeriformes. — SPARROW-LIKE BIRDS (Fig. 504). — It is necessary, because of lack of space, to refer the student to books on birds for a detailed account of the birds included in this order. On page 526 will be found a list of the principal families. Almost half, about seven thousand species and subspecies, of all the birds known belong to this order. They are grouped into sixty-four families; representatives belonging to twenty-five of these occur in North America.

Passerine birds are usually small or of medium size, but are the most highly organized of the class AVES. Their feet are four-toed and adapted for grasping. The first toe, or hallux, is directed backward, and is on a level with the other three, which are directed forward.

FIG. 503. — Downy woodpecker at entrance to nest-hole in a dead poplar tree. Her bill is filled with insects which she has captured on near-by trees and is about to feed to her young within the hole. (Photo by Hegner.)

Two superfamilies of the PASSERIFORMES have North American representatives, the CLAMATORES and the OSCINES. The CLAMATORES are non-melodious birds, with a syrinx which is ineffective as a musical apparatus. Only two families occur in this country: (1) the COTINGIDÆ or chatterers, with one species recorded from Arizona; and (2) the TYRANNIDÆ, or tyrant fly-catchers, with a large number of common species, such as the kingbird, phœbe, and wood-pewee.

The OSCINES are the singing birds. Twenty-five of the forty-nine families are known from North America. Many of the "singing-birds" are almost voiceless, but their structure necessitates their inclusion in the superfamily.

4. A General Account of the Class Aves

a. *Form and Function*

The bodies of birds have become adapted to various environments. This adaptation is best shown by the wings, tails, feet, and bills.

Wings. — The wings of most birds are used as organs of flight, and the more time spent in the air, the longer and stronger they become. Birds like the swallows, gulls, and albatrosses have long, pointed wings characteristic of aerial birds; whereas terrestrial birds, such as the bob-white and song-sparrow, possess

Fig. 504. — Types of common passerine birds.   (From Judd, Bul. 17, Bur. Biol. Survey, U. S. Dep't Agric.) **A**, kingbird, *Tyrannus tyrannus* (TYRANNIDÆ). **B**, blue jay, *Cyanocitta cristata* (CORVIDÆ).   **C**, bobolink, *Dolichonyx oryzivorus* (ICTERIDÆ).   **D**, song-sparrow, *Melospiza melodia* (FRINGILLIDÆ).   **E**, barn-swallow, *Hirundo erythrogastra* (HIRUNDINIDÆ).   **F**, cedar waxwing, *Bombycilla cedrorum* (Bombycillidæ).   **G**, house wren, *Troglodytes aedon* (TROGLODYTIDÆ). **H**, mocking bird, *Mimus polyglottus* (MIMIDÆ).

short, rounded wings which enable them to fly rapidly for short distances. Many species of birds that spend their lives mostly in the water possess wings, but are unable to fly. For example, the wings of the penguins (Fig. 486) are like flippers and covered with scale-like feathers; they are moved alternately and are the sole organs of locomotion in swimming under water, the legs being used simply as a rudder. Other sea-birds, like the auks and murres (ALCIDÆ), use their wings effectively in diving beneath the waves.

Among the flightless birds belong a number of terrestrial species, like the ostrich (Fig. 480), rhea (Fig. 481), emeu (Fig. 482), and kiwi (Fig. 485). These birds all possess the remnants of wings,

Fig. 505. — **A**, lyre-bird, *Menura superba*. (From Evans.) **B**, bird of paradise, *Paradisea rubra*. (From Brehm.)

but these are, for the most part, of no use in locomotion, and in some (Fig. 485) are practically concealed beneath the feathers. Their legs are, on the other hand, very well developed, and quickly carry them out of danger.

The primitive use of wings was for climbing. *Archæopteryx* (Fig. 477) was provided with three strong claws on its fore limbs. Of living birds the young of the hoactzin, a peculiar bird inhabiting South America, should be mentioned, since it is able to climb about before it can fly, by the aid of two claws on each fore limb.

Wings may also serve as organs of offense and defense, or as musical instruments; for example, the " drumming " of the ruffed grouse.

Tails. — During flight the tail acts as an aerial rudder, and a long-tailed bird is able to fly in short curves, or follow an erratic course without difficulty. The tail is light, and therefore easy to manage, and the tail-feathers (*rectrices*, Fig. 471) are firmly supported by the terminal bone of fused vertebræ, the pygostyle (Fig. 471). Movement of the tail is allowed by the freely movable

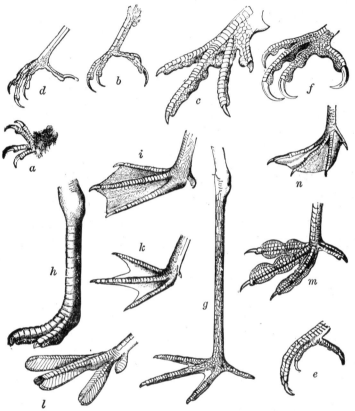

FIG. 506. — The most important forms of birds' feet. *a*, clinging foot of a swift, *Cypselus;* *b*, climbing foot of woodpecker, *Picus;* *c*, scratching foot of pheasant, *Phasianus;* *d*, perching foot of ouzel, *Turdus;* *e*, foot of kingfisher, *Alecdo;* *f*, seizing foot of falcon, *Falco;* *g*, wading foot of stork, *Mycteria;* *h*, running foot of ostrich, *Struthio;* *i*, swimming foot of duck, *Mergus;* *k*, wading foot of avocet, *Recurvirostra;* *l*, diving foot of grebe, *Podicepes;* *m*, wading foot of coot, *Fulica;* *n*, swimming foot of tropic-bird, *Phaeton.* (From Sedgwick's Zoology: *b, c, d, f, n,* from règne animal.)

vertebræ just preceding the pygostyle. While perching the tail acts as a " balancer." Birds that cling to the sides of trees, like the woodpeckers (Fig. 503), or to the sides of other objects, like the chimney-swift, brace themselves by means of their tails.

In many birds the tail of the male differs from that of the female, being more beautiful in the former, and serving as a sexual character. Two of the most famous of these dimorphic species are the lyre-bird (Fig. 505, A) and the birds of paradise (Fig. 505, B).

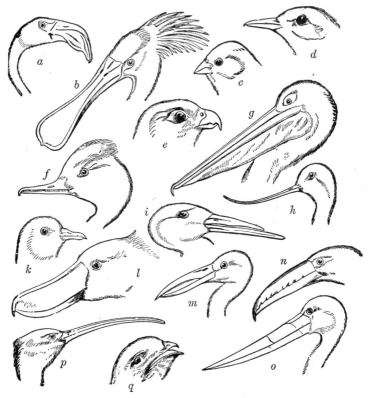

FIG. 507. — The most important forms of birds' beaks. *a*, flamingo, *Phœnicopterus;* *b*, spoonbill, *Platalea;* *c*, yellow bunting, *Emberiza;* *d*, thrush, *Turuds;* *e*, falcon, *Falco;* *f*, duck, *Mergus;* *g*, pelican, *Pelicanus;* *h*, avocet, *Recurvirostra;* *i*, black skimmer, *Rhynchops;* *k*, pigeon, *Columba;* *l*, shoebill, *Balœniceps;* *m*, stork, *Anastomus;* *n*, aracari, *Pteroglossus;* *o*, stork, *Mycteria;* *p*, bird of paradise, *Falcinellus;* *q*, swift, *Cypselus.* (From Sedgwick's Zoology: *a, b, c, d, k,* after Naumann; *g, i, m, o,* after règne animal; *l,* after Brehm.)

Feet. — The feet (Fig. 506) are used for locomotion, for obtaining food, for building nests, and for offensive and defensive purposes. Ground-birds usually have strong feet, fitted for running (Fig. 506, *h*), or scratching (*c*); perching birds (see p. 546) possess feet adapted for grasping a perch (*d*); aerial birds

use their feet very little, and these organs are consequently weak
(*a*, *e*); swimming birds (*i*, *l*, *n*) and wading birds (*g*, *k*, *m*) are
provided with toes that are more or less completely lobed; birds
of prey possess strong feet with sharp claws (*f*) for capturing other
animals; woodpeckers have feet (*b*) adapted for clinging to the
bark of trees.

Bills. — The bills of birds (Fig. 507) serve as hands, and their
most important function is to procure food. Since bills are also
used to construct nests, to preen feathers, and to perform other
duties, their adaptations are such as to make them serve several
purposes. In preening the feathers a drop of oil is pressed from
the oil-gland at the base of the tail and spread by means of the
bill.

Seed-eating birds possess short, strong bills for crushing seeds
(Fig. 507, *c*); birds that eat insects have longer and weaker bills
(*d*, *q*); birds of prey are provided with strong, curved beaks fitted
for tearing flesh (*e*); the pelicans (*g*) and skimmers (*i*) scoop up
fishes and other animals from the water; and the avocet (*h*) uses
its long, curved bill like a scythe, swinging it from side to side
near the bottom in shallow water and securing food it cannot see;
the bill of the woodpecker serves as a chisel; and that of the woodcock as a probe for capturing small animals in the muddy shores
of ponds and streams. Many other examples might be cited.

b. *The Colors of Birds*

Birds are among the most beautifully colored of all animals.
This color is due to pigments within the feathers (chemical colors)
or to structural peculiarities, such as prismatic shapes which break
up the rays of light into their component colors (physical colors),
or to both causes. Nestling birds possess distinctively colored
feathers which later give way to the " immature plumage "; this
is worn usually throughout the first winter, and is generally dull
in color, often resembling the plumage of the adult female. Males
and females frequently differ in color (sexual dimorphism), especially during the breeding season, when the male acquires a
brightly colored coat. The attempt to explain this difference
has led to the theory of sexual selection.[1]

One important use of color is its protective value to the bird.

[1] Darwin, The Descent of Man and Selection in Relation to Sex.

The colors and color patterns of birds, as well as other animals, are such as to conceal these animals amid their surroundings.[1]

c. *Bird Songs*

The songs of birds, as explained on page 522, are produced by the air passing through the syrinx. For one who wishes to study birds, a knowledge of bird songs is indispensable, since one hears a great many more birds than he is able to see. Songs should be distinguished from call-notes. The former are usually heard during the breeding season, and are generally limited to the males. Call-notes, on the other hand, are uttered throughout the year, and correspond in their meaning and effect to our conversation. By means of call-notes a bird is able to express anxiety or fear, and to communicate to a limited extent with other birds.

d. *Bird Flight*

One of the most important functions of birds is that of flight. The bodies of flying birds are structurally adapted so as to offer little resistance to the air; the wings are placed high up on the trunk to prevent the body from turning over; and the bones are hollow and the body contains air-sacs, which decrease the specific gravity.

In flying, the tip of the wing describes a figure 8 as it is brought downward and forward and then backward and upward (Fig.

Fig. 508. — Gull flying. (From Headley, after Marey.)

508). The wing works on the principle of the inclined plane, and both the down and up strokes propel the bird forward. The body is sustained in the air by the downward strokes, which force it upward.

A great many birds are able to glide, and a number are fond of sailing or soaring. Birds are able to glide or skim by spreading their wings and then moving forward by means of their acquired velocity. In soaring, birds do not depend upon acquired velocity, but apparently rely upon favorable air currents.

[1] Thayer, Concealing Coloration in the Animal Kingdom.

The rate of speed at which birds fly varies considerably. The carrier-pigeon in this country maintains an average racing speed of about thirty-five miles per hour. Ninety miles per hour has been recorded for ducks (Forrester), but this rate is not sustained for any great length of time. During long flights the distances traveled per day are comparatively short, *e.g.* an albatross is known to have covered over three thousand miles in twelve days or two hundred and fifty miles per day, and a carrier-pigeon flying from Pensacola, Florida, to Fall River, Massachusetts, a distance of over a thousand miles, attained a daily average of seventy-six miles.

e. *Bird Migration*

Formerly birds were supposed to hibernate during the winter in caves, hollow trees, or, in the case of swallows, in the mud at the bottom of lakes and ponds. This is now known to be incorrect, and when birds disappear in the fall they depart to spend the winter in a more congenial southern climate.

Migration means moving from one place to another, and the idea of distance is emphasized. Birds are the most famous of all animals from the standpoint of their migrations. As winter approaches in the north temperate zone, they gather together in flocks and move southward, returning on the advent of the following spring. Birds that breed farther north spend the winter in parts of the temperate zone.

Not all birds migrate; for example, the great horned owl and bob-white remain with us throughout the winter. Certain other birds move southward only when the weather becomes very severe.

One of the most remarkable of all migratory birds is the golden plover. These plovers arrive in the " barren grounds " above the Arctic Circle the first week in June. In August they fly to Labrador, where they feast on the crowberry and become very fat. After a few weeks, they reach the coast of Nova Scotia, and then set out for South America over twenty-four hundred miles of ocean. They may or may not visit the Bermuda Islands and the West Indies. After a rest of three or four weeks in the West Indies or northern South America, the birds depart and are next heard from on their arrival in southern Brazil and Argentine. Here they spend the summer, from September to March, and then disappear. Apparently they fly over northern South America and Central America, and over the central portion of North America, reaching their breeding grounds in the Arctic Circle the first week in June. The elliptical course they follow is approximately twenty thousand miles in length, and this remarkable journey is undertaken every year for the sake of spending ten weeks in the bleak, treeless, frozen wastes of the Arctic Region.

Most birds migrate on clear nights at an altitude sometimes of a mile or more. Each species has a more or less definite time of migration, and one can predict with some degree of accuracy the date when it will arrive in a given locality. The speed of migration is, as a rule, rather slow, and a daily rate of twenty-five miles is about the average.

During their migrations, birds are often killed in great numbers by striking against objects, such as the Washington Monument, lighthouses, and telegraph wires. Over fifteen hundred birds were killed in one night by dashing against the Bartholdi Statue in New York Harbor. Birds may also be driven out to sea or be killed by severe storms.

Many theories have been advanced to account for the migration of birds, such as the temperature and condition of the food supply. Other theories attempt to explain how birds find their way during migration. The best of these seems to be the " follow-the-leader " theory. According to this, birds that have once been over the course find their way by means of landmarks and the inexperienced birds follow these leaders.

f. *The Nests, Eggs, and Young of Birds*

Some birds, like the hawks and owls, mate for life, but the majority of them live together for a single season only. The nesting period varies according to the species. The eggs of the great horned owl are often deposited before the snow has left the ground, but most birds are forced to wait until April or later, when the supply of insects is sufficient to feed their young.

The nest site is chosen with considerable care, and is determined upon from the standpoint of protection. As a rule, birds conceal their nests, or else build them in places that are practically inaccessible; for example, the nest of the song sparrow is hidden beneath a tuft of grass, whereas that of the great blue-heron is placed in the top of the tallest tree.

Many species, like the auk and certain other sea-birds, and the night-hawk and whippoorwill, make no pretence to build a nest, but lay their one or more eggs directly upon the ground. The killdeer and other plovers deposit their eggs in a small, crudely lined hollow in the ground. The great horned owl lays its eggs in an old hawk's or squirrel's nest. The mourning-dove builds a loose platform of twigs. There are all stages of complexity between this simple attempt and the beautifully woven, hanging nest of the Baltimore oriole. Certain features distinguish the nest of one bird from that of another; thus the nest of the chipping sparrow almost invariably contains a lining of horsehair, that of the shrike contains feathers, that of the American goldfinch is lined with thistle-down, and the nests of the ruby-throated humming-bird and the wood pewee are covered externally with lichens.

A few birds not only do not build nests, but even refuse to incubate their eggs and take care of their offspring. This is true of the European cuckoo and the American cowbird. The breeding habits of the latter are very interesting. There are more male cowbirds than females and each female therefore mates with several males, — a condition known as polyandry. The females seek out the nests of other birds, usually those smaller than themselves, in which to lay their eggs. The young cowbirds are carefully reared by their foster parents, and often starve out the rightful owners.

The eggs of birds vary in size, color, and number. The smallest eggs are those of certain humming-birds, measuring less than half an inch long; the largest eggs are those of the extinct elephant-birds of Madagascar, *Æpyornis*, which measure over thirteen inches in length (see p. 532).

As a rule, eggs laid in dark places, such as those of the bank-swallow, kingfisher, woodpecker, and owl, are white. Many eggs are colored, some possessing a uniform ground color; others, spots of various hues; and still others, both a ground color and spots. These colors usually vary but slightly in the eggs laid by different individuals of the same species, and those of one species are, in most cases, easily distinguished from those of another species.

The eggs laid at a setting vary in number from one to about twenty. For example, the murre lays one; the mourning dove, two; the red-tailed hawk, two or three; the robin, three or four; the blue jay, four or five; the bank swallow, six; the flicker, six to eight; the ruffed grouse, eight to fourteen; the bob-white, ten to eighteen.

The average period of incubation for passerine birds is about twelve days. The eggs of the ostrich hatch in about forty-five days. In some cases the female alone incubates; in other cases both male and female assist in incubation; and in a few birds, such as the ostrich, the male performs practically all of this duty.

Two general classes of young are recognized: (1) those that are able to run about, like young chickens, soon after hatching, known as precocious birds; and (2) those that remain in the nest for a greater or less period before they are able to take care of themselves. The latter are known as altricial birds.

g. *The Economic Importance of Birds*

Commercial Value. — Without taking into consideration the more than three million dollars annually derived from poultry products in this country, we may say that the principal sources of revenue derived from birds are the flesh of game birds, the eggs of certain colonial sea-birds, the feathers of many species of use for millinery purposes, and the excreta and ejecta of certain species, which have accumulated on tropical islands and are known as guano.

Guano contains two important elements of use in fertilizing the soil, phosphoric acid and nitrogen. The Chincha Islands off the coast of Peru have been for centuries the habitation of large numbers of sea-birds, whose excreta and remains have dried and formed a deposit in some places a hundred feet thick. The supply on these islands is now almost exhausted, though in 1853 the Peruvian government estimated the amount at that time at 12,376,100 tons. There are many other deposits in the rainless latitudes of the Pacific, but none as rich as were those of the Chinchas.

Birds are in some localities persecuted to a considerable extent for their eggs, which are used as food. This is true of certain gulls, terns, herons, murres, and ducks. Egging is not carried on now as much as formerly, since many of the colonies have been driven away from their breeding places, or the government has prohibited the practice. In 1854 more than five hundred thousand murres' eggs were collected on the Farallone Islands and sold in the markets of San Francisco in two months.

The game-birds have been and still are in certain localities a common article of food. Most of them, however, have been so persistently hunted by sportsmen and market men that they are now of no great commercial importance. Several species, like the wood-duck and heath-hen, have been brought to the verge of extinction. The repeating shotgun, introduction of cold-storage methods, and easy transportation facilities soon depleted the vast flocks of prairie-chickens and other game-birds of the Middle West. One New York dealer in 1864 received twenty tons of these birds in one consignment. The hunting and transportation of game-birds is now regulated by law in most localities.

The use of birds' skins and feathers as ornaments has been for many years a source of income for many hunters, middlemen, and milliners. Laws and public sentiment are slowly overcoming the barbarous custom of killing birds for their plumes, and it is hoped that the women of the country will soon cease to demand hats trimmed with the remains of birds.

The Value of Birds as Destroyers of Injurious Animals. — Within the past two decades detailed investigations have been carried on by the United States Department of Agriculture, state governments, and private parties in order to learn the relations of birds to man with regard to the destruction of injurious animals. The results of these researches may be found in government publications or in books such as Weed and Dearborn's *Birds in their Relation to Man,* and Forbush's *Useful Birds and their Protection.*

A very large proportion of the food of birds consists of insects. Figure 509 shows diagrammatically the food of nestling and adult house wrens, birds that are very common about gardens. Practically all of the insects devoured by birds are injurious to plants or animals and consequently harmful to man.

Another large element in the food of birds consists of small mammals, such as field-mice, ground-squirrels, and rabbits. For many years hawks, owls, and other birds of prey have been killed whenever possible, because they were supposed to be injurious on account of the poultry and game-birds they captured. Careful investigations by Dr. A. K. Fisher have shown, however, that at least six species are entirely beneficial; that the majority (over thirty species) are chiefly beneficial; that seven species are as beneficial as they are harmful; and that only the gyrfalcons, duck-hawk, sharp-shinned hawk, Cooper's hawk (Fig. 495), and goshawk are harmful.

As examples of beneficial birds of prey may be mentioned (1) the rough-leg hawk, which feeds almost entirely on meadow mice during its six months' sojourn in the United States, (2) the red-tailed hawk, or "hen hawk," sixty-six per cent of whose food consists of injurious mammals and only seven per cent of

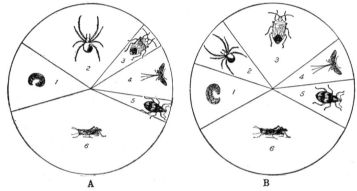

A　　　　　　　　　　　B

Fig. 509. — Diagram showing the kind and comparative quantity of food of the nestling (A) and adult (B) house wren. (From Judd, Bul. 17, Bur. Biol. Survey, U. S. Dep't Agric.)

poultry, and (3) the golden eagle, which is highly beneficial in certain localities because of the noxious rodents it destroys. The Cooper's hawk (Fig. 495) is the real "chicken hawk"; its food is made up largely of poultry, pigeons, and wild birds, but also includes the harmful English sparrows.

The beneficial qualities of birds are well shown by Dr. S. D. Judd[1] from a seven years' study of conditions on a small farm near Marshall Hall, Maryland. Modern methods of investigation led Dr. Judd to the following conclusions: —

"At Marshall Hall the English sparrow, the sharp-shinned and Cooper hawks, and the great horned owl are, as everywhere, inimical to the farmers' interests and should be killed at every opportunity. The sapsucker punctures orchard trees extensively and should be shot. The study of the crow is unfavorable in

[1] Bulletin No. 17 of the Division of the Biological Survey of the United States Department of Agriculture.

results so far as these particular farms are concerned, partly because of special conditions. Its work in removing carrion and destroying insects is serviceable, but it does so much damage to game, poultry, fruit, and grain that it more than counterbalances this good and should be reduced in numbers. The crow blackbird appears to be purely beneficial to these farms during the breeding season and feeds extensively on weed seed during migration, but at the latter time it is very injurious to grain. More detailed observations are necessary to determine its proper status at Marshall Hall.

" The remaining species probably do more good than harm, and except under unusual conditions should receive encouragement by the owners of the farms. Certain species, such as flycatchers, swallows, and warblers, prey to some extent upon useful parasitic insects, but, on the whole, the habits of these insectivorous birds are productive of considerable good. Together with the vireos, cuckoos, and woodpeckers (exclusive of the sapsuckers), they are the most valuable conservators of foliage on the farms. The quail, meadow-lark, orchard oriole, mocking-bird, house wren, grasshopper sparrow, and chipping sparrow feed on insects of the cultivated fields, particularly during the breeding season, when the nestlings of practically all species eat enormous numbers of caterpillars and grasshoppers.

" The most evident service is the wholesale destruction of weed seed. Even if birds were useful in no other way, their preservation would still be desirable, since in destroying large quantities of weed seed they array themselves on the side of the Marshall Hall farmer against invaders that dispute with him, inch by inch, the possession of his fields. The most active weed destroyers are the quail, dove, cowbird, red-winged blackbird, meadow-lark, and a dozen species of native sparrows. The utility of these species in destroying weed seed is probably at least as great wherever the birds may be found as investigation has shown it to be at Marshall Hall."

h. *Domesticated Birds*

Birds have for many centuries been under the control of man, and have produced for him hundreds of millions of dollars' worth of food and feathers every year. The common hen was probably derived from the red jungle-fowl, *Gallus gallus*, of northeastern and central India. The varieties of chickens that have been derived from this species are almost infinite.

The domestic pigeons are descendants of the wild, blue-rock pigeon, *Columba livia* (Fig. 470), which ranges from Europe through the Mediterranean countries to central Asia and China. Breeders have produced over a score of varieties from this ancestral species, such as the carriers, pouters, fantails, and tumblers. Young pigeons, called squabs, constitute a valuable article of food.

Of less importance are the geese, ducks, turkeys, peacocks, swans, and guinea-fowls. The geese are supposed to be derived from the graylag goose, *Anser anser*, which at the present time nests in the northern British Islands. Most of our domestic breeds of ducks have sprung from the mallard, *Anas boscas*. This beautiful bird inhabits both North America and temperate Europe and Asia. The common peacock, *Pavo cristatus*, of the Indian peninsula, Ceylon, and Assam, has been in domestication at least from the time of Solomon. It has been distributed by man over most of the world. The swan is, like the peacock, used now chiefly as an ornament. The mute swan, *Cygnus olor*, of Central Europe and Central Asia, is the common domesticated species. The guinea-fowl, *Numida meleagris*, is a native of West Africa. Farmers usually keep a few of them to " frighten away the hawks."

The turkey is a domesticated bird that has been brought under control within the past four centuries. Our Puritan ancestors found the wild turkey abundant in New England. It was introduced into Europe early in the sixteenth century and soon became a valuable domestic animal. In its wild state, it is now almost extinct except in some of the remoter localities. Our domestic turkeys are descendants of the Mexican wild turkey.

CHAPTER XXI

SUBPHYLUM VERTEBRATA: CLASS VII. MAMMALIA [1]

THE mammals are popularly known as "animals." The name of the class is derived from the fact that most mammals possess mammary glands which secrete milk for the nourishment of their young. Mammals also possess a covering of hair at some time in their existence and are distinguished by this characteristic as certainly as birds are by their feathers. With few exceptions adult mammals are provided with at least a small number of hairs.

The seventy-five hundred or more species of living mammals, and the three thousand or more species of fossil mammals may be grouped into two subclasses, (1) PROTOTHERIA, or egg-laying mammals, and (2) EUTHERIA, or viviparous mammals.

The three living genera of the PROTOTHERIA are included in one order which is confined to Australia, Tasmania, and New Guinea. They are the spiny ant-eater and duckbills (Fig. 513).

The EUTHERIA may be grouped into two divisions: —

I. DIDELPHIA, or marsupials, such as the opossum and kangaroo, with a pouch in which the young are carried after birth, and without a typical placenta (see p. 569).

II. MONODELPHIA, or placentals, with a typical placenta before birth, and more highly developed young.

The MONODELPHIA may be subdivided into four sections: —

(A) UNGUICULATA, or clawed mammals, such as the moles, bats, dogs, cats, seals, squirrels, mice, ant-eaters, and sloths.

(B) PRIMATES, with fingers usually terminating in "nails," such as the lemurs, monkeys, apes, and man.

---

[1] The rabbit is a satisfactory type for the study of mammalian anatomy if there is time for its dissection. Everyone should know something of the more common mammals such as is given in the review of the principal orders and families. Among the more interesting features of mammals are hair, scales, claws, etc., cutaneous glands and teeth. Because of their close relationship to man the development of mammals is of particular importance.

561

(*C*) UNGULATA, or hoofed animals, such as the pigs, deer, sheep, oxen, horses, and elephants, and

(*D*) CETACEA, or whales, which have probably been derived from the unguiculate division.

1. THE RABBIT

The rabbit belongs to the order of gnawing mammals — the RODENTIA or GLIRES. This order is made up of a number of families, one of which, the LEPORIDÆ, contains about sixty species of rabbits and hares. Rabbits are generally common in North America, both wild and in a state of domestication. They are, therefore, usually easy to obtain. This fact, together with their convenient size, have made them favorite objects for the introduction of students to mammalian anatomy. The following account, however, is not intended as a laboratory guide, but simply as a means of pointing out some of the more obvious mammalian characteristics with the aid of an animal that can be examined easily in the class room.

External Features. — The rabbit (Fig. 510) is a four-footed animal (quadruped) adapted for *leaping*. It possesses an external

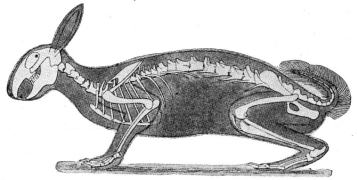

FIG. 510. — Lateral view of skeleton with outline of body of the rabbit. (From Parker and Haswell.)

covering of *hair*, two large external *ears*, or *pinnæ*, and separate genital and anal apertures. The mouth is bounded by soft, fleshy *lips* which aid in seizing and holding food. At the end of the snout are two obvious slits, the *nostrils*. The large *eyes*, one on either side of the head, are protected by an upper and a lower *eyelid* bordered by thin eyelashes, and a white, hairless third eyelid, or *nictitating membrane*, which may be drawn over the eyeball from the anterior angle. Above and below the eyes and on either side of the snout are long, sensitive hairs, the *whiskers* or *vibrissæ*.

The trunk may be separated into an anterior portion, the *thorax*, which is supported laterally by the ribs, and a posterior portion, the *abdomen*. The *tail* is short. Beneath it is the *anus*, and just in front of this is the *urinogenital aperture*. On either side of the anus and just anterior to it is a hairless depression, the *perinæal pouch* into which a strong-smelling secretion is poured by the perinæal glands. Four or five pairs of small papillæ, the *teats* or *mammæ*, are situated in pairs on the ventral surface of the thorax and abdomen. At the end of the teats open the ducts of the *mammary* or *milk glands*.

The *fore limbs* of the rabbit are used, as in the frog, for holding up the anterior part of the body. They possess five *clawed digits* each. The *hind limbs* are longer and more powerful than the fore limbs and serve as leaping organs. They are provided with only four digits; the one corresponding to the great toe in man is absent. The rabbit places the sole of its foot upon the ground, and is, therefore, said to be *plantigrade* (L. *planta*, the sole of the foot; *gradior*, walk).

The Skeleton. — An outline of the skeleton is shown in Fig. 510. It consists principally of bone, but a small amount of cartilage is also present. As in the fishes, amphibians, reptiles, and birds, there are *cartilage-bones*, preformed in cartilage, and *membrane-bones*, arising by the ossification of dermal portions of the skin. A third type, called *sesamoid bones*, occurs in the tendons of some of the limb-muscles, the action of which they modify; for example, the knee-cap.

The *axial skeleton* consists, as in the pigeon, of a skull, ribs, sternum, and vertebral column. The skull (Fig. 511) is formed of both cartilage- and membrane-bones, and only a small amount of cartilage. The individual bones are immovably united to one another, and their boundaries are in many cases obliterated in the adult and can only be made out in the embryo. The following points are worthy of special mention : The occipital ring is completely ossified and there are *two occipital condyles* (Fig. 511); the cranial and olfactory cavities are separated by a bony cribriform plate; the lower jaw articulates directly with the squamosal; three small but distinct *auditory ossicles* are present; and there is no distinct parasphenoid on the under surface.

The *teeth* are cutaneous structures, as are the scales and teeth of the dogfish-shark (p. 383), and are developed from the mucous membrane of the mouth. Each tooth possesses an outer, hard covering, called *enamel*, a central softer substance, called *dentine*, and about the base and in the surface folds a bony layer, the *cement*. The teeth of the rabbit remain open at the base and continue to grow throughout life, thus supplying new material to replace that worn away in grinding its vegetable food.

The rabbit lacks canine teeth, and the incisors (Fig. 511) are widely separated from the grinding teeth. There are two pairs of

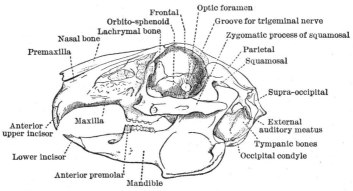

FIG. 511. — Side view of skull of the rabbit.   (From Shipley and MacBride.)

incisors lodged in sockets (alveoli) in the premaxillæ of the upper jaw, and one pair projecting forward from the anterior end of the lower jaw. Only the outer, curved surface of the incisors is covered with enamel, and since the inner dentine wears away more rapidly than the enamel, a chisel-shaped form results that is admirably fitted for gnawing. The grinding teeth are called premolars and molars. The *premolars* develop after a preceding set of " milk " teeth have fallen out; the *molars* have no deciduous predecessors. The *upper jaw* contains three pairs of anterior premolars and three pairs of posterior molars. The last molar is smaller than the others. The *lower jaw* is provided with two pairs of premolars and three pairs of molars; the last molar is small.

The *vertebral column*, as in other vertebrates, supports the body, and protects the spinal cord. The *vertebræ* move upon one another;

are separated by *intervertebral disks* of fibrocartilage, except in the sacrum; and are connected by *intervertebral ligaments.* The vertebræ of the neck, or *cervical vertebræ*, are almost always seven in number; those of the chest, the *thoracic vertebræ*, bear movably articulated ribs; those of the trunk region are called *lumbar vertebræ;* the three or more *sacral vertebræ* are fused together and support the pelvis; and the *caudal vertebræ*, about sixteen in number, form the skeletal axis of the tail.

The *ribs* and *sternum* constitute the framework of the thorax, and not only protect the vital organs in that region, but also play an important rôle in respiration. There are twelve, or sometimes thirteen, pairs of ribs (Fig. 510). The first seven pairs articulate with the sternum; the others do not reach the sternum. The *sternum* is a long, laterally compressed structure consisting mostly of bone. It is situated in the ventral wall of the thorax, and is transversely divided into six segments, or sternebræ.

The *pectoral girdle* consists of two scapulæ, two imperfect clavicles, and two knob-like coracoids. Each half of the *pelvic girdle* is called an *innominate bone*, and is made up of the *ilium*, *ischium*, and *pubis* fused together. The concavity in the innominate bone in which the head of the femur articulates is called the *acetabulum.*

The *ankle-joint* of the rabbit lies between the *tibia* and *fibula* above, and the *tarsal bones* below. The fourth and fifth *carpal bones* and corresponding tarsal bones are fused together, forming, in the fore limb, the *unciform bone*, and in the hind limb the *cuboid bone.* One of the *sesamoid bones* of the hind limb which is situated on the front of the distal end of the femur is called the kneepan, or *patella.* The *tibiale* is fused with the *intermedium* of the tarsus to form the *astragalus;* and the *fibulare*, which lies along its outer side. is called the *calcaneum.*

Internal Anatomy. — Unlike other vertebrates, the body-cavity of the rabbit and mammals in general is divided by a transverse muscular partition, called the *diaphragm*, into two parts, an anterior thoracic portion containing the heart and lungs, and a posterior portion containing the abdominal viscera.

The Digestive System. — The mouth or buccal cavity bears on the anterior portion of the roof a series of transverse ridges against which the tongue works. That part of the roof which has a bone foundation is known as the *hard palate.* Posterior to this is a muscular flap, the *soft palate*, which separates the mouth from the pharynx. At the sides of the posterior part of the soft palate are a pair of small masses of lymphoid tissue containing pits of unknown function, called the *tonsils*. The *tongue* is attached to the floor of the mouth. It bears a number of *taste papillæ* on the anterior part and sides. The two orifices of the *eustachian tubes* and the two apertures of the *nasopalatine canals*, which connect the nasal and buccal cavities, are situated in the roof of the mouth behind and above the soft palate. There are four pairs of *salivary glands*: (1) the parotids, (2) the infraorbitals, (3) the submaxillaries, and (4) the sublinguals. They pour their secretions into the mouth cavity.

The posterior continuation of the mouth cavity is called the *pharynx*. In the floor of the pharynx is the respiratory opening, the *glottis*, which is covered by a bilobed cartilaginous flap, the *epiglottis*, during the act of swallowing. The pharynx leads into the narrow, muscular *œsophagus*. Following this is the *stomach;* then comes the U-shaped *duodenum*, into which the pancreatic duct from the *pancreas* and the bile duct from the *liver* open.

The *small intestine*, which is seven or eight feet in length, leads into the *colon*, which is continued as the *rectum*. At the anterior end of the colon a large, thin-walled tube, the *cæcum*, is given off. This cæcum is about an inch in diameter and twenty inches long; it ends in a thick-walled, finger-like process about four inches long, called the *vermiform appendix*. A large cæcum is characteristic of most herbivorous animals with simple stomachs.

The rabbit possesses the following *ductless glands*: the *spleen*, the *thymus*, the *thyroid*, and the *suprarenals*.

The Circulatory System. — The *blood corpuscles* of the rabbit are unlike those of the lower vertebrates, being smaller, round instead of oval, biconcave, and without nuclei. The *heart* is four chambered, as in the pigeon, but the main blood-vessel, the *aorta*, arising from the left ventricle, has only the left arch, whereas in birds the right arch persists. The right systemic arch of the rabbit is represented by the *innominate artery*, which is the common trunk of the right carotid and subclavian arteries. An *hepatic-portal system* is present, but no renal-portal system.

The *lymphatic system* is important in rabbits and other mammals. The fluid portion of the blood, which, because of the blood pressure, escapes through the walls of the capillaries into the spaces among the tissues, is collected into lymph vessels. These vessels pass through so-called *lymph glands,* and finally empty into the large veins in the neck. The lymphatics which collect nutriment from the intestine are called *lacteals.*

The Respiratory System. — The rabbit and all other mammals breathe air by means of *lungs.* The glottis opens into the *larynx,* from which a tube called the *trachea* or *windpipe* arises. The trachea is held open by incomplete rings of cartilage; it divides into two *bronchi,* one bronchus going to each lung. The larynx is supported by a number of cartilages and across its cavity extend two elastic folds called the *vocal cords.* The lungs are conical in shape, and lie freely in the thoracic cavity suspended by the bronchi.

Air is drawn into the lungs by the enlargement of the thoracic cavity. This is accomplished both by pulling the ribs forward and thus separating them, as in most reptiles, and by means of the diaphragm. The diaphragm is normally arched forward and when it contracts it flattens, thus enlarging the thoracic cavity. The increased size of this cavity results in the expansion of the lungs, because of the air pressure within them, and the *inspiration* of air through the nostrils. Air is pumped out of the lungs (*expiration*) by the contraction of the elastic pulmonary vesicles, and of the thoracic wall and diaphragm.

The Excretory System. — The *urine* excreted by the two *kidneys* is carried by two slender tubes, the *ureters,* into a thin-walled, muscular sac, the *urinary bladder.* At intervals the walls of the bladder contract, forcing the urine out of the body through the *urinogenital aperture.*

The Nervous System. — The rabbit possesses a brain, cranial nerves, spinal cord, spinal nerves, and a sympathetic nervous system.

The *brain* (Fig. 512), as in other mammals, differs from that of the lower vertebrates in the large size of the *cerebral hemispheres* and *cerebellum.* The cerebral hemispheres are slightly marked by depressions, or *sulci,* which divide the surface into lobes or *convolutions* not present in the pigeon. The *olfactory lobes* are very large and club-shaped. The *optic lobes* are each divided by a transverse furrow into two. The cerebellum is divided into three parts, a central portion and two lateral lobes.

The Sense Organs. — The *eyes* of mammals are without a pecten such as is present in birds. The large *outer ear,* or *pinna,* serves to collect sound waves; the *middle ear* transmits the vibrations of the *tympanic membrane*, or *eardrum*, by means of three *auditory ossicles*, which extend across the tympanic cavity, to the inner ear. The *cochlea* of the *inner ear* is spirally coiled, and not simply curved as in the pigeon. The *nasal cavities* are very large, indicating a highly developed sense of smell.

The Reproductive System. — The two *testes* of the male lie in oval pouches of skin, called *scrotal sacs*, one on either side of the copulatory organ, or *penis*. They may be drawn back into the abdominal cavity through the narrow *inguinal canals*. The *spermatozoa* pass from the testes into irregular convoluted tubes called

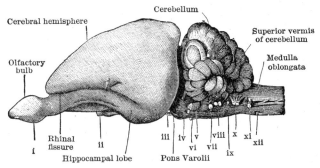

Fig. 512. — Side view of brain of the rabbit. (From Wiedersheim.)

the *epididymes;* they then enter the *vasa deferentia* which lead into the abdominal cavity and open into a medium sac, the *uterus masculinus*, attached to the dorsal surface of the urinogenital canal, or *urethra*. During *copulation* the spermatozoa pass into the urethra and are transferred to the female by the penis. Surrounding the vasa deferentia is a *prostate gland* which opens by short ducts into the urethra, and just behind are a pair of *Cowper's glands*. The secretions from these glands are added to the spermatozoa, making the seminal mass more fluid.

The two *ovaries* of the female are oval bodies exhibiting small, rounded projections on the surface; these are the outlines of the *Graafian follicles*, each of which contains an ovum. The *oviducts* consist of an anterior *Fallopian tube* and a middle *uterus;* the uteri unite posteriorly to form the *vagina*. The anterior end of the Fallopian tube is wide and funnel-shaped; it carries the ova from the ovary to the uterus, where the young are developed. The urinogenital canal, or *vestibule*, is a wide, median tube. On its ventral wall lies a small rod-like body, the *clitoris*, corresponding to the penis of the male.

The ova undergo *holoblastic segmentation* in the oviduct; they then pass into the uterus, where they receive nourishment from the blood of the mother through a structure called the *placenta*, which is formed from the fœtal membranes and united with the mucous membrane of the uterine wall. The interval between fertilization and birth, known as the *period of gestation*, is thirty days. Eight or ten young may be produced at a birth, and a new litter may be born every month for a large part of the year. Young rabbits breed when three months old.

2. A Brief Classification of Living Mammals[1]

As stated on page 632, there are about seventy-five hundred species of living mammals, and three thousand or more species of fossil forms known to man. The living mammals may be grouped into two subclasses and eighteen orders.

Class Mammalia. — Mammals or " Animals." — Warm-blooded vertebrates with a covering of hair at some stage in their existence, and with cutaneous glands in the female, which secrete milk for the nourishment of the young.

Subclass I. **Prototheria.** — Egg-laying Mammals.
    Order 1. **Monotremata.** — Monotremes. — Examples: *Ornithorhynchus*, duckbill (Fig. 513); *Echidna*, spiny ant-eater.
Subclass II. **Eutheria.** — Viviparous Mammals.
    Division I. Didelphia (Metatheria). — Marsupials.
    Order 1. **Marsupialia.** — Marsupials. — Mammals which usually carry their young in a marsupium or pouch; allantoic placenta usually absent.
        Suborder 1. Polyrotodontia. — Chiefly Carnivorous Marsupials. — Marsupials with eight or ten incisors in the upper jaw, and at least three pairs in the lower jaw. Examples: *Didelphis*, opossum (Fig. 514); *Thylacomys*, rabbit bandicoot.
        Suborder 2. Diprotodontia. — Mostly Herbivorous Marsupials. — Marsupials with not more than three pairs

[1] Modified from Osborn's *Age of Mammals*.

of incisors in the upper jaw, and usually one pair of large incisors in the lower jaw. Examples: *Cœnolestes*, cœnolestes; *Phalanger*, cuscus; *Macropus*, kangaroo and wallaby (Fig. 515).

Division II. MONODELPHIA (PLACENTALIA, EUTHERIA). — EUTHERIA nourished before birth by a typical placenta; young never carried in a pouch.

Section A. UNGUICULATA. — CLAWED MAMMALS.

Order 1. Insectivora. — INSECTIVORES. — Small, usually terrestrial, clawed mammals; feet plantigrade, generally pentadactyle; molars enamelled, tuberculated, and rooted. Examples: *Erinaceus*, hedgehog; *Condylura*, star-nosed mole; *Sorex*, shrew (Fig. 516).

Order 2. Dermoptera. — DERMOPTERA. — Two genera of flying mammals resembling insectivores in the structure of the skull and the canine teeth. They inhabit the forests of Malaysia and Philippine Islands, and are popularly called flying lemurs.

Order 3. Chiroptera. — BATS. — Clawed mammals with fore limbs modified for flight. Examples: *Pteropus*, flying fox; *Desmodus*, blood-sucking vampire; *Myotis*, brown bats (Fig. 517).

Order 4. Carnivora (FERÆ). — FLESH-EATING MAMMALS. — Clawed carnivorous mammals with large, projecting canine teeth; incisors small; premolars adapted for cutting flesh.

Suborder 1. Fissipedia. — CHIEFLY TERRESTRIAL CARNIVORES. — Chiefly terrestrial carnivores with separated digits. Examples: *Canis*, dog, fox, etc.; *Procyon*, raccoon (Fig. 519); *Mephitis*, skunk (Fig. 520); *Hyæna*, hyæna; *Felis*, cat, lion, etc.

Suborder 2. Pinnipedia. — SEALS and WALRUSES. — Aquatic carnivores with digits united by a membrane. Examples: *Zalophus*, California sea lion; *Callotaria*, fur seal; *Phoca*, harbor seal; *Odobænus*, walrus (Fig. 521).

Order 5. Rodentia (GLIRES). — RODENTS or GNAWING ANIMALS.

Suborder 1. Duplicidentata. — HARES and PICAS. — Rodents with two pairs of incisors in the upper jaw. Examples: *Lagomys*, pica; *Lepus*, cottontail.

Suborder 2. Simplicidentata. — RODENTS PROPER. — Rodents with one pair of incisors in the upper jaw. Examples: *Sciurus*, squirrel; *Castor*, beaver; *Geomys*, pocket gopher (Fig. 523); *Mus*, mice, rats; *Erethizon*, Canada porcupine; *Cavia*, guinea pig.

Order 6. Edentata. — AMERICAN EDENTATES. — Clawed EUTHERIA without enamel on the teeth; teeth absent from anterior part of jaw. Examples: *Myrmecophaga*, great ant-eater (Fig. 525); *Bradypus*, three-toed sloth; *Tatusia*, nine-banded armadillo (Fig. 526).

Order 7. Pholidota. — SCALY ANT-EATERS. — Clawed EUTHERIA with a covering of large, overlapping, horny scales; teeth absent; tongue long and protractile. Example: *Manis*, pangolin (Fig. 527).

Order 8. Tubulidentata. — AARD VARKS. — One genus *Orycteropus*, with two species of burrowing mammals, confined to Africa. They are called Cape ant-eaters.

Section B. PRIMATES.[1]— MAMMALS WITH " NAILS."

Order 9. Primates. — LEMURS, MONKEYS, MAN. — EUTHERIA with " nails "; great toe or thumb or both are opposable to other digits; brain large.

Suborder 1. Lemuroidea. — LEMUROIDS. — PRIMATES with front teeth separated by a space in the middle line. Example: *Lemur*, lemur (Fig. 528).

Suborder 2. Anthropoidea — MONKEYS, APES, MAN. — PRIMATES with front teeth in contact in middle line. Examples: *Cebus*, capuchin; *Ateles*, spider monkeys; *Cynocephalus*, baboon; *Simia*, orang-utan (Fig. 532); *Gorilla*, gorilla (Fig. 533); *Homo*, man.

Section C. UNGULATA. HOOFED MAMMALS.

Order 10. Artiodactyla. — EVEN-TOED UNGULATES. — UNGULATA with an even number of digits; the axis of symmetry passes between digits three and four. Examples: *Sus*, pig; *Dicotyles*, peccary; *Hippopotamus*, hippopota-

[1] The position of the PRIMATES in the midst of the mammalian series instead of at the end, where they are usually placed, may seem strange to students, but man, the apes, and other mammals belonging to this group retain a larger number of primitive characters than do the orders that are placed above them in this classification. The primates excel principally in the development of the nervous system, but are comparatively primitive when the bones, muscles, teeth, and other organs are taken into account.

mus; *Camelus*, camel; *Giraffa*, giraffe; *Cervus*, deer, etc.; *Alces*, moose; *Bos*, domestic cattle; *Bison*, bison (Fig. 536).

Order 11. Perissodactyla. — ODD-TOED UNGULATES. — UNGULATA with an uneven number of digits; the axis of symmetry passes through digit three. Examples: *Equus*, horse, ass, zebra (Fig. 538); *Tapirus*, tapir; *Rhinoceros*, rhinoceros (Fig. 539).

Order 12. Proboscidea. — ELEPHANTS. — UNGULATA with long, prehensile proboscis; incisors form tusks; molars very broad. Examples: *Elephas*, Asiatic elephant; *Loxodonta*, African elephant (Fig. 540).

Order 13. Sirenia. — SEA-COWS. — Aquatic EUTHERIA of the ungulate type; tail with horizontal fin; fore limbs fin-like; hind limbs absent. Examples: *Halicore*, dugong; *Manatus*, manatee (Fig. 541).

Order 14. Hyracoidea. — HYRACAS or CONEYS. — Small rodent-like mammals, with short ears and reduced tail; fore limbs with four digits; hind limbs with three digits. There is a single living genus, *Procavia*, and about eighteen species, in Africa. One species, *P. syriaca*, reaches Syria; it is the coney of the Bible.

Section D. CETACEA. — WHALES AND DOLPHINS. — Aquatic mammals probably derived from the UNGUICULATA or UNGULATA.

Order 15. Odontoceti (DENTICETI). — TOOTHED WHALES. CETACEA with teeth, at least on the lower jaw; no whalebone. Examples: *Delphinus*, dolphin (Fig. 542); *Phocæna*, porpoise; *Grampus*, grampus.

Order 16. Mystacoceti. — WHALEBONE WHALES. — CETACEA without teeth in adult; mouth provided with plates of whalebone. Examples: *Balænoptera*, fin whale; *Balæna*, right whale.

3. A REVIEW OF THE PRINCIPAL ORDERS AND FAMILIES OF LIVING MAMMALS

Order Monotremata. — EGG-LAYING MAMMALS. — The MONOTREMES are primitive mammals confined to Australia, New Guinea, and Tasmania. Their most conspicuous peculiarity is their egg-laying habit, since they are the only mammals that reproduce in this way. The two oviducts do not unite to form a vagina, but open into a cloaca along with the intestine and urethra, as in birds and reptiles (hence the term *Monotremata*: Gr. *monos*, one; *trema*, an opening). In certain respects the skeleton agrees with that of the reptiles.

The young before hatching live on the yolk contained in the egg. After hatching, the young are for a time nourished by milk from the mammary glands. These glands do not open at the end of a papilla, or teat, but pour their secretions upon the hair of the abdomen. The young either suck or lick the milk from this hair.

There are three genera, each containing a single species. The spiny ant-eater, *Echidna aculeata*, is from fifteen to eighteen inches in length. It has a prolonged snout, a mouth without teeth, an extensile tongue, and a covering of stiff spines mixed with long, coarse hairs. It lives in burrows and feeds upon ants. The egg is placed by the lips of the mother within a fold of skin on the abdomen; here it is protected until hatched. *Præchidna*, the long-snouted echidna, is confined to New Guinea.

Fig. 513. — The duckbill, *Ornithorhynchus anatinus*. (From Shipley and MacBride.)

The duckbill or platypus, *Ornithorhynchus anatinus* (Fig. 513), is about as large as *Echidna*, but is adapted for life in the water. It possesses webbed feet, a thick covering of waterproof fur like that of a beaver, and a duck-like bill with which it probes in the mud under water for worms and insects. The heels of the male are provided with strong horny spurs connected with a duct from a venom gland in the thigh. During the daytime the duckbill sleeps in a grass-lined, underground chamber at the end of a long burrow in the bank, the entrance of which is under water. In this chamber one or two eggs are laid and the young reared.

Order Marsupialia. — MARSUPIALS or POUCHED MAMMALS. — The MARSUPIALS occur mainly in Australia and neighboring islands, but a few are natives of America. Their method of reproduction is peculiar. The eggs, which are without shells, absorb food from the uterus; they are not laid, as in the monotremes, but hatch within the mother's body and the young are born in an immature condition. The mother transfers them with her lips to a pouch on the abdomen, where they are fed, by means of teats, upon milk from the mammary glands.

The opossums (DIDELPHIIDÆ) and kangaroos and wallabies (MACROPODIDÆ) are well-known groups. The opossums are

FIG. 514. — The opossum, *Didelphis virginiana*. (Photo by Hegner.)

confined to America. There are four genera and about twenty-five species; only one of these is common in the United States, the Virginia opossum, *Didelphis virginiana* (Fig. 514). The opossum occurs in the Southern and Middle states. It sleeps during the day, usually in a hollow tree or stump, but is active at night, seeking insects, eggs, young birds and mammals, berries, nuts, etc., which constitute its food. When disturbed the opossum frequently feigns death, or " plays possum." Two or three litters of from six to fourteen young each are produced per year. The young remain with the mother for about two months, at first in the pouch and later often riding about on her back. Opossums are used as food in the south, and, when properly roasted, are excellent.

Other American marsupials that should be mentioned are the murine opossum, *Marmosa murina*, which is no bigger than a mouse; and the yapock, the only member of the genus *Chironectes*, which is the size of a rat, has webbed feet, and lives in the water, catching small fish, crustaceans, and aquatic insects.

The kangaroos and wallabies (MACROPODIDÆ) are represented by about sixty species distributed all over the Australian region. They range in size from four or five feet in height to that of a small rabbit. The fore limbs are very small and are used principally for grasping (Fig. 515), whereas the hind limbs and tail are strongly developed, enabling the animals to move about rapidly by a series of leaps. The kangaroos are vegetarians, feeding on grass, herbs, and roots. Most of them are terrestrial, but a few are arboreal. The natives of Australia hunt them both for sport and for food. In some localities they are injurious, since they eat the grass necessary for feeding the cattle and sheep.

The other families of marsupials are with the exception of the EPANORTHIDÆ, which contains the South American genus *Cænolestes*, confined to the Australian region. They are (1) the banded ant-eaters (MYRMECOBIIDÆ), (2) the pouched mice, dasyures, and Tasmanian devil (DASYURIDÆ), (3) the thylacines and sparassodonts (THYLACYNIDÆ), (4) the bandicoots (PERAMELIDÆ), (5) the pouched

FIG. 515.—The rock wallaby, *Petrogale xanthopus*, with young in pouch. (From Shipley and MacBride, after Vogt and Specht.)

moles (NOTORYCTIDÆ), (6) the phalangers (PHALANGERIDÆ), and (7) the wombats (PHASCOLOMYIDÆ).

Order Insectivora. — INSECTIVORES. — These are small mammals covered with fur. They are considered the most primitive of the mammals that nourish their young before birth by means of a placenta. INSECTIVORES are entirely absent from the Australian region and most of South America. They are nocturnal in habit and feed principally on insects which they seize with their projecting front teeth and cut into pieces with the sharp-pointed cusps on their hind teeth. Most of them are terrestrial, but a number are subterrestrial (*i.e.* burrow); a few are aquatic, and some are arboreal.

The two families of insectivores represented in North America are the TALPIDÆ, containing the moles and shrew moles, and the SORICIDÆ, or shrews. The moles are stout, with short fore legs, fore feet adapted for digging, rudimentary eyes, and without external ears. The common mole, *Scalops aquaticus*, ranges from southern Canada to Florida. It burrows just beneath the surface of the ground, and is of considerable benefit because of the insects it destroys, though its upheaved tunnels soon disfigure a lawn. The rate of progress underground is astonishing. One will tunnel a foot in three minutes, and a single specimen under normal conditions is known to have made a runway sixty-eight feet long in a period of twenty-five hours. (Hornaday.)

The shrews (SORICIDÆ) have pointed heads, rat-like feet, small eyes, a distinct neck, and small external ears. About thirty-five species occur in North America north of Mexico; some of them are among the smallest of all mammals. They live in burrows or on the surface of the ground. The common or long-tailed shrew, *Sorex personatus* (Fig. 516), inhabits the northern part of the United States. It is about three and three quarters inches in length and

FIG. 516. — The long-tailed shrew, *Sorex personatus.*
(From Ingersoll.)

resembles a mouse in appearance. The short-tailed shrew, *Blarina brevicauda*, is also a resident of the Northern states.

Other families of insectivores are (1) the Madagascar tenrecs (CENTETIDÆ), (2) the solenodonts (SOLENODONTIDÆ) of Cuba and Haiti, (3) the golden moles (CHRYSOCHLORIDÆ) of South Africa, (4) the hedgehogs (ERINACEIDÆ) of Europe, Asia, and North Africa, (5) the Oriental tree shrews (TUPAIIDÆ) of India and Borneo, and (6) the jumping shrews (MACROSCELIDIDÆ) of Africa.

Order Chiroptera. — BATS. — The bats are easily distinguished from other mammals by the modification of their fore limbs for flight. The fore arm and fingers are elongated and connected with each other and with the hind feet, and usually the tail, by a thin leathery membrane. Because of their remarkable powers of locomotion bats are very widely distributed, occurring on small islands devoid of other mammals. There are more than six hundred species of bats. Most of them are small and chiefly nocturnal. During the day they go into retirement and hang head downward suspended by the claws of one or both legs. At night

FIG. 517.— A bat, *Synotus barbastellus.* (From Newman, after Vogt and Specht.)

bats fly about actively in search of insects. Some of them live on fruit, and a few suck the blood of other mammals.

The fruit-eating bats (suborder MEGACHIROPTERA; Family PTEROPIDÆ) occur in Africa, Asia, Australia, and the East Indies. The largest of these are the flying " foxes " (*Pteropus*). One species (*P. edulis*) has a wing expanse of five feet and a body only one foot in length. The fruit bats feed on fruit, especially figs and guava, and move about in companies.

Almost half of all the species of bats belong to the family VESPER-TILIONIDÆ. The brown bat, *Vespertilio fuscus*, is a common species inhabiting the United States. The little brown bat, *Myotis lucifugus*, is abundant in eastern North America. It is less than three and a half inches in length.

The true vampire bats belong to the family PHYLLOSTOMIDÆ and live in South America. They live on the blood of horses, cattle, and other warm-blooded animals, and sometimes attack sleeping human beings. Their front teeth are very sharp, but the back teeth have practically disappeared. The skin is cut by the front teeth, and the oozing blood is lapped up.

Some of the other families of bats are (1) the long-eared bats (EMBALLONURIDÆ), (2) the noseleaf bats (RHINOLOPHIDÆ), (3) the funnel-eared bats (NATALIDÆ), (4) the hare-lipped bats (NOCTILIONIDÆ), (5) the MOLOSSIDÆ, which are more at home on their legs than other bats and can scamper about almost like mice, and (6) the THYROPTERIDÆ, which have sucking discs on the thumbs and soles of the feet, enabling them to adhere to a smooth surface.

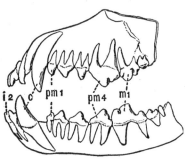

FIG. 518. — Teeth of dog. *i 2*, second incisor; *c*, canine; *pm 1*, *pm 4*, first and fourth premolars; *m 1*, first molar. (From Shipley and MacBride.)

Order Carnivora. — FLESH-EATING MAMMALS. — Not all of the carnivores are flesh-eating; many of them are omnivorous, and a few are chiefly vegetarian. The teeth of carnivores (Fig. 518) are perhaps the most characteristic feature of the order. The front teeth, or incisors (*i 2*), are small and of little use; the canines (*c*), or eye-teeth, are very large and pointed, enabling the animal to capture and kill its prey; the premolars (*pm 1*, *pm 4*) and the first molar in the lower jaw (*m 1*) have sharp-cutting edges; the other molars are broad, crushing teeth; the fourth premolar of the upper jaw (*pm 4*) and the first molar of the lower jaw (*m 1*) bite on one another like a pair of scissors, and are called carnassial teeth.

The living carnivores may be grouped into eleven families, of

which eight belong to the suborder FISSIPEDIA, or chiefly terrestrial CARNIVORA, and three to the suborder PINNIPEDIA, or
aquatic CARNIVORA. The five families of FISSIPEDIA occurring
in North America north of Mexico, and the approximate number
of species in each, are as follows (Hornaday): —

FAMILY	COMMON NAME	APPROXIMATE NUMBER OF SPECIES NORTH OF MEXICO
Canidæ	Dogs	22
Procyonidæ	Raccoons	3
Ursidæ	Bears	12
Mustelidæ	Martens	46
Felidæ	Cats	8

The other families are the civets and mungooses (VIVERRIDÆ)
of Europe, Asia, and Africa, the aard wolves (PROTETIDÆ) of
Africa, and the hyænas (HYÆNIDÆ) of Africa and Asia.

The CANIDÆ are represented in North America by the wolves
and foxes. These animals walk on their toes (digitigrade), possess
blunt, non-retractile claws, and have a more or less elongated
muzzle. The red fox, *Vulpes fulvus*, ranges from northern North
America south to Georgia. It is persistently hunted by the poultry raiser because of its fondness for chickens, but the benefits
derived from the destruction of field mice, rabbits, ground squirrels, woodchucks, and insects, which constitute the larger part
of a fox's food, probably more than repay the loss of a few fowls.
Foxes seek their food most actively in the morning and evening
twilight. They are monogamous; mate in February and March;
and bring forth, on the average, five young in April or May. The
black phase of the red fox is called by furriers " silver fox," and
high prices are paid for skins of this phase. Silver fox farming may
be carried on successfully, and it seems probable " that under
proper management fox raising will be developed into a profitable
industry." (Osgood.)

The arctic, or blue fox, *Vulpes lagopus*, inhabits the Arctic
regions, where it lives in burrows, and feeds on wild fowl and
small mammals, especially lemmings and polar hares. In the
winter its fur may become perfectly white, enabling it to creep
upon its prey unseen. The gray fox, *Urocyon cinereoargenteus*,
is the common species in the eastern part of North America. It

is partial to the forests of uncultivated regions, and makes its home more frequently in a hollow tree or stump than in a burrow.

The genus *Canis* is represented in North America by the gray or timber wolf, *C. occidentalis*, and the coyote, or prairie-wolf, *C. latrans*. The gray wolf ranges over the Great Plains and the Rocky Mountains. It is over four feet in length and very powerful. Wolves hunt in packs, and are able to capture deer and other large animals. They destroy great numbers of calves, colts, and sheep, and are shot, trapped, or poisoned whenever possible. Many states pay a high bounty for wolf scalps. The young, usually five in number, are born early in May.

Coyotes are common on the plains and deserts of the West. Their pointed ears and drooping tails distinguish them easily from dogs. They are fond of poultry, lambs, and sheep, but if these are properly protected, turn their attention to rabbits, mice, and other noxious mammals, thereby becoming an ally of the farmer.

The PROCYONIDÆ are mostly confined to America. The commonest species is the raccoon, *Procyon lotor* (Fig. 519). This

form, as well as the Texas bassaris, and the Mexican coati, which also occur in North America, can be recognized at once by their black- and white-ringed tail. The raccoon walks on its entire foot (plantigrade), and is about two and a half feet in length. It prefers to live in a hollow tree, and is omnivorous. Its flesh is considered by many people an excellent article of food.

FIG. 519. — The raccoon, *Procyon lotor.* (From Beddard.)

The best-known bears (URSIDÆ) of North America are the polar bear, black bear, grizzly bear, and the large Alaska brown bear. They are all plantigrade, and have a thick, clumsy body and rudimentary tail. The polar bear, *Thalarctos maritimus*, frequents the coasts of the Arctic Ocean, feeding principally upon seals, walruses, and fish. The black, brown, or cinnamon bear, *Ursus americanus*, is a smaller species abundant throughout the forested regions of North America, where not exterminated. It is omnivorous, being especially fond of fish, blueberries, and honey. The grizzly bear, *Ursus horribilis*, of the Rocky Mountains is now rare except in the Yellowstone Park and certain other limited localities.

The martens (MUSTELIDÆ) constitute a large family of small fur-bearing animals. The best known of the forty-six or more species inhabiting North America north of Mexico are the otter, mink, weasel, marten, wolverine, skunk, and badger. The otter, *Lutra canadensis*, is over three feet in length. It makes its home in a burrow in the bank of a lake or stream and is very fond of water, being adapted for swimming by webbed feet and a flattened tail. Fish constitute its chief food. Otter fur is very valuable, but cannot be obtained now except in certain parts of Alaska, where the natives capture the sea otter, *Latax lutris*.

The mink, *Putorius vision*, is less than two feet in length, and dark brown in color. Like the otter, it is fond of water. Its food consists of birds, small mammals, and fish. The weasel, *Putorius noveboracensis*, is one of the smallest of the MUSTELIDÆ. It is very bloodthirsty, often killing a great many more birds and small mammals than it can eat. The skunks, *Spilogale* and *Mephitis* (Fig. 520), are notorious because of the powerful odor of the secretion which they can eject from a pair of scent glands at the base of the tail. They feed upon poultry, but pay for their board by killing grubs and other noxious insects. The badger, *Taxidea taxus*, is over two feet in length. It inhabits western North America, ranging east to Wisconsin; lives in a burrow in the ground; and feeds on small mammals. The wolverine, *Gulo luscus*, is one of the larger martens. It occurs in the northern United States. Wolverines are fierce, greedy animals, and great thieves, stealing bait from traps, and even the traps themselves.

The family FELIDÆ includes the cat, puma, leopard, lion, tiger, lynx, and cheetah. The principal species inhabiting North America are the wildcat, Canada lynx, puma, and jaguar. The wildcat, *Lynx ruffus*, also called bay lynx, bob cat, or catamount, is a stub-tailed animal about three feet in length, and weighs up to eighteen pounds. It was formerly common, but is now restricted to the forests of thinly settled localities. Its food consists of rabbits, poultry, and other birds and mammals. The Canada lynx, or " loup cervier," *Lynx canadensis*, is slightly larger than the wildcat, and can be recognized by a tuft of stiff, black

hairs projecting upward from each ear. It occurs in the northern
United States and in Canada. The puma, cougar, mountain
lion, or panther, *Felis cougar*, reaches a length of over eight feet,
of which the tail constitutes about three feet. Pumas make their
homes in rocky caverns, or in forests. They prey upon many
kinds of animals, frequently causing much damage by killing young

FIG. 520. — Skunk. (From Ingersoll.)

colts; but they do not attack man unless cornered. The jaguar,
Felis onca, is the largest American cat, but only occasionally enters
the southern United States from Mexico, where it is common.
It is spotted and has a shorter tail than the puma. The jaguar
is afraid of man, but is a dangerous enemy of deer, horses, cattle,
and other animals.

The largest living cat is the tiger, *Felis tigris*, and related species, whose body reaches a length of ten feet; it is most abundant in southern Asia. The lion, *Felis leo*, is found in Africa and certain parts of Asia; it is slightly smaller than the tiger. The cheetah, or hunting leopard, *Acinonyx jubatus*, occurs in parts of Asia and Africa. In India it is trained to capture game.

The aquatic carnivores (suborder PINNIPEDIA) are greatly modified for life in the water. The hands and feet are fully webbed, and serve as swimming organs, and the body has acquired a fishlike form suitable for progress through the water. They are chiefly marine, but a few inhabit fresh water, or swim up rivers. The three families are the eared seals (OTARIIDÆ), the walruses (ODOBÆNIDÆ), and the earless seals (PHOCIDÆ); all of them have representatives on American shores.

The family OTARIIDÆ includes the sea-lions, fur seals, and sea-bears. The fur seal, *Otoes alascanus*, breeds on the Pribilof Islands in Bering Sea, but at other times occurs along the coast of California. Fur seals are polygamous, and a single old male maintains control over from six to thirty females. One young is produced each year. The three-year-old males, called " bachelors," are the ones killed for their fur. The California sea-lion, *Zalophus californianus*, is the member of this family most often seen in captivity. Squids, shellfish, and crabs are its principal articles of food. Its fur is short, coarse, and valueless.

The family ODOBÆNIDÆ contains two living species, the Atlantic walrus, *Odobænus rosmarus* (Fig. 521), and the Pacific

FIG. 521. — The walrus, *Odobænus rosmarus*. (From Flower and Lydekker.)

walrus, *O. obesus*. An adult male walrus is ten or twelve feet long and weighs almost a ton. The canine teeth of the upper jaw are very long, and are used to dig up mollusks and crustaceans from the muddy bottoms, and to climb up on the blocks of ice in the Arctic seas, where it lives. Walruses have been almost exterminated for their ivory, skins, and oil.

The seals belong to the family PHOCIDÆ. The harbor seal, *Phoca vitulina*, inhabits the North Atlantic; the ringed seal, *P.*

hispida, and the harp seal, *P. grœnlandica,* live in the Arctic seas; Pallas' seal, *P. largha,* is the seal of the North Pacific.

Order Rodentia (GLIRES). — GNAWING MAMMALS. — The rodents are characterized by their long, chisel-shaped incisors (Fig. 511), which are adapted for gnawing, and the absence of canines, leaving a gap between the incisors and pre-molars. They are all small or of moderate size, and number over fourteen hundred species, constituting the largest order of mammals. South America is richest in the number of species. The best-known North American families are the rabbits and hares (LEPORIDÆ), the squirrels (SCIURIDÆ), the beavers (CAS-

TORIDÆ), the pocket-gophers (GEOMYIDÆ), the rats, mice, etc. (MURIDÆ), and the porcupines (CŒNDIDÆ).

The LEPORIDÆ, or rabbits and hares, differ from most other rodents in the possession of a pair of small incisors just behind the pair of large incisors in the upper jaw. The more common Ameri-can species are the cot-tontail, or gray rabbit,

FIG. 522. — Striped gopher at entrance to hole in ground. (Photo by Hegner.)

Sylvilagus floridanus mallurus, the varying hare, or snow-shoe rabbit, *S. americanus,* and the jack-rabbit, *S. campestris.*

The family SCIURIDÆ includes the woodchucks, prairie-dogs, tree-squirrels, chipmunks, ground-squirrels, and flying squirrels. There are about one hundred and seventy species and geographic races in North America. The common tree-squirrels (genus *Sciurus*) are the gray, fox, and red squirrels; these are all excel-lent climbers, and possess large, bushy tails. They become quite tame if unmolested, and with the probable exception of the red squirrel or chickaree, should be protected.

The chipmunks or rock squirrels (genera *Eutamias* and *Ta-mias*) are small animals living usually on the ground among rocks. The ground-squirrels (genera *Citellus, Callospermophilus,* and

Ammospermophilus) are sometimes called gophers (Fig. 522). They are inhabitants of open country and dig burrows in the ground. Their food consists of grain which they carry into their burrows in cheek-pouches. The prairie-" dogs " (genus *Cynomys*) are burrowing rodents that live on our western plains in colonies of from forty to one thousand. They feed upon grass and other vegetation. The woodchucks, or ground-" hogs " (genus *Marmota*), also live in burrows; but are usually not colonial, and prefer hillsides or pasture land for their homes. They feed on clover and other grass. The flying squirrels (genus *Sciuropterus*) are

FIG. 523. — Pocket-gopher.   (Photo by Hegner.)

delicate nocturnal rodents that spend the day asleep in a nest, usually in a cavity in a tree. They possess a thin fold of skin between the fore and hind limbs on either side, which, when spread out, acts like a parachute to sustain the animal in the air.

The beavers (CASTORIDÆ) are the largest gnawing animals in North America. They are adapted for life in the water, possessing webbed hind feet and a broad flat tail. The dams of wood, grass, and mud made by beavers are constructed for the purpose of forming ponds in which houses are built with underwater entrances.

The pocket-gophers (GEOMYIDÆ) possess large cheek-pouches, which open outside of the mouth, and strong fore feet provided with large claws suitable for digging (Fig. 523). They occur in the western and southeastern states, where they burrow into meadows and throw out mounds of earth. Grain and vegetables are carried in the pouches and such quantities are destroyed as to make these rodents quite injurious.

Fig. 524. — The Norwegian lemming, *Myodes lemmus*. (From Ingersoll.)

The family MURIDÆ includes the muskrats, lemmings (Fig. 524), meadow-mice, white-footed mice, and rats. About one-fourth of our mammals belong to this family. They are all small, the muskrat being one of the largest American species. The common house mouse, *Mus musculus*, the Norway rat, *Epemys norvegicus*, and black rat, *E. rattus*, have all been introduced into this country from the Old World.

The porcupines (CŒNDIDÆ) are characterized by the presence of spines, which normally lie back, but can be elevated by muscles in the skin. The Canada porcupine, *Erethizon dorsatus*, ranges over northern North America.

Order Edentata. — AMERICAN EDENTATES. — The edentates are mainly inhabitants of South America; only one species, the nine-banded armadillo, reaches the southern boundary of the United States. They have been grouped into three families: the American ant-eaters (MYRMECOPHAGIDÆ), the sloths (BRADYPODIDÆ), and the armadillos (DASYPODIDÆ).

Fig. 525. — The great ant-eater, *Myrmecophaga jubata*. (From Flower and Lydekker, after Sclater.)

The great ant-eater, *Myrmecophaga jubata* (Fig. 525), measures about seven feet in length, possesses a long, narrow snout, and is provided with long claws on the fore feet which are used to tear open ant-hills. Its tongue is long and slender and serves to capture the ants upon which the animal feeds.

The sloths inhabit the tropical forests of Central and South America. They live in the tree-tops, and hang to the underside of the branches by means of two or three long, curved claws. Their food consists of leaves and buds.

The armadillos are curious mammals with an armor of bony scutes. When disturbed, they roll up into a ball, in which condition they are not easily injured. The nine-banded armadillo, *Tatusia novemcincta* (Fig. 526), ranges from southern

FIG. 526.— The nine-banded armadillo, *Tatusia novemcincta*. (From Flower and Lydekker.)

Texas to Paraguay. It is about two feet long, and lives on the open plains, feeding chiefly upon worms and insects.

Order Pholidota. — SCALY ANT-EATERS. — This order contains a single genus (*Manis*) and seven species of peculiar mammals, called pangolins (Fig. 527), inhabiting Africa and eastern Asia. Their bodies are protected by overlapping epidermal scales which can be erected. Like the armadillo, they can roll themselves into a ball. The tongue is long and extensile; it is used to capture white ants or termites, upon which they feed. Pangolins walk on the dorsal surface of the claws of the fore feet and on the soles of the hind feet. They are terrestrial, burrowing, or arboreal, and from one to five feet in length.

FIG. 527.— The white-bellied pangolin, *Manis tricuspis*. (From Flower and Lydekker.)

Order Primates. — LEMURS, MONKEYS, APES, MAN. — There are two suborders and eight families of living primates; the lemurs (LEMURIDÆ), aye-ayes (CHIROMYIDÆ), tarsiers (TARSIIDÆ), marmosets (HAPALIDÆ), South American monkeys (CEBIDÆ), Old-World monkeys (CERCOPITHECIDÆ), anthropoid apes (SIMIIDÆ), and mankind (HOMINIDÆ). It is customary to place these animals at the end of the vertebrate series, but they excel the UNGULATA and CETACEA chiefly in the large size of the brain, and retain many primitive characters, some of which are found elsewhere only among the lowest placental mammals, the INSECTIVORA.

FIG. 528. — Ruffed lemur. (From Elliott. Courtesy American Museum of Natural History.)

The primates inhabit chiefly the warm parts of the world. They are mostly arboreal in habit, and are able to climb about among the trees because the great toe and thumb are opposable to the other digits, adapting the hands and feet for grasping. A few primates lead a solitary life, but most of them go about in companies. Fruits, seeds, insects, eggs, and birds are the principal articles of food. One young is usually produced at a birth; it is cared for with great solicitude.

The lemurs (LEMURIDÆ) are quadrupeds and small or moderate in size; they are covered with fur, and usually possess a long tail (Fig. 528). The face is elongated; the brain case is relatively small, and the hind limbs are always longer than the fore limbs. The fifty living species are mostly confined to Madagascar and

FIG. 529. — White throated capuchin, a South American monkey. (From Elliott. Courtesy American Museum of Natural History.)

neighboring islands; the rest inhabit Africa and the Oriental region. Lemurs are mostly nocturnal. They feed on fruit and various other substances, and are all arboreal.

The marmosets (HAPALIDÆ) are small arboreal primates ranging from Central America to Brazil. The great toe has a flat nail, but the other digits bear claws; the tail and ears are long; the brain case is large; the thumb is not opposable, and there is a wide space between the nostril openings. They feed upon fruit and insects, and produce three young at a birth.

The South American monkeys (CEBIDÆ) are arboreal and of small or medium size (Fig. 529); the thumb, as well as the great toe, is opposable; all the digits possess nails; the tail is usually long and prehensile, aiding in climbing; the space between the nostril openings is wide; there is no vermiform appendix. The

FIG. 530. — Bengal macaque, an Old World monkey. (From Elliott. Courtesy American Museum of Natural History.)

principal groups are the howlers, sakis, squirrel monkeys, and spider monkeys.

The howling monkeys (genus *Alouatta*) range from South America to Mexico. They possess a resonating apparatus, with which they increase the power of the howls they are in the habit of emitting, probably for the purpose of frightening away enemies. The sakis (genus *Pithecia*) inhabit northern South America; they have long, bushy tails which are non-prehensile. The squirrel monkeys (genus *Chrysothrix*) are very active species inhabiting central and northern South America. The spider monkeys (genus *Ateles*) are slender, long-limbed forms ranging north-ward into southern Mexico. They possess a very prehensile tail, but the thumb is lacking.

The Old World monkeys (CERCOPITHECIDÆ) are mostly quad-rupedal, and have hind limbs about as long as the fore limbs (Fig.

FIG. 531. — The hoolock, a gibbon. (From Elliott. Courtesy American Museum of Natural History.)

530). They usually possess a long tail, which is never prehensile; their buttocks are provided with thick patches of callous skin on which they rest when in a sitting posture; their nostrils are separated by a narrow space; and many of them have cheek-pouches. The Indian and African monkeys belong to this family.

Only one species, the Barbary ape, enters Europe; this peculiar tailless form is found on the Rock of Gibraltar.

The anthropoid apes (SIMIIDÆ) are the primates most nearly related to man. The tail is absent; the fore limbs are longer than the legs; locomotion is often bipedal, and when walking the feet tend to turn in, and the knuckles help preserve equilibrium. There are four genera in the family: (1) *Hylobates*, or gibbons,

FIG. 532. — The Bornean orang-utan. (From Elliott. Courtesy American Museum of Natural History.)

(2) *Pongo* (*Simia*), or orang-utans, (3) *Gorilla*, or gorillas, and (4) *Pan* (*Anthropopithecus*), or chimpanzees.

The gibbons (Fig. 531) are arboreal; they have a slender body and limbs; are omnivorous; reach a height of not over three feet; and when walking are not assisted by the hands. There are several species inhabiting southeastern Asia and the East Indies.

There are one or probably two or more species of orang-utans (Fig. 532), confined to Borneo and Sumatra. They live principally in the tree-tops, where they construct a sort of nest for themselves. Orang-utans are herbivorous, about four and a half feet in height, and when walking use their knuckles as well as their feet. The brain of this species is more nearly like that of man than the brain of any other animal.

The gorilla, *Gorilla gorilla* (Fig. 533), inhabits the forests of western Africa. It is arboreal; feeds mainly on vegetation; has large canine teeth; reaches a height of five and a half feet and a weight of about five hundred pounds; walks on the soles of its feet aided by the backs of the hands; and is ferocious and untamable.

Fig. 533. — The gorilla, *Gorilla gorilla*. (From Flower and Lydekker.)

The chimpanzee, *Pan* (*Anthropopithecus*) *troglodytes* (Fig. 534), also lives in West Africa. It resembles the gorilla, but has shorter arms and a smoother, rounder skull. In many respects the chimpanzee is more nearly like man than any other living mammal. It is easily tamed.

The family HOMINIDÆ contains the single living species, *Homo sapiens*, or man. Man differs from the other primates in the size of the brain, which is about twice as large as that of the highest monkey, and in his erect, bipedal locomotion. The hairy covering is not well developed, and the great toe is not opposable. The mental development of man has enabled him to accommodate himself to every climate, and to dominate all other animals. Some fossil remains of a primate that were found in the upper Pliocene on the island of Java have been designated by Haeckel as "the last link" between the apes and man, and the animal to which they belonged has been given the name *Pithecanthropus erectus*.

The human race may be divided into three primary groups (Sedgwick): (1) the Negroid races, (2) the Mongolian, and (3) the Caucasian. The Negroid races possess frizzly hair, dark skin, a broad, flat nose, thick lips, prominent eyes, and large teeth. They are the African Negroes, the South African Bushmen, the Central African and Philippine Pygmies, the Melanesians, Tasmanians, and Australians.

The Mongolian races possess black, straight hair, a yellowish skin, a broad face with prominent cheek-bones, a small nose, sunken narrow eyes, and teeth of moderate size. They are the inhabitants of northern and central Asia, the Lapps, Finns, Magyars, Turks, Esquimaux, Malay, brown Polynesians, and American Indians.

Fig. 534. — Chimpanzee. (From Elliott. Courtesy American Museum of Natural History.)

The Caucasian, or white races, possess soft, straight hair, a well-developed beard, retreating cheek-bones, a narrow prominent nose, and small teeth. There are two main varieties: (1) the Xanthochroi, with fair, white skin, ranging from northern Europe into North Africa and western Asia; and (2) the Melanochroi, with black hair, and white to black skin, inhabiting southern Europe, northern Africa, and southwestern Asia.

An extinct species of man, *Homo neanderthalensis*, has been named from remains found in a limestone cave in the Neanderthal, near Düsseldorf, Germany. The skull is distinctly human, and is the most primitive and least specialized of any known.

Order Artiodactyla. — EVEN-TOED HOOFED MAMMALS. — This order contains the majority of the " game " animals, and includes the pigs (SUIDÆ), peccaries (TAYASSUIDÆ), hippopotami (HIPPO-POTAMIDÆ), camels and llamas (CAMELIDÆ), chevrotains (TRA-GULIDÆ), giraffes (GIRAFFIDÆ), deer (CERVIDÆ), pronghorn antelopes (ANTILOCAPRIDÆ), and antelopes, sheep, goats, cattle, etc. (BOVIDÆ). These animals are characterized by the presence of an even number of hoofed toes; the axis of symmetry passes between digits three and four. The families TAYASSUIDÆ, CER-VIDÆ, ANTILOCAPRIDÆ, and BOVIDÆ are represented in North America.

The term *ruminant* has been given to the animals belonging to the camel, chevrotain, deer, giraffe, pronghorn, and ox families,

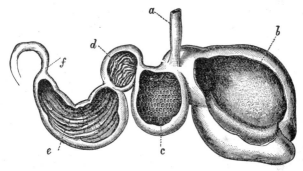

FIG. 535. — Stomach of a ruminant, opened to show internal structure. *a*, œsophagus; *b*, rumen; *c*, reticulum; *d*, psalterium; *e*, abomasum; *f*, duodenum. (From Flower and Lydekker.)

since they ruminate or chew their cud. The food of these animals is swallowed without sufficient mastication; it is later regurgitated in small quantities and thoroughly chewed. This method of feeding enables " these comparatively defenseless animals to gather nutriment in a short time and then retreat to a safe place to prepare it for digestion." A typical ruminant possesses a stomach consisting of four chambers (Fig. 535): the first two, the rumen (*b*) and the reticulum (*c*), belong to the cardiac division; and the other two, the psalterium (*d*) and the abomasum (*e*), belong to the pyloric division. The food is first taken into the rumen (*b*), where it is moistened and softened; it passes back

into the mouth as " cuds " and is ground up by the molar teeth
and mixed with saliva. When the cuds are swallowed, they are
received by the reticulum (c), then pass into the psalterium (d),
and finally into the abomasum (e).

The peccaries (TAYASSUIDÆ) are pig-like animals confined to
America. They possess large, prominent canine teeth, and incisors in both jaws, but are without horns. The Texas peccary,
Tayassu angulatum, occurs in Texas. It looks like a small black
pig; is nocturnal; goes about in companies; and feeds on nuts
and roots.

The deer (CERVIDÆ) constitute the majority of the American
hoofed mammals. Their horns or antlers are solid, and are shed
annually. The best-known species are the wapiti or elk, Virginia deer, mule deer, with round horns, and the caribou and moose,
with flat horns.

The moose, *Alces americanus*, is the largest member of the
family and possesses the most massive antlers. It inhabits the
woods of the northern United States and British America, and
feeds on bark, twigs, leaves, moss, and lichens. A larger and
darker race occurs in Alaska. The woodland caribou, *Rangifer
caribou*, lives in the forested parts of northern Maine and Mon-
tana, and British America. The female caribou is our only female
deer that bears antlers. The reindeer also belongs to the genus
Rangifer.

The wapiti or elk, *Cervus canadensis*, is the largest round-horned
deer. It is easily bred in confinement, and is common in zoological parks. The Virginia or white-tailed deer, *Odocoileus virginianus*, is the best known and most widely distributed of all our
species. It is an inhabitant of forests. The mule deer or black-
tailed deer, *Odocoileus hemionus*, is a large, high-headed species,
which prefers open country. It browses on twigs and leaves,
and also grazes when the grass is good. Two fawns are usually
produced at a birth.

The pronghorn antelopes (ANTILOCAPRIDÆ) are confined to
the open country of western North America. Their horns are
hollow, branched, and shed annually. There is but a single species,
Antilocapra americana.

The family BOVIDÆ contains the gnus, hartebeests, dik-diks,
waterbucks, gazelles, elands, chamois, Rocky Mountain goats,
sheep, goats, musk-oxen, oxen, and bison. These are all rumi-

nants (see p. 668), and both males and females usually possess unbranched, hollow horns, which fit over bony prominences on the skull and are not shed annually. The best-known American forms are the bison, musk-ox, bighorn, and mountain goat.

The bison, *Bison bison* (Fig. 536), up to the year 1870, ranged over a large part of the Great Plains and other portions of North America. It was persistently hunted, chiefly for its hide, until most of the species had been killed. In 1903 it was estimated that about six hundred wild individuals and one thousand captive specimens still existed. The musk-ox, *Ovibos moschatus,*

Fig. 536. — Bison. (Photo by Hegner.)

lives on the Arctic barrens of North America. It has a long, shaggy coat, and the male has a strong, musky smell. The Esquimaux use it for many purposes. The bighorn, or mountain sheep, *Ovis cervina* (Fig. 537), is an inhabitant of the slopes of the Rocky and Sierra mountains above timber line. It seeks the more sheltered valleys in the winter. The mountain goat, *Oreamnos montanus*, occurs in the higher Rocky and Cascade mountains to Alaska. It is covered with long, white hair; has slender black horns; and is an expert climber.

Among the ARTIODACTYLA not found in North America are: (1) the wild boar, *Sus scrofa*, of Europe; (2) the wart hog, *Phacochœrus œthiopicus*, of Africa; (3) the hippopotamus, *Hippopotamus amphibius*, of Africa; (4) the camel, *Camelus bactrianus*, of Asia; (5) the dromedary, *Camelus dromedarius*, of Arabia; (6) the llama, *Lama glama*, of South America; (7) the chevrotains, *Tragulus* and *Hyæmoschus*, of India, Malay, and Africa, among the smallest living ruminants; (8) the okapi, *Ocapia johnstoni*, of the Congo; (9) the giraffe, *Giraffa camelopardalis*, of Africa; (10) the

Fig. 537. — Rocky mountain bighorn or mountain sheep.   (From Ingersoll.)

gazelles, *Gazella*, of Africa and Asia; (11) the chamois, *Rupicapra*, of southern Europe and southwestern Asia; (12) the buffaloes, *Bubalus*, of Africa and Asia; and (13) the yak, *Poëphagus*, of the Himalayas and Thibet.

Order Perissodactyla. — ODD-TOED HOOFED MAMMALS. — The horses (EQUIDÆ), tapirs (TAPIRIDÆ), and rhinoceroses (RHINOCEROTIDÆ) belong to this order. They are characterized by the presence of an odd number of hoofed toes; the axis of symmetry passes through the third digit. None of the PERISSO- DACTYLA are native to the United States, but many remains of extinct species have been found.

The horses, zebras, and asses of the family EQUIDÆ have but one functional toe on each foot, and two lateral splints. The

FIG. 538. — Zebra. (From Lydekker.)

common horse, *Equus caballus*, of which over sixty domesticated races exist, is not now known in a wild state. There are several species of wild asses in Asia and Africa. The Nubian ass, *Equus africanus*, is probably the parent of the domestic donkey. The zebras are confined to Africa, and may be divided into several specific types with numerous subspecies. The common zebra is *Equus zebra* (Fig. 538).

The tapirs (TAPIRIDÆ) have four toes on the fore feet and three on the hind feet. They occur in Central and South America,

Sumatra, Java, and the Malay Peninsula. The American tapirs have a long, prehensile nose. They feed on soft plants and are hunted for their flesh.

The rhinoceroses (Fig. 539) are large, thick-skinned mammals with one or two epidermal horns on the nasal and frontal bones.

The Indian species has one horn; the Sumatran form has two, as has also the white rhinoceros of Africa.

Order Proboscidea. — ELEPHANTS. — There are two genera of elephants, each with one living species. The Asiatic elephant, *Elephas indicus*,

FIG. 539. — African rhinoceros. (From Newman, after Lydekker.)

inhabits the jungles of India; the African elephant, *Loxodonta africanus* (Fig. 540), lives in tropical forests and is hunted for its tusks. Both species possess five digits on each foot; are covered by a thick, loose skin (therefore called pachyderms) with a thin coat of hair; have a long, muscular proboscis with nasal openings at the tip; are

FIG. 540. — The African elephant, *Loxodonta africanus*. (From Beddard, after Baker.)

provided with tusks which develop from the incisors; possess small eyes and tail and enormous ears; and are without canine teeth. The skull is massive, because the bones are thickened and contain air spaces, and the grinding teeth are very large and possess complicated ridges.

Order Sirenia. — SEA-COWS. — This order contains four species of manatees, one on the Atlantic coast of Africa, and three on the Atlantic coast of America; and three species of dugongs (genus *Dugong*) on the shores of the Red Sea, Indian Ocean, and Australia.

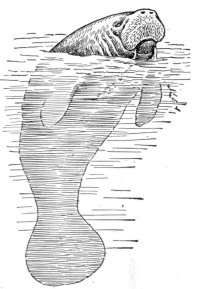

Steller's sea-cow (*Rhytina*) formerly inhabited the north Pacific, but became extinct about 1768 because its fearlessness enabled hunters to kill it easily. Sea-cows differ considerably in structure from whales. Their bones are heavy, enabling them to remain on the bottom; the teeth are broad and crushing; the lips are large and movable and are used to seize seaweeds and other water-plants upon which they feed; the fore limbs are flexible flippers; and the tail is rounded and not notched as in whales. The Florida

FIG. 541. — Florida manatee. (From Newman, after Fuertes.)

manatee, *Trichechus latirostris* (Fig. 541), is about nine feet in length. It is now nearly extinct.

Order Odontoceti (DENTICETI). — TOOTHED WHALES. — Four families belong to this order: (1) the PLATANISTIDÆ, or river dolphins; (2) the DELPHINIDÆ, or dolphins, porpoises, grampuses, and killer whales; (3) the DELPHINAPTERIDÆ, or belugas and narwhales; and (4) the PHYSETERIDÆ, or sperm whales and beaked whales.

Whales are adapted to life in the water. They possess a very large head with elongated face and jaw bones; the fore limbs are modified as paddles; the tail is flattened horizontally and forms two lobes, the " flukes "; the eyes are small, and there is no external ear. The nostrils form a single semilunar opening, and the air, which is forced from it, condenses in the cold atmosphere, appearing like a spout of water. Beneath the skin is a thick layer of fat, or " blubber," which retains the body heat. The teeth are numerous, and conical in shape.

The common dolphin, *Delphinus delphis* (Fig. 542), is about seven feet in length; it is common in the Mediterranean, along

FIG. 542. — The dolphin, *Delphinus delphis*. (From Sedgwick's Zoology.)

the western coast of Europe, and in the warmer portions of the Atlantic. The sperm-whale, *Physeter macrocephalus* (Fig. 544), reaches a length of seventy-five feet, and is the largest toothed whale. Its oil, spermaceti, and blubber are sought by whalers. Cephalopods (p. 264) are its principal food. The narwhale, *Monodon monoceras*, inhabits Arctic seas; one of its upper teeth

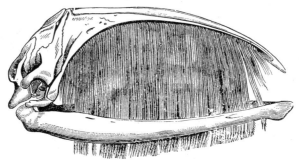

FIG. 543. — Skull of Greenland whale, *Balæna mysticetus*, with the whale-bone. (From Sedgwick's Zoology, after règne animal.)

is a horizontal, twisted tusk about five feet in length. The killer-whale, *Orca orca*, occurs in all oceans, is about twenty feet in length, and, as its name implies, is a fierce predatory mammal, killing fish, seals, and other whales.

Order Mystacoceti. — WHALEBONE WHALES. — The single family (BALÆNIDÆ) of whalebone whales includes the gray whale,

Rhacianectes glaucus, of the north Pacific, the rorqual and fin-whales (*Balænoptera*), the hump-backed whale, *Megaptera boops,* of the Atlantic and Pacific, and the right whales (*Balæna*). These whales possess teeth only in the embryo; they are provided in the adult stage with numerous plates of baleen or whalebone, which are horny and frayed out at the end (Fig. 543). In feeding the whale takes large quantities of water into its mouth, and then forces it out through the sieve-like whalebone, retaining any small organisms that may have entered with the water.

The sulphur-bottom whale, *Balænoptera sulfureus,* is the largest whale, and the largest living animal, reaching a length of ninety-five feet, and a weight of about 294,000 pounds; it inhabits the

Fig. 544. — The sperm whale, *Physeter macrocephalus.* (From Flower and Lydekker.)

Pacific from California to Central America. The Greenland whale or bow-head, *Balæna mysticetus,* occurs in polar seas; and reaches a length of about sixty feet. It yields nearly three hundred barrels of oil, and about three thousand pounds of the best whale-bone. *Balænoptera musculus* is a sulphur-bottom whale occurring in the Atlantic and caught off the coast of Newfoundland.

4. General Remarks on the Mammalia

a. *Integumentary Structures*

Hair. — The hairs that distinguish mammals from all other animals are related phylogenetically to the feathers of birds and the scales of reptiles. They are cornified modifications of the epidermis (p. 360, Fig. 347, *Se. SM*) which project out from pits in the skin, called *hair follicles.* The *hair shaft* (*H*) broadens at the base, extending around a highly vascular *papilla* at the bottom of the pit. When hairs are shed, new hairs usually arise to take their place. Secretions from the *sebaceous glands* (*D*) keep the hairs glossy.

The two main types of hairs are (1) *contour hairs* which are long and strong, and (2) *woolly hairs* which are shorter and constitute the under fur. In some animals the woolly hairs have a rough surface, as in the sheep, which causes them to cohere and gives them their felting quality. Certain of the stronger hairs may be moved by muscular fibers. The muscles of the dermis are responsible for the erection of spines or the bristling of the other hairs.

Scales. — Scales are present on the bodies of a few mammals, notably in the pangolin (Fig. 527) and on the tail of certain rodents, such as the beaver, rats, and mice.

Claws, Nails, Hoofs, etc. — The claws of the UNGUICULATA, the nails of the PRIMATES, and the hoofs of the UNGULATA are all modifications of the horny covering on the dorsal surface of the distal ends of the digits. The chief forms are shown in Figure 545. When on the ground the foot rests partially or entirely upon the pads or tori (*b*). Dermal papillæ occur on the tori, often forming concentric lines such as those that produce the fingerprints of man. The sole-horn (*S*) is softer than the nail-plate (*N*).

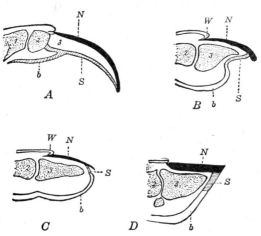

FIG. 545. — Diagrammatic longitudinal sections through the distal ends of the digits of mammals. **A**, spiny anteater, *Echidna*. **B**, an unguiculate. **C**, man. **D**, horse. 1–3, phalanges; *b*, torus; *N*, nail-plate; *S*, sole-horn; *W*, bed of claw or nail. (From Wiedersheim, after Gegenbaur and Boas.)

Other epidermal horny thickenings are the *horn-sheaths* of the ox and other ruminants, the *nasal horns* of the rhinoceros, and the " whalebone " (baleen, Fig. 543) of certain whales. *Dermal plates* of bone form the exoskeleton of the armadillos (Fig. 526).

Cutaneous Glands. — Mammals possess a greater number of glands than reptiles or birds; these are for the most part sebaceous and sweat-glands, or modifications of them. The *sebaceous glands* usually open into the hair-follicles (p. 360, Fig. 347, *D*), and secrete a greasy substance which keeps the surface soft and the hair glossy. The *sweat-glands* (Fig. 347, *SD*) secrete a fluid composed chiefly of water containing a small amount of solid matter in solution; this fluid evaporates, thereby cooling the skin and regulating the bodily temperature. The *lachrymal glands*, whose secretions keep the eyeballs moist, the *scent glands* of many mammals, and the *mammary glands*, are all modifications of cutaneous glands.

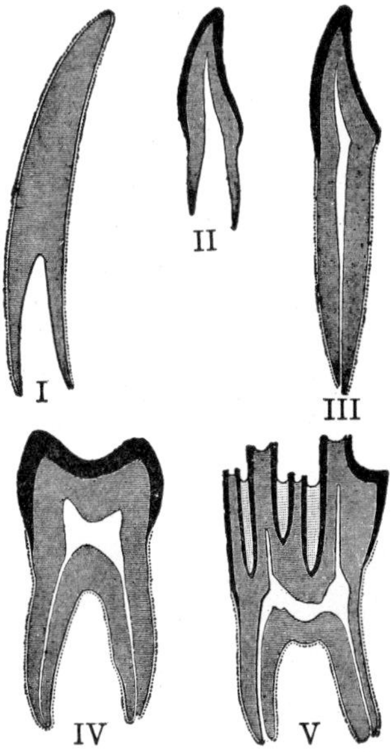

b. *The Teeth of Mammals*

The teeth of mammals are of considerable value in classification, and indicate also the food habits of their possessors. Most mammals are provided with teeth, but the whalebone whales, the monotremes, and many edentates are without them in the adult stage, and in some forms (*e.g.* the spiny anteater, *Echidna*) they have never been found even in the embryo.

FIG. 546. — Diagrammatic section of various forms of teeth. **I**, incisor or tusk of elephant with pulp cavity open at base. **II**, human incisor, during development, with pulp cavity open at base. **III**, completely formed human incisor, opening of pulp cavity small. **IV**, human molar with broad crown and two roots. **V**, molar of ox, enamel deeply folded and depressions filled with cement. Enamel, black; pulp, white; dentine, horizontal lines; cement, dots. (From Flower and Lydekker.)

The teeth are embedded in sockets in the bone, but arise independently of the endoskeleton, taking their origin from calcifications of the mucous membrane of the mouth. The principal forms of teeth and the relations of the three constituents are shown in Figure 546. The *enamel* (in black) is the outer hard substance; the *dentine* (horizontal lines) constitutes the largest portion of the tooth; and the *cement* (dotted) usually covers the part of the tooth embedded in the tissues of the jaw. The central *pulp-cavity* of the tooth contains nerves, blood-vessels, and connective tissue. Teeth have an open pulp-cavity during growth (Fig. 546, II), which in some cases continues throughout life (Fig. 546, I).

The teeth of fishes, reptiles, and amphibians are, with few exceptions, all similar, and the dentition of these animals is therefore said to be *homodont*. The dentition of mammals, on the other hand, is almost always *heterodont*, there being usually four kinds of teeth in each jaw: (1) the chisel-shaped *incisors* in front (Fig. 518, *i 2*), (2) the conical *canines* (*c*), (3) the anterior grinding teeth or *premolars* (*pm 1 — pm 4*), and (4) the posterior grinding teeth or *molars* (*m 1*).

In most mammals the first set of teeth, known as the *milk dentition*, is pushed out by the permanent teeth, which last throughout the life of the animals. The milk molars are followed by the premolars, but the permanent molars have no predecessors.

It is customary to indicate the number of each kind of teeth possessed by a mammal by a formula expressed in the form of a fraction, of which the numerator refers to those in one half of the upper jaw, and the denominator to those in one half of the lower jaw. For example, the dog (Fig. 518) possesses three incisors (*i*), one canine (*c*), four premolars (*pm*), and two molars (*m*), in one half of the upper jaw, and three incisors, one canine, four premolars, and three molars in one half of the lower jaw. The dental formula of the dog is therefore written $i \cdot \dfrac{3}{3}$; $c \cdot \dfrac{1}{1}$; $pm \cdot \dfrac{4}{4}$; $m \cdot \dfrac{2}{3}$, or in simpler form $\dfrac{3 \cdot 1 \cdot 4 \cdot 2}{3 \cdot 1 \cdot 4 \cdot 3}$. The total number of teeth in the dog may be learned by adding these numbers and multiplying by two.

The relation of the form of the teeth to the food habits of the animal may be shown by the following examples: The dolphins (Fig. 542) have a large number of sharp conical teeth adapted for capturing fish (compare teeth of perch, p. 396); the carnivorous animals, like the dog (Fig. 518), are provided with large canine teeth for capturing and killing their prey, small and almost useless incisors, and molars with sharp edges for cutting or crushing; herbivorous animals, like the ox, possess broad incisors for biting off vegetation, no canines, and large grinding molars (Fig. 546, *V*); rodents, like the rabbit (Fig. 511), have incisors that grow throughout life, but are worn down by gnawing, thereby maintaining a serviceable length and a keen cutting edge; insectivores, such as the shrew (Fig. 516), seize insects with their projecting incisors and cut them into pieces with the pointed cusps on their premolars and molars; and man and other omnivorous animals are provided with teeth fitted for masticating both animal and vegetable matter.

c. The Development of Mammals

The eggs of most mammals develop within the body of the mother; the exceptions are the monotremes (p. 572), which lay eggs. During their development the eggs of mammals, as well as those of birds and reptiles, produce two membranes: (1) the amnion, and (2) the allantois. Because of the presence of these membranes, the mammals, birds, and reptiles are often grouped together as AMNIOTA, while the amphibians, fishes, elasmobranchs, and cyclostomes, which do not possess these membranes, are designated as ANAMNIOTA.

The segmentation of mammals' eggs is complete (except in monotremes), and takes place either in the oviduct, as in the rabbit, or in the uterus, as in the sheep. Figure 547 illustrates by a series of diagrams the formation of the embryonic membranes of a mammal. The processes are briefly noted beneath the diagrams.

The placenta which is present in some marsupials and all the other EUTHERIA arises in the following manner: " In the uterus the embryo becomes connected with the uterine wall by means of its outer epithelial layer, now known as the trophoblast. This later becomes coated wholly or in part on its inner side by somatic mesoblast, and constitutes the membrane known as the subzonal membrane. . . . Later on, the mesoblast of the peripheral part of the allantois becomes applied to the subzonal membrane and the two structures constitute the embryonic membrane called the chorion. . . . The chorion develops vascular villi which enter into close relation with the uterine wall. In this manner there is developed a relatively large surface, permeated with branches from the fœtal vessels, the blood of which is in intimate osmotic connection with the blood of the uterine wall. This connection of the chorion of the fœtus with the uterine walls gives rise to the placenta, by means of which the nourishment and respiration of the fœtus are provided for in the body of the mother. . . . The placenta presents great variations, in the individual orders, in its special development and in the mode of its connection with the uterine walls." (Sedgwick.)

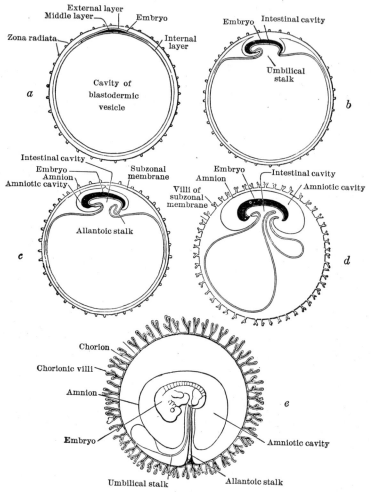

Fig. 547. — Diagrammatic figures illustrating the formation of the fœtal membranes of a mammal. **a**, embryo before appearance of amnion; **b**, embryo with yolk-sac and developing amnion; **c**, embryo with amnion closing and developing allantois; **d**, embryo with villous subzonal membrane, and with mouth and anus; **e**, embryo in which vascular layer of allantois is applied to subzonal membrane, and has grown into the villi of the latter, yolk-sac reduced, amniotic cavity increasing. (From Sedgwick's Zoology, after Kölliker.)

d. *Hibernation*

The problem of maintaining life during the winter is solved by most birds by migrating. Mammals, on the other hand, usually remain active, like the rabbit, or hibernate. During hibernation the temperature of the body decreases and the animal falls into a profound torpor. A cold-blooded animal, like the frog, can be almost entirely frozen without being injured, but warm-blooded animals must protect themselves from the cold; they therefore seek a sheltered spot, such as a burrow in the ground, in which to spend the winter. Furthermore, at this time the fur of mammals is very thick and consequently helps to retain the body heat.

The temperature of the body of hibernating animals becomes considerably lower than normal; for example, a ground squirrel which hibernated in a temperature of 35.6° F. had a body temperature exactly the same. (Semper.) Respiration almost ceases; the heart beats very slowly; and no food is taken into the body, but the fat masses stored up in the autumn are consumed, and the animal awakens in the spring in an emaciated condition.

The woodchuck is the most profound sleeper of our common mammals; it feeds on red clover in the autumn, goes into its burrow about October 1, and does not come out until April 1. The bear does not sleep so profoundly, for if there is plenty of food and the temperature is mild, he will not hibernate at all. When the bear does hibernate, he scoops out a den under a log or among the roots of a hollow tree. The raccoon and gray squirrel sleep during the severest part of the winter; the skunk spends January and February in his hole; the chipmunk wakes up occasionally to feed; and the red squirrel is abroad practically all winter. Many other mammals hibernate for a greater or less period of time.

e. *Migration*

Comparatively few mammals migrate; this may be due in part to their inadequate means of locomotion. Among those that do migrate are the fur-seal, reindeer, bison, bat, and lemming. The fur-seals in American waters breed on the Pribilof Islands in Bering Sea, where they remain from about May 1 to September 15. They then put out to sea, spending the winter months making a circuit of about six thousand miles.

The reindeer of Spitzbergen migrate regularly to the central portion of the island in summer and back to the seacoast in the autumn, where they feed upon seaweed. The bisons used to range over a large part of North America, making regular spring and fall migrations; they covered an area of about thirty-six hundred miles from north to south, and two thousand miles from east to west.

The lemmings of Scandinavia (Fig. 524) are celebrated for their curious migrations. They are small rodents about three inches in length.

" At intervals, averaging about a dozen years apart, lemmings suddenly appear in cultivated districts in central Norway and Sweden, where ordinarily none live, and in a year or two multiply into hordes which go traveling straight west toward the Atlantic, or east toward the Gulf of Bothnia, as the case may be, regardless of how the valleys trend, climbing a mountain instead of going around it, and, undeterred by any river or lake, keep persistently onward until finally some survivors reach the sea, into which they plunge and perish." They are said to march in " parallel lines three feet apart " and " gnaw through hay and corn stacks rather than go round." (Pennant.)

f. *Domesticated Mammals*

The most common domesticated mammals are the dog, horse, ass, ox, sheep, goat, pig, and cat. The dog was probably the first mammal to be domesticated. Dogs have been the companions of man for many centuries; they have become changed while under domestication, until there are now more than two hundred breeds. In many cases local wild species of the genus *Canis* have been tamed; for example, the original Arctic sledge dogs were half-tamed gray wolves, and the dogs kept by our northwestern Indians were tamed coyotes.

The immediate ancestors of the horse are not known, and there are at the present time no wild horses from which it could have arisen. It has probably developed from animals inhabiting the semiarid plains of central Asia. The more remote ancestors of the horse are well known (see Chap. XXII).

The ass is the favorite beast of burden in Eastern countries. In this country the cross between a female horse and male ass is known as a mule. The common ass of Europe and America is descended, through the early Egyptian domestication, from the African wild ass, *Equus africanus.*

The oxen of Europe and America were probably derived from the aurochs, *Bos primigenius,* of Europe. The sacred or humped cattle of India, *Bos indicus,* doubtless developed from one of the wild races that still roam the Himalayan foot-hills.

Sheep have been domesticated for so many centuries that their ancestors are not known, but there are many wild sheep of the same genus (*Ovis*) from which they may have originated. Goats have also been domesticated since the earliest times, and their wild relatives are abundant in many parts of the world.

The domesticated pigs are descended from the European wild boar, *Sus scrofa,* and the Indian wild boar, *Sus cristatus.*

The common house cat has a complicated ancestral history. Its remote ancestor was probably the Egyptian cat, *Felis libyca,* from which the Mediterranean cat, *F. mediterranea,* the wild-cat, *F. catus,* the jungle cat, *F. chaus,* the steppe cat, *F. caudata,* and the Indian desert cat, *F. ornata,* descended. The European and American domesticated cats were derived either from the Egyptian cat or the Mediterranean cat, which soon became crossed with the wildcat. The spotted Indian domesticated cats are derived from the Indian desert cat. A number of crosses have been made between the various wild and domesticated cats, resulting in a large variety of mixed breeds.

g. *Fossil Mammals*

Fourteen of the thirty-two orders of mammals are known only from fossil forms (H. F. Osborn). The earliest known remains of mammals are from the Triassic period, a period which began about ten million years ago (see Table XVII). The genera *Dromatherium* and *Micronodon,* taken in the Upper Triassic of North America, have been referred tentatively to the first order of mammals, the PROTODONTA. The mammals of both the Triassic and Jurassic periods were small. A number of genera of marsupials (MULTITUBERCULATA) and the lowest placental mammals, the TRITUBERCULATA or Mesozoic insectivores, are referred to the Jurassic period. In Cretaceous times the evolution of the existing orders of placental mammals took place.

There are, however, very few remains; the genera *Ptilodus* and *Meniscœssus* are marsupials (MULTITUBERCULATA) from the Upper Cretaceous of North America.

The Cenozoic Era is called the "Age of Mammals," since this interval of about three million years, between the Mesozoic Era and the present time, witnessed the ascendency of mammals and the inauguration of their dominance over all other animals. The mammalian characteristics of the periods in the Cenozoic Era may be outlined briefly as follows (Osborn) : —

The Eocene is "characterized by the first appearance of many of the ancestors of the modernized mammals and the gradual

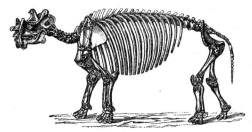

FIG. 548. — Skeleton of *Uintatherium mirabile*. (From Flower and Lydekker, after Marsh.)

disappearance of many of the archaic types characteristic of the Age of Reptiles " (Mesozoic Era).

The Oligocene is "characterized by the appearance of many existing types of mammals and the gradual disappearance of many of the older types."

The Miocene is an early stage of modernization, "in which lived many mammals closely similar to existing forms."

The Pliocene witnessed "a vast modernization of the mammals in which all the existing orders and families are known, as well as many of the existing genera, but few or no existing species."

The Pleistocene is "a life period in which the majority of the recent forms of mammals appear and in which there occurs the last glacial period and a great natural extinction of earlier forms in all parts of the world."

The Holocene, or recent time, is "characterized by the world-wide destruction and elimination of mammals through the agency of man."

Among the fossil mammals found in North America are the archaic ungulate, *Uintatherium mirabile* (Fig. 548), which was about as large as the largest existing elephants, and possessed three pairs of conspicuous protuberances upon the dorsal surface of its head; the enormous tortoise armadillo, *Glyptodon clavipes*

Fig. 549. — *Glyptodon clavipes*, a fossil edentate resembling the armadillo
(From Weysse, after Owen.)

(Fig. 549), which was almost nine feet in length, and was provided with an arched shell of immovable bony plates; and the mastodon (Fig. 550), of Europe, Asia, and South Africa, as well as of North America, which resembled our modern elephants in size and shape, and of which more than thirty species have been distinguished.

Fig. 550. — Restoration of *Mastodon arvernensis*. (From H. F. Osborn.)

h. *The Economic Importance of Mammals*

The relations of mammals to man are so varied and complex that only a very general account can be given here. In the first place, DOMESTIC MAMMALS are of almost inestimable value to man. Cattle constitute the most important animal industry in this country. Next in importance to cattle are horses. Sheep are utilized extensively for meat and wool. In some countries goats are used as draft animals and furnish milk and meat. In the tropical countries of the Old World, especially in desert regions, the camel is the most important draft animal; its hair is valuable in the manufacture of fabrics and brushes. In parts of South America the llama and guanaco furnish the chief means of transportation. The elephant is in Asia used as a draft animal, for hunting, and for various other purposes; in Africa it is hunted for the ivory in its tusks.

The GAME ANIMALS are those that are pursued and taken by sportsmen. Some of the more important game mammals of North America are the moose, wapiti, deer, bears, mountain lions, foxes, wolves, coyotes, wildcats, and rabbits. Some of these are exceedingly destructive, and certain states pay a bounty for their capture; others, like the deer, are of considerable value as food, though they may be injurious to farms in thickly populated districts. The various states protect many of the game animals during certain seasons of the year and in some cases for a period of years, so as to prevent their extermination.

The majority of the FUR-BEARING ANIMALS of North America belong to the family MUSTELIDÆ of the order Carnivora. This family includes the otter, mink, weasel, marten, wolverine, and badger. Most of these animals are now scarce, and furriers are forced to use the skins of other species, such as the skunk, muskrat, raccoon, fox, lynx, black bear, and rabbit.

The RODENTIA, or GNAWING MAMMALS, are on the whole injurious, since they include such notorious pests as the rabbits, rats, and mice. Rabbits are vegetarians, feeding on leaves, stems, flowers, seeds, buds, bark, and fruit. They damage especially clover, alfalfa, peas, cabbages, and the bark of trees. Young fruit, forest, and ornamental trees and shrubs in nurseries are subject to injury from rabbits, and frequently the branches and twigs within reach are cut off, or the bark is removed near the base of the trunk, thus girdling the tree and causing its death. MICE feed principally on stems, leaves, seeds, bulbs, roots, and other kinds of vegetation. A single field mouse devours in one year from twenty to thirty-six pounds of green vegetation, and a thousand mice in one meadow would require at least twelve tons annually. Damage is done to meadows and pastures, to grains and forage, to garden crops, to small fruits, to nursery stock, to orchards, to forest trees, and to parks and lawns.

" The RAT is the worst mammalian pest known to man. Its depredations throughout the world result in losses amounting to hundreds of millions of dollars annually. But these losses, great as they are, are of less importance than the fact that rats carry from house to house and from seaport to seaport the germs of the dreaded plague." (Lantz.) The amount of loss due to rats in the United States is not known; in Germany the loss is estimated at $50,000,000 per year. The losses in this country are as follows: a large part of the crops of cultivated grains are often destroyed by rats; " the loss of poultry due to rats is probably greater than that inflicted by foxes, minks, weasels, skunks, hawks, and owls combined " (Lantz); rats are a serious pest in game preserves, feeding upon the eggs and young of pheasants, etc.; fruits and vegetables both before and after being gathered are damaged by rats; and miscellaneous merchandise in stores, markets, and warehouses suffers injuries second only to that done to grains. Rats eat bulbs, flowers, and seeds in greenhouses, set fire to buildings by gnawing matches, depreciate the value of buildings and furniture, and are injurious in many other ways.

PREDACEOUS MAMMALS feed upon the flesh of other animals; if these animals are beneficial to man, the predaceous mammal may be considered injurious, but if the animals preyed upon are harmful to man, the predaceous mammal is beneficial. The harmful predaceous mammals include the wolves and cougars, which subsist largely upon big game, sheep, cattle, and horses, and the house cat, which destroys millions of birds in this country annually.

The other predaceous mammals are occasionally harmful, but usually beneficial. Coyotes and wildcats, if poultry and sheep are properly protected, devote their attention to rabbits and other small mammals, and insects. The fox destroys great numbers of field-mice, rabbits, ground squirrels, and insects. The mink often commits depredations upon poultry, but more than pays for this by destroying meadow-mice and muskrats. The weasel has a similar bill of fare. The skunk destroys immense numbers of mice, grubs, and noxious insects. The badger feeds largely upon ground squirrels and other burrowing mammals and insects.

There is great danger in introducing mammals into this country. The brown rat reached this country about 1775, and is now, as pointed out above, our worst mammalian pest. Rabbits which were introduced into Australia about 1864 soon became so numerous that legislative action was taken for their destruction. The mungoose of India destroys rats, lizards, and snakes; it was introduced into Jamaica and other tropical islands and at first proved very beneficial, but later it became a great pest, destroying poultry, birds, young domesticated animals, and even fruit. These disastrous results from the introduction of foreign species of mammals led Congress to prohibit the importation of most reptiles, birds, and mammals unless special permission is obtained from the Department of Agriculture.

CHAPTER XXII

THE ANCESTORS AND INTERRELATIONS OF THE VERTEBRATES

THE purpose of this chapter is to point out the probable relations between the vertebrates and invertebrates, to unify our account of the vertebrates by discussing the interrelations of the class, and to indicate the extent of our knowledge concerning the ancestors of vertebrates secured by the study of fossil forms.

1. THE RELATIONS BETWEEN VERTEBRATES AND INVERTEBRATES

A problem that has commanded the attention of many eminent scientists has been to trace the ancestry of the vertebrates to some invertebrate form. Investigations along this line have resulted in a number of theories, each with many adherents ready to argue in its favor. It is impossible in this place to give an account of each of these theories, but that their differences are considerable may be inferred from the fact that scientists have derived the vertebrates from the annelids, nemerteans, insects, arachnids, flatworms, and echinoderms.

The origin of vertebrates from the echinoderms through the ENTEROPNEUSTA (p. 346, Fig. 332) and *Amphioxus* (p. 352, Fig. 341) seems to have so many points in its favor that this theory will be sketched briefly in the following paragraphs as an illustration of the method used in tracing vertebrate descent.

We have seen that there are a number of subphyla in the phylum CHORDATA that contain animals of a lower grade than the vertebrates. These are: (1) the ENTEROPNEUSTA (Figs. 332–336), which includes a few worm-like species; (2) the TUNICATA (Figs. 337–340), which contains a number of sac-like animals that exhibit chordate characteristics chiefly in the immature stages; and (3) the CEPHALOCHORDA, which has but a single genus — *Amphioxus* (Figs. 341–344).

A careful study of *Amphioxus* has brought forth convincing evidence that this animal is really a modified ancestor of the vertebrates. The essential structural characteristics which are possessed in common by *Amphioxus* and the vertebrates are the presence of (1) a notochord, (2) a dorsal nervous system, (3) a pharynx perforated by gill-slits, and (4) a mid-ventral endostyle.

If we accept *Amphioxus* as the invertebrate most nearly allied to the vertebrates, we may then seek for an ancestor of this form. Such an ancestor is supplied by the sea-squirts or TUNICATA (pp. 348 to 351). The adult tunicates (Fig. 338) have retained very few of their primitive characteristics, but the larva, as shown in Figure 339, possesses a typical notochord, a neural tube, a series of gill-slits, and an endostyle, which are similar in position and development to these structures in *Amphioxus;* and it seems probable that the adult tunicate once existed as an animal like the larval tunicate of to-day, and that this remote ancestor was not only the progenitor of the modern tunicates, but was also the direct ancestor of the group to which *Amphioxus* belongs.

The search for a vertebrate ancestor more remote than the tunicates leads to a consideration of the marine worm-like animals of the subphylum ENTEROPNEUSTA. These species, as previously shown (p. 346, Figs. 332 and 333), are provided with clearly defined gill-slits, a structure which may be homologous to the notochord of the vertebrates, and four longitudinal nerve-cords of which the dorsal is slightly more pronounced than the ventral and lateral ones. It appears, therefore, that the ENTEROPNEUSTA may possibly be vertebrate ancestors of an earlier stage than the tunicates.

We must look to the larvæ of the ENTEROPNEUSTA for the link which may connect this lowest of the chordates with the invertebrates and thus complete our hypothetical line of vertebrate descent. The egg of the enteropneuston *Balanoglossus* develops into a small larva called *Tornaria* (Fig. 334), which floats in the sea, is transparent, has a bilateral symmetry, and is provided with bands of cilia for locomotion. This larva corresponds in habitat and structure almost exactly to the larvæ of the starfish and other echinoderms. This similarity leads to the conclusion that a form resembling these larvæ was the very remote progenitor of both the echinoderms and the chordates, and that " The lineal descendants of this hypothetical ancestor chose two paths, the one leading to the ECHINODERMATA, the other to *Balanoglossus*, the TUNICATA, *Amphioxus*, and eventually the VERTEBRATA."

"The question of the descent of the CHORDATA is not solved by accepting their relationship to the ENTEROPNEUSTA, since this latter group holds an uncommonly isolated position. Only from the structure of the *Balanoglossus* larva can there be concluded a distant connection with the echinoderms. We must resign ourselves to the thought that at the present time we are not in a condition to assert from what ancestral form the CHORDATA, and with them *Balanoglossus*, are to be derived. The origin of the vertebrates is lost in the obscurity of forms unknown to us." (Wilder.)

2. THE PHYLOGENESIS OF VERTEBRATES [1]

Anatomical and paleontological investigations are continually changing our ideas regarding the interrelations of the vertebrates, and we can indicate only provisionally the possible line of descent of the vertebrates and the relations of one group to another. Reference to Figure 551 will make the following paragraphs clear.

The lowest vertebrates, *i.e.* the forms most nearly related to *Amphioxus*, are the CYCLOSTOMES. These (see Chap. XV, Fig. 352) are eel-like vertebrates without jaws and with a cartilaginous skeleton. Next above the CYCLOSTOMES come the ELASMOBRANCHS (sharks, skates, etc.; see Chap. XVI, Fig. 358), which also possess a cartilaginous skeleton, but are provided with jaws. The direct descendants of the ELASMOBRANCHS appear to be the ganoid fishes (CHONDROSTEI, CROSSOPTERYGII, LEPIDOSTEI, and AMIOIDEI), which constituted the dominant group during the Devonian Period (see Table XVII). Some of the ganoids have a skeleton entirely of cartilage; others are equipped with both cartilage and bone, but all of them possess gill-covers, which are absent in CYCLOSTOMES and ELASMOBRANCHS. The bony fishes (TELEOSTS) are probably the descendants of the bony ganoids. The lung-fishes (DIPNOI) represent an independent lateral branch from the ELASMOBRANCHS; they are by many considered a connecting link between the fishes and amphibians, but this is probably not the case.

[1] For a more detailed account of this subject, see Wilder's History of the Human Body, Chapter II.

The AMPHIBIANS may be traced back to the ganoids and seem to have developed through the STEGOCEPHALIA, a group now extinct, which are the probable ancestors of not only the modern AMPHIBIA, but also of the REPTILIA.

The most primitive living reptiles are the RHYNCHOCEPHALIA; these are represented by the single living species *Sphenodon punc-*

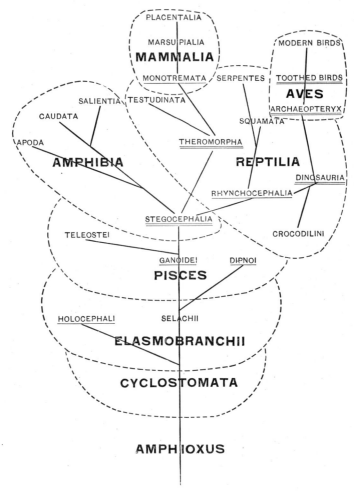

FIG. 551. — Phylogenetic tree of vertebrates. Double underscoring indicates an extinct group; single underscoring, those that have but a few living representatives. The boundaries of the classes are represented by dotted lines. (Modified after Wilder.)

tatum (Fig. 450) of New Zealand. From this group have come the Squamata, Serpentes, and Crocodilini, and some of the extinct reptiles. The Testudinata seem more closely allied to the extinct Theromorpha.

The birds have sprung from dinosaurian ancestors. They are very closely related to the reptiles, and the earliest known form (*Archæopteryx*) might almost be called a flying reptile. The toothed birds are considered the forerunners of the modern toothless birds.

The Mammalia are of special interest, since this class of vertebrates includes man. The earliest living mammals, the Monotremata, are descended from reptilian ancestors, the Theromorpha, which are known only from fossil remains. Above the monotremes are placed the Marsupialia, and finally the Placentalia, which are the highest of all animals. The Primates, the group that includes man, seem to have descended from the primitive Insectivora. The line of descent within the group is probably somewhat as follows: —

1. Monotremata. Egg-laying Mammals.
2. Marsupialia. Marsupials.
3. Insectivora. Insectivores.
4. Lemuridæ. Lemurs.
5. Cercopithecidæ. Old World Monkeys with Tails.
6. Simiidæ. Anthropoid Apes.
7. Pithecanthropus. An Extinct " Ape-Man."
8. Homo neanderthalensis. The Extinct Neanderthal Man.
9. Homo sapiens. Modern Man.

3. The Fossil Remains of Vertebrates

a. *Succession of Life in General*

The fossil remains of animals that lived millions of years ago give us authentic records of the fauna present upon the earth's surface at that time. These records, unfortunately, are fragmentary, since only the hard parts of the animals were preserved, and these, when discovered, are almost always broken and incomplete, making the reconstruction of many parts necessary. From the evidence obtained from fossils, paleozoologists have constructed a table (Table XVII) showing the geological periods, arranged in the order of their succession, and the time of origin of the different groups of animals.

TABLE XVII

THE DISTRIBUTION OF THE FOSSIL REMAINS OF ANIMALS
IN THE EARTH'S CRUST

Era	Period	Duration in Years (Walcott)	Animals Characteristic of the Period
Cenozoic (Era of Mammals)	Recent Pleistocene Pliocene Miocene Eocene	3,000,000	Man; mammals, mostly of species still living. Mammals abundant; belonging to numerous extinct families and orders.
Mesozoic (Era of Reptiles)	Cretaceous Jurassic Triassic	7,200,000	Bird-like reptiles; flying reptiles; toothed birds; first snakes; bony-fishes abound; sharks again numerous. First birds; giant reptiles; clams and snails abundant. First mammals (a marsupial); sharks reduced to few forms; bony-fishes appear.
Paleozoic (Era of Invertebrates)	Permian Carboniferous (Age of Amphibians) Devonian (Age of Fishes) Silurian (Age of Invertebrates) Cambrian	17,500,000	Life transitional between Paleozoic and Mesozoic eras. Earliest true reptiles. Amphibians; lung-fishes; first cray-fishes; insects abundant; spiders; fresh-water mussels. First amphibian; sharks; first land shells (snails); mollusks abundant; first crabs. First truly terrestrial or air-breathing animals; first insects; corals abundant; mailed fishes; brachiopods; trilobites; mollusks. Invertebrates only.
Archæan	Laurentian		Simple marine invertebrates.

Such a table shows that the invertebrates appeared first, since their remains occur in the oldest strata, unaccompanied by the remains of vertebrates; that the invertebrates became more complex in the succeeding periods; that the fishes (low in the scale of vertebrate life) were the first vertebrates to appear; and that these were followed by the amphibians, reptiles, birds, and mammals in just the order that would be expected from a study of the structure of these vertebrates.

b. The Evolution of the Horse [1]

One of the best methods of illustrating the value of studying fossil animals is to give a brief description of a succession of connecting links such as are exhibited by the evolution of the horse. The horses now inhabiting America are descendants of domesticated animals which were brought to this country by the early settlers from Europe, but in prehistoric times the ancestors of our modern horse were native here, and some of the finest fossil remains of these ancestors have been found in America.

The evolution of the horse has been traced back through at least twelve distinct stages extending through the Cenozoic Era or the Era of Mammals. A brief description of five of these stages together with Figure 552 will serve to illustrate the principal changes that took place during this evolution. The structural features that became modified during this era of about 3,000,000 years were such as to adapt the horse to life on the open plains, where its food consisted of dry silicious grasses.

The feet gradually lost the side toes, and only the middle toe and splints of the second and fourth digits remain in our modern horses. The limbs became longer, enabling the animal to move about more rapidly; this change was correlated with an elongation of the head and neck, which was necessary in order to reach the ground. The front teeth were modified as chisel-like cropping structures, and the back teeth evolved from simple molars into wonderfully effective grinding organs with tortuous ridges of enamel and with supporting and protecting layers of dentine and cement. During the later periods the molars elongated, and thus became adapted for grinding the dry silicious grasses which caused them to wear down more rapidly than the softer vegetation. During this evolution the body gradually increased in size from that of the earliest known form, which was about as large as a domestic cat, to that of the horse of to-day.

[1] For a detailed account of this subject, see "The Evolution of the Horse" by W. D. Matthew. The Quarterly Review of Biology, Vol. 1, April, 1926.

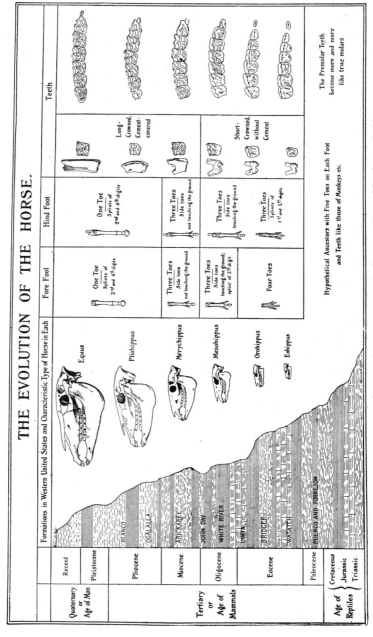

FIG. 552. — Diagrams showing the evolution of the horse. (From Matthew, 1926.)

(1) *Hyracotherium* and *Eohippus* (Fig. 553). These animals lived during the lower Eocene Period. Only the skull of *Hyracotherium* has been discovered, but this shows it to be the most primitive stage known. *Eohippus* was named from remains found in the Lower Eocene of Wyoming and New Mexico; its fore feet have four complete toes and the splint of the fifth, and the hind feet have three complete toes and the splint of the fifth.

(2) *Protorohippus* and *Orohippus*. These forms lived during the Middle Eocene Period and were about as large as a small dog.

Fig. 553. — Restoration of the four-toed horse, the oldest known ancestor of the modern horse; only 16 inches high. (From Matthew after Knight.)

The feet are similar to those of *Eohippus*, except that the splint of the fifth digit has entirely disappeared. Remains of an animal called *Epihippus* are recorded from the Upper Eocene.

(3) *Mesohippus*. This animal belongs to the Oligocene Period, and reached the size of a sheep. Its fore feet possess three complete toes and a splint of the fifth digit, and the hind feet also possess three complete toes, but no splint. All three toes touched the ground, but the middle toe is larger and bore most of the weight of the body. *Anchitherium* from the Lower Miocene is larger than *Mesohippus; Parahippus* and *Hypohippus* from the Middle Miocene were as large as a Shetland pony.

(4) *Protohippus* and *Pliohippus*. In these animals from the Middle and Upper Miocene there are three toes on each foot, but the middle one is large, and the side toes are smaller and do not touch the ground. The crowns of the upper molars are long and provided with an effective grinding surface of ridges of cement. *Hipparion* which lived during the Pliocene Period is larger than *Protohippus* and has a more complicated tooth pattern.

(5) *Equus*. The modern horses of the Pleistocene and Recent periods have lost the first and fifth digits entirely, and the second and fourth digits are represented by splints. The third toe alone sustains the weight of the body. The crowns of the molar teeth are much elongated, the skull has lengthened, and the body is considerably larger than that of any of its ancestors.

At the present time true wild horses occur only in Asia (the Asiatic Wild Ass, *Equus hemionus*, and Przewalsky's Horse, *E. pryzewalskii*) and in Africa (the African Wild Ass, *E. asinus*, and the Zebras, *E. zebra*, *E. burchelli*, and *E. quagga*). The mustangs and broncos of our Western Plains and South America are not true wild horses, but are descendants of domesticated horses brought over from Europe.

The evolution of the elephant, dog, and many other animals has been carefully worked out by paleontologists, but none quite so much in detail as that of the horse. Nevertheless, they show how much is possible toward a knowledge of the ancestors of vertebrates from a study of fossil forms.

INDEX

All numbers refer to pages. Words in italics are names of genera; words in capitals and small capitals are names of families, orders, or of higher divisions. Numbers in bold face type are numbers of pages on which there are figures.

A

Abductor muscle, 446.
Absorption, 433.
ACANTHIIDAE, 312.
ACANTHOCEPHALA, **168**.
ACARINA, **339**.
Accommodation, 523.
Accretion, 9.
Acetabulum, 445, 565.
ACINETARIA, **64**, 65.
Acipenser, **409**.
ACŒLOMATA, 220.
Acontia, **126**, 127.
ACRIDIIDÆ, 308, **309**.
Acris, 465.
ACTINIARIA, 131.
Actinomma, **40**, 41.
ACTINOPODA, **40**.
ACTINOZOA, 125.
Adaptation, 371.
Adductor muscle, 446.
ADELOCHORDA, 345.
ADEPHAGA, **323**.
Adjustor, 207.
Adrenal bodies, 442.
Aedes, 319.
ÆPYORNITHIFORMES, 532.
Aërial, 6.
Æstivate, 483.
Afferent nerves, 206.
AGAMIDÆ, 494.
Agkistrodon, **505**.
AGLOSSA, 463.
AGLYPHA, 500.
Air-bladder, 392.
Air-sacs, 521.
Aix, 536, **537**.
Albatrosses, 534.
Alces, 596.
ALCIDÆ, 541.
ALCYONACEA, 130.
ALCYONARIA, 130.
Allantois, 607.
Alligator, 491.
Allolobophora, 199.

Alouatta, 590.
Alternation of generations, 115.
Alveolar theory, 9.
Alveoli, 434.
Alytes, 467.
Amblyopsis, **417**.
Amblyrhynchus, 495.
Ambulacra, 178.
Ambystoma, **462**.
Ameiurus, **413**.
Ametabola, 301.
Amia, 410, **411**.
Amitosis, 12–**13**.
Amnion, 607.
AMNIOTA, 607.
Amœba, **28**–38; anatomy, **28**; behavior, 33; metabolism, 29; reproduction, 31.
Amœbocyte, 182, 256.
Amœboid movement, **34**.
AMPHIBIA, 3, 428.
Amphiblastula, 93, **94**.
Amphicœlous vertebræ, **394**.
AMPHINEURA, 229.
Amphioxus, **85**, 352–357, **352**, **353**, **355**, **356**, 617.
AMPHIPODA, **268**.
AMPHISBÆNIDÆ, 497.
Amphitrite, **215**.
Amphiuma, 460.
Ampullæ, **180**, 367.
Amylopsin, 433.
Anabolism, 17.
Anaconda, 500.
Analogous organs, 75.
ANAMNIOTA, 607.
ANASPIDACEA, 267.
ANATIDÆ, 536.
Anatomy, 23.
Anchitherium, 625.
Ancylostoma, 162.
Anguilla, **418**.
Anguis, **496**.
Angulo-splenials, 443.
Animal communities, 371.
Animal habitats, 371.
Animal mind, 38.

627